STAR TREK
ROLEPLAYING GAME

Design Christian Moore, Ross Isaacs, Kenneth Hite, Steven S. Long

Development Kenneth Hite

Star Trek® Line Developer Kenneth Hite

Icon System Design Christian Moore, Steven S. Long *with* Kenneth Hite, Ross Isaacs

Authors James L. Cambias (Space, New Life, Menagerie, and New Civilizations), Jackie Cassada and Nicky Rea (To Boldly Go, Where No Man Has Gone Before), Kenneth Hite (passim), Robin D. Laws (Federation, Starfleet, fictional vignettes), Steven S. Long (Character Creation, Characteristics, Action, Rewards, Starships, Starship Combat), S. John Ross (Constructing an Episode), John Snead (Starship Locations, Technology)

Editing Janice Sellers

Additional Project-specific Contributions Christian Moore

Proofreading Janice Sellers, Bruce Harlick

Product Development, Paramount (and Continued Spiritual Guidance) Chip Carter

Proofreading and Fact Checking, Bill Maxwell

Additional Design, Development, and Contributions Steve Bishop, Bill Bridges, Richard E. Dansky, Matthew Grau, Andrew Greenberg, Daniel Greenberg, Danny Landers, Tim O'Brien, Owen Seyler, Tammie Webb

Graphic Design Anthony N. Vayos

Layout Bruce Harlick, Sheila Ralston, Alvaro Riet

Art Direction Anthony N. Vayos, Matt Colville

Original Art Randy Asplund (ships), Joe Corroney (creatures), Gordon Purcell (archetypes and adventure), Walter Velez (Yorktown crew)

Maps and Schematics Charles Ryan, Kenneth Hite

Bridge Diagram Courtesy of Star Trek: The Magazine

Special Thanks Chip Carter (for benevolent undersea despotism), Greg Orman and Bernard Cahill (for thinking outside the box), Jay Longino and Inman Young (for train conducting), Ryan Moore and Lessa Isaacs (hoteliers extraordinary), Don Mappin (for keeping Memory Alpha safe from Zetarians), Guy McLimore and Greg Poehlein (for paving the way), Greg Stafford (for keeping the Other Western Mythology), Susan Pinsonneault and Phil Brucato (for shaping me up), and Robin Laws (for TOSsiness above and beyond the call of duty). Thanks to Bruce Baugh, Rich "Denebianguy" Dansky, John Nephew, S. John Ross, Greg Stolze, Jeff Tidball, John Tynes, and Dustin Wright, for knowing. Props to Ross Isaacs. Finally, thanks to Harold Hite for tuning it in and Mary Hite for understanding, and as always to Sheila Ralston, for everything.

Dedication To Gene L. Coon and Robert H. Justman, without whom the *Enterprise* could never have flown.

Disclaimer While Last Unicorn Games has researched extensively to make this the most authentic *Star Trek®* Roleplaying Game possible, the depth of information necessary for a fully-realized roleplaying game is not always revealed during a weekly television show. While we have tried to extrapolate logically within the flavor of *Star Trek®*, we have taken some liberties and players should remember that only the events, characters, and places that appear on the show or in films are canon.

STAR TREK
ROLEPLAYING GAME

Paramount

A VIACOM COMPANY

LAST UNICORN GAMES

Last Unicorn Games, Inc.
9520 Jefferson Blvd., Suite C
Culver City, CA 90232

Distributed to the book trade by Simon & Schuster
1230 Avenue of the Americas, New York, NY 10020

First Printing – 1999   Printed in Canada

Visit us on the web at *www.lastunicorngames.com*

TABLE OF CONTENTS

Chances are, you know the answer to this one. There is no greater universe for the dyed-in-the-velour fan of swashbuckling action and optimistic adventure than the galaxy of the United Federation of Planets in the 23rd century. It is a universe of exploding planets, bizarre aliens, and most of all, iconic characters. Who doesn't feel a thrill at the legendary names: Kirk, Spock, McCoy, the *Enterprise*? This game takes you from the helm of a *Constitution*-class starship to planets threatened by the Klingon menace. From the Prime Directive to the phaser rifle, *Star Trek* saw the future as it should be thirty years ago. Last Unicorn Games is excited to show it to you again now.

WHAT IS A ROLEPLAYING GAME?

Chances are, you know the answer to this one, too, although you may not know it. After school, when you were a kid, you'd watch *Star Trek* on TV, and then you'd play *Star Trek* in the backyard with your friends. Fingers pointed, you'd phaser down the luckless Klingons. A vacant lot became Vulcan, and the starships zoomed in your imagination. With a roleplaying game, you can do all of that, and you don't even need the vacant lot. Better yet, there's even a way to tell if you hit the bad guy.

A roleplaying game, like a TV show, is about telling a story. Players take the roles of the main characters, the heroic Starfleet officers who keep the galaxy safe from giant amoebas and Romulan birds of prey. But rather than read someone else's script, you write your own lines, set your own stage directions. The Narrator becomes the director, the set designer, and the producer; she decides what this week's episode will be about, and acts out the roles of everyone else – the guest stars, the villains, and the red-shirted security man who dies in the first act. She also keeps track of the rules, so that everybody knows what they can do, and whether the deflector shields will hold up. Between all of you, evil is vanquished and the galaxy is saved. Everybody wins, because everybody has a good time.

WHAT IS THE *STAR TREK* ROLEPLAYING GAME?

It's all of the above, complete in one book but as expandable as the Human horizon. Your adventures can be written in the stars next to those of the legendary crew of the *U.S.S. Enterprise*, or even surpass them – here, your imagination tells the stories without worrying about special effects budgets.

Players can start right away with the Archetype characters on pages 42-45; just copy them onto the character sheet, or out of the book, and take off! The Action rules on pages 97-120 hold everything you need to know to play the game. They're designed to be simple and fast, and to stay out of your way while you're having fun. If you want to build characters yourself, use the Character Creation rules on pages 40-61. The Narrator should eventually be familiar with the entire book, but you only really need a love of *Star Trek*, an imagination, and a fistful of dice to begin. There's some advice from seasoned Narrators on pages 237-262, just before a complete ready-to-play adventure, The Danurian Factor (with eight more ready-to-run characters). We've included guides and rules for Starfleet technology and starship combat; for aliens and monsters; for promotion and death. It's all in here, and it's all out there, beyond Antares, on the final frontier.

So boldly go – *where no man has gone before.*

The following game terms appear throughout the *Star Trek Roleplaying Game*. Each of the terms is described more completely in the appropriate section of the book indicated after the definition; we have collected them here for ease of reference.

Action: Almost anything a character does can be described by an action. Making an attack, dodging a blow and using a skill are all actions. Actions are divided into Immediate Actions, which take no time in combat (for example, dropping a weapon), and Timed Actions (actions which take time in combat and must be declared; for example, making or dodging an attack). See page 108.

Advantage: Special abilities, benefits, or advantages that a character possesses. Examples include having a Contact in Starfleet Command, being especially adept at Engineering tasks, or having a particularly acute sense. Advantages cost a number of Development Points equal to their value; for example, a +2 Advantage costs 2 Development Points. See pages 84-90.

Attribute: A character's innate capabilities, such as his agility or intelligence. There are five attributes: Fitness, Coordination, Intellect, Presence, and Psi. Attributes range in value from 1 to 5 (and, rarely, higher). See page 63-64.

Attribute Test: A Test (*q.v.*) made using only an attribute (no skill is involved). See page 103.

c: The scientific notation for the speed of light. For example, a starship moving at .25*c* moves at one quarter the speed of light.

Combined Test: A Test made by several characters working together. The best Test Result acts as a base, and each additional successful result adds +1 to it; failures may subtract from the total or delay completion of the task. See page 105.

Courage Points: Courage represents a character's bravery, ingenuity and fortitude in the face of adversity. Characters use Courage Points to improve rolls and increase Test results. See page 102.

Crew: With a capital "C," it refers to the player characters. The personnel of a starship are its "crew" with a small "c." They, and everyone else not a player character, are the Supporting Cast. See page 251.

d6: A six-sided die. Six-sided dice are used to make all Tests in the *Star Trek Roleplaying Game*.

Development Points: Points which characters use to buy attributes, edges, and advantages. Characters receive a certain number of Development Points at each stage of their Background History. See page 46.

Difficulty: How easy or hard it is to accomplish a task. Each task is given a Difficulty (or Difficulty Number) indicating how hard it is—the higher the number, the harder the task. Difficulty Numbers are organized into categories (from lowest to highest, Routine [3-5], Moderate [6-8], Challenging [9-11], Difficult [12-14], and Nearly Impossible [15+]). When trying to accomplish a task, a character rolls a Test (*q.v.*); if his Test result equals or exceeds the Difficulty, he succeeds. See page 99.

Disadvantage: Limitations, hindrances, or other problems that afflict a character. Examples include having a Sworn Enemy, being Physically Impaired (for example, blind) or being Impulsive. See pages 90-96.

Drama Die: When a player rolls a Test, one of the dice he rolls is a different color. This die is called the Drama Die. If the Drama Die rolls a 6, it indicates a great degree of success; if it rolls a 1, it may indicate a great failure. See page 100.

Dramatic Failure: A failed Test that is six or more below the Difficulty Number (for example, a Test Result of 5 when the Difficulty is 12). This indicates a grievous failure that may have terrible consequences for the character. See page 102.

Dramatic Success: A successful Test that is six or more above the Difficulty Number (for example, a Test Result of 12 when the Difficulty is 5). This indicates an amazing success that may have especially beneficial results for the character. See page 102.

Edge: Aspects of attributes that represent a character's particular level of talent (or lack of talent) with some functions of an attribute. For example, the edges associated with Intellect are Perception and Logic. Edges range in value from +2 to -2, and act as modifiers to related Tests. See page 64.

Extended Test: A Test requiring an extensive amount of time, or which is broken up into segments so that the Narrator can gauge the character's progress by requiring multiple Skill Tests. See page 104.

Initiative: Determines who goes first in combat or similar situations. Characters in combat must make Initiative Tests based on the Skill they are about to use, modified by their Reaction edge. See page 107.

Level: A character's level of ability in a skill or attribute. For example, a character who buys a skill has a level of 1 in that skill; as his ability improves, the level increases to 2, 3, 4, and so on. See page 46.

Opposed Test: A Test (*q.v.*) which is opposed or resisted by another character; for example, a character who uses his Stealth skill to sneak past a guard will engage in an Opposed Test with the guard, who uses his Search skill in an attempt to locate the character. The character who rolls the highest Test Result in an Opposed Test wins the Test. See page 104.

Overlay: A character creation tool that represents the character's profession, such as Engineer or Doctor. Each Overlay includes the basic Skills and other abilities needed to perform the profession. See page 49.

Renown: Renown measures how well-known a character is. Renown has five Aspects (Initiative, Aggression, Skill, Discipline, and Openness), and can be positive or negative. Each character starts the game with 1 point of Renown in one Aspect (player's choice). See page 60.

Resistance: A character's ability to withstand damage. Resistance equals a character's (Fitness + Vitality). If the character wears armor or other protection, it will add to his Resistance. See page 61.

Result: Test Result. See Test.

Round: A measure of time in combat, equal to five seconds. See page 98.

Skill: A character's learned abilities, aptitudes, and knowledges. Examples include the ability to fire energy weapons, the ability to diagnose illness and perform surgery, and the ability to operate ship's sensors. Skills range in value from 1 to 5 (and, rarely, higher). Most skills have specializations (*q.v.*). See pages 64-83.

Skill Test: A Test (*q.v.*) in which a character rolls a number of dice equal to the attribute upon which a skill is based, and adds the highest result on any die to his skill level. If the total equals or exceeds the Difficulty (*q.v.*) Number for the task, the character succeeds. See page 98.

Specialization: Areas of particular expertise and ability within a skill. Many skills require a character to specialize, since they are so broad that few characters will ever learn all aspects of the skill in depth. See page 65.

Template: A character creation tool that represents the character's species, such as Human or Vulcan. Each Template includes the basic attributes and other abilities common to an average member of the race. See pages 47-49.

Test: Dice rolls used to determine whether a character succeeds with a particular action. Most Tests are based on a skill plus an attribute, but there are also Tests based solely on an attribute. Typically, the highest die rolled in a Test is added to the relevant skill level; if that total, or Test Result, equals or exceeds the Difficulty (*q.v.*) of a task, the character succeeds. See pages 98-105.

Test Modifier: These include edges, poor visibility, using the off hand, being wounded, or trying to perform tasks in zero gravity. See pages 105-106.

Wound Level: An indication of a character's current injury status. There are seven Wound Levels: Healthy, Stunned, Injured, Wounded, Incapacitated, Near Death, and Killed. A character can withstand a number of points of damage equal to his Resistance per Wound Level; when he takes more damage than that, he drops to the next level. See page 116.

Captain Duffy's rollicking haymaker caught the burly Centauran full on the jaw, sending him windmilling backward into a stack of conference chairs, which tumbled all around him. The Centauran reeled for a moment, worked his facial muscles to shake off the blow, and started to struggle back up to his feet.

Duffy clenched his fist at the half-stunned alien. "The second one is just like the first," he warned. The Centauran sank back into the jumble of downed chairs.

THE FEDERATION

Lt. Basta completed his override of the door's locking mechanism and burst through the threshold, the Federation President in tow.

"My god, Captain! You've just punched out the Centauran ambassador!"

"Not quite," Duffy replied, as the Centauran's form began to shimmer, bubble, and contort. In seconds the figure resolved itself into a floating, pulsing mote of energy. The energy being bobbed and weaved in the air, then made a sudden dive toward President McLaren. Basta threw his body between the alien and the President, pushing McLaren back toward the wall. Duffy's phaser was already in hand. He fired at the alien. It skittered wildly across the length of the room, then vanished through the ceiling.

Duffy and Basta rushed to the President's side. He brushed them off, quickly regaining both his balance and his dignity. "No need to fuss, gentlemen. I was a Starfleet commander when you were both still teething."

"What in the sainted name of Antonio Carlos Jobim was that thing?" Basta asked.

"I don't know," said Duffy, "but I'm sure as hell going to find out."

History

The story of the United Federation of Planets is also the story of Humankind. Although Humans are only one of the five founding races of the Federation, the humanistic values developed through the hard-won experience of Earth history define its mission and shape the rules that guide it. The very existence of the Federation is a testament to those values: hope, tolerance, and courage. To understand the Federation, you have to start with Earth.

BEGINNINGS

Millions of years ago, beings from deep space seeded Earth with humanoid life, and the fruit of their work has looked to the stars ever since. Some cultures, such as the Preservers, carried samples of Humanity to other planets, and unknown entities intervened to protect (or interfere with) *homo sapiens* on its own world as well.

Humanity's own journey toward the stars began during its nuclear era, in circumstances emblematic of man's struggles with himself. Space exploration was both an expression of man's eternal hunger for knowledge and achievement, and an extension of his thirst for conflict. Two political empires, embroiled in a decades-long cold war, competed with one another for victories in the so-called space race. In 1961, Soviet cosmonaut Yuri Gargarin became the first Human to achieve orbital spaceflight. U.S. astronaut Neil Armstrong, in 1969, was the first man to walk on Earth's moon.

THE EUGENICS WARS

Many of the ever-accelerating technological developments of this period were double-edged, offering mankind seemingly unlimited potential for good—or for ill. The greedy and power-hungry hijacked the initial promise of genetic engineering technology, intended at first to cure inherited ailments. Instead, they seized upon various selective breeding and genetic enhancement procedures to create a new breed of superhuman warriors.

The supposed "supermen" turned on their masters, deposed the lawful governments of over forty nations, proclaimed themselves warlords and tyrants, and then went to war with one another. History remembers these conflicts as the Eugenics Wars. The most notorious of these tyrants, Khan Noonian Singh,

CHRONOLOGY

1961	Soviet cosmonaut Yuri Gargarin becomes the first Human in space
1968	American orbital weapons platform explodes on launch
1969	American astronaut Neil Armstrong becomes the first Human on the Moon
1977	American space shuttle *Enterprise* tested
1992-1996	Eugenics Wars
2002	Jackson Roykirk launches *Nomad* probe
2009	Christopher Mission to Saturn
2053	World War III
2063	Zefram Cochrane invents the warp drive; Vulcan-Human first contact
2064	*S.S. Valiant* launched on deep-space exploratory mission
2103	Colonization of Mars
2113	United Earth Republic establishes the United Earth Space Probe Agency (UESPA)
2156-2160	Earth-Romulan War
2160	Terran Conventions of Epsilon Eridani draft Articles of Federation
2161	Foundation of the United Federation of Planets; UESPA folded into Starfleet
2218	Disastrous first contact with the Klingons
2220	Prime Directive adopted
2242	Battle of Donatu V ends series of Federation-Klingon border wars
2245	Launch of the *U.S.S. Enterprise*
2252	Spock becomes the first Vulcan in Starfleet
2253	Garth of Izar defeats Axanar
2264	James T. Kirk begins his five-year mission in command of the *Enterprise*
2265	Axanar admitted to the Federation
2266	Romulan attacks across Neutral Zone resume
2267	Organian Peace Treaty; first contact with the Gorn
2268	Romulan-Klingon alliance; UFP skirmish with the Tholians
2269	Federation data library at Memory Alpha seriously damaged

conquered one fourth of the planet. In 1996, humanity rose up and overthrew the genetically engineered despots, and Khan vanished in the turmoil. The use of genetic engineering techniques on sentient species remains, to this day, illegal throughout the Federation.

Khan's exile was later discovered to be a voluntary emigration in the earliest interplanetary craft. Humanity's nobler side also ventured into space in those confused times, as probes like Jackson Roykirk's *Nomad* succeeded the *Voyager* series and the Christopher Mission to Saturn in 2009 blazed new trails.

FIRST UNITY MOVEMENT

It took great unity to throw off the shackles of the genetic warlords. In the decade that followed the Eugenics Wars, leaders all around the globe tried to build on that unity to foster a new era of international cooperation. Although this early blossoming of idealism soon fizzled, its tenets would be remembered through coming dark times.

WORLD WAR III

Mystery shrouds the conflict known as World War III, because much of the historical record of that era vanished in the course of its military campaigns, which saw sustained bombing campaigns against civilian targets, the deployment of biogenic weapons, and electronic terrorism designed to destroy information and communications. One figure from the period, a Colonel Green of the U.S. military, is remembered as instigator of the worst genocidal excesses of World War III. Today's historians estimate the death toll at 37 million, although this figure is open to dispute. What is clear is that the hopes of Humankind suffered a serious setback. Although historians debate the root causes of the conflict—overpopulation, resource depletion, and eroding respect for personal liberty are the most common suggestions—the average student today understands that it was ultimately a failure of the Human spirit.

FIRST CONTACT

The Human response to this crisis again took two forms. Li Kuan, a gifted strategist, attempted to unite Earth by force, but fell prey to his own dictatorial ambition. The Eastern Coalition he led remained a powerful symbol of world unity to many humans, but an adventurous pilot named Zefram Cochrane rekindled mankind's capacity to dream of a better life. From the most devastated area of Earth, Cochrane constructed and successfully flew the *Phoenix*, the first spacecraft to break the light barrier. A passing survey vessel manned by scientists from the planet Vulcan spotted the telltale warp signature of Cochrane's ship.

Shortly after he touched back down on Earth, they initiated the first overt contact between mankind and another intelligent species. The incident captured the imaginations of Earth's demoralized peoples, triggering a renewed determination not only to explore the stars (the deep-space vessel *Valiant* was the second warp craft launched, from the European Hegemony), but to remake their own troubled societies.

This determination paid off three years later when newly commissioned Earth vessels initiated their own first contact, with the people of nearby Alpha Centauri. The Centaurans provided Humans with terraforming technology to aid in their rebuilding efforts. In exchange, they received warp-drive technology from Earth.

The Vulcans, Centaurans, and Humans forged an informal three-way alliance, a precursor to the full Federation. For forty years they engaged in peaceful trade and cultural exchange activities, materially and spiritually enriching all three races.

BIRTHING PAINS

Then yet another outbreak of nationalistic fervor on Earth threatened to strangle the burgeoning alliance in its cradle. Four decades of reconstruction on Earth left its people anxious for expansion to the rest of its solar system. Earth nations worked in concert to colonize Mars; by 2103 it was inhabited and self-sustaining. The Fundamental Declarations of the Martian Colonies, inspired by the Vulcan Theorems of Governance and the United States Constitution, eloquently proclaimed the universal rights of all sentient beings.

Unfortunately, the journey to the stars inspired greed as well as greatness. In the wake of this hopeful beginning, Earth's leaders came down with a bad case of avarice, forgetting the lessons of the past. Power blocs competed ferociously for colonial territory, arming their space craft for the first time. The European Hegemony grabbed the moons of Jupiter. The United States struck out in search of interstellar worlds to capture.

The Vulcans and Centaurans watched this development with increasing concern; Humanity was now showing its ugly face, its capacity for greed and violence. When European and South American spacecraft clashed near Alpha Centauri, endangering the crews of nearby Centauran ships, the Vulcans and Centaurans banded together to issue a diplomatic ultimatum: If Earth could not unify itself and send a single, representative delegation to a settlement conference, both planets would end relations with Humankind.

Despite the indignant responses of certain political leaders, whose threatened sense of personal power led them to propose military action against the busybody aliens, cooler heads ultimately prevailed. Average citizens, shocked and shamed by the necessity of the Vulcan-Centauran ultimatum, pressured their leaders to reach a one-world accord. They chose the heroic Zefram Cochrane as spokesman for their cause. Mars colonists declared their independence from any single Earth government, while signaling their willingness to rejoin a one-world regime.

The Europeans and Americans started Earth's long progress toward unified government, declaring the United Earth Republic in 2113. By 2130, United Earth represented and subsumed most Terran governments; the last straggler, Australia, joined in 2150.

FIRST ENEMIES: THE ROMULANS

Not long after the good sense of the Human people prevailed over the warlike impulses of their leaders, the United Earth Republic found itself embroiled in its first true interstellar war. The enemy was the Romulan Star Empire; the dispute was territorial. Neither side looked its foe in the face; the apex of ship-to-ship communication technology was still the subspace radio. Following the near-destruction of the UESPA starship *U.S.S. Endeavor*, arrogant-sounding Romulan officers demanded that Earth ships depart from a vast area of space. The Earth commanders, though offended by the rank aggression of the Romulans, offered to meet and work out a solution. The Romulans rebuffed them. President Patel chose not to tolerate the bully tactics of this faceless enemy; Earth would have full access to space. UESPA sent the *U.S.S. Armstrong* to intentionally violate the Romulan ultimatum, as a fleet of Earth ships, their hulls freshly reinforced, their weapons arrays equipped with atomic missiles, waited within warp distance for the conflict to begin. The Romulans attacked; they had atomic weapons, too, and destroyed the *Armstrong*. The rest of the Earth fleet dropped out of warp and obliterated the Romulan vessel in retaliation.

Over the next four years, Human and Romulan space armadas battled throughout the area now known as the Neutral Zone, although Romulan raiders struck deep into Human space. The Romulans laid claim to a bigger fleet, manned by suicidally courageous crews ready to sacrifice their own lives in the name of victory. Terrans boasted superior maneuverability, thanks to their warp-drive technology, as well as wily captains always ready to bend the rules and take their Romulan counterparts off-guard. Casualties were high on both sides; many of today's Starfleet officers still revere the names of forebears killed in this formative struggle.

The Earth fleet wore down the Romulans one ship at a time, in a grinding war of attrition. The tide turned at the Battle of Cheron, when Earth's resourceful admirals managed to lure a full two thirds of the remaining Romulan fleet into a trap, destroying it to the last vessel. The humiliated Romulans sued for peace, and in 2160 the two powers negotiated the treaty, establishing the untouchable Neutral Zone between Earth and Romulan territory, by radio. The Earth commanders still didn't get to look their vanquished enemies in the eye.

FEDERATION

Immediately after the conclusion of the war, and less than a decade after the completion of its own one-world government, Earth took its first step toward one galaxy government, sponsoring the so-called Terran Conventions of Epsilon Eridani, a round of diplomatic talks between what would become the founding races of the Federation. In addition to the Vulcans and Centaurans, the participants included the hot-blooded, blue-skinned Andorians and the blunt-snouted, brusque Tellarites. The talks succeeded beyond the expectations of the participants; the leaders of the five races watched as their new unifying entity, the United Federation of Planets, fell easily into place, as if destined to do so. Only a year later, in 2161, the United Federation of Planets became a reality.

A period of euphoria followed. The trade, cultural, and military exchanges inspired by the alliance brought increased prosperity to all five founding cultures. Good times spurred social advances. Earth was able virtually to eliminate poverty on the homeworld and on Mars. The idealistic society people had long dreamed of blossomed with surprising speed. Greed became an anachronism. Want became a memory. Every schoolchild grew up knowing that he would be part of the dawning of a new era.

THE EXPLORATION ERA

The economic expansion was part and parcel of a broader move to investigate, survey, and colonize countless solar systems. Colonization efforts, often coordinated between several of the five founding species, had already begun during the days of the informal alliance. The optimism of the post-Federation years fueled them further. The Federation celebrated colonists and explorers alike as great frontier heroes. Colonists suffered enormous challenges, risking death on dozens of distant, sometimes inhospitable, worlds. The explorers, part of the new combined star fleet of the five worlds (called, appropriately enough, Starfleet) faced these same dangers, and quickly learned that the armaments they'd equipped their vessels with were necessary in a universe populated not only by peaceful, open alien races, but by a variety of menacing species and strange threats. The new flagship vessels, the *Daedalus*-class ships, proved their ruggedness and versatility (and that of their crews and captains) in the face of these many dangers. Ships such as the *U.S.S. Horizon*, the *Daedalus* herself, and the lost *U.S.S. Archon* became legendary not only in Starfleet but throughout the quadrant, among beings who had never seen a Human.

Starfleet's initial policy was to contact all intelligent lifeforms, in order to learn about them and arrange mutually beneficial exchanges of goods and technologies. Many of these first contacts were successful. Some races, such as the Vulcanoid Rigelians, applied for, and won, membership in the Federation shortly after establishing initial relations. Some in Starfleet voiced concerns about contact with species whose cultural development was less advanced than the Federation member races. Although some less developed planets quickly found a role in the Federation, others (such as the people of Sigma Iotia II) found their cultures distorted by first contact.

Even the species who rejected Starfleet overtures were more aloof than hostile. With the early, disastrous encounter with the Romulans now over half a century in the past, citizens of the Federation expected that all future contacts would be benign. Optimism became naïveté, setting the scene for the arrival of one of the Federation's fiercest enemies.

THE KLINGONS

In 2218, a Starfleet ship on a diplomatic mission encountered members of a previously unknown race—the Klingons. The Klingons tricked the crew of the U.S.S. Ranger into expecting a peaceful diplomatic encounter. Instead, they slew every member of the Federation delegation, captured their vessel, and summarily executed the rest of the crew. The Klingons dismissed further, more cautious attempts at contact; Klingon commanders declared themselves exemplars of a courageous warrior people who lived only for conquest. The people of the Federation were weak, they crowed, and could expect only to be enslaved when the inevitable triumph of the Klingon Empire came. For the next five years, every encounter was a hair-trigger affair; more than once a Starfleet captain found himself powering up his weapons. Time after time, the Klingons backed down, waiting until the moment was right.

The Klingons, having completed their military build-up (using technology stolen from the captured Ranger), launched a sneak attack against the Federation colony of Ardan IV in 2223. For the next nine years, nearly every encounter between a Starfleet and a Klingon vessel resulted in a skirmish, or even a battle to the death. The most famous conflict of the war was the Battle of Donatu V, in which more ships were deployed—and destroyed—than in any fight in Federation (or Klingon) history. Federation victory at Donatu V turned the tide of the conflict. In its aftermath, even the bloodthirsty Klingons showed a willingness to withdraw when challenged. The war cooled without ending.

THE PRIME DIRECTIVE

The failure of first contact with the Klingons haunted Federation officials. The Federation Council debated its entire policy of undiscriminating overtures to all intelligent lifeforms. The debate took on a life of its own, concerning itself with the right of the Federation to interfere in the historical development of other species. Council members hammered out the terms of the Prime Directive, a doctrine of noninterference which would henceforth guide all contact between Starfleet crews and new races. They strictly forbade potentially distorting contact with cultures that had yet to achieve warp capability. With some exceptions for primitive planets contacted earlier, the Prime Directive became Starfleet General Order No. 1 in 2220. Although the policy supposedly supersedes all other considerations (hence the name), it sometimes proves difficult to live up to under actual field conditions.

NEW SHIPS AND NEW THREATS

2245 saw the commissioning of perhaps the most celebrated ship in Starfleet history, the U.S.S. Enterprise. The new Constitution-class vessels, such as the Enterprise, represented a big leap forward in starship engineering. Their clear superiority over their predecessors gave pause to the steeliest Klingon commanders. The brilliant, mercurial Captain Robert April helmed the Enterprise for its maiden five-year voyage. The nature of its first mission remains to this day a top secret of the Federation; both Romulan and Orion spies have in recent years been apprehended trying to steal classified files describing this mysterious incident. April's celebrated exploits as captain of the Enterprise include the emergency evacuation of Ursa II, the destruction of the oxygen vampires of the Altair nebula, and the rescue of the Midnight Six from the radioactive pocket dimension on the fringes of the Neutral Zone. He also established what has become a long tradition for Enterprise captains, by testing the limits of the Prime Directive.

While attending a cultural exchange event on Signara, a planet friendly to the Federation, which had chosen to not to apply for Federation status, April stumbled across a conspiracy hatched by a coterie of Signaran legislators. Their intent was to overthrow Signaran democracy through a massive hoax that claimed alien infiltration of all levels of their society. Although the affair was none of the Federation's business, April outconspired the conspirators, finally exposing the primary plotter in a pugilistic contest. April was subjected to a board of inquiry and officially reprimanded by the Federation Council. He was neither demoted nor stripped of his command, though, and his career progressed unimpeded by this incident, or by the six other such incidents later in his command.

Starfleet Command promoted April at the end of his second five-year tour as Enterprise captain. After nearly ten years in service as an admiral, April stepped aside to take a position as special lecturer at Starfleet Academy, where his anecdote-packed lectures for the starship tactics and astropolitics courses remain ferociously well attended. April also serves the Federation well as an ambassador-at-large, traveling on diplomatic business to many planets that he himself first discovered.

KODOS

One of the worst disasters of the colonization movement shocked the Federation in 2246, when the isolated colony of Tarsus IV suffered a famine. An unbalanced individual named Kodos took advantage of the emergency

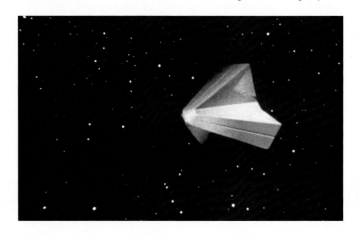

CAPTAIN CHRISTOPHER PIKE

Captain Christopher Pike took over the bridge of the *Enterprise* in 2250, serving as captain until 2263. Notable events of his tenure include the discovery of Talos IV, a planet inhabited by mentally advanced beings so powerful that the Federation imposed General Order 7, quarantining the planet from Federation contact on pain of death.

The *Enterprise*'s survey of the planet Eridios nearly led to total disaster. The *Enterprise*'s warp signature created powerful resonance waves within the crust of Eridios, composed of a dilithium-kemacite crystalline matrix. Only Pike's quick-thinking order to vaporize the surface of the planet with the ship's weapons prevented Eridios' crustal matrix from ripping apart all of spacetime. Even now, temporal rifts remain common in the Eridios system. Although no ship has discovered any other such planet, Pike's General Order 24 remains on the books just in case. Pike also unlocked the sinister secrets of the resort asteroid Cronari, saving many prominent Federation vacationers from death at the hands of a transdimensional doomsday cult, and saved the vital medicinal flora of Beta II.

Pike turned the *Enterprise* over to James T. Kirk in 2263. In 2266 he suffered severe, incurable radiation burns in an accident aboard a training vessel. The psychically powerful Talosians then contrived to bring Pike to their quarantined planet, where they offered him a life free from the shackles of his ruined physical body. Presumably, he remains on Talos IV to this day.

had never turned down a willing applicant, and that it had no right to interfere in the internal affairs of would-be members.

Axanari leaders took the questions about its status as an outright rejection, and, offended by the mention of their inferior technology, decided to prove their worthiness. They conquered several neighboring worlds and presented them to the Federation Council as tribute. Ambassador T'Pavis threatened to pull Vulcan out of the Federation if Axanari aggression went unchecked, and Andorian Admiral Farsha, seeing a grave threat, added his arguments to hers. This stand swayed the more cautious members; a fleet of ships, commanded by Captain Garth of Izar, hurtled toward Axanar to demand their immediate withdrawal from the conquered planets. This further offended the Axanari, who refused to stand down. A series of deadly engagements followed, pitting the numerically superior Axanari fleet against the more advanced *Constitution*-class vessels of the Federation. Garth's tactical brilliance, bolstered by the bravery of his Starfleet crews, carried the day for the Federation. The Axanari surrendered and abandoned their conquered planets. Their leaders resigned in disgrace, leaving new officials to negotiate peace terms with the Federation. Captain Garth proved as gifted in peace as he was in war, negotiating an agreement which laid the grounds for a future alliance. One of the junior members of the Federation delegation was a cadet on the *U.S.S. Republic*, one James T. Kirk. Kirk, despite his low rank, ended up taking a decisive role, uncovering an old-guard assassination plot against the new Axanari leadership. Kirk was awarded the Palm Leaf of Axanar Peace Mission during the treaty signing ceremony.

CHALLENGE AND CHANGE

In the last twenty-five years, the Federation has seen the potential, and the problems, of its expansion increase. Fortunately, the brave men and women of Starfleet remained up to every challenge. Captain Gan Laikan's *U.S.S. Asimov* visited more new planets, and charted more new worlds, than any other Starfleet vessel, and the Andorian crew of Captain Igrilan's *U.S.S. Eagle* has earned more decorations for heroism than any other command in the fleet. But from 2263 to the present day, many of the most crucial developments in Federation history have involved Captain James T. Kirk and the *Enterprise*.

In 2265, Kirk discovered the fate of the lost *Valiant* on the edge of the galaxy, and tracked the final voyage of the *Archon* to Beta III two years later. Kirk wrapped up two more, bloodier historical mysteries when he unmasked Kodos the Executioner and discovered the ancient sleeper ship holding the tyrant superman Khan Noonian Singh. The *Enterprise* thwarted the first Romulan attack in over a century in 2266, fended off a Tholian trap which had claimed the *U.S.S. Defiant* in 2268, and parried Klingon thrusts both before and after advanced energy beings enforced the Organian Peace Treaty of 2267 on both sides. The *Enterprise* also holds an important place in the expansion of Federation knowledge, if only because of its role in the discovery of the time-traveling "slingshot effect" in 2267. Kirk and the *Enterprise* made first contact with scores of races, including the nearly extinct First Federation, the maternal Horta of Janus VI, the wily Gorn, and the noncorporeal Metrons and

conditions to stage a coup against the colony's legitimate rulers. He proceeded to "solve" the food crisis by selecting half of the colony's population—four thousand people all told—to die. Kodos personally chose the victims according to his own twisted eugenic theories, earning himself the nickname Kodos the Executioner. The crew of the *U.S.S. Constellation*, led by Captain Matt Decker, responded to a covert distress call sent by survivors and retook Tarsus IV. Kodos was presumed killed in the fierce house-to-house fighting. The name of Kodos the Executioner is now a hateful reminder that even in enlightened times, mankind's darker instincts still hold sway over some.

THE AXANAR REBELLION

The Federation faced its worst internal crisis since its foundation over the issue of Axanar's application for UFP membership. The Axanari, a proud people with a rigidly hierarchical social structure, all but demanded membership in 2252. They pointed to their interstellar spaceships and tight sense of discipline as hallmarks of their development as a civilization. Their application split the Federation Council. One faction, led by the Centaurans and Vulcans, argued that the Axanari class system was too oppressive; its lower castes lived in virtual slavery. Besides, the Axanari didn't technically qualify for membership because their ships weren't propelled by true warp technology. Other members, spearheaded by the Tellarites and Andorians, argued that the Federation

Melkotians. Although some criticize Kirk for his seemingly cavalier attitude toward the Prime Directive, he has been dauntless in its enforcement on planets from Omega IV to Ekos to Planet 892-IV.

TODAY

By now, many issues pull the worlds of the Federation ever closer together. Romulan raids on Tau Ceti and Klingon infiltrators on Capella IV strike at the core of the Federation, even as Orion pirates attempt to loosen the hold of peaceful trade on the fringes. With the admission of Axanar in 2265 and Coridan in 2267, old rivalries within the Federation heal even as its enemies combine in alliance. Although the all-Vulcan *U.S.S. Intrepid* was lost near the Gamma 7A system last year, ever-increasing numbers of Vulcans are following Commander Spock into Starfleet service.

As 2269 dawns, Kirk's first five-year mission in the *Enterprise* is ending, but the age of exploration and adventure is far from over. This remains a time of excitement and danger, of continuing colonization and invention. Vast sectors of space remain mysterious, providing plenty of opportunity for intrepid Starfleet officers to write the next chapter of Federation history.

Organization and Activities

Although the Federation is nearly a hundred years old, it in large part remains a loose alliance of member species who recognize political and cultural integration as an ideal which as of yet has been put only imperfectly into practice. For more details on the Federation (and its next hundred years), see **The Price of Freedom: The United Federation of Planets** supplement.

GOVERNMENT

A hundred years from now, the Federation will no doubt have evolved into a centrally governed confederation efficiently managed by a stable, highly complex, bureaucratic structure. This is not that Federation. In 2269 Federation structure and operations remain surprisingly flexible. The planets of the Federation improvise their way through the political challenges posed by the great age of exploration. Like the Starfleet captains who courageously illuminate the still-unplumbed depths of the galaxy, the Federation officials of 2269 must evaluate each situation as it arises.

CONSTITUTION

The Constitution, drafted in 2160 and ratified the following year, establishes a framework for the operations of government and provides fundamental guarantees of individual rights for Federation citizens.

Framework

The Constitution establishes that a president will preside over a Federation council, on which each member planet has one voting seat. The President exercises a great deal of leeway in making executive decisions, so much so

that enemy propagandists (like the Klingons) can get away with portraying the Federation as a dictatorship. In fact the President reports to the Council, in which the true power of the Federation rests.

The Council

The framers of the Constitution, innovative deal-makers to a man, knew first-hand the importance of wiggle room to the diplomatic process. Not wanting to hamstring those who followed in their footsteps, they filled the Federation Constitution with principles and broad statements, keeping rigid rules and structures to a minimum. The Constitution codifies very little about the make-up of the council, except to say that each member planet selects its councilor in whatever way it sees fit. It outlines the broad powers of the Council but specifies only the sketchiest of parliamentary procedures. It doesn't even tell the Council how often it should meet. Currently the Council convenes only on a contingency basis, when there is a matter of top-level policy to resolve, such as the strategic response to a crisis or a new candidate planet's application for Federation membership. Many member states tap high-ranking diplomats to fill the chairs of the Council chamber; thus many Councilors are also ambassa-

PROMINENT CURRENT COUNCIL MEMBERS

The virtuous, strong-willed **Sarek** of Vulcan often dominates debate at Council conferences, especially since recent heart surgery restored his health and sense of purpose. His logic and moral authority demand respect from even his most truculent colleagues.

Councilors know the Tiburonese Ambassador **Threta** as both a skilled negotiator and a notorious lothario always on the lookout for new romantic conquests. His great personal charm and empathy for other's points of view allows him considerable success in both of these callings.

The gravel-voiced Tellarite **Morpro** intimidates less confident colleagues with her take-no-prisoners negotiating style. A stickler for rules and a dedicated upholder of tradition, Morpro pursues Tellarite diplomatic objectives with the unwavering certainty of a mathematical formula.

dors. Technically, decisions on the Council are made on a simple majority-vote basis; if more than half of the Councilors agree on a piece of legislation, it is enacted into law. Amendments to the Constitution, however, require a two-thirds majority of the Council as a whole, and the votes of three out of five of the founding members (that is, the Centaurans, Humans, Vulcans, Tellarites, and Andorians). Because the broad principles of the Constitution can be interpreted in various ways, eloquent Councilors can, if they so desire, block proposed actions or laws by questioning their constitutionality. This may seem like a recipe for chaos, but it preserves the vital, living energy of the Council, shaping it into an institution which must continually be renewed by the best and brightest politicians and diplomats in the galaxy. Getting things done is never easy, but that's how the framers intended it. Taking a leaf from Thomas Jefferson of Earth and Jora Kanta of Tellar, the framers reasoned that the best guarantee of freedom from tyranny was to see to it that passing a new law is a very hard thing to do. The process discourages rash decisions.

Council meetings are often stirring to behold, as the most eloquent debaters and sagacious political philosophers in the galaxy gather to engage one another in duels of knowledge, wisdom, and wit. Councilors work to persuade each other outside formal sessions as well; an effective Councilor must reach out to other planets for support. This, too, was part of the founders' design.

There is no set location for Council meetings, although Article Thirteen of the Constitution establishes the permanent seat of the Federation Council on Earth. It is a measure of the caution with which even established members of the Federation regard one another that many major conferences still occur in neutral locations, such as the asteroid Babel. Much to the chagrin of security officers, the headstrong Councilors often choose to meet in interesting new locations rather than the safe confines of Federation Hall in San Francisco. New surroundings stimulate new thinking, or so the rationalization goes. Unfortunately, interesting locations tend to be hard to secure, and more than one conference—as Councilors like to call especially important meetings—has been rendered a little too exciting by attempts at assassination or sabotage.

President

The head of the executive branch is elected by a majority vote of the Federation Council and serves for a six-year term. The Constitution does not limit the number of terms the President may serve, but current custom dictates that he should enthusiastically decline all entreaties to seek an additional term when his first has expired. The President's primary duty is to implement faithfully the laws and policies laid out by the Council. He is almost invariably also his home planet's Council member; otherwise he would be unable to propose new regulations or participate in Council debates. The typical President musters influence beyond his single vote as a Council member, since he wouldn't have been elected in the first place without the respect of the others.

The President is subject to recall at any time. Recall requires a three-fourths vote of the Council. No president has ever been recalled, or even seriously threatened with recall.

The President's chief duties lie in the realms of diplomacy and defense. In diplomatic matters, he may serve as chief negotiator during high-level meet-

PRESIDENT MCLAREN

Current Federation President Lorne McLaren, a lantern-jawed, white-haired Human who wears authority like a favorite old jacket, works hard to duck ceremonial functions whenever possible. As a result, he can almost never be found in his official quarters at Empyrean House in Paris, Earth. He wouldn't get away with this if he weren't so well loved by the bulk of the Council. McLaren prefers to spend his time on defense issues. Unlike most of his predecessors, McLaren is himself a former Starfleet commander; his hard-bitten manner makes it easy for those who meet him to picture him barking out orders on the bridge of a starship. Sometimes the Starfleet admiralty wishes he weren't quite so full of hands-on experience. He's too apt to get into operational details best left to lower-ranking officers, they complain. Even more annoyingly, when he does micromanage, he's usually right. At the same time he busts the chops of high-ranking rear-echelon types, McLaren staunchly supports the right of captains and commodores to make gut decisions in the field. His attitude toward the bending of rules such as the Prime Directive can almost be summed up as "boys will be boys"; this approach troubles some of the literalists on the Council but seems to work. McLaren took office last year; his term expires in 2274.

ings with foreign powers, or appoint an official to appear as his representative. The President takes no diplomatic initiatives without the explicit authorization of the Council.

The President exercises broad authority in matters of defense, because military decisions must often be made on the spur of the moment. The Council can make general policy concerning Starfleet operations, and may choose to review Presidential decisions on constitutional grounds. In practice, the Council allows the President to implement defense policies with a minimum of guessing. Its primary check on the President's control of defense lies in the allocation of resources; if the President wants to build a new fleet, the Council must agree to pick up the tab.

Federation Presidents face a bewildering array of ceremonial duties. Traditionally, they do their best to fob these duties off on past Presidents and advisors. Even the most successful in this regard spend over half of their time officiating at ceremonies, delivering speeches, christening vessels, attending official arts events, and entertaining visiting dignitaries.

The Secretariat

The Federation President draws upon the knowledge and experience of an advisory panel called the Secretariat. Members of the Secretariat do not wield executive powers or head permanent departments of bureaucrats. They're appointed by the President and may be dismissed by him at any time, although since Federation Councilors hold the leading Secretariat posts, the President seldom uses these powers without calculating the political cost. Most serve on an *ad hoc* basis, traveling to the presidential offices as the need arises. Sometimes they take on specific missions, and are assigned resources and personnel to aid them in the accomplishment of same. These resources may include starships; Starfleet sometimes orders its captains to aid a Secretariat member in the completion of an especially risky task. Clashes of authority between captains and presidential secretaries on such missions are regrettably common.

Although the President changes the specialties represented on the Secretariat according to circumstances, certain positions are so obviously necessary that they are almost always represented. These seats include Commerce Secretary, Science Advisor, Chief Diplomat, Attorney General, and a Secretary of Planetary Affairs. Most of these are self-explanatory; the Planetary Affairs advisor deals with conflicts that arise between member planets. President McLaren, himself a military expert, has dropped the traditional post of Defense Secretary.

Starfleet

The most important organization overseen by the Federation President is Starfleet. It's so important it gets its own chapter, starting on page 25.

Science Council

The Science Council is a think tank devoted to research and technology. If you were to draw up a list of the greatest scientific minds of the last century, from Richard Daystrom to Roger Korby, almost all of them would be past or present members of the Science Council. It allocates resources to research projects throughout Federation space. It sponsors conferences that promote knowledge exchange between far-flung researchers. Other conferences grapple with the effect of technological change on the Federation and its neighbors. The Council itself is headquartered in Geneva, Switzerland, but its conferences and research projects are peppered throughout the Federation, with especially important centers on Vulcan and Tellar.

Starfleet personnel get involved with Science Council projects when those projects go awry—as they are prone to do from time to time—or when enemies of the Federation choose them as targets for espionage or sabotage. Starfleet routinely assigns starships to carry out surveys and experiments under the supervision of senior Science Council researchers. Academics can be a handful even when everything goes as expected; such missions do not always go as expected. Scientists expose themselves to all sorts of weird viruses, types of radiation, and alien influences in the course of their work; every so often a Science Council member goes insane and causes the kind of trouble only a Starfleet crew can handle.

Federation Court

The judicial branch of the 23rd-century Federation has yet to progress beyond the status of a quasijudicial body. Member planets, still protective of their own sovereignty, have withheld enforcement powers from the judiciary. The Federation Court issues rulings on disputes between members, but those rulings are binding only if both parties agree beforehand to submit to them. When both parties to a dispute are willing, then, the court serves as a mediation service. The vast bulk of intra-Federation disputes are resolved not through the Federation, but through bilateral diplomatic talks between the relevant parties.

Analysts from the Tellarite Institute of Political Science predict that the Federation Court will eventually transform into a Supreme Court, as the Federation itself continues its ongoing evolution toward a true centralized government.

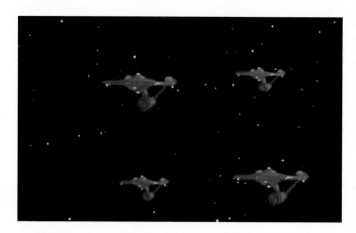

Infiltrators, spies, and saboteurs are interested in the court only when it has the power to resolve something. Thus, Starfleet officers are likely to find themselves embroiled in its affairs only when important issues are subject to pending arbitration.

MEMBERSHIP

To qualify for membership in the Federation, a candidate planet must meet the following criteria:

- It must be a starfaring culture, with true faster-than-light capability.
- It must have a single world government with a record of internal stability.
- It must be at peace with its neighbors, and likely to remain so.
- It must be willing and able to lend its resources to support Federation activities.
- It must be willing to accept the principles embodied in the Federation Constitution. (Current thinking among the Federation Council is on the lenient side where the finer points of the universal rights of sentient beings are concerned. For example, some member states, such as Ardana, maintain caste systems which deny certain rights to individuals based on birth status. Council members believe that it is dangerous and even immoral to demand dramatic cultural changes from candidate worlds, even when those planets display a radically different understanding of individual rights. A growing minority among the Council continues to challenge this long-established balance between the right of a culture to maintain its heritage and the right of all Federation citizens to expect equal treatment under the law. If a single political issue stands to drive a wedge between Council members in the decades to come, this is that issue.)

When a planet joins the Federation, it expects to gain specific benefits, in exchange for fulfilling certain obligations.

Benefits

One reason candidates apply for Federation membership is economic. The Federation monitors and regulates the most lucrative trade routes in the known galaxy. With the recent addition of dilithium-rich Coridan to its ranks, the Federation claims a supply of every major natural resource somewhere within its space. Membership in the Federation grants access to a rock-solid universal financial system and bolsters the stability of domestic markets. The mere possibility of Federation membership is enough to lift a planetary economy out of the doldrums.

Likewise, Federation membership provides immediate access to an array of technological marvels ranging from the terraforming techniques of Alpha Centauri, to the starships of Earth, to the medical advances of Vulcan science.

The Federation guarantees the security of all of its members. Few individual planets can field a navy as powerful as Starfleet. Planets on likely pathways of Klingon or Romulan conquest have special motivation to join the Federation, before it's too late.

The Federation Council maintains a hefty budget for emergency relief. Experienced Starfleet personnel supervise efforts to combat plagues, relieve famines, and evacuate victims of natural disasters.

The Council itself represents a pool of the best diplomatic talent in the quadrant. Ambassadors of the Federation regularly lend their aid to member planets engaged in negotiations with foreign powers.

Obligations

Members are expected to contribute to the Federation institutions that provide the above benefits. They must contribute material or financial resources to maintain Starfleet, fund the efforts of the Science Council, keep trade regulators in business, and deliver emergency services. They must allow Starfleet and other Federation organizations right of free movement through their territories. They must provide reasonable facilities for Federation operations on their soil.

ECONOMY

The Federation boasts the longest period of unfettered economic expansion in galactic history. Its founding worlds completely eliminated poverty during the first few decades of the colonization movement. Most other long-term members are now well on the way to doing so.

Experts attribute the astounding success of the Federation economy to four factors: the free flow of goods and information within its boundaries, near-universal access to education for its people, technologies like fusion plants and automated factories that lower costs for energy and materials, and new demand created by the colonization movement.

The stability of the Federation, and the well-being of its people, depend upon the protection of interstellar commerce and of the colonies that fuel it. The vibrant economy allows Federation shipyards to continue pumping out the superior starships that make Starfleet a force to be reckoned with. Starfleet captains often find themselves protecting food shipments from contamination, running off space pirates, investigating damage to communications relays, and saving colonists from a wide variety of threats.

CURRENCY

Federation officials unveiled the Federation credit about forty years ago. Its introduction solved a chronic problem with interstellar trade: currency fluctuation and speculation. The credit serves as universal currency everywhere in the Federation. Starfleet conducts all of its business in credits. Some planets, most notably Earth, abandoned their old monetary systems and now rely entirely on the credit. Others cleave to their currency for internal use, reserving the use of the credit for interstellar transactions.

On some non-Federation worlds, you can convert credits to the local currency. This is possible only on worlds with a history of long-term, friendly contact with the Federation. On remote or newly discovered worlds, it should

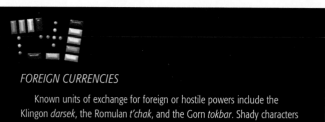

go without saying that a Federation credit isn't worth a plugged *tokbar*. Currencies of hostile civilizations are tough to come by; only a handful of neutral trading worlds offer direct exchange between Federation credits (or local currencies of member worlds) and Klingon *darseks* or Romulan *t'chaks*.

When currency fails, engage in barter. Cargo holds of larger Starfleet vessels assigned to contact new starfaring civilizations contain supplies of desirable trade goods, from medicines to rare minerals. Starfleet is generally forbidden from overt contact with prewarp species; they don't trade in bangles and beads.

Federation diplomats often arrange for transfers of large shipments of goods when opening relations with newly discovered neighbors. Starfleet ships often escort the trading vessels delivering such shipments.

CHANGED ATTITUDES

The unprecedented strength of the Federation economy over the past ninety years changed not only peoples' material circumstances but their entire way of thinking about money and wealth. When everyone's basic needs are taken care of, personal priorities change. People still strive for status and recognition. Getting rich is simply no longer a good way of going about it. In a galaxy where everybody enjoys relatively easy access to luxury goods, owning fine clothes, rare jewelry, or other appurtenances of wealth fails to impress. Most Federation citizens regard greed as a weird and primitive impulse. In the Federation, it's not what you own, it's what you *do* that counts. The late 23rd century is a time of heroes: stalwart Starfleet officers, brave colonists, bold scientists, intrepid traders. Today's ambitious people want to change the galaxy for the better, thereby winning honors and admiration, and ideally a place in the history books. A balance sheet laden with zeroes, in and of itself, just isn't considered noteworthy. Successful traders win admiration for building things and improving lives, and for overcoming the risks and difficulties that face the creator of a business empire.

Expect to find these attitudes firmly entrenched within Starfleet. Starfleet officers see money as a handy thing to have around when shore leave rolls around, but are otherwise unconcerned with it. Most officers spend much less than they earn, and couldn't even tell you their current account balances. Promotions and commendations measure success. Luxury is for civilians. Aside from the occasional curio to decorate one's quarters or to give to someone else as a token of esteem, a Starfleet officer requisitions all his important possessions from headquarters. You might find the odd Starfleet

crewman with a collection of rare artifacts; if so, she's no doubt an expert in a related field of study who produces important academic papers in her off-duty hours.

FOREIGN POLICY

The Federation aims to include every known spacefaring civilization in its ranks, so that all peoples may join together in an interstellar utopia of limitless prosperity and personal fulfillment. That's the ideal, anyway. In practice, of course, Council members know that many foreign civilizations are xenophobic, hostile, or simply too independent to join any kind of Federation. While always holding out the hope that every civilization will eventually reform itself into an ideal candidate for Federation membership, the Council designs policies to encourage other spacefaring powers to be as neighborly as possible.

SECURITY

Above all, Federation foreign policy seeks to ensure the security of its people from aggression and conquest. Negotiation is the favored tactic; the Federation may be ready to fight, but only as an absolute last resort. The Federation never starts a fight. Preemptive strikes, even in cases where eventual aggression from another power seems inevitable, are strictly forbidden. However, it isn't shy about displaying its defense capabilities to discourage would-be conquerors from trying anything. As it proved in the Klingon Wars and the Axanar Rebellion, the Federation fights tenaciously to defend itself and its allies. Even in battle, the Federation maintains lofty principles. It doesn't use biogenic weapons or attack civilian targets. Starfleet captains don't destroy helpless enemies when a surrender is possible. Their duty is to win, not to inflict suffering on the enemy.

ALLIANCE

The Federation wants to ally with as many neighbors as possible. The ideal alliance is full Federation membership for the new neighbor—provided the neighbor fulfills the criteria needed to join. If not, Federation diplomatic teams willingly help the prospective candidate achieve a stable world govern-

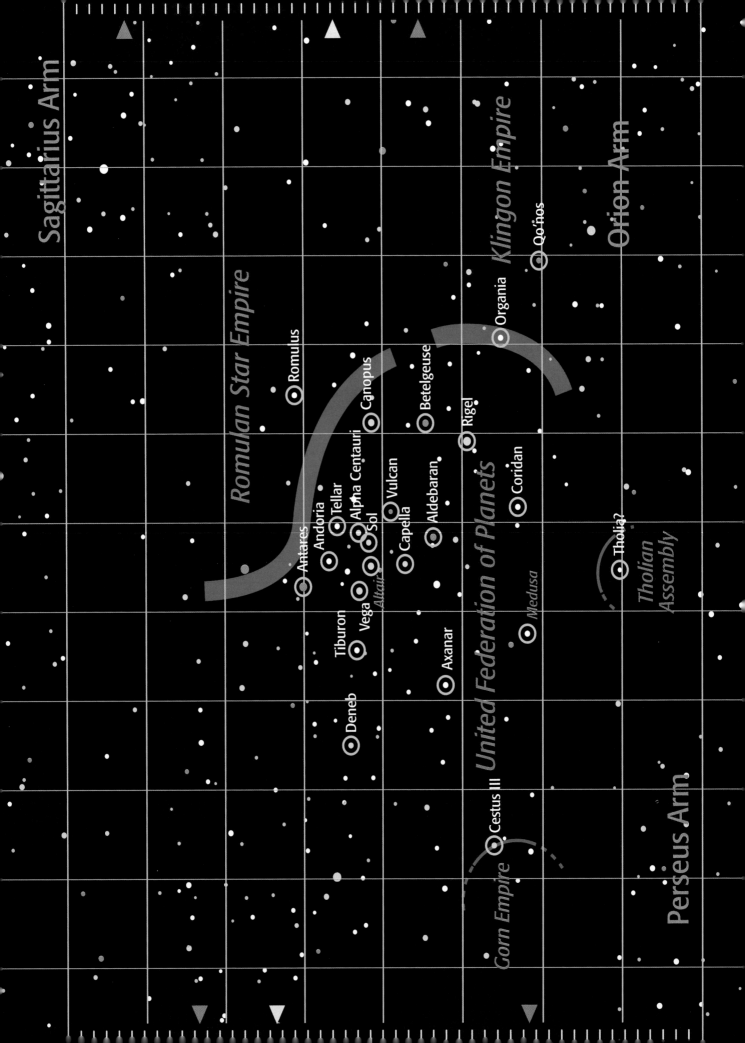

ment or make peace with its neighbors. They won't provide warp technology to those who lack it, though.

If a neighbor is unwilling or unable to join the Federation, diplomats instead seek alliances with it. The most basic type of alliance is the nonaggression pact, which guarantees that neither side will attack the other. Federation negotiators usually press for closer ties than that. They usually seek trade agreements, which reduce or eliminate tariffs and other barriers to the flow of goods and services between the two powers. Nothing promotes integration between neighbors like mutual economic interests; several planets that started out as mere trade partners of the Federation have later gone on to join it. Federation diplomats also covet cultural or technological exchange agreements, which provide for the flow of ideas from one party to the other.

FEDERATION SPACE

The Federation defines its territory as space surrounding its various member planets. The vastness of this space boggles the mind. Federation territory is not contiguous—that is, there is plenty of unexplored, dangerous, or foreign-occupied space in between the sometimes far-flung member planets. Envision it as a series of bubbles around member planets; the bubbles sometimes connect, but not always. Holes and gray areas on the interstellar maps far outnumber explored space. The Federation's so-called borders with hostile neighbors share this Swiss cheese quality. The Neutral Zone, as laid out in the 2160 treaty between Earth and the Romulans (now honored by the Federation), cuts a jagged swath through the stellar map, encompassing a vast gulf of unexplored space. The Klingon Neutral Zone, its borders drawn and imposed by the Organians, is likewise vague and ever-shifting.

THE SPACELANES

The so-called "spacelanes" are secure, easily navigable standard routes between member planets and the Federation's trade allies. Their security depends on the continued vigilance of Starfleet, which protects shipping from invaders, pirates, hostile unmanned ships, and dangerous spacefaring organisms. Vessels on patrol duty routinely survey the spacelanes for the sudden appearance of spatial anomalies, comets, radiation storms, and other natural hazards to shipping.

Starfleet vessels represent only a fraction of interstellar traffic within the Federation. Most vessels belong to private or state-sponsored commercial ventures. Passenger vessels also claim a big percentage of space traffic; many passenger fleets devote their entire capacity to ferrying emigrants to the colonies. Research vessels, even the sizeable Vulcan Science Academy fleet, make up a small percentage of traffic.

The Federation designates certain routes within its space as vital to commerce and patrols them heavily. These include the Rigel-to-Andoria corridor, routes from Tellar to several heavily colonized regions, and the bubble of space surrounding Vulcan, Sol, and Alpha Centauri.

Member Species

Although the UFP consists of several dozen member planets, certain member species will take a greater role in your game than others. The races most likely to belong to, or interact with, Starfleet are described below.

HUMANS

The Humans of Earth dominate Starfleet and take a pivotal role in the history of the Federation. Their dual natures are legendary throughout the quadrant. On one hand, they are capable of extraordinary courage, idealism, and altruism. On the other, they can display incredible violence, cruelty, and short-sightedness. They show considerable resourcefulness and tenacity in either direction. Although they're learning to control their darker qualities and have done great things for their allies in the Federation, many species remain wary of them.

Humans are plucky, determined, brave, and sometimes rash. Insatiably curious, they seek answers wherever there are questions. Many indulge a hedonistic streak, taking great pleasure in the sensual pleasures of the dining table, the well-stocked bar, and elsewhere.

That said, they're also a highly variable lot. Name an extreme of character, and we'll find you a Human who embodies that trait. As soon as you make a generalization about humankind, you'll meet a Human who explodes it.

23rd-century Humans are proud of their history, viewing its dark spots as anomalies in a slow struggle toward progress. Individuals maintain sentimental ties to the ancient nations of their ancestry. Despite their incomprehensibility to outsiders, the distinctions between Scots and Indians, or Portuguese and Japanese, remain important to Humans. They subject themselves to the folk music of their ancient nations, profess a preference for their traditional foods, affect their costume at ceremonial events, and make frequent conversational references to the great heroes of their particular ethnic persuasion. Even more curiously, they ascribe certain character traits to their ancestral groups, striving to live up to their own customary traits, while teasing others among them with good-natured jokes referencing their supposed ethnic qualities.

Humans respond well to command structures, especially that of Starfleet—after all, they designed it based on their own military history. Again their dual

natures come into play: They are capable of great discipline, but at the same time are adept at thinking "out of the box", solving problems with sudden leaps of intuition. The Human version of discipline allows people to work toward a common goal without losing touch with each participant's fundamental individuality. To command a Human successfully, you must earn his respect. Expect to be politely but firmly questioned if the reasons for your actions are unclear; Humans work best when they understand the goal and agree with the means chosen to accomplish it.

Humans fight the same way they do everything else: tenaciously, unpredictably, passionately. Earth's many old ethnic groups generated a staggering variety of fighting arts, from the unarmed martial techniques of the East to the high-spirited brawling tactics still practiced in barrooms throughout Federation space.

Humans pursue their leisure activities with the same fervor they employ in public life, devoting great energies to chosen pursuits, which they sometimes call "hobbies." Hobbies may be mental or physical in nature. Popular hobbies include arts and art appreciation, athletics, crafts, and the pursuit of science.

As much as any species in the galaxy, Humans venerate heroes whose accomplishments span a wide variety of fields. Playwright William Shakespeare, active in the 16th century, remains the most-quoted Human. Other Human heroes include political leaders Abraham Lincoln and Mahatma Gandhi, warp-drive pioneer and peace activist Zefram Cochrane, landscape artist Hokusai, composers W. S. Bach and Wolfgang Mozart, athlete Jesse Owens, explorers Christopher Columbus and Neil Armstrong, military leader Joan of Arc, architect Buckminster Fuller, futurist Isaac Asimov, and scientists Isaac Newton, Albert Einstein, and Fang Lizhi.

ANDORIANS

The passionate, honor-driven Andorians take pride in their beautiful blue skin, fine white hair, and twin antennae. Their antennae grant them unusual sensory abilities: They detect subtle environmental changes and can sense extremes of the audio band inaudible to most other species. These capabilities make Andorians natural communications specialists. Hailing from a frigid homeworld, Andorians enjoy bracing, chilly temperatures and suffer silently when faced with hot weather.

Andorians recall their warrior heritage with pride. Their clan structure, once the root cause of terrible warfare, remains a source of dignity and a cause for contention. Grudges between clans still run deep, even though they're now dealt with in the contained environment of the dueling arena. Quick to take offense and slow to abandon a grudge, Andorians consider themselves dishonored if they fail to gain satisfaction when slighted. Their code of honor allows them to wait a considerable while before springing their revenge, however.

Andorians know that the best way to resolve a dispute is through ritualized hand-to-hand combat, at which they excel. Fiercely competitive but not stupid, they've learned to give outlanders the benefit of the doubt before issuing a challenge. The phrase "Did you *really* mean to say that, sir?" crops up often in touchy negotiations between Andorians and others. If the alien really *did* mean to say that, the duel is on, and any kind of special treatment goes out the airlock.

Outsiders see Andorians as taciturn and secretive; this perception flows from another aspect of their honor-bound culture. Andorians admire the ability to keep one's mouth shut, especially when sensitive information is involved. They despise gossips and other invaders of personal privacy. They also dislike indecision, and feel contempt for people who back down from their decisions or are unwilling to fight for strongly held beliefs. Long-windedness drives them crazy, too. No point in using a long sentence where a short one will do; if you can sum up your thoughts in a grunt or snort, so much the better.

Forthright Andorian thinking also expresses itself in their legendary desire for clear organizational structures. Andorian efficiency experts have done much to streamline the internal structures of the Federation. In Federation politics, Andorians frequently find themselves at odds with the blunt-spoken, prolix Tellarites, who love both to proliferate procedure and to talk about it endlessly. Andorians believe passionately in a clear chain of authority and are a dream to command, unless a commander is insensitive enough to transgress against their honor. The Andorian honor code forbids the breaking of laws; the concept of a foolish or unjust law that deserves to be broken is utterly alien to Andorian thinking. However, the idea that one can circumvent the apparent intent of a law while still cleverly obeying it to the letter is not so unfamiliar. Andorians make very good lawyers.

Andorians fight with zeal, ferocity, and skill. Hand-to-hand, one-on-one combat is their specialty. In all areas, they strive to live life to its fullest extent. They favor physical pursuits; if you can't feel it in your heart and in your bones, why bother? They channel their aggressive instincts into sports which pit one individual against another. Music fills the artistic lives of Andorians, because you can feel the pulse of the instruments in your body as you listen to it.

Andorian heroes include Lor'Vela, the great peacemaker who ended the clan wars that threatened to destroy Andorian society, and Sheras, one of the founders of the Federation and framers of its constitution. 19th-century duelist Atra is revered as the greatest Andorian fighting man, the planet's greatest exemplar of honor, and a tragic hero doomed by a love he could not deny. Ancient composer Falo'To originated most of the rhythmic conventions of Andorian music.

AXANARI

The Axanari claim a dubious distinction as the only people to have joined the Federation after going to war with it. Today's Axanari see the Axanar Rebellion (see page 12) as both a hideous misunderstanding and a historical turning point. For centuries, the Axanari lived within a rigid caste system in which the lower echelons were virtual slaves. The massive failure of the elite classes—who first misunderstood the Federation sufficiently to think they wanted some planets conquered for them, and compounded the mistake by refusing to back down when otherwise informed—caused great social upheaval on Axanar. A bloodless revolution—the Social Awakening, to use the Axanari term—followed. They abolished their caste system almost overnight, chaotically selecting new leaders from all classes to negotiate peace terms with the Federation. After a period of proving their good intentions, the Axanari overcame the mistrust of the Federation Council; they gained admission to the UFP four years ago. They now strive to prove themselves as worthy contributors to the Federation, working to atone for the blunders of their old leaders and old system. They have good reason to worry about the mistrust of colleagues: Any Starfleet officer as old or older than Kirk probably fought against the Axanari fleet, and well remembers comrades killed in the fighting. Some Axanari carry around gigantic chips on their shoulders, always ready to take offense at perceived slights; they hate the old regime that got them into war with the Federation and go to any lengths to distance themselves angrily from it. Others sheepishly curry favor with other Federation species, hoping to prove that they're friendly, thoughtful, and not at all the reflexively warlike conclusion-jumpers they're made out to be.

The crucial blunder of the Axanar Rebellion may be rooted in Axanari physiology. A variety of large predators with highly sophisticated camouflage abilities hunted the ancient hominid ancestors of the Axanari. In response, the Axanari evolved acute perceptual abilities, especially in the area of pattern recognition. These senses allowed them to spot predators, and then assisted in the development of intelligence. Today's Axanari see, hear, and smell better than most intelligent species. Their brains process perceptual information at a phenomenal rate, allowing them to identify the hidden patterns in what they see. This process looks like amazing intuition to others, but there's nothing psychic about it. Alas, if there's no pattern to detect, they'll often find one anyway. No Axanari language contains the phrase "I don't know." When you ask an Axanari a question, he makes a definite judgment one way or the other, even if insufficient evidence exists to draw any conclusion. He then treats his inference as conclusive fact and stands on it with absolute certitude.

This sense of certitude led Axanar's peoples into violent conflict, which ultimately led to the forcible institution of the old caste system. Axanari now face an identity crisis; their changing social system and attitudes don't provide the bedrock certainty the Axanari brain craves. Most Axanari feel lost, desperately searching for new certainties. Many hope to find these irrefutable truths in the Federation and in Starfleet.

Physically, Axanari are tall humanoids with varying complexions; a fine, whitish, dustlike secretion covers their skin and protects them from the high radiation levels of their homeworld. Axanari body and head hair comes in an

array of bright colors unknown to the Human head: violet, electric blue, Kelly green, fire-engine red, and orange-peel orange. Head hair is long and thick, allowing Axanari to twist and braid it into tall, sculptured castles of hair. Perhaps by contrast, they wear long, plainly decorated robes.

Axanari throw themselves into any task with gusto, but perhaps not much forethought. They fight eagerly, preferring to hurtle pell-mell into their foes, scattering them through sheer aggression and enthusiasm. They may have thrown off the caste system, but centuries of ingrained behavior don't vanish overnight; they respond almost joyfully to the exercise of strong authority. Woe betide the officer, however, who attempts to order an Axanari to do something that contravenes his personal list of certitudes.

Axanar's new heroes include Dura Ma, the young high-caste who first proclaimed the death of the old system; Quasa Koquasi, the former low-caste who now leads the planetary government, and Namyl Ruhart, the first Axanari to take a commission as a Starfleet officer.

CENTAURANS

Aside from Humans, Centaurans are the best-represented race in Starfleet. Their amazing physical and physiological similarity to Humans allows them to serve in great numbers on the primarily Human-built starships of the fleet. Even Centaurans can seldom tell the two races apart at a glance. Various theories seek to explain why the natives of Alpha Centauri are such close physiological kin to Humans. Only a few minor differences of internal anatomy separate the two races. Philosophical differences are more acute.

Peoples of all races agree that Alpha Centauri is the most beautiful of the Federation homeworlds; just gazing at an image of one of its green, harmonious landscapes can bring peace to the stormiest heart. Prolonged exposure to beauty has left an indelible mark on the Centauran soul. The highest compliment you can pay a Centauran is to call him peaceful, thoughtful, and spiritual. Centaurans seek out beauty throughout the galaxy; where they find no beauty, they try to make some. This attitude (and the unpredictable weather of a planet with three suns) spurred the development of Alpha Centauri's most famous technological discipline, terraforming. Their superior knowledge of biosystems sprang from their attempts to create lovely and harmonious ecosystems. Centaurans used both specialties to help Earth recover from the damage done by its Third World War.

Centauran attitudes toward Humans are often portrayed as "love-hate." Centaurans deplore Human rashness and violence, at the same time as they admire the vitality and resilience of Earth culture. They unequivocally admire the serenity and pacifism of the Vulcans, and take political inspiration from Vulcan's foreign policy.

Collective memories of rights abuses during the terrible Plague Years provide a motivating sense of shame for the Centauran people. They have sworn never again to permit themselves to allow the fears of the majority to override the sacred freedoms of the individual. If you're making a decision that favors expediency over principle, expect spirited argument from any Centaurans in your midst.

Centaurans see themselves as long-term thinkers. A favorite proverb says, "Worry about tomorrow, and today will take care of itself." To embark on a course of action without exhaustively exploring all of its possible ramifications is completely irresponsible. This tendency irritates less introverted Federation partners like Earth and Andoria, while drawing praise from Vulcans and Tellarites.

On a starship, a Centauran's habitual hesitation and introspection often prove to be his worst enemy. Commanders belonging to other species say that Centaurans find it difficult to obey a snap order unhesitatingly. In an emergency situation, even a sliver of a pause can be deadly, so Centaurans face a bad reputation among certain Starfleet captains, which they must strive mightily to overcome. On the other hand, they enjoy a positive image as far-thinking rear-echelon strategists.

Centaurans are not famed for their love of combat, although they're certainly not washouts in Starfleet Academy self-defense classes. Their home-grown martial arts emphasize holds and other maneuvers that render an opponent helpless without doing him permanent harm.

Common pursuits include the visual arts, literature, and artistic gardening. Holography, a field in which a variety of exciting technical advances loom on the horizon, attracts more avid practitioners every day. Centauran sports emphasize competition against the clock, or are subjectively graded by panels of judges on aesthetic grounds. Centaurans regard team and combat-based sports as hopelessly vulgar.

Centaurans venerate 17th-century vaccine discoverer and political savior Dr. Kulei Asephas as their greatest hero. Current celebrities include nonconformist sculptor Sherei Aacra and intrepid Starfleet explorer Gan Leikan.

TELLARITES

Tellarites are short-statured humanoids with porcine snouts. Males are hirsute. Females are … somewhat less hirsute. Tellarites are a proud people. They have a great deal to be proud of. They are precise. They are highly mathematical. They are pragmatic. When they have something to say to you, they say it. No weasel words, no shilly-shallying around the point. If you don't understand the point the first time, they'll repeat it. Again, if necessary. And again. When they know they are right, Tellarites don't back down. And Tellarites almost always know they are right.

Tellarites are skeptical. They don't trust people who are always going on and on about spirituality. Or philosophy. Or aesthetics. Or any kind of other nonsense you can never accurately measure. They're just trying to confuse you, that's what Tellarites say.

Tellarites are engineers. They understand how things work. How they're put together. How they come apart. How they can be improved. This is good.

Tellarites were social engineers. That wasn't so good. They came up with all kinds of different supposedly perfect societies. Then all these supposedly perfect societies fought each other, in what the Tellarites call the Voice Wars, and proved none of them was so perfect after all. Finally the Tellarites came to their senses, and realized that peace and unity were what worked. That was what was practical.

Tellarites like procedure. Procedure is good when you can trust it always to be the same. Big bureaucratic structures work extremely well, and are highly practical, if their procedures work properly. To have good procedures, you need good forms. Other races don't always understand this, and complain about having to fill out forms, and how the Tellarites want to make the Federation more bureaucratic, more systematic. That's because they don't know how to fill out forms properly, is what the Tellarites say.

Just because Tellarites like to talk plainly doesn't mean they don't like to talk. They like to talk a lot. Debate is good, because it allows you to explain how everything works. Long debates are better, because people who understand and appreciate the procedures can use them to make things work properly.

Tellarites would sooner make things than wreck them. But that does not mean they don't know how to fight. Ranged weapons are the best. Tellarites

think that people who prefer fists to phasers aren't thinking straight. Somebody went to the trouble of inventing phasers for a reason, you know.

Tellarites like to solve math puzzles. They like to design and build gadgets, just for the fun of it. Old technologies are still interesting and fun to work with, even if they are no longer the most practical. The great inventions of the past are still great, and should still be admired. Clockwork items are in a way more beautiful than the silicon and circuitry devices of today. Tellarites also like to debate, just for the fun of it. They also like good food and good drink. The body is a machine, too, and needs its fuel.

Some commanders don't like Tellarites because they question impractical orders and fuzzy thinking. They say Tellarites don't understand morale and don't always get along with others. But no one will fix that warp core for you faster than a Tellarite. Also, Tellarites never give up once they've fixed their minds on something. They'll keep working until the problem is solved.

Gnarr the Shipbuilder is a Tellarite hero; he designed the ships Starfleet flies. Tarnoc is another hero. He gave the Federation Constitution what structure it has. He set up the Federation commerce system, too. Both of them were right. They kept arguing with those who disagreed, until things were right.

TIBURONESE

The people of Tiburon are humanoid, on average several inches taller than humans, and have large and elaborately flanged ears.

The Tiburonese live in a highly technological society still scarred by a history of alien conquest. Modern Tiburonese are a hybrid of two races: the pastoral original Tiburonese and the Ucali, authoritarian invaders from another Class M planet in the Tiburon system. After losing a power struggle at home, a Ucali faction used prewarp ships to migrate to Tiburon, then conquered and subjugated its people. By treating all bodily pleasures as taboo, Ucali culture molded its young people into aggressive bullies fit only for conquest and domination. For centuries, the Ucali prospered at the expense of their forced laborers, the old Tiburonese. They even allowed the notorious butcher Zora to conduct atrocities on the Tiburonese in the name of scientific experimentation. But the Tiburonese possessed, in addition to an inexhaustible appetite for sensual pleasure, an innate cleverness that allowed them, over time, to subvert the self-denying ethos of their conquerors. Slowly they tempted their captors into a life of gratification and pleasure, until one day the Ucali underwent a cultural meltdown. Their youth rebelled, refusing to follow the orders of a corrupt old guard that preached rules it itself no longer obeyed. Anarchy followed. Even the government of the Ucali homeworld collapsed.

In the ensuing centuries, the Tiburonese and Ucali interbred to the point where they became indistinguishable. After a long era of technological stagnation—people were too busy having fun to think about machines and science—a Tiburonese renaissance redirected Ucali technical expertise toward the pursuit of pleasure and knowledge. The Tiburonese began to explore the stars.

Tiburonese believe that they exist in order to experience joy, and that the denial of pleasure serves as tyranny's handmaiden. They rely on technology to provide them with creature comforts; robotic devices perform almost all economic activity on Tiburon, leaving its people to enjoy a life of leisure. Some critics, as did the late exile Dr. Sevrin, claim that overreliance on technology has weakened the Tiburonese. It does seem to have suppressed their immune systems; the incurable and deadly disease synthococcus novae now infects thousands of Tiburonese.

Tiburonese are renowned for their expertise in robotics and other applications of high technology. They've also earned a reputation as masters of the erotic arts. Tiburonese treat the satisfaction of curiosity as a crucial pleasure and thus make good explorers. They also delight in subverting intolerant or authoritarian regimes. Since joining the Federation forty years ago, they've pushed it to take a more active role in deposing despotic rulers, arguing that there are higher virtues than the noninterference espoused by the Prime Directive.

Although used to having things done for them, Tiburonese aren't all lazy, fun-addled dilettantes. Charming and technologically adept, they perform admirably as negotiators and science officers. The more straitlaced officers in Starfleet dislike their sly humor and propensity for getting maximum results through minimum effort.

Almost every Tiburonese in Starfleet has at one time or another used the phrase "I'm a lover, not a fighter." The only thing they enjoy about fighting is complaining afterward about the bruises they've received.

Tiburonese heroes include the polymathic experimenter Neprin, who pioneered emotional cybernetics and atmospheric ionization, and Alari, whose seduction of the Ucali High Suzerain is regarded as the first step in the Grand Subversion.

VULCANS

Once a turbulent race ruled by passions so fierce that they nearly destroyed themselves, the Vulcans long ago transformed into paragons of logic and pacifism. They did so by adopting a forbidding mental regimen of emotional suppression through meditation and philosophical contemplation. The philosophy of logic, elusive to other species, makes Vulcans superb scientists and mediators. The dispassionate mode of inquiry that is the scientific method suits them perfectly. Countless tomes of Vulcan philosophy expound upon the logic of peace and cooperation; the trained Vulcan mind takes to diplomacy like a fish to water.

Vulcans are humanoid but have a physiology dramatically different from other species. Vulcan features are aquiline, their ears and eyebrows pointed. Having evolved on a harsh, rugged planet, their strength and endurance is much greater than a Human's. Vulcan's powerful sun caused its people to evolve inner eyelids to grant them protection from its radiation. Vulcan hearing is, of the races listed in this section, second only to that of the Andorians. Vulcan senses exceed the Human in psionic abilities as well, most famously the mind-meld, which allows a Vulcan to share the thoughts and experiences of another sentient being.

People from emotional cultures, particularly Humans, like to twit Vulcans about the virtues of the passionate life, forgetting that the untrained emotions of a Vulcan are much more powerful and erratic than their own. For a Vulcan, emotion is not just undesirable, but dangerous. Hints of this primitive emotion-

alism survive in the circumstances of Vulcan mating: Every seven years, a Vulcan is seized by *pon farr* and suffers an irresistible urge to join with his chosen mate. If unable to do so, the Vulcan suffers a possibly fatal neurochemical imbalance. In rare cases, a betrothed Vulcan bride may demand a fight to the death to determine who she will mate with. The emotion-laden facts of Vulcan biology and ritual remain a source of deep embarrassment to the Vulcans; even their Starfleet colleagues remain surprisingly ignorant of anything but the vaguest outlines.

Vulcans well understand the logic of the chain of command; the few of them who deign to join Starfleet enjoy a reputation for loyalty and good judgment. In the 2360's, despite their pivotal role in its creation, Vulcans remain uncomfortable mixing with the other races of the Federation. They prefer to journey through space together, in survey ships of the Vulcan Science Academy. They realize that their apparent coldness confuses and annoys many Humans and others, and see powerful logic in remaining aloof from a species whose violent and impulsive nature reminds them so vividly of their own dark and warlike past. A Vulcan choosing Starfleet over the Science Academy can expect the strong disapproval of his family, although the example of Spock and the sacrifice of the *U.S.S. Intrepid* drive young Vulcans into the service in slowly increasing numbers.

Vulcans fight only when logic provides no alternative, preferring nonlethal means of disabling opponents. The most famous technique for doing so is the Vulcan nerve pinch, which renders the recipient unconscious through applied acupressure.

Vulcan arts are austere and intellectual in nature. Vulcans don't do things for "fun"—a concept puzzling to them—but do recognize the necessity of relaxation. Preferred activities include meditation, scientific inquiry, musical mathematics, immersion in abstruse philosophy texts, and cerebral games such as three-dimensional chess.

It is logical to admire and emulate individuals of great achievement. A list of esteemed Vulcans begins with Surak, the great philosopher who created the system of logic and meditation that saved Vulcans from themselves. Among living Vulcans, the priestess T'Pau warrants great admiration for her poise and rectitude.

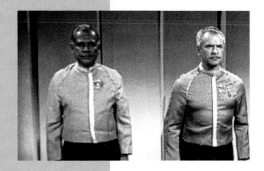

Seel could not restrain himself: "Hmpf!" he observed, studying the alien vessel on the ship's viewscreen. "What a shoddy design! It's a wonder that contraption can fly at all!"

Captain Diamond smiled; his truculent helmsman had always been a chauvinist in matters of ship construction. "It's a previously unknown species, Mr. Seel—you can hardly blame them for failing to hire Tellarite engineering consultants."

"Moreover," said Mr. Aroumti, "sensors detect a true warp engine aboard that ship."

"Which means, according to the Prime Directive, that we're allowed to contact them," said Diamond, happily completing his first officer's thought. "I was hoping they'd have a warp drive, because I'd really like to know what they're doing with our communications relay. Open a channel, Lieutenant."

Lieutenant Danna complied, not without a certain nervousness. First-contact situations were fraught with peril. The six-inch scar on her left thigh was testament to that, a souvenir of the ship's first brush with the Matapedians. Everything had worked out okay in the end, thanks to Captain Diamond's quick thinking. Moments like this still made her edgy, though.

The image of a humanoid appeared on the viewscreen, replacing that of the ungainly vessel. Its occupant was equally peculiar. The being's right side looked completely different from its left. Its right side was garbed in a shiny, metallic material; the right side of its head was hairless, the skin pale. The being's left side was hairy, olive-skinned, sharp-toothed; that half was clothed in animal hide and furs.

STARFLEET

"I am Captain Achilles Diamond of the starship Solzhenitsyn. I represent the United Federation of Planets. We are interested in peaceful interchange with our interstellar neighbors. And we're also wondering why your ship is dismantling our communications equipment."

The pilot of the other ship spoke from the left side of his mouth. "I am Harth. Seven times have I ridden the ka storm. Fourteen heads of the vunath have I taken. From the cup of the elmar I have supped. I have wet my lips with the blood of Osos. I own forty-nine slaves, and seven herds of sohax."

"Pleased to meet you, Harth. Now, about those relays …?"

The being then spoke from the right side of its mouth, in a higher, flutelike tone. "You address Harth. My score on the Examination Universal was 1,293. My paintings are on display in the Royal Museum of Alcansar. My epigrams are quoted nine times in the Ealsa Codex."

Diamond rolled his eyes. This was going to require all the diplomacy he could muster.

The Legacy Begins

The founders of the Federation created Starfleet during the Terran Convention talks of 2160; its birth coincided with that of the Federation itself. Since Earth's space navy (itself an ad hoc creation under the United Earth Space Probe Agency) was by far the largest and most modern of any of the Federation's founding planets, it made sense for the United Earth Republic to transfer UESPA authority to the newly born Starfleet. This established a tradition of Human space service that continues to this day—even now, Starfleet is mostly Human crews and officers flying Human-built ships (albeit with important design elements from Tellar and Andoria).

The framers of the Federation Constitution envisioned a fivefold mission for Starfleet: It would explore the galaxy, defend member planets, aid in the advancement of science, patrol the spacelanes, and promote galactic communications. Starfleet has done these things, and more, since its creation a hundred years ago.

GENERAL ORDERS

When you hear an officer called a "by the book" man, the book referred to is the Starfleet Manual of General Orders and Regulations. Most crew members just call it "The Book." A few pretentious types prefer to say SMGOR (pronounced sem-GOR), because they think service jargon sounds more impressive, especially when you're pronouncing an acronym as if it's a word.

The Book is always subject to revision. Revisions may be called for by Starfleet High Command, the President, or the Federation Council. Most revisions are additions and amendments. The one exception to this general tendency occurred in 2220, when debate over the drafting of the Prime Directive inspired a top-to-bottom procedural overhaul. Starfleet Command renumbered the list of general orders in order to give the Prime Directive pride of place in the manual, making the point that it superseded all other Starfleet regulations.

You'll note that the following is not a complete list of Federation general orders and regulations. After all, the Starfleet Manual is much thicker than the game rules you hold in your hand. In other words, we've left room for you to invent your own general orders and regulations as dictated by the needs of the stories you choose to tell. Make sure that your new regulations fit the spirit

of Starfleet. Remember that it is an idealistic organization operating in a tough universe, and that its rear echelon wants to strike a balance between consistency of operations and freedom of field commanders to do what needs to be done to accomplish the task at hand. If you do make up your own general orders or regulations, don't forget to make a note of them for future reference!

If a rule seems all-encompassing in nature, make it a general order. These set out the goals of the organization. Regulations, on the other hand, are detail-oriented, providing standard operating procedures used to achieve the above goals. Orders fall between the two extremes; they're neither broadly philosophical nor concerned with operational minutiae.

GENERAL ORDER ONE: THE PRIME DIRECTIVE

This one gets its own section. See page 28, below.

GENERAL ORDER TWO: PROTECT FEDERATION CITIZENS

Starfleet officers swear to protect Federation citizens from harm or loss of liberty. By invoking General Order Two, an officer declares that he is abandoning his current mission, or altering its terms in order to counteract an immediate and pressing threat to Federation citizens. For example, a starship captain sent to rendezvous with a scientific survey team would invoke General Order Two in order to answer a distress call from a Federation vessel instead of picking up the survey team on time. This order is so commonly invoked that only the most officious officers feel the need to cite it as they zoom off to deal with a newly discovered crisis.

GENERAL ORDER THREE: DESTRUCT SEQUENCE

General Order Three allows the current commanding officer to start the ship's computer-controlled destruct sequence, which will blow up the ship at a time specified by the officer, killing everyone on board. Officers should do this only to deal with situations where the threat to Starfleet and the Federation is so great that it justifies the loss of a ship. Captains use G.O. 3 when their ships are occupied by hostile forces and all other means of regaining control of the vessel have been exhausted. It is also highly useful as a bluff, although an unwritten general order of Starfleet surely reads, "Only bluff when you're prepared to be called on it." Obviously, G.O. 3 is easier to invoke if all Federation personnel can be evacuated from the ship before it blows. The protocols for initiating destruct sequences vary by ship class. *Constitution*-class vessels require verbal commands, with correct code group sequences, to be given by the commanding officer and two other senior officers to begin self-destruct. The sequence can be aborted until the five-second mark, at which point there's nothing to do but count along with the computer until the ship explodes.

GENERAL ORDER FOUR: NOTWITHSTANDING PROTOCOL

By invoking this protocol, flag officers (see page 30) can issue mission objectives which cannot be countermanded by any other general order. They use this protocol only for missions so sensitive that their failure would threaten the survival of the Federation itself, or would put thousands of lives at risk.

GENERAL ORDER FIVE: WELFARE OF THE CREW

This order affirms the high priority Starfleet places on the lives and freedom of its personnel. Invocation of General Order Five allows a commanding officer to disregard mission orders or regulations in order to protect a crewman or crewmen from imminent danger or imprisonment. General Order Five cannot be called upon during missions formulated under the Notwithstanding Protocol, immediately above, or in contravention of the Prime Directive.

GENERAL ORDER SEVEN: THE TALOS QUARANTINE

This general order forbids all Starfleet personnel from visiting or even contacting the mentally advanced humanoids of Talos IV, and was put into place by a panicked Federation Council after reading Captain Christopher Pike's *Enterprise* log accounts of the ship's mission to that planet in 2254. Talosian abilities seemed positively godlike, and the Federation Council deadlocked while attempting to formulate foreign policy objectives dealing with such powerful entities. So they just declared Talos off-limits and hoped the Talosians would ignore them, which they did.

The panic at the time was so extreme that the penalty for disobeying G.O. 7 is death. Since 2254, concern about superadvanced entities has waned. A second encounter with the Talosians in 2266 showed them in a more benign light. The *Enterprise* has encountered entities, such as Trelane of Gothos, who make Talosian powers seem limited by comparison, but a more confident Council has now chosen to let sleeping dogs lie where relations with godlike aliens are concerned. Whether the death penalty would be enforced today for a violation of G.O. 7 remains to be seen, but for now it remains on the books.

GENERAL ORDER EIGHT: COUNTERESPIONAGE PROTOCOLS

Commanding officers may invoke General Order Eight to cancel any routine mission (as defined under Order 118.D—see below) in order to pursue evidence of espionage against the Federation. They are expected to stop the flow of intelligence damaging to Federation security; if they unmask and apprehend the culprits, so much the better.

GENERAL ORDER NINE: STRATEGIC RESOURCE PROTECTION

G.O. 9 requires commanding officers to abandon routine missions in order to protect Starfleet bases, shipyards, and vessels from imminent danger. Certain planetary resources likewise qualify as strategic resources and must be protected at all costs. Some resources, like the dilithium deposits on the planet Coridan, are so important that even Category C missions (see Order 118, below) should be aborted in order to protect them.

GENERAL ORDER TWELVE: APPROACH WITH CAUTION

This order dictates that ships approaching spaceships with which they have not exchanged communications should exercise extreme caution. It was instituted after a incident in 2231 near Archanis IV in which Klingons captured a Tiburonese pleasure cruiser, tricking it up so that it seemed to be adrift in space and full of wounded Federation passengers. When rescue teams from the *U.S.S. Antares* beamed aboard, they were taken as hostages by the Klingons.

GENERAL ORDER FIFTEEN: FLAG OFFICER ESCORTS

G.O. 15 requires all admiral-level officers to take an armed escort into any dangerous area. President McLaren can take credit for this one; he managed to get himself captured by Orion pirates during his days as an admiral. His staff loves to cite G.O. 15 whenever the President goes anywhere hazardous.

GENERAL ORDER TWENTY-FOUR: PLANETARY DESTRUCTION

This calls for bridge crew to commence bombardment of a planet's surface within a specified period of time. The officer giving the order, or any of his superiors, may countermand it before the time elapses. Perhaps the most surprising G.O. on the books, this owes its existence to an incident from the Captain Pike era, described on page 12.

ORDER 104.B: CHAIN OF COMMAND

This passage lays out Starfleet's rank structure and affirms the right of superior officers to countermand the orders of juniors, or to take over their assignments outright. High-ranking characters should bark out the number of this order when pulling rank and if faced with the protests of a junior.

ORDER 104.C: FITNESS FOR DUTY

104.C provides the protocol under which the Chief Medical Officer can relieve a commander of duty, if, in the judgment of the medical officer, the commander is mentally or physically unfit to perform. In an assignment where possession, madness, and exotic health crises are all too common, order 104.C has proved its usefulness time and time again. (Any medical officer may relieve a lower-ranking crew member of duty for health reasons; senior officers may be relieved by higher-ranking members of the medical department, or by the Chief Medical Officer.)

ORDER 118: MISSION PRIORITIES

118 states that all missions assigned by flag officers must be classified in order of importance, so that the commanding officers charged with carrying them out know whether or not they can break away from those missions to attend to emergencies that crop up in the field. The different mission priorities break down like this:

Category A (Vital Mission)

The very survival of the Federation is at stake. Interruption of this mission is unthinkable. All Class A missions are assigned according to General Order Four, the Notwithstanding Protocol (see above), which means that the lives of all Starfleet personnel are expendable in the completion of the mission. Also called a Priority One command.

Category B (Urgent Mission)

Lives hang in the balance. Only new orders, or news of a crisis with even higher stakes, permit the commanding officer to delay its execution.

Category C (Strategic Mission)

Although successful completion of the mission will substantially advance the interests of the Federation, lives are not at stake. If the commanding officer learns of a serious emergency only his crew can attend to, he should delay or abort the original mission.

Category D (Routine Mission)

These everyday assignments take up the bulk of a crew's time and should be delayed for any distress signal.

ENFORCING THE PRIME DIRECTIVE

The most important (and seemingly most inflexible) rule of the Federation, the Prime Directive upholds the inviolability of natural cultural evolution and prevents Federation crews from interfering in the normal course of a planet's development. On the surface, this directive appears cut and dried. In action, however, the Prime Directive lends itself to many interpretations, some of which involve the apparent breaking of its strictures. One of the most challenging situations facing a crew aboard a Federation starship sent to encounter new cultures consists of deciding when their actions conflict with the Prime Directive. Does eradicating an indigenous disease on a colony not advanced enough to develop a cure on its own constitute a violation of the noninterference clause? Can your Crew of *Star Trek Roleplaying Game* characters prevent a world-destroying war between two opposing nations without upsetting the natural development of the planet? What happens if obeying the Prime Directive leaves a world vulnerable to interference by enemies of the Federation, such as the Klingons or the Romulans?

These dilemmas provide characters with plenty of room for both roleplaying and action-based games. Follow-up episodes can arise when characters' decisions to interfere spark an investigative trial (with dramatic review board or even court-martial scenes) by Starfleet for possible violations of the Prime Directive. The idea of breaking the letter of a law in order to uphold its spirit is not uncommon in *Star Trek*.

REGULATION 19: OBEYING LOCAL JURISDICTIONS

When on Federation member planets, Starfleet officers must obey all local laws. If a Starfleet crewman is charged with a local offense, his case will be handled by a Starfleet board of inquiry or court-martial, depending on the seriousness of the law allegedly broken. Prosecution proceeds as a joint effort of Starfleet and local law enforcement officials.

When on a friendly, non-Federation planet, Starfleet officers must likewise obey local laws. Starfleet will not act to rescue alleged lawbreakers from local due process, but will aid defendants, if necessary, by providing appropriate legal counsel.

Starfleet makes no guarantee that it will abide by the laws of hostile powers. Romulans and Klingons exercise nothing resembling due process. Starfleet personnel charged with crimes in these jurisdictions may require rescue missions, under the auspices of General Order Five.

REGULATION 46A: COMMUNICATIONS SECURITY

This regulation forbids communications on uncoded channels during battle, in situations where the enemy can reasonably assumed to be monitoring your transmissions.

THE PRIME DIRECTIVE

The Prime Directive forbids any interference in the normal development of an alien society. The directive treats the safety of Starfleet personnel and vessels as expendable to further this goal. Although the principle of noninterference applies to all cultures, from the most basic hunter-gatherer peoples to ancient, starfaring civilizations, the drafters of the Directive were especially concerned with prewarp societies. The discovery that one's species is not the only intelligent lifeform in the galaxy is profoundly jarring for any society, no matter how stable. This knowledge alone can radically alter the course of a culture: Sometimes it inspires fear and a reactionary, often repressive, retreat to old values; other cultures may rush headlong to abandon traditional social structures in favor of a half-understood imitation of the visitors from space.

Although Starfleet upholds the Prime Directive as its most important principle, it also frankly admits that it can be mighty difficult to apply. Many field commanders end up breaching it, or at least pushing its limits, at least once during their careers. Some, naturally, are more cautious than others in its application. Courses in the Prime Directive at Starfleet Academy (compulsory for all students) not only study the philosophy underlying G.O. 1, but look at case studies to determine when it should be rigidly applied and when it needs to be bent a little. Events of the past few years have provided a rich new body of case lore for today's students; so much has happened, in fact, that standard officer retraining programs now include an obligatory Prime Directive refresher course.

The planet Sigma Iotia II provides a textbook example of the dangers of cultural contamination. One hundred years ago, a book accidentally left behind by a crew member of the *U.S.S. Horizon* transformed the naturally imitative Iotian people into a civilization of gangsters styled after the Chicago mobsters of 1920's Earth. The contamination occurred before the drafting of the Prime Directive, and was discovered only a year ago.

The worst violation of the Prime Directive also occurred only a year ago, in 2268. Federation cultural observer and noted historian John Gill, stationed on the planet Ekos, knowingly broke the Directive in an effort to bring stability to its disordered society. In a stroke of colossal misjudgment, he introduced theories of social control from Earth's notorious Nazi regime. The *Enterprise* crew, headed by Gill's former Starfleet Academy student James T. Kirk, overthrew Ekos' fascist regime. Gill did not survive to face charges for his violation of the Prime Directive: His Ekosian protégé murdered him during the uprising.

A second serious violation was exposed last year. Captain Ronald Tracey, sole survivor of a viral epidemic aboard the *U.S.S. Exeter*, provided phaser weapons to one side of a local conflict on the planet Omega IV, favoring the Kohm villagers over the Yang raiders. He did so in exchange for protection as he worked for his own enrichment, hoping to discover the secret of immortality and parlay it into a personal fortune. Arrested by Captain Kirk and charged with gross violations of the Prime Directive, Tracey now serves a twenty-year sentence in the Tantalus Penal Colony.

James T. Kirk figures in Prime Directive case studies not only as a thwarter of Directive violators, but as a commander who has himself tested the limits of the Directive on multiple occasions. However, in each instance a Starfleet review board determined that his actions were justifiable.

In 2267, Kirk destroyed the computer that regulated the development of Beta III because it imposed an oppressive regime on the people. Later that year, Kirk destroyed the computer that regulated ritualized warfare between the planets Eminiar and Vendikar. Near the end of the year, Kirk destroyed the computer that kept the people of Gamma Trianguli VI in a state of immortal pastoral innocence. In each case, Kirk successfully argued that the computers had hijacked the "normal development" of their respective cultures, and that

their destruction restored the normal development envisioned by the drafters of the Directive. Although the decision to accept Kirk's doctrine was controversial in some Federation Council circles, President McLaren repeatedly refused to reverse it, and the Council has yet to draft an explicit amendment to the Directive overturning the Kirk Precedent.

Kirk's most recent exoneration on Prime Directive grounds aroused much less disagreement. In 2268, Kirk armed one tribe of hill people on the planet Neural, allowing them to defend themselves against another tribe which had been armed by the Klingons, who gave them flintlocks. Even though he felt a personal connection to the people of the hill tribe, Kirk maintained the balance of power, arming the tribe with weapons no more powerful than those the Klingons were handing out to their chosen tribesmen. Thus, he countered the cultural interference of another outside power while minimizing the impact of his own involvement.

Instructors for the Prime Directive course take their students through a series of roleplaying exercises to illustrate what happens when Starfleet officers stand charged with Prime Directive violations. First, staged simulations present a variety of scenarios posing the student with a problem tempting him to contravene the Directive. The student knows that certain apparent violations are in fact acceptable, so the correct response is never obvious. After the conclusion of the simulation, instructors debrief the student, asking him a series of questions about his decision. Through this process, the student learns the criteria used by Starfleet to determine the seriousness of violations. The questions are as follows:

How vulnerable was the subject culture?

The more vulnerable the culture, the worse the violation. Prewarp cultures are more susceptible to societal deformation than starfaring ones. Postcontact societies are more resistant to abnormal development than precontact cultures. Entrenched, traditional cultures are less apt to be affected than young, dynamic ones. Some species are more imitative than others.

Was the culture subject to previous negative interference in its normal development?

Convincingly arguing that your actions simply rectified a previous cultural deformation by an outside force, or a computer which stultifies a previously dynamic society, is an officer's best defense. Starfleet also usually excuses

actions taken to counter the interference of hostile forces such as Klingon or Romulan infiltrators.

What actually happened?

If lives were saved, or an oppressive regime overthrown, the violation is less serious than if the incident led to loss of life or personal liberties. Good results alone do not justify a violation, but are taken into account as part of a spectrum of mitigating factors. After all, it's impossible to determine immediately after an incident whether the long-term repercussions of a violation will be for good or for ill.

Starfleet prosecutors look at each alleged Directive violation and decide how severe its obvious consequences were. Officers charged with obviously egregious violations face court-martial and the attending possibility of lengthy prison terms. If a prosecutor decides that his case is weak, or the violation not so serious, he opts for a board of review, a process with less dire consequences for convicted defendants. For more on Starfleet justice, see page 35.

Command Structure

Despite occasional rogues, madmen, and interstellar cowboys, the bulk of Starfleet is composed of dedicated, disciplined men and women who achieve the Federation's lofty goals by working within a tightly organized command structure.

THE OTHER OFFICER RULE

When Starfleet officers other than the main cast of the *Star Trek* TV series take a major role in an episode, they're almost invariably there to cause some kind of trouble for Kirk and company. If they're the main focus of an episode you can count on them to be insane, criminal, or reckless. Call this the "other officer rule" of classic *Star Trek* storytelling. (This convention goes beyond *Star Trek*. In pretty well any adventure series you care to name, the series regulars solve problems, while guest characters either create them or highlight their importance. If a guest star plays a cop on a police show, there's a good chance he's a rogue cop or causes some other kind of trouble for the regular characters.)

The same should be true of your series; player character Crew members are the focus of your stories, and should be left to their own devices to solve the central problem of the story line. In the course of your series, plenty of the major Starfleet NPC's might turn out to be rogues, madmen, or other troublemakers. Do not interpret this to mean that Starfleet has a huge number of problem officers! Remember, the adventures of your Crew are not representative of everyday reality for every team of Starfleet officers. Your Crew's adventures are always the most interesting thing happening anywhere in the galaxy. Never confuse a perennially useful plot device with a statistical sample. The vast majority of Starfleet officers are ethical, dedicated, and mentally stable.

RANKS AND CHAIN OF COMMAND

Ranks determine the relative authority of all Starfleet officers. The chain of command dictates the circumstances under which a higher-ranking officer can expect to be obeyed by a lower-ranking one. Starfleet protocol emphasizes this important distinction. In general, if an officer is not assigned to report to you, you can issue orders to him only under certain specific circumstances laid out in Order 104.B of The Book (see page 27 above). He must obey you only in emergencies.

FLAG OFFICERS

Flag officers claim the highest ranks in Starfleet. Although considerable pomp and circumstance attend their every move, the glory surrounding a flag officer is mostly ceremonial. Flag officers no longer command individual ships or bases. They attend policy conferences, formulate strategy, supervise the bureaucracy of Starfleet, and launch inspection tours. Some field officers yearn for the respect accorded an admiral; others fear the day they'll be torn screaming from their bridge chairs and chained to a desk at Starfleet headquarters. Metaphorically speaking, of course.

The Flag Officer ranks, from highest to lowest are:

Fleet Admiral
Admiral
Fleet Captain

The rank of Fleet Captain is awarded to exemplary captains destined for Starfleet Command service. Admirals are administrators and planners, not fighting commanders, although creative ones find excuses to "visit the field" regularly. Fleet Admirals command fleets of starships, some from strategic starbases, but most from a network of facilities and orbital stations on Earth centered on Starfleet Command in San Francisco. The Chief-in-Command, Starfleet's most senior fleet admiral, reports directly to the Federation President. The current C-in-C is Terence Lockhart ("the Old Man"), a crotchety battleship of a man whose ironclad spirit keeps a firm grip on his increasingly frail body. Sparks fly in Lockhart's relationship with President McLaren;

McLaren started as Lockhart's protégé and is now his boss. Those who know them compare them to a father and son who don't always expect to get along, and who would never be caught dead admitting to the fierce love that binds them together. The tough, gruff, and unsentimental Lockhart shows little patience for bureaucratic procedures, leaving them to his admirals. He believes his real function is to provide inspiration to the rank and file, and general guidance to his staff. He keeps threatening to retire, but no one can imagine him actually doing so. Few think that McLaren could ever bring himself to ask him to step down, at least not until his health fails completely. Truth be told, they expect the Old Man to keel over in office, if he's not in fact immortal.

LINE OFFICERS

Line officers carry out the policies made by the flag officers. Some perform administrative duties at headquarters or at the various starbases Starfleet maintains throughout its territory. Most, however, are on active duty assignments, and most of these serve aboard starships of various sizes.

Here are the Line Officer ranks, in desending order:

Commodore
Captain
Commander
Lieutenant Commander
Lieutenant
Lieutenant (Junior Grade)
Ensign

Commodores, the highest-ranking officers to take regular field duty, can be seen almost as supercaptains. Like captains, they serve as commanding officers on bases or starships. Unlike captains, their powers supersede the normal chain of command; they can at any time issue valid orders to any officer ranked from captain on down, assignments to the contrary. They can even take

PROVISIONAL OFFICERS

Dangerous circumstances in the field can catapult low-ranking officers into positions normally out of their reach when the officers who normally hold such positions are killed, incapacitated, captured, possessed, or declared unfit for duty. Chain of command dictates who moves up to take the place of a missing superior to become Acting Security Chief, Acting Chief Medical Officer, or whatever.

When a commanding officer leaves the ship—as commanding officers are wont to do—protocol demands that he designate an acting CO. Almost invariably he picks the highest-ranking senior officer. Sometimes, given the Starfleet habit of taking most of the senior officers along on any interesting planetside mission, the commanding officer has to reach pretty far down the roster for his temporary stand-in.

over a captain's base or starship with a single barked verbal command. A captain can, on his personal authority, countermand a commodore's orders if such orders would needlessly hazard the captain's crew—but Starfleet review boards can judge such objections harshly indeed.

ASSIGNMENTS

Due to the chain of command, an officer's assignment is as important as his rank; it determines not only his current responsibilities, but whom he can expect to take orders from.

COMMANDING OFFICER

A commanding officer (CO for short) is in charge of a Starfleet installation, base, or starship. Everyone else assigned to that installation, base, or ship reports to him and must accept direct orders from him. In normal circumstances, the CO gives orders to his senior officers, who then pass them on to the junior officers assigned to their departments. Regardless of rank, a CO is referred to as "captain" in conversation.

Characteristic phrase: "I need you to do it in ten minutes!"

FIRST OFFICER

The First Officer serves as aide, sounding-board, confidant, and general second-in-command to the CO. Under the CO's supervision, he performs the day-to-day administrative tasks, such as the compilation of duty rosters, that keep the ship or base running smoothly. Although it is unusual for him to do so, the First Officer is permitted to issue orders to junior officers assigned to other department heads. "Number One" is a common nickname for First Officers.

First Officers sometimes take double duty, serving also as science, security, navigation, or communications officers. First Officer duty mandates a presence on the bridge, so chief engineers and medical officers serve as First Officer only on a provisional basis. The First Officer must be at least one rank lower than his commanding officer.

Characteristic phrase: "Captain, you are aware of Starfleet regulations on this matter …?"

SENIOR OFFICERS

Every CO counts on a small team of senior officers to head departments and provide advice to him in their areas of expertise. Each senior officer in turn supervises a coterie of junior officers who report to him, fulfilling the tasks expected of his department. The First Officer is always considered a senior officer, whether or not he also heads a department.

Science Officer

The Science Officer oversees all scientific research, surveying, and analysis. He is an expert in one or more specific fields, but broadly familiar with all branches of the sciences. His junior officers are also specialists who have been encouraged to familiarize themselves with other fields. The size of a science department varies widely depending on the mission of a particular ship, base, or installation.

Characteristic phrase: "Sensors detect life signs aboard the derelict vessel, Captain."

Security Chief

The Security Chief sees to the safety of crew members and civilians on the ship or base. His junior officers conduct regular sensor sweeps for signs of hostile activity, patrol the ship or base and duly report any unusual activity, and rush to the scene when trouble arises. Security officers escort troublemakers to the brig and then ensure that they remain incarcerated until the authorized time of their release. On-duty security officers remain armed at all times.

Characteristic phrase: "Captain, intruder alert on deck four!"

Chief Engineer

The Chief Engineer's crucial duty is to attend to the good repair and smooth operations of the ship or base to which he is assigned. His junior officers execute routine maintenance procedures, conduct regular checks to make sure that everything is in proper working order, and rush to repair systems damage wherever and whenever it occurs.

Characteristic phrase: "Captain, I can't hold her together much longer!"

Chief Medical Officer

The Chief Medical Officer, bound by the Hippocratic Oath as well as by his duty to Starfleet, tends to the health of any victims of disease or injury he encounters, whether or not they are crew members or even Federation citizens. His medical staff also takes responsibility for routine and preventive health care for the crew of the starship or base.

Characteristic phrases: "I'm a doctor, not a magician!" "He's dead, Captain."

Starfleet Uniforms

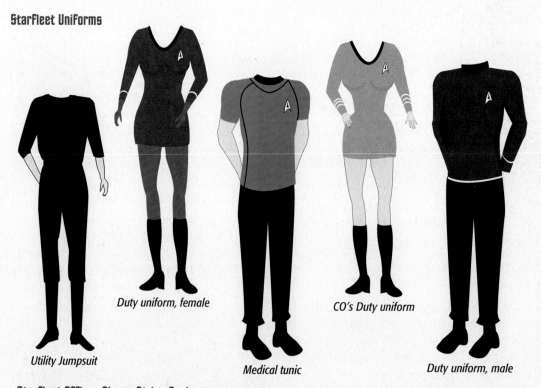

Utility Jumpsuit

Duty uniform, female

Medical tunic

CO's Duty uniform

Duty uniform, male

Starfleet Officer Sleeve Stripe Ranks

ENSIGN &
CREWMEMBER

Command
division

LIEUTENANT

Command
division

LIEUTENANT
COMMANDER

Engineering
and Security
division

COMMANDER

Science
division

CAPTAIN

Command
division

COMMODORE

Command
division

RANK AND GAME PLAY

When Kirk faces a crisis, you don't see him joining his senior officers in a meeting room to sit around a table and invite everyone's input. He stands on the bridge, probably asking his senior officers for information. Once he has the facts he needs, he quickly reaches a decision, and the senior officers carry it out. Only if his decision seems completely out of left field does he get so much as a raised eyebrow from his loyal senior officers.

While the Kirk approach to command is an excellent means of protecting the Federation, you need to adopt a trick or two to use it in an interactive game which will be fun for all participants, not just the player taking the role of captain. Furthermore, the typical group of roleplaying gamers takes much longer to reach a decision than Captain Kirk does. Most gamers like to argue back and forth, mull over options, and carefully weigh the consequences of their characters' actions.

To do this while still maintaining the chain of command element which is so much a part of *Star Trek*, we strongly recommend that players take a time out when there's an important decision to be made. Speaking out of character, they should reach a consensus on what the ranking officer's orders will be—with the Narrator prodding the players to keep it moving when their discussions bog down or become repetitive. (Players can slip back into character when there are questions to be answered with the characters' knowledge skills.)

Once the players know what the plan is, they resume speaking as their characters. The player playing the Captain issues the orders, the others carry them out, and everyone waits to see what the results will be. This way, the *players* all get equal input into decisions, even though the *characters* do not.

Mission Specialists

Certain special jobs are assigned to junior officers. Officers filling these high-status posts report directly to the captain. Commanding officers only rarely call on them for advice; they're valued for their skills in a particular, well defined task, rather than for a body of knowledge. These mission specialists (a term found in The Book but rarely used in the field) operate outside the usual departments, reporting to the First Officer. There are enough specialists of any given type aboard a ship or base to allow the position to be staffed during each shift. Junior officers from other departments act as alternates when the usual mission specialists are for whatever reason unavailable for duty. Usually one mission specialist of each type is recognized as the most experienced or capable; he takes over in crisis situations.

Helmsman

The helmsman pilots the ship, controlling its speed and direction. He takes evasive maneuvers during combat, avoids asteroids and other spaceborne obstacles, and generally gets the ship where it's going in one piece. Obviously, bases and installations lack helmsmen.

Characteristic phrase: "They're still on our tail, Captain!"

Communications Officer

The communications officer directs incoming transmissions to their proper destinations and opens channels to vessels or bases the commanding officer wants to communicate with.

Characteristic phrase: "They're hailing us, Captain."

Navigator

Navigators serve only on ships; they plan the course of a ship's travels. Depending on the mission, they may be called upon to plot the fastest route, or the safest one; usually they take both factors into consideration. Navigators and helmsmen are often cross-trained.

Characteristic phrase: "But Captain, that'll take us straight into the heart of the Hecate Nebula!"

Junior Officers

Junior officers staff the various departments outlined above and fill other slots on the ship as need be such as Records Officer, Transporter Chief, Life Support Chief, Head of Nursing, and so forth.

In the early days of UESPA, small elite crews filled every post, making decisions on the spot, leading from the front, and accepting the dangers and excitement of new planets and first-contact missions as their duty and their due. This tradition is still alive in Starfleet today. Although theorists in Starfleet Command question the logic of risking a ship's command staff on possibly fatal missions, any officer with the guts and brains to rise to a command position seldom wishes to delegate the jobs calling for the most guts and brains in the galaxy to others. In short, commanders, senior officers, and mission specialists have all the fun. Junior officers get to be killed or—if they're lucky—rescued.

The ship's scientific and professional staff (sociologists, historians, astrophysicists, etc.) and yeomen (personal assistants to department heads and commanders) fill similar roles in story terms, unless they're player characters, in which case they're no doubt marked for greatness.

Characteristic phrase: "Unngh!"

BRANCHES AND UNIFORMS

Starfleet divides its personnel into three general branches, primarily to facilitate tactical deployments and provide a variety of clear "career tracks" for its officers. However, the loose nature of fleet organization means that officers often transfer between branches—an astrophysicist can transfer to the helm, or an engineer move into planetology. An officer's branch dictates the color of his tunic, with some latitude (which increases with rank) for personal choices.

COMMAND

Most ship and base commanders come from this branch, which contains personnel trained in crisis resolution, ship tactics, and administration. This branch also contains the helm, navigational, and weapons control personnel, along with other departments which value both long-range planning and quick decision skills. Command personnel are often seconded to other departments. The command branch tunic is gold.

SCIENCE

This branch includes the science officer and his subordinates along with the myriad of scientific specialists on any Starfleet vessel (including social scientists such as historians and sociologists). Starfleet's medical corps is also part of the science branch, and many Starfleet biologists and biochemists serve both in scientific and medical roles on board ship. The science branch tunic is blue.

ENGINEERING AND SECURITY

Both of these divisions deal with practical solutions to immediate problems, and with the maintenance of conditions conducive to smooth operation of the ship or facility. Whether their common branch sprang from such functional theories or from the tendency of early atomic pile crews on old spacecraft to be burly, brawling types is unknown.

Either way, this branch encompasses most trained technical and maintenance personnel (which overlap with the science branch in some duties) and the ship's primary interior defensive and offensive personnel (whose expertise similarly overlaps with the command branch). The engineering and security branch tunic is red.

STAFF ASSIGNMENTS

Not all Starfleet officers serve aboard starships and bases. Unless you're taking part in an unusual *Star Trek Roleplaying Game* series, these assignments are likely suitable only for Supporting Cast.

GOVERNOR

Starfleet governs a small handful of Federation colonies. These are either very young colonies or are especially imperiled in some way. Federation's nat-ural preference is for civilian governments which are accountable to their citizens. The goal of any decent Starfleet governor is to make himself obsolete, laying the groundwork for a stable transition to local autonomy. The chief executive officer takes the title of Governor; his rank might be anything from Commodore on up. A mixture of Starfleet and local civilian personnel make up the rest of his executive branch.

ACADEMY INSTRUCTOR

Assignments to Starfleet Academy bring prestige, the honor of influencing a new generation of officers, and a renewing charge of youthful enthusiasm. Some Starfleet officers thrive in this environment because they are born teachers. Others gratefully take teaching positions when they are for some reason unable to continue their field careers, or as a very active version of retirement. Field officers often make guest lecture appearances at the Academy to tell cadets what it's really like out in deep space.

AIDE

Some line officers pull aide duty to flag officers. These desk jobs are attractive to some but anathema to most.

ATTACHÉ

Federation member planets, candidates for membership, and allied worlds outside the UFP may all request the ongoing assistance of Starfleet personnel. These officers live and work planetside, in concert with civilian officials of the host planet. Each attaché assignment is tailor-made to the circumstances. Typical assignments are as follows:

CULTURAL ATTACHÉ

This largely ceremonial position serves to cement good relations between Starfleet and host planets throughout the galaxy. Rigors of duty include atten-

THE UNBEARABLE LIGHTNESS OF BEING A REDSHIRT

Players who have watched enough episodes of *Star Trek* may be nervous about playing security personnel, given the seemingly magnetic way that the red tunic attracts phaser fire, poison spines, or deadly gas clouds. The Narrator (and any potential player) needs to distinguish between Crew security officers, who should be in no greater danger than any other player characters, and Supporting Cast redshirts, who can (and often should) die whenever the story demands a dramatic demonstration of the alien menace.

dance at rituals, arts events, athletic tournaments, and cocktail parties. Starfleet headquarters saves these assignments as graceful career-enders for officers who have served the institution well, but are now not needed in a more active role.

DIPLOMATIC ATTACHÉ

Diplomatic attachés assist civilian Federation bureaucrats in building relations with the host planet, either as an ally or a prospective Federation member. They lend their security, science, or other expertise to Federation officials, rather than to representatives of the host planet. They may simply act as observers reporting back to the Federation.

SECURITY ATTACHÉ

A security attaché participates directly in defense efforts on the host planet. Unlike the above assignment, this can actually be an exciting and dangerous mission, especially on worlds threatened by hostile forces. The attaché may work on planetary defense networks, serve aboard a ship in the host planet's fleet, or engage in counterespionage activities. Starship crews may be temporarily assigned to such duties pending the arrival of a permanent security attaché team.

TECHNICAL ATTACHÉ

As technical attaché, an officer works directly on research or engineering projects crucial to the host planet. The attaché may help design and build starships, bases, or other installations. He may oversee scientific surveys or research projects.

DISCIPLINARY ACTION

Officers accused of disobeying Federation law or Starfleet orders and regulations face disciplinary action, of varying natures and of varying severity. Confinement to quarters may accompany or replace any form of command discipline, at an individual commander's discretion.

SANCTIONS

Penalties for offenses range from reprimand to the death penalty. The different types of sanctions are as follows, from mildest to harshest.

Reprimand

The officer who committed the offense must stand at respectful attention while he receives a verbal dressing-down, to which he is not permitted to respond, except to agree with the statement at its conclusion. The officer delivering the reprimand then attaches it to the subject's service record, where it will lessen his chances for further promotion. Reprimands are only rarely expunged from the record, usually when extenuating circumstances are later discovered.

Demotion

The officer is reduced in rank. He may or may not also be reassigned to a less desirable post.

Brig

The offender reports to the brig (see page 133), a small prison area on his ship or base, where he is incarcerated for a period of time not to exceed thirty days. Afterward he returns to active duty. A sentence to the brig is usually accompanied by a reprimand or demotion.

Dishonorable Discharge

Starfleet kicks the offender out of its ranks. His service record reflects the reasons for his dismissal, making it difficult for him to find a position of responsibility in civilian life. Some dishonorably discharged officers drift into Orion or other neutral-planet service; others redeem themselves by working bravely as colony world police, or as freelance explorers.

Jail

The offender serves up to a year's incarceration in a low-security prison facility on a starbase or Federation planet. Good behavior earns swift transfer to a community-service project, where he can work off his debt to society. Dishonorable discharge invariably accompanies a jail term.

Penal Colony

Court officials remand the freshly convicted man to the custody of security officers for immediate transport to a correctional facility. These facilities, located on isolated, barren, and otherwise uninhabited asteroids or planetoids, are called penal colonies. Sentences range from a year to life. Needless to say, you also get a dishonorable discharge with your penal colony sentence.

Death

Although never applied, the death penalty remains on the books for certain offenses, most exotically for disobeying General Order Seven, forbidding contact with the Talosians (see page 27).

DISCIPLINARY PROCEDURES

Three different disciplinary procedures apply to offenses by Starfleet personnel. The more serious the offense, the more forbidding and formal the disciplinary procedure.

COMMAND DISCIPLINE

Any nonsenior officer can be directly disciplined by his commander. If he finds the accused guilty, the commander can confine him to quarters, reprimand him, demote him, or sentence him to the brig. If he deems the offense too serious for these remedies, or doubts his objectivity, he can refer the case to a board of inquiry or court-martial.

BOARD OF INQUIRY

A board of inquiry is a panel of high-ranking officers who sit in judgment of serious but noncriminal offenses. They may acquit the defendant or subject him to any sanction which does not deprive him of his liberty. In addition to these sanctions, they may issue a nonbinding recommendation that the defendant's commanding officer sentence him to a brief stay in the brig.

Any charge against a senior, commanding, or flag officer is referred to a board of inquiry. If the board determines that the charge is unworthy of consideration, or lacks sufficient evidence, it dismisses the case without hearing witnesses. This happens more often than not. If the board decides that the offense is criminal in nature, it refers the case to a court-martial.

COURT-MARTIAL

Courts-martial are formal trials, with Starfleet judges and attorneys. Rigorous standards of evidence apply. The defendant is presumed innocent until proven guilty and is afforded due process of law. Guilty verdicts result in sanctions. Courts-martial of senior officers are exceedingly rare. However, courts-martial are common enough to support Starfleet's Judge Advocate General corps, and a number of busy defense lawyers, the most famous of which is the wise and wily Samuel T. Cogley, who has rescued more than one defendant, including James T. Kirk, from frame-up attempts or other tricky legal situations.

INTERSPECIES COOPERATION

In the 23rd century, widespread cooperation between the different cultures of the Federation is still an ideal for tomorrow, instead of a reality of the present day. Federation members believe in cooperation, but not necessarily at close range. The maxim remains, "Distance makes good neighbors." Even the founding races of the Federation are still tentatively getting to know each other. The few institutions which have managed a high degree of integration engender little pride: They're prisons and asylums.

Starfleet provides the prime example of this trend. Humans make up the vast majority of Starfleet personnel. The Centaurans, visually indistinguishable from Humans, clock in at a distant second. All other species are still rarities on the Starfleet roster. For example, even though Humans and Vulcans recently celebrated the two hundredth anniversary of their first contact, Spock, the very first Vulcan to join Starfleet, did so only about sixteen years ago. He enlisted in the face of serious pressure from his family; they wanted him to join the Vulcan Science Academy, an all-Vulcan institution which also explores the spaceways according to its own research-oriented agenda.

Other Federation races likewise stick together. Tellarite engineering teams entertain few job applications from members of other species. Andorian trade vessels are staffed entirely by Andorians. Tiburonese resorts employ only a few non-Tiburonese. And so on. Part of this separation is cultural, but much of it is simply practical. Although 23rd-century technology can accomplish many things, designing a starship which can provide comfortable (or even adequate) medical and environmental facilities for vastly different races remains a forbiddingly difficult task. Until ship design and technology take another significant jump ahead, minority species on a Starfleet ship will face discomforts both physical and psychological. Only the toughest and most dedicated can serve as a "fish out of water" as long as Spock has.

Nonhuman Starfleet officers can expect the same kind of treatment Spock receives. He's a trusted and valued member of the crew, regarded as a friend by his captain and senior officers. Still, they find his alien heritage remarkable, continually referring to it. Most of the time those references take the form of good-natured jokes, but even Spock's two best friends on the *Enterprise* feel perfectly comfortable telling him that the Human approach to emotion is superior to the Vulcan one. By another era's standards, this might seem staggeringly insensitive. In 2369, it's just the way things are, and everybody understands that. What's a couple of green blood jokes between friends?

MISSIONS

Starship crews can expect to perform a mix of the following missions. Certain smaller vessels are specialized to particular mission types. Crews of larger ships, like those of the *Constitution* class, may be called upon to perform any mission at any time. That's why assignments to bigger ships are more coveted; they offer the widest opportunity for excitement and adventure.

COLONIZATION

Starships aid the colonization effort by patrolling passenger routes and providing emergency assistance when required. Some ships also aid in planetary terraforming efforts, either by providing scientific expertise, transport, or raw power. Depending on the emergency, the aid might consist of disaster relief, defense against a threat, investigation of a troubling mystery, or assistance in the restoration of law and order after a local crisis.

DEFENSE

Fortunately, the Federation is not at war with its neighbors right now. If it were, the bulk of Starfleet missions would be military in nature. Some would

be attacks against enemy targets. Most would be defensive: Ships would be assigned to guard specific installations, planets, bases, and trade routes. Other ships would accompany crucial freighter shipments on convoy and escort missions.

Starfleet wards off peacetime complacency by staging war games and other security-related training exercises. These exercises hardly ever go wrong, which is not to say that they lack the potential for disaster.

EXPLORATION

Federation surveys to date have barely scratched the surface when it comes to mapping the vast depths of space. Preliminary deep-space exploration remains a high priority for Starfleet command. Crews exploring deep space learn to expect the unexpected.

Most of the sectors of space Starfleet has mapped have been only sketchily examined. After preliminary surveys record the broad outlines of a solar system, follow-up missions accumulate more detailed data on each planet. These longer tours of duty allow crew members to catalog geographical features, climate, biology, mineral content, and other matters of interest to science. Surveys of planets inhabited by prewarp intelligent beings are carried out by sensor sweep only. Exploratory teams go planetside for close-up studies of planets without sentient life. Sometimes crews encounter the most bizarre dangers on a planet only on these "routine" planetary survey missions.

At the conclusion of an intensive survey of this sort, standard procedure requires the crew to leave behind a series of unmanned, orbital probes. These probes periodically take sensor readings, which are then relayed through subspace to various starbases, where science teams monitor the data for the appearance of new anomalies. Anything really strange results in a new starship visit to check out the anomaly first-hand.

PATROL

Patrol duties are the least glamorous in the fleet, but are the most important, because they protect and maintain Federation space. Patrol ships check communications relays and unmanned scientific monitoring stations to make sure they're still in working order. They travel the central trade routes, ready to

provide emergency assistance to disabled civilian vessels. They maintain an armed presence to discourage piracy and chase down rogue vessels whenever they're bold enough to poke their nacelles into Federation territory.

Ships on border patrol form the first line of defense against incursions from hostile vessels, whether known enemies such as Romulan and Klingon raiders, or unknown enemies from the fringes of the Federation.

SCIENCE

Science experiments conducted under the auspices of the Federation Science Council are often performed on starships. These range from tests of new weaponry to studies of the effects of a given type of particle emission on a space-time distortion. Most experiments go off without a hitch, but some attract the unwanted attention of hostile entities or spies. Others fail in such a way as to threaten the safety of the crew and visiting scientists.

ALERT MODES

Although most Starfleet missions are danger-free, a well trained CO stays alert, knowing that a routine situation can plunge into crisis in the blink of an eye. Two alert modes warn crew members of possible danger.

YELLOW ALERT

The issuance of a yellow alert tells all crew members to drop their routine duties and brace themselves for incoming weapon fire or other sources of damage to the ship. Sleeping personnel wake, dress, and equip themselves. Off-duty personnel stand in quarters for assignment to their departments. Security personnel arm themselves. All crew members keep a special eye out for anything out of the ordinary, reporting any strange readings or occurrences to their department heads.

RED ALERT

All personnel head to battle stations. Security personnel take predetermined positions at strategic locations throughout the ship. Medical personnel report to sickbay or station themselves in predetermined places where injuries are likely to occur. Engineering crews head to critical systems and ready their repair kits.

STARBASES

The Federation asserts its sovereignty in space through a network of starbases. Many, but not all, of these installations are space stations. Stations are placed in strategic locations that lack nearby Federation Class M planets.

The Federation's starbase network provides a wide range of services. Starbases act as supply posts for Federation vessels, stocking everything from spare parts to food. They provide opportunities for rest and recreation. They house administrative offices, process reports, and keep records. They engage in scientific monitoring. They act as trade hubs, warehousing shipments and breaking cargoes down into smaller units for further transportation. While all starbases provide each of the above services, most are noted for superiority in one or two areas.

Starfleet currently keeps seventeen starbases in active service. They are not numbered from one to seventeen, because some of the lower-numbered starbases were long ago decommissioned. Starbase 200, a trading hub near Coridan, was so numbered in honor of the recent 200th anniversary of Human-Vulcan contact, rather than implying the existence of two hundred bases. In order to give each Narrator leeway to create his own starbases, we'll describe only some of them here.

Starbase 2

Location: A space station between Beta Auriga and Camus II.
Primary Service: Starbase 2 offers a fully equipped and staffed medical unit, one of the finest in Starfleet. Crew members suffering from grievous injuries or mysterious illnesses can expect top-quality treatment here. Missions to investigate the source of bizarre epidemics may begin at Starbase 2.
Commanding Officer: The dashing and unconventional Dr. Aubrey Townsend runs a tight ship, thanks to a long-suffering team of senior medical officers who nurture his brilliance and cover for his organizational indifference. When he's not busy making medical history, Dr. Townsend's breaking hearts on his nursing staff.

Starbase 4

Location: A starbase located in the Lyris Corridor, a standard route for many passenger vessels taking emigrants to the colonies.
Primary Service: Starbase 4 serves primarily as a rest stop for travelers and a supply post for shipping. It also houses a large administrative unit of the Federation's department of colonial management. The department is staffed largely by efficient yet condescending Tellarite bureaucrats. In anticipation of emergencies requiring mass evacuation of colonists, it offers temporary housing for up to two hundred thousand people; almost all housing units are unused at any given time. A civilian court headquartered here administers justice for colonies too new to maintain justice systems of their own. Starfleet officers who apprehend civilian criminals should bring them here for imprisonment and trial. (Starbase 11 handles courts-martial.)
Commanding Officer: Commodore Jack Kerr, a patrician fellow with an air of natural authority, demands high standards of efficiency and decorum from his officers. The occasional facial twitch hints at dark currents within the man, perhaps related to atrocities witnessed during the Axanar Rebellion. He keeps as tight a rein on his emotions as on the daily operations of the starbase.

Starbase 6

Location: A space station past Aldebaran.
Primary Service: Starbase 6 provides the most famous amenities for rest and

relaxation of any Starfleet installation. Run by Tiburonese civilians, the base offers personnel a surprising array of recreational activities. Its regular athletic tournaments attract competitors from all over the Federation. Starfleet erects a zone of official privacy over its officers' activities at Starbase 6, as long as they're discreet enough to keep their passions behind closed doors.
Commanding Officer: Commander George Reed adopts the air of a cruise line social director when welcoming visiting officers, but should not be taken for a fool. In private, he is a brooding, intense man, frustrated by his inability to secure a command assignment on a starship. His success at Starbase 6 ironically impedes his career; no visiting flag officer can imagine drinking in the Crystal Bar without good old George warming a stool beside him.

Starbase 9

Location: A space station close to Pyris VII.
Primary Service: Primarily a resupply post, this base hosts a larger-than-usual science complement, which studies incoming transmissions from unmanned monitoring stations left behind by Starfleet explorers. When something strange occurs in deep space, the officers of Starbase 9 are the first to hear about it.
Commanding Officer: Bald, bold, and gregarious Commodore Lee Block whiles away his time chatting with visiting field officers and awaiting his imminent promotion to Rear Admiral. He doesn't want to take any chances that this simple assignment might trip him up, and closely screens incoming scientific data for possible threats to Federation security.

Starbase 10

Location: A space station near Gamma Hydra IV, near the Neutral Zone.
Primary Service: The most important duty here is the monitoring of Romulan activity along the border region. Starbase 10 lacks the relaxed atmosphere of more secure bases; everyone is constantly on edge here, wondering just who might be an impostor working for Romulan intelligence. Starbase 10 harbors a mostly empty, state-of-the-art medical facility, in anticipation of a possible second war with the Romulans.
Commanding Officer: Commodore Gerald Williams, a cagey Cockney with extensive experience as a field officer, was appointed to head Starbase 10 two years ago, after the CO scheduled to take command disgraced himself through his rash actions aboard the *Enterprise*. Underlying Williams' habitual good humor is a determination not to let the Romulans put anything past him.

Starbase 11

Location: Located on a planetside base on the beautiful, blue-clouded colony of Yko.
Primary Service: The largest cluster of Starfleet administrative offices outside Earth is found in this distant outpost. Any kind of Starfleet business, from award ceremonies to courts-martial, may be conducted here.
Commanding Officer: Commodore Jose Mendez oversees station business with stern efficiency.

The rocks in front of them shimmered and partially melted. Neither Captain Duffy nor the fresh-scrubbed young cadet at his side could help leaning back as waves of heat radiated from the bubbling rock. Duffy watched as the cadet's eyebrows singed from the heat; they curled up and dropped off. Duffy figured his own had to be doing the same. Eyebrows were one thing, but if one of those crab-faced aliens actually hit them with that heat beam, it would be over for both of them. The crabs' aim was nothing to brag about, but eventually he and the kid would run out of rocks to hide behind, and then…

Duffy turned to the kid. The poor fellow's knuckles were white, his shaking hand clenched tight around the grip of a phaser pistol. Just a boy, really. Duffy remembered his own cadet days. He'd gotten himself into a few unauthorized scrapes, but nothing like this. "What's your name again, son?"

CHARACTERS

"Cadet Abbott, sir!"

"Listen to me very carefully, Abbott. I know you're worried. Anyone would be in this situation. But if you trust me, you'll make it. You got that?"

"Yes, sir."

"We're going to make a run for it when I give the signal, Abbott, and you're going to be fine." Abbott wasn't looking fine. He was looking nauseous. "You'll go on to a distinguished career. What mission specialty were you planning on, Abbott?"

"Uh, I hadn't decided, sir."

Another beam hit the rocks. Spatters of molten rock hit the fabric of Duffy's uniform, sizzling through to burn his flesh.

"Well, decide now!"

"Uh … engineering, sir!"

"All right, Abbott, you're going to live to be a fine engineer… If you follow me—NOW!"

Creating a Character

The core of any storytelling experience is character; people to whom things happen. In the *Star Trek Roleplaying Game*, the most important characters are the ones you, as players, portray and inhabit—what we refer to as the Crew. Like the crew of a starship, without them, nothing runs and the ship stands dead in space. Without your character, the story is hollow. The difference between you as players in the *Star Trek Roleplaying Game* and the actors portraying roles in the *Star Trek* television series is that where they were prisoners of the script, speaking lines written for their characters by others, you can write your own lines, make your own decisions. You, as players, collaborate with the Narrator to build the story. Early on, it's best to keep to simple situations and formal puzzles, as you get to know the character you're writing. Over the course of play, though, the player character becomes an alter ego, with his own desires and personality. But before any of this can happen, you must create a character.

Creating a character takes a certain amount of effort. Your characters should be fully realized individuals, with detailed backgrounds, motivations, and behavior. This chapter provides you with all the guidelines needed to create a beginning character. The *Star Trek Roleplaying Game* allows players to create a character and begin playing in only a few minutes. Start with an initial concept. Then, using the steps explained here, translate your rough idea into a character with innate capabilities, skills, talents, and abilities. These abilities are expressed in game terms with numbers and rules.

Initially, these statistics may seem dry. When an author begins to think about a novel, he creates a detailed description of his main characters—their likes and dislikes, past histories, concerns, and motivations. He does not typically describe his characters as Fitness 2 and Tricorder 3. These ratings, however, are a sort of shorthand that quantify a character's skills and abilities—a way for the character to interact with the rules system.

DEVELOPING THE INITIAL CONCEPT

Creating a character begins with an initial conception—a general idea of what type of character you want to play. This usually involves choosing a species and profession (Vulcan science officer, Human commander, Tiburonian

WHAT DO I PLAY?

Roleplaying games offer the fun and exciting opportunity to create an original character—one you conceive of and flesh out by yourself, rather than simply playing a known character from a television show, book, or movie. While you might enjoy playing Captain Kirk or Commander Spock, they've had their adventures. Create your own characters, ones as intriguing and exciting as Kirk and Spock, and tell your own stories, perhaps ones as spectacular and history-making as those of the *U.S.S. Enterprise.*

Before narrating the *Star Trek Roleplaying Game*, the Narrator should discuss character ideas with her players. One player might want to play the Chief Engineer, while another has an idea for an eager junior officer. Talking about this in advance allows all of you to figure out how the members of the Crew fit together, the types of stories the players envision their characters participating in, and the types of stories most appropriate for the series. Remember, the story focuses on the player characters—they're heroes, and adventure always seems to find them, regardless of where they are or what they're doing. Of course, the Narrator may find it difficult to concoct reasons for crewmen from three separate departments or areas of the ship to work together or get into trouble episode after episode, so the players should help out by creating characters who have some reason to work together. Perhaps they all hold roughly the same rank (maybe they're all mid-level or senior officers, or all fresh-faced Academy graduates) so that they work on the same types of assignments and have other reasons to come together to solve problems. Some may even have interpersonal relationships, such as being married or related in some way.

Narrators may not want to let Crew members hold positions like Captain or First Officer, at least not at the start of the game. They need time to prove themselves and work their way up in the ranks (and, in the real world, for the players to become comfortable with their characters and the game rules). However, it's usually all right to let players' characters be the ship's department heads—Chief Engineer, Chief Medical Officer, Chief of Security, Helmsman, Science Officer and the like—who run departments on the ship and have crewmen serving under them. Characters who want to hold such a position must buy the Department Head advantage—and, of course, have the Narrator's permission.

Remember, characters don't have to head departments to work on the bridge or to do important work. The Chief Engineer relies on a lot of other engineers to get the work done, and the Navigator can't man the navigation station all the time. Commanding officers often choose qualified crewmen, regardless of rank, to perform important missions or tasks. Thus, a motley group of characters—some department heads, some high-ranking officers, others junior crewmen—may be thrown together to undertake a mission.

Furthermore, Starfleet assignments are flexible. Crewmen don't do the same job, day in and day out; as new or unusual circumstances arise, officers are assigned to, and expected to perform competently, a wide variety of duties. A Crew member might help chart a star system one week, and the next week assist with a diplomatic mission. Groups of crewmen who work well together—like the members of your Crew—may find themselves working together episode after episode on many different kinds of missions.

science officer), and perhaps some general personality traits (brash, bold, crusty, curious, or the like).

Notice, however, how this basic idea doesn't even begin to describe the complexity and subtle nuances of those characters. Kirk is a Human commander, but where's his romantic side? Spock is a Vulcan science officer, but that sparse description ignores his Human half. At this stage, the characters are reduced to their most basic components. They are simply cardboard cutouts, not fully fleshed-out individuals.

Next, develop your character's personality. As a springboard, think about how he looks, and what attitude or demeanor he displays to others. Is that what he's really like, or just the face he shows his shipmates? A character who seems uptight or temperamental might actually be very warm and friendly around those who take the time to get to know him well.

As you create your character, try to get more and more specific, fleshing out your initial concept. As you design a character, ask yourself "Why?" a lot. If your general character concept involves a character who wants to travel a lot, ask why he feels that way. Is he escaping an unpleasant situation at home, possessed of wanderlust, or just eager to "experience life" in a way he couldn't in only one place? His motivations for attending the Academy won't be the same as someone forced into it by domineering parents. The more of these questions you ask and answer, the more you'll learn about your character, and the more fun you'll have designing him.

Talk with your Narrator as you think about your character. She'll probably have some suggestions for you, possibly ones which will help the character function better (or play a more important role) in the series she has planned (or in specific episodes).

Certain concepts might not be appropriate for life in Starfleet, such as escaped criminals or underhanded con men. However, that doesn't mean you can't play that character—just that he probably isn't a member of Starfleet. If you'd like to play such a character, discuss it with your Narrator and see if you can fit it into the series she plans to run. After all, characters who strive to overcome disreputable pasts or their own inherent flaws are one of the themes of *Star Trek*.

CHARACTER COMPATIBILITY AND CONFLICT

Your character should fit in reasonably well the other members of the Crew (the group of player characters). A Crew with two helmsmen or three Tiburonians isn't as much fun, or as easy to prepare episodes for, as one with a wide mix of professions, races, and personalities. Work with the other players to make sure you're not duplicating something one of them wants to do, and that each character is distinct. If two players want to play very similar characters, perhaps they can work different shifts, or have other skills or personality quirks which make each of them important to the game.

Of course, the Crew members should be compatible—a group of characters who quarrel constantly just makes the game no fun for anyone. Friendly rivalries, joking, and even mild friction are all right—even good for the dramatic side of the game—but shouldn't be taken to the extent that they spoil the series.

NON-STARFLEET CHARACTERS

The *Star Trek Roleplaying Game* assumes that the players' characters belong to Starfleet. But sometimes a player wants to play a character associated with some other aspect of the Federation—a Vulcan ambassador, a Tiburonian scientist, or a Federation reporter, for example. The Narrator can have a difficult time fitting these types of characters into the typical *Star Trek RPG* game—why would they join the crew of a starship, episode after episode? Several ways exist to handle this situation.

First, you can use the character as a "special guest star" who appears only occasionally, as the series permits. The Narrator will tell you in advance if, say, your Andorian merchant would be appropriate for a particular episode, allowing you to play him while the Narrator uses your regular character as an NPC.

Second, you might try letting each player who wants to play two or more characters at a time: a Tiburonian helmsman and a Human historian, for example. For each episode, the player chooses which character he wants to play (or the Narrator tells him which one suits the episode better).

Third, the Narrator can tailor specific episodes or groups of episodes to a particular character. For a "story arc" involving extended negotiations between two warring alien races, rather than playing his usual Human engineer, the player brings out his Vulcan ambassador character. This allows the Narrator to focus more closely on that specific character, and the situation that forms the basis for the story arc.

Fourth, the Narrator and player can create a reason for a non-Starfleet character to be on board the starship for an extended period. Perhaps the nature of the campaign and the Vulcan ambassador character can be changed just a little to make them fit together well—for example, maybe Starfleet assigns the ship to a series of diplomatic missions, assigning the Vulcan ambassador (a former Starfleet captain) to the ship to ensure their success. This is perhaps the easiest solution, since it meets both Narrator and player needs, but it may involve a little more work on the Narrator's part.

Of course, you could also come up with a character who has absolutely no Starfleet or Federation connection—for example, a con man or errant artist. Perhaps the Narrator can tailor part of the series to draw the character into Starfleet. Alternately, you can always run and play a *Star Trek Roleplaying Game* series with all non-Starfleet characters; just because the rules assume the characters belong to Starfleet doesn't mean they have to. Space is big.

When creating a non-Starfleet character, the player should work with the Narrator to create an Overlay which properly represents the character's profession. Use the existing Overlays as guidelines, or consult other supplemental products from Last Unicorn.

During character creation, Bill thinks it would be interesting if his Axanari Security Officer were intolerant of Tiburonians. His explanation is that a Tiburonian ship destroyed the ship on which his character's best friend served. In talking with the Narrator, Bill describes a character who avoids Tiburonians and refers to them sneeringly. The Narrator thinks this is going too far—after all, this character must work closely with Starfleet officers (possibly including Tiburonians), and Starfleet won't tolerate such prejudice. So, he suggests Bill tone down his character's anti-Tiburonian sentiments a bit.

CHARACTER ARCHETYPES

If you want to start playing right away, without taking time to create your own character, choose one of the *Archetypes*—pregenerated characters described on pages 42-45. They've already got a Template, Overlay, Background History, and everything else needed for you to start the game right away. Take five Development Points to personalize the basic character a bit (increase an attribute or skill, or choose an advantage you like)—in short, make him more your own creation. You'll be ready to start playing in just a couple of minutes. (See the Development Point Cost Table, on page 52, for details on what things cost.)

Matt wants to play a Centauran Medical officer, so he chooses that archetype. Looking over the character, he decides he wants his character, Dr. Artan, to have a gift for languages, so he spends 6 Development Points to buy one level of proficiency each in Vulcan and Andorian. With another 2 Development Points, he gives Dr. Artan an advantage—Language Ability. Having spent more than 5 Development Points, Matt must give the good doctor some disadvantages. He decides that Dr. Artan tends to obsess about curing patients, neglecting other tasks to give them superhumanly good care. Since Obsessive Tendencies is a 3 point disadvantage, Dr. Artan is now balanced and ready to enter play. Matt notes (saving and curing patients) next to Obsessive Tendencies on the character sheet, to further define Dr. Artan's personality.

ARCHETYPES

ANDORIAN SCIENCE OFFICER

ATTRIBUTES
> Fitness 4
>> Vitality +2
> Coordination 2
> Intellect 2
>> Logic -1
>> Perception +2
> Presence 2
>> Willpower +1
> Psi 0

SKILLS
> Computer (choose specialization) 2 (3)
> Culture (Andorian) 2 (3)
> Dodge 1
> Energy Weapon (Phaser) 1 (2)
> First Aid (Andorian) 1 (2)
> History (Andorian) 1 (2)
>> (Federation) (2)
> Language
>> Andorian 2
>> Federation Standard 1
> Law (Starfleet Regulations) 1 (2)
> Life Sciences (Biology) 1 (2)
> Material Engineering (Civil Engineering) 1 (2)
> Personal Equipment (Tricorder) 2 (3)
> Physical Sciences (Physics) 1 (2)
> Planetary Sciences (Chemistry) 1 (2)
> Mathematics (2)
> Planetside Survival (Arctic) 2 (3)
> Primitive Weaponry (Chaka) 2 (3)
> Shipboard Systems (Sensors) 2 (4)
> Library Computer (3)
> Space Sciences (Astronomy) 2 (4)
>> (Astrophysics) (4)
> Systems Engineering (Computer Systems) 1 (2)
> Vehicle Operations (Shuttlecraft) 1 (2)
> World Knowledge (Andoria) 1 (2)

TRAITS
> Curious +1, Excellent Hearing +2 (due to antennae), High Pain Threshold +2; Poor Sight –2

COURAGE: 3

RENOWN: 1
> Aggression 1

Axanari Security Officer

Attributes

Fitness 3
Coordination 2
   Dexterity +1
Intellect 2
   Perception +2
Presence 2
   Empathy -1
   Willpower +2
Psi 0

Skills

Athletics (Climbing) 1 (2)
   (Running) (2)
   (Leaping) (2)
Computer (Data Alteration/Hacking) 1 (2)
Culture (Axanari) 2 (3)
Dodge 1
Energy Weapon (Phaser) 2 (4)
History (Axanari) 1 (2)
   (Federation) (2)
Language
   Axanari 2
   Federation Standard 1
Law (Starfleet Regulations) 1 (2)
Personal Equipment (Tricorder) 1 (2)
Physical Sciences (Mathematics) 1 (2)
   (Physics) (2)
Planetary Science (Geology) 1 (2)
Planetary Tactics (Shipboard) 1 (2)
Planetside Survival (Forest) 1 (2)
   (Mountains) (2)
Security (Security Systems) 2 (4)
   (Law Enforcement) (4)
Shipboard Systems (Tactical) 1 (2)
Strategic Operations (Invasion Defense) 1 (2)
Systems Engineering (Security) 1 (2)
Unarmed Combat (Starfleet Martial Arts) 1 (2)
Vehicle Operations (Shuttlecraft) 1 (2)
World Knowledge (Axanar, choose two other worlds) 1 (2) and (2) and (2)

Traits

Excellent Chemoreception +1, Excellent Hearing +2, Excellent Sight +2, Pattern Recognition +3, Promotion (Lieutenant JG) +1, Radiation Resistance +1; Impulsive -1, Stubborn –1

Courage: 3

Renown: 1

Discipline 1

Centauran Medical Officer

Attributes

Fitness 2
Coordination 2
Intellect 2
   Logic +2
Presence 2
   Empathy +2
Psi 0

Skills

Artistic Expression (Painting) 2 (3)
Athletics (Running) 1 (2)
Computer (Research) 1 (2)
Culture (Centauran) 2 (3)
Dodge 1
Energy Weapon (Phaser) 1 (2)
First Aid (Wound/Combat Trauma) 2 (3)
   (Centauran) (3)
History (Centauran) 1 (2)
   (Federation) (2)
Language
   Centauran 2
Federation Standard 1
Law (Starfleet Regulations) 1 (2)
Life Sciences (Exobiology) 2 (3)
   (Biology) (4)
   (Zoology) (3)
Medical Science (General Medicine) 2 (3)
   (Centauran) (3)
   (Psychology) (3)
Personal Equipment (Medical Tricorder) 2 (3)
Physical Sciences (Chemistry) 2 (3)
Planetside Survival (Desert) 1 (2)
Shipboard Systems (Medical Systems) 2 (3)
Vehicle Operations (Shuttlecraft) 1 (2)
World Knowledge (Alpha Centauri) 1 (2)

Traits

Sexy +2, Patron +2; Arrogant –1, Code of Honor (Hippocratic Oath) –2, Fanatic (about saving and preserving sentient life) -3

Courage: 3

Renown: 1

Openness 1

HUMAN COMMAND OFFICER

ATTRIBUTES

Fitness 3
   Vitality +1
Coordination 3
   Reaction +1
Intellect 3
Presence 3
   Willpower +2
Psi 0

SKILLS

Administration
(Starship Administration) 2 (3)
   (Starfleet) (3)
   (Logistics) (3)
Athletics (Running) 2 (3)
   (Lifting) (3)
Command (Starship Command) 2 (3)
Computer (Programming) 1 (2)
Culture (Human) 2 (3)
Dodge 1
Energy Weapon (Phaser) 1 (2)
History (Human) 1 (2)
   (Federation) (2)
Language
   Federation Standard 3
Law (Starfleet Regulations) 2 (3)
Personal Equipment (Communicator) 1 (2)
Planetside Survival (Forest) 1 (2)
Shipboard Systems (Helm) 1 (2)
Space Sciences (Astronomy) 1 (2)
Starship Tactics (Starfleet) 2 (3)
   (Planetary Support Tactics) (3)
   (Klingon) (3)
Vehicle Operations (Shuttlecraft) 1 (3)
World Knowledge (Earth or other homeworld) 1 (2)

TRAITS

Bold +1, Contact (Starfleet) +1; Rival (in Starfleet) -2

COURAGE: 5

RENOWN: 1
   Skill 1

TELLARITE COMMUNICATIONS OFFICER

ATTRIBUTES

Fitness 3
   Vitality +1
Coordination 2
   Reaction +1
Intellect 3
   Perception +1
Presence 3
   Empathy –1
   Willpower +1
Psi 0

SKILLS

Administration (Starship) 1 (2)
Athletics (Lifting) 1 (2)
Computer (Research) 2 (3)
   (Programming) (3)
Culture (Tellarite) 2 (3)
Dodge 1
Energy Weapon (Phaser) 1 (2)
History (Tellarite) 1 (2)
   (Federation) (2)
Language
   Tellarite 2
   Federation Standard 1
Law (Starfleet Regulations) 1 (2)
Personal Equipment (Communicator) 1 (2)
Persuasion (Debate) 2 (3)
Physical Sciences (Physics) 1 (2)
Planetside Survival (Mountains) 1 (2)
Propulsion Engineering (Warp Drive) 1 (2)
Shipboard Systems (Communications) 2 (3)
   (Sensors) (3)
   (Helm) (3)
Weapons Systems (3)
Space Science (Astronomy) 1 (2)
   (Stellar Navigation) (2)
Systems Engineering (Communications) 2 (4)
   (Computer Systems) (3)
Unarmed Combat (Starfleet Martial Arts) 1 (2)
Vehicle Operation (Shuttlecraft) 2 (3)
World Knowledge (Tellar) 1 (2)

TRAITS

NIGHT VISION +2; ARGUMENTATIVE –1

COURAGE: 3

RENOWN: 1
   Initiative 1

TIBURONIAN ENGINEER

ATTRIBUTES

Fitness 2
  Vitality +1
Coordination 3
Intellect 3
  Perception +1
Presence 2
  Empathy +1
Psi 0

SKILLS

Athletics (Running) 2 (3)
  (Lifting) (3)
Computer (Modeling) 2 (3)
Culture (Tiburonian) 2 (3)
Dodge 1
Energy Weapon (Phaser) 1 (2)
Gaming (Poker) 1 (2)
History (Tiburonian) 1 (2)
  (Federation) 1 (2)
Language
  Tiburonian 2
  Federation Standard 1
Law (Starfleet Regulations) 1 (2)
Material Engineering (Structural/Spaceframe) 1 (2)
  (Starship Design) (2)
Personal Equipment (Tricorder) 1 (2)
Physical Science (Physics) 1 (2)
Planetside Survival (Forest) 1 (2)
Propulsion Engineering (Warp Drive) 2 (4)
  (Impulse) (3)
Shipboard Systems (Helm) 2 (3)
  (Weapons Systems) (3)
  (Sensors) (3)
Space Sciences (Stellar Navigation) 1 (2)
Starship Tactics (Klingon) 1 (2)
  (Romulan) (2)
Systems Engineering (Computer Systems) 1 (2)
Vehicle Operations (Shuttlecraft) 1 (2)
  (Sailboats) (2)
World Knowledge (Tiburon) 1 (2)

TRAITS

Curious +1, Promotion (Lieutenant) +3; Hedonist –1, Vengeful -1

COURAGE: 3

RENOWN: 1

Openness 1

VULCAN HELMSMAN

ATTRIBUTES

Fitness 3
  Strength +1
Coordination 3
Intellect 2
  Logic +1
  Perception +1
Presence 2
  Empathy –1
  Willpower +1
Psi 1
  Range -1

SKILLS

Administration (Starship) 1 (2)
Athletics (Lifting) 1 (2)
Computer (Research) 1 (2)
Culture (Vulcan) 2 (3)
Dodge 1
Energy Weapon (Phaser) 1 (2)
History (Vulcan) 1 (2)
  (Federation) (2)
Language
  Vulcan 2
  Federation Standard 1
  Klingon 1
Law (Starfleet Regulations) 1 (2)
Mind Meld 2
Personal Equipment (Tricorder) 1 (2)
Planetary Tactics (Klingon) 1 (2)
Planetary Science (Ecology) 1 (2)
Planetside Survival (Desert) 1 (2)
Shipboard Systems (Helm) 2 (3)
  (Sensors) (3)
Space Sciences (Astrogation) 2 (3)
  (Astronomy) (3)
  (Stellar Cartography) (3)
Starship Tactics (Klingon) 1 (2)
Systems Engineering (Helm) 1 (2)
Unarmed Combat (Nerve Pinch) 2 (3)
  (Starfleet Martial Arts) (3)
Vehicle Operation (Shuttlecraft) 2 (3)
World Knowledge (Vulcan) 1 (2)

TRAITS

Bold +1, Curious +1; Code of Honor (Vulcan) -3, Hides Emotions –2, Intolerant (Klingons) -1

COURAGE: 3

RENOWN: 1

Skill 1

The Character Creation Process

If you'd rather not use an archetype, you can create your character by following these four steps:

1) Choose a Template: Templates define a character's species—Human, Vulcan, or anything else the player wants and the Narrator allows in her series. The Template provides the basic attributes and skills of an average member of the species.

2) Choose an Overlay: After selecting your species, choose your profession, represented by an Overlay. When combined with a Template, an Overlay provides a picture of a detailed member of Federation society who is just about ready to play.

3) Customize your character with Development Points, Advantages, Disadvantages, and a detailed Background: *Star Trek Roleplaying Game* characters aren't generic, "average" members of their respective species—each one is distinctive and special. One way to make your character that way is to use the Background History system to trace his life up to the time the game begins—from childhood, to Academy training, to tours of duty. Each stage in the History provides you with Development Points to improve and customize your character.

4) Finishing touches: Finally, determine your character's Renown, Courage Points, and rank.

THE BASICS OF CHARACTER CREATION

Players (and Narrators) build *Star Trek Roleplaying Game* characters with three basic elements: attributes and edges, advantages and disadvantages, and skills. This chapter provides information about each of these. When you create your character, you receive some attributes, skills and traits for free from the Template and Overlay you choose. You can purchase others with Development Points, which are discussed below.

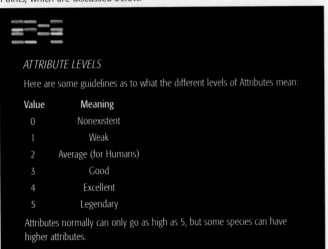

ATTRIBUTE LEVELS

Here are some guidelines as to what the different levels of Attributes mean:

Value	Meaning
0	Nonexistent
1	Weak
2	Average (for Humans)
3	Good
4	Excellent
5	Legendary

Attributes normally can only go as high as 5, but some species can have higher attributes.

Attributes represent a character's innate physical and mental characteristics—everything from how strong he is, to how fast his reflexes are, to how intelligent he is. Attribute scores are "open-ended," meaning there is no limit to how high they can go, though normally they range from 1 to 5. Your character's base attributes come from his Template, which represents his species.

Edges represent aspects of an attribute. Each attribute has two of them, expressed in plus or minus values ranging from +2 to –2. Edges provide a way to distinguish and conceptualize characters, and to make attributes more flexible. For example, two characters might both have Presence 2, but one is more willful (he has a positive Willpower edge).

Skills, unlike attributes and edges, aren't innate. They represent a character's learned abilities and knowledge—everything from shooting a phaser, to using a communications system, to playing the Vulcan lute. Skills are rated from 1 to 5; the higher character's rating in a skill, the more he knows about it and how to perform it. An Orion pirate with Dodge 3 is better able to dodge blows than a Tellarite scientist with Dodge 1.

Most skills deal with broad, complex subjects. For many of them, a character must choose a specialization indicating his area of particular expertise. For example, a character who knows the Shipboard Systems skill could choose to specialize in such areas as Communications, Sensors, Helm, or some other shipboard system. Being specialized doesn't mean the character can't use his skill in other ways—he understands the basics of the field, and can still attempt a Skill Test in related areas—he just doesn't know as much about them and isn't likely to perform such Tests as well. For example, a character who specializes in Shipboard Systems (Communications) still understands the basics for operating all starship control panels; in a pinch, he could fire the phasers. An Engineer specializing in Propulsion Engineering (Warp Drive) can apply that knowledge to a variety of tasks. If necessary, he could try to repair the impulse drive or the emergency rockets on the shuttlecraft.

A character's *advantages* represent his "special" abilities—the things he has a knack for and is best at (and usually enjoys the most)—or some benefit or superiority he has over other characters (like a High Pain Threshold or a Contact). Most Crew members should have at least one or two advantages; they're one of the things which makes them distinctive "heroes" and not everyday NPCs.

However, many characters also have bad habits, have suffered cruel twists of fate, or have the deck stacked against them in other ways. In the Icon System, these drawbacks and flaws are represented with *disadvantages*. Remember, in many cases being a hero has as much to do with overcoming one's own limitations as it does with winning a fight or solving some problem. Disadvantages help simulate these limitations, thereby breathing life into the character and stimulating roleplaying. Taking a disadvantage also gives your character more Development Points to spend in other areas.

DEVELOPMENT POINTS

Players spend *Development Points* to obtain new skills or specializations, improve existing skills, attributes and edges, and the like. Every character element in the *Star Trek Roleplaying Game* costs a number of points, based on its usefulness in game play (see the table on page 52). Increasing your Intellect from 2 to 3, for example, costs two Development Points. During the character creation process, you receive Development Points to spend to individualize your character.

STEP ONE: THE TEMPLATE

Once you've got a concept in mind for your character, you can choose the appropriate Template. The Template represents an average specimen of the character's species—Human or Axanari, for example. It provides the character's innate qualities, inherited characteristics, and cultural aspects.

Pages 47-49 provide Templates for various Federation member species. Choose the one which fits your concept. Templates are free; they do not cost Development Points.

A Template gives you three things: your character's basic attributes; the basic background skills he'd learn growing up in his society (such as his native language); and possibly some inherent advantages or disadvantages (like Tiburonians' hedonism).

Template attributes define the character at his most basic level: how strong he is, how intelligent, whether he has psionic ability. Every character has five basic attributes—Fitness, Coordination, Intellect, Presence, and Psi. The numbers appearing in brackets are the maximum levels a character of that species can possess. For example, Humans cannot possess a Fitness greater than 5. Record the numbers listed on the Template on your character sheet. Later during the character creation process, you'll have the chance to change them, thus personalizing your character.

Skills and abilities represent what every character of a given species knows; a Tiburonian character, for example, knows the history, customs and language of his people. Record the skills and skill levels listed on the Template on your character sheet.

A few Templates list advantages and disadvantages common to the species. All Tiburonians, for example, have the disadvantage Hedonist. Record any advantages or disadvantages on your character sheet.

ANDORIAN

Hailing from the frigid planet Andoria, the blue-skinned Andorians have snowy white hair and antennae. Passionate, and often warlike, they channel their aggressiveness into ritualized duels and other activities (see page 20 for more details).

ATTRIBUTES

Fitness 3 [6]
    Vitality +1
Coordination 2 [5]
Intellect 2 [5]
    Logic -1
    Perception +1

Presence 2 [5]
Psi 0 [5]

SKILLS

Culture (Andorian) 2 (3)
History (Andorian) 1 (2)
Language
    Andorian 2
Primitive Weaponry (Chaka) 2 (3)
Science, Any (choose specialization) 1 (2)
World Knowledge (Andoria) 1 (2)

TYPICAL ADVANTAGES/DISADVANTAGES

Excellent Hearing +2 (due to antennae)
High Pain Threshold +2

AXANARI

The Axanari are tall humanoids—the average Axanari is about two meters tall, but quite a few are even taller. Their brownish skins are covered with dust-like white secretions which help protect them from radiation; Axanari hair comes in a rainbow of colors. They are known for their stubbornness and impulsiveness, but also for their keen senses and deductive abilities (see page 21 for more details).

ATTRIBUTES

Fitness 3 [6]
Coordination 2 [5]
Intellect 2 [5]
    Logic -1
    Perception +2
Presence 2 [5]
    Empathy -1
    Willpower +1
Psi 0 [5]

SKILLS

Athletics (choose specialization) 1 (2)
Culture (Axanari) 2 (3)
History (Axanari) 1 (2)
Language
    Axanari 2
Science, Any (choose specialization) 1 (2)
World Knowledge (Axanar) 1 (2)

TYPICAL ADVANTAGES/DISADVANTAGES

Excellent Chemoreception +1
Excellent Hearing +2
Excellent Sight +2
Pattern Recognition +3

Radiation Resistance +1

Impulsive -1

Stubborn -1

CENTAURAN

The natives of Alpha Centauri appear virtually identical to Humans, and are often mistaken for them, though the placement of their internal organs differs significantly. A highly spiritual people, their holistic approach makes them excellent scientists and artists (see page 21 for more details).

ATTRIBUTES

Fitness 2 [5]

Coordination 2 [5]

Intellect 2 [5]

Logic +1

Presence 2 [5]

Empathy +1

Psi 0 [5]

SKILLS

Artistic Expression (choose specialization) 2 (3)

Culture (Centauran) 2 (3)

History (Centauran) 1 (2)

Language

Centauran 2

Science, Any (choose specialization) 2 (3)

World Knowledge (Alpha Centauri) 1 (2)

TYPICAL ADVANTAGES/DISADVANTAGES

Sexy +2

HUMAN

Humans come from Earth or one of the many Earth colony worlds in Federation space. Transcending their warlike natures, they founded an ideal society and ventured out into space to explore the unknown, and helped to found the United Federation of Planets (see page 8 for more details).

ATTRIBUTES

Fitness 2 [5]

Coordination 2 [5]

Intellect 2 [5]

Presence 2 [5]

Willpower +1

Psi 0 [5]

SKILLS

Athletics (choose specialization) 2 (3)

Culture (Human) 2 (3)

History (Human) 1 (2)

Language

Federation Standard 2

Science, Any (choose specialization) 1 (2)

World Knowledge (Earth or other homeworld) 1 (2)

TYPICAL ADVANTAGES/DISADVANTAGES

2 extra Courage Points

TELLARITE

Stocky, with vaguely porcine features and often unkempt-looking shocks of hair, Tellarites are renowned for their love of engineering and argument. A Tellarite will debate simply for the enjoyment it gives him (though they do not, as a rule, question the orders of their commanding officers). They make excellent engineers and scientists (see page 22 for more details).

ATTRIBUTES

Fitness 3 [6]

Coordination 2 [5]

Reaction +1

Intellect 2 [5]

Presence 2 [5]

Empathy -1

Psi 0 [5]

SKILLS

Culture (Tellarite) 2 (3)

Engineering, Any (choose two specializations) 2 (3)

History (Tellarite) 1 (2)

Language

Tellarite 2

Persuasion (Debate) 2 (3)

World Knowledge (Tellar) 1 (2)

TYPICAL ADVANTAGES/DISADVANTAGES

Night Vision +2

Argumentative –1

TIBURONIAN

Natives of Tiburon, Tiburonians are known for their sensual natures, technological acumen, and dislike of tyranny and intolerance. They are characterized by their large, elaborately shaped ears and a row of tiny bony protrusions running across the center of the top of the head and down the front of the necks (see page 23 for more details).

ATTRIBUTES

Fitness 2 [5]
Coordination 2 [5]
Intellect 2 [5]
Presence 2 [5]
    Empathy +1
Psi 0 [5]

SKILLS

Athletics (choose specialization) 2 (3)
Culture (Tiburonian) 2 (3)
Engineering, Any (choose specialization) 1 (2)
Gaming (choose specialization) 1 (2)
History (Tiburonian) 1 (2)
Language
    Tiburonian 2
Science, Any (choose specialization) 1 (2)
World Knowledge (Tiburon) 1 (2)

TYPICAL ADVANTAGES/DISADVANTAGES

Curious +1
Hedonist -1

VULCAN

Known throughout the Federation (and beyond) for their logic and emotionlessness, the Vulcans are a pillar of the Federation. Most Vulcans exhibit some form of telepathic ability, though they are better known for their curious natures and scientific achievements. Vulcans serve in an increasing variety of postings in Starfleet—from science to security (see page 23 for more details).

ATTRIBUTES

Fitness 2 [6]
    Strength +1
Coordination 2 [5]
Intellect 2 [6]
    Logic +1
Presence 2 [5]
    Empathy -1
Psi 1 [6]
    Range -1

SKILLS

Culture (Vulcan) 2 (3)
History (Vulcan) 1 (2)
Language
    Vulcan 2
Mind Meld 2
Science, Any (choose specialization) 2 (3)
Unarmed Combat (Nerve Pinch) 2 (3)
World Knowledge (Vulcan) 1 (2)

TYPICAL ADVANTAGES/DISADVANTAGES

Curious +1
Code of Honor (Vulcan) -3
Hides Emotions -2

STEP TWO: THE OVERLAY

After choosing a Template, select an Overlay, which represents your character's profession (in Starfleet, his primary duties aboard his ship). The Overlay defines what your character has learned in training and over his career, rather than his innate abilities or skills appropriate to his species. Every profession in the *Star Trek Roleplaying Game* has its own Overlay.

The following pages contain Overlays for several positions on board a starship. You should choose the appropriate Overlay for your character's conception.

The Overlay provides the skills necessary for a character to complete his duties—every commander knows how to run his ship, every Science Officer knows how to use the science station. As graduates of Starfleet Academy, all Starfleet characters also learn certain basic skills. Note the skills and skill levels listed on the Overlay on your character sheet. Later on, you will be able to choose additional skills or increase existing skill levels. Overlays are free; they do not cost Development Points.

To become the head of any department on a starship, a character has to have the *Department Head* advantage, and typically the *Promotion* advantage as well. Before buying these advantages, characters often have to know certain skills or accomplish certain things. Your Narrator can tell you more about this.

For further information about each of the professions described on pages 50-51, please refer to the chapters on *Starfleet* and *Technology*, pages 25 and 163, respectively.

STEP THREE: BACKGROUND

Your character's Template and Overlay provide a firm foundation for a well-developed character. They tell you how strong or smart he is, and what he can do. But not all Axanari security officers are the same; one might be stronger than another, or a better shot with a phaser. One may have specialized in planetary defense, while the other is an expert on starship security. The

COMMAND

Command Branch personnel serve as administrators assigned to various departments throughout Starfleet. They oversee compliance with all Starfleet regulations, assist operations and science personnel, and report to the commanding officer. Command personnel know how to lead, and how to motivate others to follow them.

To become a First Officer or Captain requires the purchase of both the *Department Head* and *Promotion Advantages*, as well as possessing knowledge of other duties (such as Helm and Weapons Systems).

Administration (Starship Administration) 2 (3)
Command (Starship Command) 2 (3)
Law (Starfleet Regulations) 2 (3)
Planetary or Starship Tactics
   (choose specialization) 2 (3)
Shipboard Systems (choose specialization) 1 (2)
Athletics (choose specialization) 1 (2)
Computer (choose specialization) 1 (2)
Dodge 1
Energy Weapon (Phaser) 1 (2)
History (Federation) 1 (2)
Language
   Federation Standard 1
Personal Equipment (choose specialization) 1 (2)
Planetside Survival (choose specialization) 1 (2)
Vehicle Operations (Shuttlecraft) 1 (2)

COMMUNICATIONS

Communications personnel ensure the integrity and security of Starfleet transmissions. They use their equipment and skills to overcome interference, encode and decode transmissions, open communications channels and similar duties.

Administration (choose specialization) 1 (2)
Computer (choose specialization) 1 (2)
Science, Any (choose related specialization) 1 (2)
Shipboard Systems (Communications) 2 (3)
Systems Engineering (Communications) 1 (2)
Vehicle Operation (Shuttlecraft) 2 (3)
Athletics (choose specialization) 1 (2)
Computer (choose specialization) 1 (2)
Dodge 1
Energy Weapon (Phaser) 1 (2)
History (Federation) 1 (2)
Language
   Federation Standard 1
Law (Starfleet Regulations) 1 (2)
Personal Equipment (choose specialization) 1 (2)
Planetside Survival (choose specialization) 1 (2)
Unarmed Combat (Starfleet Martial Arts) 1 (2)

HELM/NAVIGATION

These two related bridge officer functions involve guiding and piloting the ship. The Helm officer pilots the ship based on a course computed and laid in by the Navigator. In combat situations, both positions also assist with weapons operations.

Administration (choose specialization) 1 (2)
Shipboard Systems
   (choose either Helm or Navigation) 2 (3)
Space Sciences (Astrogation) 2 (3)
Systems Engineering
   (choose either Helm or Navigation) 1 (2)
Vehicle Operation (Shuttlecraft) 2 (3)
Athletics (choose specialization) 1 (2)
Computer (choose specialization) 1 (2)
Dodge 1
Energy Weapon (Phaser) 1 (2)
History (Federation) 1 (2)
Language
   Federation Standard 1
Law (Starfleet Regulations) 1 (2)
Personal Equipment (choose specialization) 1 (2)
Planetside Survival (choose specialization) 1 (2)
Unarmed Combat (Starfleet Martial Arts) 1 (2)

ENGINEER

An Engineer keeps his ship's systems and equipment operating at maximum efficiency. Although engineers specialize in a particular type of engineering–warp field dynamics, matter/energy conversion or materials engineering, for example–Chief Engineers must be proficient in a variety of engineering subjects.

Computer (Modeling) 2 (3)
Engineering, Any
   (choose two specializations) 2 (3) and (3)
Engineering, Any Other
   (choose specialization) 1 (2)
Physical Science (choose specialization) 1 (2)
Shipboard Systems
   (choose two specializations) 2 and (3)
Athletics (choose specialization) 1 (2)
Dodge 1
Energy Weapon (Phaser) 1 (2)
Language
   Federation Standard 1
History (Federation) 1 (2)
Law (Starfleet Regulations) 1 (2)
Personal Equipment (choose specialization) 1 (2)
Planetside Survival (choose specialization) 1 (2)
Vehicle Operations (Shuttlecraft and one other
   vehicle) 1 (2)

MEDICAL

Since starships seek out new life, they need doctors to investigate the new and unusual lifeforms that they encounter. Starfleet doctors are also responsible for ensuring that a starship's crew stays healthy both physically and mentally. Medical personnel tend to specialize in particular fields, such as surgery or toxicology.

First Aid (choose specialization) 2 (3)
Life Science (choose specialization) 1 (2)
Medical Science (choose specialization) 2 (3)
Personal Equipment (Medical Tricorder) 2 (3)
Shipboard Systems (Medical Systems) 2 (3)
Athletics (choose specialization) 1 (2)
Computer (choose specialization) 1 (2)
Dodge 1
Energy Weapon (Phaser) 1 (2)
History (Federation) 1 (2)
Language
   Federation Standard 1
Law (Starfleet Regulations) 1 (2)
Planetside Survival (choose specialization) 1 (2)
Vehicle Operations (Shuttlecraft) 1 (2)

SCIENCES

Starfleet scientists staff starship laboratories, analyze samples from strange new worlds, investigate scientific mysteries, and provide scientific solutions for the problems a starship inevitably confronts. The Science Officer is responsible for all scientific personnel, and reports directly to the commanding officer, though various scientific personnel may advise the captain in their area of specialization. A character's scientific specialties depend on the specializations he chooses.*

Computer (choose specialization) 2 (3)
Engineering, Any (choose specialization) 1 (2)
Personal Equipment (Tricorder) 2 (3)
Science, Any
   (choose two specializations) 2 (3) and (4)
Science, Any Other (choose specialization) 1 (2)
Shipboard Systems (Sensors and Library Computer) 2 (3)
Dodge 1
Energy Weapon (Phaser) 1 (2)
History (Federation) 1 (2)
Language
   Federation Standard 1
Law (Starfleet Regulations) 1 (2)
Planetside Survival (choose specialization) 1 (2)
Vehicle Operations (Shuttlecraft) 1 (2)

* Members of Starfleet's Science division typically choose an area of specialization. A Science officer with a specialization in astronomy might serve on board a starship in the stellar cartography department, mapping star systems and analyzing stellar phenomena. See *Specialization* (page 65).

SCIENTIST

In addition to the Science Officer who mans the bridge Science station, Starfleet vessels carry a host of other scientists who assist with vessels' missions. These officers include geologists, sociologists, botanists and many other specialists who devote their time to conducting pure scientific research.

Computer (choose specialization) 2 (3)
Engineering, Any (choose specialization) 1 (2)

Personal Equipment (Tricorder and specific scientific equipment) 2 (3)
Science, Any (choose two specializations) 2 (3) and (4)
Science, Any Other (choose specialization) 2 (3)
Shipboard Systems (Library Computer) 1 (2)
Dodge 1
History (Federation) 1 (2)
Language
   Federation Standard 1
Law (Starfleet Regulations) 1 (2)
Planetside Survival (choose specialization) 1 (2)
Vehicle Operations (Shuttlecraft) 1 (2)

SECURITY

Security officers serve on board a starship as combination security guards-police officers. They patrol sensitive areas (both on and off ship), beam into potentially hazardous situations to protect other crewmen, and handle military and tactical emergencies both on ship and planetside.

Energy Weapon (Phaser) 2 (3)
Planetary Tactics (Shipboard) 1 (2)
Security (Security Systems) 2 (3)
Shipboard Systems (any specialization) 1 (2)
Systems Engineering (Security) 1 (2)
Unarmed Combat (Starfleet Martial Arts) 1 (2)
Athletics (choose specialization) 1 (2)
Computer (choose specialization) 1 (2)
Dodge 1
History (Federation) 1 (2)
Language
   Federation Standard 1
Law (Starfleet Regulations) 1 (2)
Personal Equipment (choose specialization) 1 (2)
Planetside Survival (choose specialization) 1 (2)
Vehicle Operations (Shuttlecraft) 1 (2)

DEVELOPMENT POINT COSTS

Element	Development Point Cost
Attributes	2 points
Edges	1 point
Skill	3 points
Specialization	1 point
Advantages	Variable
Disadvantages	Variable

attributes and edges, new skills, additional skill levels, and other character creation elements. Elements chosen at a specific Background History stage background history stages represent events and developments that the character experienced at that period of his life. If he learned to play three-dimensional chess as a child, you would purchase Gaming (3-D Chess) during the Early Youth stage in his Background History.

Each Background History stage includes several "packages"—quick and easy groups of skills that a character can select to represent a particular type of training or background he experienced during that stage of his life. If you were assigned to Memory Alpha duty while at Starfleet Academy, you could choose the Memory Alpha Detached Duty package. If you'd rather not choose a package, you can spend that stage's Development Points on the attributes, edges, skills, advantages, and disadvantages listed with that stage or in the Universal Background List on page 53. The number of points you have to spend, and what you can spend them on, depends on particular stages in the character's

past. You must spend all Development Points for a particular Background History stage on the elements listed for that stage; you cannot "save" them or "carry them over" for later stages.

The elements you choose for your character should help to paint a picture of his life up to the point of entering play. For example, you might choose the Sworn Enemy and Vengeful disadvantages for your character. You and the Narrator might put these traits together by saying that the character's family was killed by Klingon raiders, who were driven off by Starfleet before the character himself could become their next victim. Your character has sworn revenge on the Klingon captain, who in turn has vowed to kill him.

You may come up with an idea that requires a character element not available at a particular stage. If so, talk with your Narrator and try to come up with a good explanation. A character who learned advanced mathematics as a youngster might be a child genius, while someone obsessed with Starfleet might have studied its history, protocol, or battles to the point where he's as well-versed in that knowledge as a ship captain. However, some skills, advantages and disadvantages may not be appropriate for Starfleet officers. Examples include many Dark Secrets (such as having a criminal past) or Sleight of Hand (Pick Pocket). They are included in the Icon System rules for the sake of completeness, but are marked with an icon (❖) for easy reference. If you want such an element for your character, discuss it with your Narrator; perhaps the two of you can come up with an explanation which makes the element acceptable in the series (for example, a character with a criminal record might have been falsely convicted).

As you go through the Background History, you may have additional ideas and refinements for your character. If so, follow your thoughts; you'll probably

WHAT IF I GET THE SAME SKILL TWICE?

Sometimes, you will get the same skill from two different sources during the Character Creation process. For example, an Overlay might provide a character with a skill he already received from his Template, or a Background History Package might provide a character with a skill he already received from his Overlay, or from earlier in his Background.

– If both sources provide the same skill with different specializations at the same level, the character simply knows two specializations. For instance, Tiburonians possess the skill History (Tiburon) 1 (2). Starfleet officers learn History (Federation) 1 (2). On the character sheet, this becomes History (Tiburon) 1 (2) and (Federation) (2).

– If both sources provide the same skill with different specializations at different levels, the character takes the higher level skill, and knows two specializations. For instance, a Tiburonian possesses any one Engineering skill and a chosen specialization at 1 (2); the player chooses Systems Engineering (Environmental Systems) 1 (2). Later, he chooses the Shakedown Cruise Mission, which grants Systems Engineering (any specialization) at 2 (3). The player selects Transporter Systems, so on the character sheet, this becomes Systems Engineering (Transporter Systems) 2 (3) and (Environmental Systems) (2).

– If both sources provide the same skill with the same specialization at the same level, the character adds one point either to his skill or to the specialization. For example, the "Starfleet Brat" Early Life Package grants Vehicle Operation (Shuttlecraft) at 1 (2), as does the Science Overlay. On the character sheet, this can either become Vehicle Operation (Shuttlecraft) 2 (2) or Vehicle Operation (Shuttlecraft) 1 (3).

– If both sources provide the same skill with the same specialization at different levels, the character takes the higher skill level, and can then add one point to either his skill or to the specialization. For example, a Tiburonian character begins with any Science at 1 (2); the player chooses Medical Science (Surgery) 1 (2). Upon taking the Medical Overlay, he adds Medical Science with any specialization at 2 (3). On the character sheet (if the player selects Surgery as the Overlay specialization here), that can either become Medical Science (Surgery) 3 (3) or Medical Science (Surgery) 2 (4).

– Skills without specializations (such as Dodge, or most languages) simply add. A Human character with Federation Standard 2 from his Template and Federation Standard 1 from his Overlay gets Federation Standard 3.

These traits and skills can be taken at any stage of any character's Background History.

ADVANTAGES	DISADVANTAGES	SKILLS
Ally (+2 to +5)	Argumentative (-1)	Acrobatics
Athletic Ability (+2)	Chronic Pain (-2)	Administration
Bold (+1)	Code of Honor (-2 to -5)	Artistic Expression
Contact (+1 to +3)	Dark Secret (-1 to -3)	Athletics
Curious (+1)	Dependent (-2)	Bargain
Famous Incident (varies)	Fanatic (-2 to -3)	Charm
Favors Owed (+1)	Greedy (-1)	Computer
Indomitable (+2)	Hedonist (-1)	Concealment
Medical Remedy (varies)	Hides Emotions (-2)	Culture
Patron (+2 to +4)	Hypochondria (-1)	Demolitions
Pattern Recognition (+3)	Impulsive (-1)	Diplomacy
Quick-Draw (+2)	Intolerant (-1 to -3)	Disguise
Resolute (+3)	Medical Problem (-1 to -3)	Dodge
Sexy (+2)	Obligation (-1 to -3)	Energy Weapon
Shrewd (+1)	Obsessive Tendencies (-3)	Engineering, Any
Strong Will (+2)	Pacifism (-1 to -5)	Fast Talk
Wealth (+1 to +6)	Phobia (-2 to -5)	First Aid
	Physically Impaired (-1 to -3)	Gaming
	Poor Chemoreception (if later in life, due to disease or chemical exposure) (-1)	History
		Intimidation
	Poor Hearing (if later in life, due to trauma or increasing deafness) (-1)	Languages
		Law
	Poor Sight (if later in life, due to injury, radiation, or increasing blindness) (-2)	Merchant
		Personal Equipment
	Rival (-1 to -3)	Persuasion
	Stubborn (-1)	Planetary Tactics
	Sworn Enemy (-1 to -3)	Planetside Survival
	Vengeful (-1 to -2)	Primitive Weaponry
		Science, Any
		Search
		Sleight of Hand
		Stealth
		Unarmed Combat
		Vehicle Operation
		World Knowledge

end up creating a more interesting, better developed character. By this point you're thinking about your character more, and making decisions that will make him more enjoyable for you to play.

ELEMENT COSTS

As mentioned above, during character creation you spend *Development Points* to improve attributes, and buy various game elements such as skills. (After the game begins, you can improve your character with *Experience Points*, as detailed in the *Rewards* chapter.) Here's a breakdown of costs:

Attributes

Attributes cost 2 Development Points per attribute point. Lowering an attribute from its starting value gives you 2 extra Development Points to spend (on whatever you wish, subject to the Narrator's restrictions) per attribute point lowered.

Edges

Positive edges cost 1 Development Point for each point raised; negative edges give you 1 extra Development Point to spend (on whatever you wish, subject to the Narrator's restrictions) per point. (These costs include paying for the 0 level; for example, taking an edge from -1 to +1 costs 2 Development Points—one point to go from -1 to 0, and another point to go from 0 to +1.) Characters with Psi 0 cannot lower their Range and Focus edges to gain extra Development Points.

Characters cannot change their edges more than four times during character creation (not including changes from the character's Template). Increasing or decreasing an edge by a point counts as a "change." For example, raising Ensign Tibault's Reaction and Willpower each by 1 counts as two changes, and decreasing his Logic to -1 counts as a third change. Tibault can only make one more change to his edges during character development. (With the Narrator's permission, characters can change their edges as much as they want after game play begins). If your choice of Overlay or Background History package means you'll make more than four changes to your character's edges, either get your Narrator's permission, or simply don't make the fifth (and subsequent) change(s), and instead take the additional point for each edge and spend it on something else.

Skills

Buying the first level in a new skill costs 3 Development Points. The first specialization in any skill is free (you must choose it automatically when you buy the skill; it doesn't cost you any Development Points); additional specializations within skills cost 1 Development Point each.

Improving the level of a skill the character already knows costs 3 Development Points per level (regardless of level). For example, during character creation, improving from Dodge 1 to Dodge 2 costs 3 Development Points. Characters may not start the game with any skill higher than 4 (5) (or 5 for skills, such as Dodge, which don't have specializations), except with the Narrator's permission.

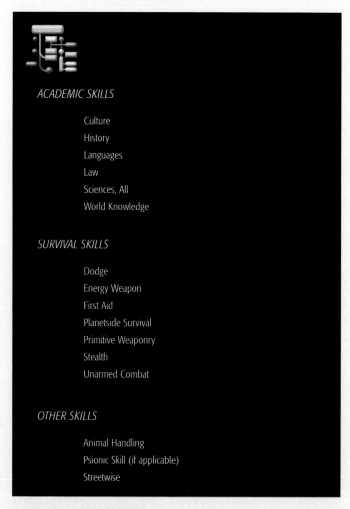

ACADEMIC SKILLS

Culture
History
Languages
Law
Sciences, All
World Knowledge

SURVIVAL SKILLS

Dodge
Energy Weapon
First Aid
Planetside Survival
Primitive Weaponry
Stealth
Unarmed Combat

OTHER SKILLS

Animal Handling
Psionic Skill (if applicable)
Streetwise

Advantages and Disadvantages

The cost of advantages varies, depending on the value of the benefit. Similarly, the value of a disadvantage is based on the severity of the flaw. The costs for them are listed later in this chapter.

There's a limit on how many disadvantages characters can take at the start of the game. Typically, a character is restricted to no more than eight points in disadvantages; anyone with more than eight points' worth of disadvantages probably couldn't pass the rigorous physical and mental screening procedures for Starfleet. Beginning Narrators may also want to restrict the number or degree of advantages characters can start with, both to make the game easier to run, and to keep the game balanced and fun for all players.

EARLY LIFE

Early Life represents a character's childhood and adolescence—essentially, his life prior to entering Starfleet Academy. When thinking about it, ask yourself: where was he born and raised? Did he live in a happy household? What did his parents do? Where was he schooled? What were his hobbies and interests? What interesting or exciting experiences did he have? All these sorts of things are reflected in the Early Life stage.

You may either choose one of the Early Life packages listed below, or spend five Development Points on the game elements listed under Early Life History or the Universal Background List. Skills purchased during this stage typically represent education and personal interests; advantages and disadvantages represent events which happened to him or privileges he acquired.

EARLY LIFE HISTORY

The character receives 5 Development Points to spend during Early Life.

Early Life Packages (each costs 5 Development Points)

Academic Upbringing: One Academic Skill (see box on pg. 54) at 1 (2), +1 to Logic Edge, Patron +2, Arrogant -1

Colony Upbringing: One Survival Skill (see box on pg. 54) at 1 (2), +1 to Vitality Edge, +1 to Perception Edge

Exploration: World Knowledge (a world the character's family explored) OR Space Sciences (Astronomy) at 1 (2), +1 Vitality Edge, Curious (+1)

Failed Colony: One Survival Skill (see box on pg. 54) at 1 (2), +1 to Vitality Edge, Alertness +2, Vengeful -1 OR Intolerant -1 (of whomever the character blames for the failure)

Famous Parents: One Intellect Skill at 1 (2), +1 Renown, Patron (your parents) +2, Obligation -1 OR Rival -1 connected to your parents' work

Military Family: History (Military) 1 (2), +1 to Dexterity OR Reaction Edge, Contact +1

Normal Upbringing: +1 to Dexterity OR Reaction Edge, Athletics (choose a Specialization for your childhood sport such as Riding or Climbing) 1 (2), add a Specialization in any Template Skill

Orphaned: Streetwise 1 (2), Charm OR Intimidation 1 (2), +1 to Empathy Edge, Hides Emotions -2

Political Upbringing: Diplomacy (with specialization reflecting your parents' career) 1 (2), Language Ability +2, Contact +1, Rival -1 (connected to parents' career)

Religious/Ideological Training: History (with specialization in past of group) 1 (2), Culture (with appropriate specialization) 1 (2), Fanatic -2 OR Pacifism -2, +1 Strength OR +1 Willpower Edge

"Starfleet Brat": Administration (Starfleet) 1 (2), Vehicle Operation (Shuttlecraft) 1 (2), Contact (Starfleet) +1, Rival (in Starfleet) -2

ATTRIBUTES AND EDGES
  Any
ADVANTAGES
  Alertness (+2)
  Alien Upbringing (+1)
  Ambidexterity (+2)
  Double-Jointed (+2)
  Eidetic Memory (+3)
  Engineering Aptitude (+3)
  Excellent Balance (+1)
  Excellent Chemoreception (+1)
  Excellent Hearing (+2)
  Excellent Metabolism (+1)
  Excellent Sight (+2)
  High Pain Threshold (+2)
  Innovative (+1)
  Language Ability (+2)
  Mathematical Ability (+3)
  Mixed Species Heritage (+6)
  Night Vision (+2)
  Peripheral Vision (+1)
  Rapid Healing (+1)
  Sense of Direction (+1)
  Sense of Time (+2)
  Tactical Genius (+3)
  Telepathic Resistance (+4)
  Toughness (+2)
DISADVANTAGES
  Bloodlust (-2)
  Low Pain Threshold (-2)
  Slow Healing (-2)
  Weak Will (-2)
  Weakness (-2)
  Zero-G Intolerance (-2)

ADDITIONAL EDUCATION

If a character displays a talent for some academic subject, he may be given the opportunity to take additional courses of study, or even attend one of the Federation's specialist schools, such as the Diplomatic College, Advanced Tactical School, or Vulcan Science Institute. Additional education does not give a character more Development Points to spend during this stage of his Background History, but provides a good explanation for buying many new and unusual skills. Other Last Unicorn Games products provide ideas for additional packages for various specialist schools. The Narrator may wish to approve any Additional Education packages.

ACADEMY LIFE

With his childhood behind him, and the future stretching before him like the uncharted reaches of the galaxy, your character applied to, and was accepted in, Starfleet Academy. There he studied, trained, and pushed himself to excel for four long, hard, rewarding years. When considering this stage, ask yourself: why did he go to the Academy? What did he study there? Which courses did he enjoy, and which ones did he loathe? Did anything unusual or significant happen while he was there? Who were his friends, rivals, favorite professors?

You receive eight Development Points to spend on the Starfleet Academy Life History stage. You can either choose one of the packages, which detail specific courses of study or academic interests, or, if none of them interest you, spend the points on the game elements listed under this stage or the Universal Background List.

Skills purchased at this stage represent Starfleet Academy courses your character took (in addition to his Overlay skills, of course, which represent the primary focus of his Academy career). Advantages and disadvantages represent unusual events he experienced.

STARFLEET ACADEMY LIFE HISTORY

A Starfleet character receives 8 Development Points to spend during Academy Life.

Starfleet Academy Specialized Training Packages
(each costs 8 Development Points)

Advanced Tactical School: Administration (Logistics) 1 (2), Starship Tactics (Planetary Support Tactics; Klingon OR Romulan) 1 (2) and (2), Bold +1

Advanced Research Engineering: Propulsion Engineering (Warp Drive) 1 (2), Material Engineering (Structural/Spaceframe OR Starship Design) 1 (2), +1 to Intellect

Colonization School: Material Engineering (Civil Engineering) 1 (2), Planetary Survival (choose specialization) 1 (2), +1 to Fitness

EVA Training: Zero-G Trained +2, Personal Equipment (Environmental Suit) 1 (2), Vehicle Operation (Work Bee) 1 (2)

Exploration Training: Space Science (choose two specializations) 1 (2) and (2), Shipboard Systems (Sensors) 1 (2), +1 to Perception Edge

First Contact Training: Diplomacy (Federation Frontier) 1 (2), +1 to Perception Edge, Social Science (choose two specializations) 1 (2) and (2)

Intelligence Training: Espionage (Traffic Analysis) 1 (2), Language (Klingon or Romulan) 1, Behavior Modification (Resistance) 1 (2), Obligation -1 (to Starfleet Intelligence)

Klingon Specialist Program: Language (Klingon) 1, Planetary Tactics (Klingon) 1 (2) Starship Tactics (Klingon) 1 (2), Intolerant (Klingons) -1

Memory Alpha Detached Duty: Culture (choose specialization) 1 (2), History (choose specialization) 1 (2), Science, Any (choose specialization) 1 (2)

Security Training: Energy Weapon (Phaser) 1 (2), Security (choose two specializations) 1 (2) and (2), +1 to Perception Edge

Starfleet Medical Academy: Life Science (choose specialization) 1 (2), First Aid (Wound/Combat Trauma) 1 (2), Medical Science (choose specialization) 1 (2), Physical Sciences (Chemistry) 1 (2), +1 to Empathy Edge, Code of Honor (Hippocratic Oath) -2, Fanatic (about saving and preserving sentient life) -3

Attributes and Edges
Any

Advantages
Alertness (+2)
Engineering Aptitude (+3)
High Pain Threshold (+2)
Innovative (+1)
Language Ability (+2)
Mathematical Ability (+3)
Tactical Genius (+3)

Disadvantages
Zero-G Intolerance (-2)

Skills
Behavior Modification (Resistance)
Command
Espionage
Heavy Weapons
Psionic Skills (if applicable)
Security
Shipboard Systems
Starship Tactics
Strategic Operations

THE CADET CRUISE

After graduating, all Academy cadets embark a one-year-long "cadet cruise" to obtain practical training. When considering this stage of your character's Background History, ask yourself: Where did he serve, and what type of mission did he perform? Was he assigned to develop skills he already knew, or given the opportunity to learn completely new skills? Did he serve well or poorly? Did anything unusual or exciting happen during his year?

Review the Tours of Duty (see below) for ideas about the types of assignments typically given for cadet cruises (other than Academy Instructor, Crosstraining, or Starfleet Command, of course). You receive one Development Point to spend during this stage of the Background History (though you may take an appropriate disadvantage to increase the number of points you have to spend). You can spend your point on the game elements listed under this stage or the Universal Background List.

STARFLEET CADET CRUISE HISTORY

Starfleet characters can spend 1 point on the game elements listed below.

ATTRIBUTES AND EDGES
Perception
Willpower
Advantages
Commendation (+1)
Promotion (almost always tied to a Famous Incident) (+1)

SKILLS
Command
Heavy Weapons
Security
Shipboard Systems
Starship Tactics
Strategic Operations

TOURS OF DUTY

After successfully completing his cadet cruise, your character begins his Starfleet career with the rank of Ensign. At this stage of his Background History, you determine what he did prior to the start of the game (skip this stage if the Narrator wants to begin the series with the characters' first assignment). As you think about it, ask yourself: What sort of assignment is your character suited for, due to the nature of his training and experiences? Where would his skills be most valuable? How long would he spend on these missions? Did he acquit himself well, or somehow earn a black mark on his record? Did anything interesting or unusual happen to him during his tour?

Most characters begin the game after having been on a single Tour of Duty lasting five years. You receive 10 Development Points to spend on this tour, either on one of the packages listed below, or on the game elements listed under this stage or the Universal Life History list. If you want your character to have served for more than one tour, and the Narrator allows this, you receive another 5 Development Points for each tour after the first. You may only spend these points on an Additional Tours package, or on the elements listed here or under the Universal Life History list.

TOURS OF DUTY HISTORY

A Starfleet character receives 10 Development Points to spend during his first posting, and 5 Development Points for each mission thereafter.

Tour of Duty Packages (First Tour costs 10 Development Points)

Academy Instruction: Any Academic Skill (choose any two specializations) (see box under Early Life History) 1 (2) and (2), Command (Military Training) 1 (2), Law (Starfleet Regulations) 1 (2), Contact +1, Argumentative -1

Crosstraining: Computer (choose specialization) 1 (2), Engineering, Any (choose specialization) 1 (2), Shipboard Systems (choose any two specializations) 1 (2) and (2)

Cultural Liaison: Culture (choose specialization) 1 (2), Language (choose one) 1, Starship Tactics (choose specialization) 1 (2), +1 to Empathy

Deep Space Exploration Mission: Planetary Science (any specialization) 1 (2), Shipboard Systems (Sensors) 1 (2), Space Sciences (Stellar Cartography) 1 (2), Bold +1

Diplomatic Mission: Diplomacy (choose specialization) 1 (2), two Languages at 1 each OR one Language at 2, Contact +1, Shrewd +1, Rival -1

Expeditionary Support: Planetary Science (choose specialization) 1 (2), Planetside Survival (choose specialization) 1 (2), Strategic Operations (Invasion Defense) 1 (2), World Knowledge (choose two specializations) 1 (2), Promotion (Lieutenant JG) +1

Frontier Patrol: Energy Weapon (Phaser) 1 (2), Security (Law Enforcement) 1 (2), Starship Tactics (Starfleet) 1 (2), Promotion (Lieutenant JG) +1

Hostile Frontier Defense Mission: Starship Tactics (Klingon; Romulan) 1 (2) and (2), Shipboard Systems (Weapons Systems; Sensors) 1 (2) and (2), Promotion (Lieutenant) (+3), Vengeful -1; OPTIONAL: Famous Incident AND any Disadvantage listed below (balance the points)

Medical/Rescue Mission: Administration (Logistics) 1 (2), First Aid 1 (2), Medical Science (choose specialization) 1 (2), Shipboard Systems (Medical Systems) 1 (2), Pacifism -2

Scientific Mission: Planetary Sciences (any two specializations) 1 (2) and (2), Shipboard Systems (Sensors) 1 (2), Space Sciences (Astronomy and any other specialization) 1 (2) and (2), Curious +1, Poor Sight -2

Shakedown Cruise: Propulsion Engineering (choose specialization) 1 (2), Systems Engineering (choose specialization) 2 (3), Innovative +1

Starbase Mission: Administration (Logistics) 1 (2), Systems Engineering (Life Support) 1 (2), Vehicle Operation (Shuttlecraft) 1 (2), Contact (Starbase Commander) +1

Starfleet Command: Administration (Starfleet) 1 (2), Law (Starfleet Regulations) 1 (2), Strategic Operations (Fleet Operations) 1 (2), Contact +1; OPTIONAL: Rival AND Promotion (balance the points)

Terraforming and Colonization Mission: Administration (Logistics) 2 (3), Life Science (Exobiology) 1 (2), Planetary Science (choose specialization) 1 (2), Intolerant (Civilians) -2

Additional Tours (cost 5 Development Points each)

Academy Instruction: Command (Military Training) 1 (2), Law (Starfleet Regulations) 1 (2), Argumentative -1

Crosstraining: Administration (Starship Administration) 1 (2), one additional Shipboard Systems specialization, Promotion (Lieutenant JG) +1

Cultural Liaison: Diplomacy (Intergalactic Affairs) 1 (2), one additional Culture specialization, +1 Renown (Openness)

Deep Space Exploration Mission: Space Sciences (Stellar Cartography) 1 (2), one additional World Knowledge specialization, +1 Renown (Initiative or Openness)

Diplomatic Mission: Diplomacy (choose specialization) 1 (2), two additional World Knowledge specializations OR one additional World Knowledge specialization and -1 Renown (Aggression)

Expeditionary Support: Administration (Logistics) 1 (2), one additional Planetside Survival specialization, one additional World Knowledge specialization

Frontier Patrol: Strategic Operations (Defense In Depth) 1 (2), one additional Starship Tactics Specialization, +1 to Vitality

RENOWN ASPECTS

Initiative: Initiative covers risk-taking, experimentalism, boldness, and willingness to disobey orders. Characters with high Initiative Renown are seen as mavericks or daredevils. Captain James Kirk has a high Initiative Renown; he is well known for his willingness to take risks (and succeed despite the odds). Negative Initiative Renown indicates a character regarded as dependable (or, less favorably, as predictable, hidebound, and cautious).

Aggression: Aggression represents a character's reputation for resorting to violence or the threat of violence to solve problems. High Aggression Renown indicates that the character is known as a hothead or warmonger (an undesirable quality in the Federation, for the most part); negative Aggression Renown means a reputation for pacifism (which peoples such as the Klingons see as weakness).

Skill: Skill covers personal skill, ability, competence, resourcefulness, and similar traits. "Hands-on" engineers like Scotty or brilliant tacticians like Kirk have high Skill Renown. Of course, a lucky character or someone good at faking it could have a high Skill Renown even though he's not actually very skilled.

Discipline: Discipline represents the character's reputation for conformity to and consideration for the larger group, and for its rules and restrictions. Repeatedly violating orders (especially for personal reasons) usually earns a character negative Discipline Renown (though it might also tie in to positive Initiative Renown).

Openness: Openness indicates a reputation for the willingness to consider and adapt to the views of others, to be affected by foreign influence, and to accept outside opinions or reviews. Negative Openness Renown indicates xenophobia, chauvinism, or cultural conservatism (such as that of Dr. Sevrin).

Hostile Frontier Defense Mission: Starship Tactics (Klingon OR Romulan) 1 (2), +2 Renown (Discipline and/or Skill); OPTIONAL: Famous Incident AND any Disadvantage (see box below) (balance the points)

Medical/Rescue Mission: First Aid 1 (2), Shipboard Systems (Medical Systems) 1 (2), Impulsive -1

Scientific Mission: Space Sciences (Astronomy and any other specialization) 1 (2) and (2), +1 Renown (Skill or Openness)

ADVANCED CHARACTER CREATION

You can use the detailed character creation rules in this chapter to create just about any type of *Star Trek Roleplaying Game* character. After you learn the rules better, or if you're already an experienced roleplayer, you may not need or want to go through all those steps. Instead, you can simply take a number of Development Points (exactly how many depends on how effective and capable you want starting characters to be) and spend them.

For starting characters similar to characters built with the Basic Character Creation Process, you can spend 125 points on the game elements you desire for your character (this represents a character with one tour of duty). Be sure to figure out when the various advancements or changes in your character's life took place, so that you can construct a good background for him.

Shakedown Cruise: Engineering, Any (choose specialization) 1 (2), +2 Renown (Initiative and/or Skill)

Space Station/Starbase Mission: Administration (Logistics) 1 (2), Patron (Starbase Commander) +2

Starfleet Command: Administration (Starfleet) 1 (2), Law (Starfleet Regulations) 1 (2), -1 Reaction or Vitality edge

Terraforming and Colonization Mission: Planetary Science (choose specialization) 1 (2), +2 Renown (Skill and/or Discipline)

ATTRIBUTES AND EDGES
Perception
Willpower

ADVANTAGES
Alertness (+2)
Commendation (+1 to +3)
Department Head (+1 to +4)
Innovative (+1)
Promotion (+0 to +6)

DISADVANTAGES
Bloodlust (almost always tied to Vengeful) (-2)
Chronic Pain (-2)
Low Pain Threshold (-2)
Medical Problem (-1 to -3)

Physically Impaired (-1 to -2)
Poor Chemoreception (-1)
Poor Hearing (-1)
Poor Sight (-2)
Slow Healing (-2)
Weakness (-2)

SKILLS
Command
Espionage
Heavy Weapons
Psionic Skills (if applicable)
Security
Shipboard Systems
Starship Tactics
Strategic Operations

Tours Of Duty Assignments

Academy Instructor
Starfleet assigned the character as an instructor at the Academy. This is often done when a cadet shows particular promise in a subject, or when a serving officer must take a "desk job" due to age or infirmity.

Crosstraining
Perhaps in preparation for a climb up the Command ladder, the character filled many different duty stations on the ship, to learn as much as possible about how it and its crew functions.

Cultural Liaison
The character served on a ship or colony run primarily by members of a species other than his own (for example, a Human posted to the Andorian-dominated *U.S.S. Eagle*). Here he learned about that race's culture and language, as well as how to relate to other species in general.

Deep Space Exploration Mission
The character served on a voyage of discovery, most likely on a science vessel, into uncharted areas of the galaxy beyond (or within) the Federation's borders.

Diplomatic Mission
The character was assigned to the Starfleet Diplomatic Corps, where he assisted in delicate negotiations or tense standoffs with various alien species.

Expeditionary Support
The character's starship checked on and provided support services to scientific expeditions, explorers, colonists, and the like as its primary mission.

Frontier Patrol
The character's starship patrolled the frontiers of Federation space to enforce Federation law, be on the lookout for invasion forces, protect colonies, and hunt down raiders.

Hostile Frontier Defense
The character served along one of the tense border regions of the Federation, possibly near either Klingons or Romulan space. He may have engaged in localized skirmishes, border disputes, or other contained frontier actions.

Medical/Rescue Mission
The character served on a hospital ship, or on a ship engaged in famine, plague, or other disaster relief.

Scientific Mission
Almost certainly on a science vessel, the character fulfilled Starfleet's fundamental mandate, adding to the store of knowledge about the galaxy.

Shakedown Cruise
The character served on a vessel's maiden voyage (possibly an experimental ship or the first in its class), helping to test its limits and repair any unexpected breakdowns.

Starbase Mission
The character was posted to one of Starfleet's many starbases to perform duties relating to the base's administration.

Starfleet Command
The character received an assignment to Starfleet Command on Earth, where he worked in one of its many departments (such as Research and Exploration).

Terraforming and Colonization
The character assisted with one or more colonization and terraforming missions, helping to develop a new planet for Federation citizens. His duties may have included building shelters, chasing off raiders or pirates, assisting with colony logistics, and the like.

STEP FOUR: FINISHING TOUCHES

By now you've got a well developed character, with everything from basic game statistics, to a detailed background, to a few special things to set him apart from the crowd. All that's left is to calculate a few finishing touches that he needs prior to beginning play, such as his starting Courage and Renown, and promotions and rank.

COURAGE POINTS

Every character receives 3 Courage Points, which he can use to obtain automatic successes (see the *Action* chapter, page 102), thus allowing him to perform heroically in stressful or dangerous situations. For rules regarding the use and recovery of Courage Points, see pages 102, 103. Record your Courage Points on your character sheet.

RENOWN

Renown measures your character's fame or reputation—the higher it is, the greater the number of people who have heard of him or his exploits. For example, if a character has low Renown, only other crewmen on the same deck of his starship might know who he is; but people throughout the Federation have heard of one with high Renown (like Captain Kirk).

In addition to representing general fame or notoriety, Renown is divided into five Aspects: Initiative, Aggression, Skill, Discipline, and Openness. Characters gain Renown in those individual Aspects; the total of those Aspects is the character's overall Renown.

Starting characters begin play with 1 Renown, in any Aspect of the player's choosing.

An Aspect of Renown can be positive or negative. A character with a -5 Skill Renown is known for his incompetence; a character with a +5 Skill Renown is just as widely known for his ability. When calculating a character's total Renown for any reason (such as Renown Tests; see the *Action* chapter, page 106), only the degree of Renown is considered, not whether it is positive or negative. (For rules on increasing and altering Renown in play, see *Rewards*, page 124.)

RANK

Unless a player chooses the *Promotion* advantage during character creation, all Starfleet characters start the game at the rank of Ensign.

WOUND LEVELS

Every character can resist a number of points of damage equal to his Fitness + Vitality. This total is known as his *Resistance*. Note this number on your character sheet.

Every character also has seven Wound Levels that describe the effects of damage he suffers from combat, accidents, and other dangers. At each level, a character has a number of Wound Points also equal to his Fitness + Vitality. Calculate your character's Wound Level points and write them on your character sheet in the space provided. See the *Combat* section of the *Action* chapter, page 107, for further information.

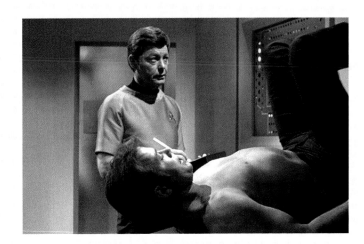

CHARACTER CREATION QUICK-REFERENCE OUTLINE

I. The Basic Character Creation Process

    A. Choose a Template (your character's species)
    B. Choose an Overlay (your character's profession)
    C. Detail your character's background using the Background History stages
    D. Put on the finishing touches: Courage Points, Renown, rank

II. Essential Elements Of Character Creation

    A. Attributes: Attributes represent a character's innate capabilities, such as his agility or intelligence. There are five attributes: Fitness, Coordination, Intellect, Presence, and Psi. Human attributes generally range in value from 1 to 5.
    B. Edges: Edges are aspects of attributes that represent a character's particular level of talent (or lack of talent) with some functions of an attribute. For example, the edges associated with Intellect are *Perception* and *Logic*. Edges range in value from +2 to -2, and act as modifiers to related Tests.
    C. Skills: Skills are a character's learned abilities and aptitudes. Examples are the ability to fire energy weapons, to diagnose illness and per-

form surgery, and to operate a ship's sensors. Most skills have *specializations*, which represent areas of particular expertise and ability. Skills range in value from 1 to 5 (and, rarely, higher).
    D. Advantages: These are special abilities, benefits or advantages that a character possesses. Examples include having a Contact in Starfleet Command, being especially adept at Engineering tasks, or having a particularly acute sense of hearing.
    E. Disadvantages: The opposite of advantages, disadvantages are limitations, hindrances, or other problems which afflict a character. Examples include having a Sworn Enemy, suffering from a Physical Impairment (such as blindness), or compulsively hiding one's emotions.
    F. Courage Points: Players spend Courage Points to add points to Test Results. Each character starts the game with 3 Courage Points.
    G. Renown: Renown is a measure of how well known a character is. Renown has five Aspects (Initiative, Aggression, Skill, Discipline and Openness), and can be positive or negative. Each character starts the game with 1 point of Renown in one Aspect (player's choice).
    H. Rank: Determine the character's Rank, per the rules on pages 88-89.

Element	Development Point Cost
Attributes	2 points
Edges	1 point
Skill	3 points
Specialization	1 point
Advantages	Variable
Disadvantages	Variable

III. Character Creation Tools

    A. Templates: Templates represent a character's species, such as Human or Vulcan. They include the basic attributes, skills and other elements common to average members of that species. Templates do not cost Development Points; each character chooses one for free.

B. Overlays: Overlays represent a character's profession, such as Engineer or Doctor. An Overlay includes the basic skills and other abilities needed to perform that profession. Overlays do not cost Development Points; each character chooses one for free.

C. Background History: A character's background helps the player trace the character's development from early life, to his term of study at the Academy, to his cadet cruise, to his tours of duty prior to the beginning of play.

Each stage of a character's Background History (Universal Background Development, Early Life, Academy Life, Cadet Cruise, Tours of Duty) lists a number of predesigned packages from which the player can choose, OR, she can spend a number of Development Points on appropriate character creation elements listed under that stage's History.

Early Life:	5
Academy Life:	8
Cadet Cruise:	1
Tour(s) of Duty:	10 (first tour); 5 (each additional tour)

IV. Quick And Easy Character Generation

A. Select a Character Archetype (see pages 42-45) and personalize it using 5 additional Development Points.

EXAMPLE OF CHARACTER CREATION

Steve decides he wants to create a Tiburonian security officer. He starts thinking about the character, Tyshon—what prompted him to choose a career in security? He concludes that it's a family tradition; Tyshon's grandfather was a law enforcement official on Tiburon, and his father served in Starfleet in a similar capacity. Tyshon is proud to carry on the family legacy. While he enjoys a good time as much as the next Tiburonian, Tyshon is a little more serious and dedicated to duty than most of his fellows.

Steve begins by choosing the Tiburonian Template and Security Overlay. That gives him the bare bones of his character. His Template includes two unspecified skills, a Science skill and an Engineering skill. For the Science he chooses Physical Science (Physics)—Tyshon enjoyed the subject in school and studied hard because he knew he wanted to get into Starfleet, where such knowledge would be important. He selects Systems Engineering (Security), since spending time with his grandfather and father as he was growing up exposed him to security equipment a lot, and he enjoyed tinkering with technology in his spare time. He also gets to choose an Athletics specialization; he selects Running, since that's Tyshon's favorite form of exercise.

The Security Overlay provides the basic skills which Tyshon needs to do his job. During his training and career, Tyshon has learned not only the basics of life in Starfleet, but how to patrol and defend a ship's corridors, how to work with and repair Starfleet security systems, and the ins and outs of

Federation security procedures. Steve selects Weapons Systems as Tyshon's Shipboard Systems specialization—Tyshon, like many Security personnel, loves phasers no matter how big they are. Two of the Overlay's skills, Athletics and Systems Engineering (Security), overlap ones he already has, so Steve applies the "What If I Get The Same Skill Twice?" rules (page 52). Since the skill level and specialization level for Athletics overlap, Steve simply selects another specialization—Lifting, which Tyshon engaged in to build up his muscles during training—and notes it on the character sheet next to Running. For Systems Engineering he can either increase the skill level or the specialization level. He opts to do the former, since Tyshon is more of a generalist sort of person than a specialist—Steve wants Tyshon to know how to do a lot of things, rather than doing one or two things very well.

Now Steve can personalize Tyshon a bit more by determining his Background History. For Early Life, he doesn't see a "Police Brat" package, or any other packages which suit his idea about Tyshon's childhood, so he opts to increase Tyshon's attributes instead, since Tyshon is something of a "health nut" who keeps in good shape both physically and mentally. He increases Fitness and Coordination each by 1 point, and also buys a +1 Reaction edge.

The choice for Academy Life is obvious—Security Training. Steve notes the appropriate skills on Tyshon's character sheet. Again he has some skill duplication, this time in Energy Weapons and Security. Steve opts to increase Tyshon's Energy Weapon (Phaser) to 2 (4)—he's gotten in a lot of practice with his phaser—and uses the two additional specializations of Security to take one more specialization at level 3 (Law Enforcement) and then increase his base skill level to 3 as well. He now has a thorough grounding in all aspects of Starfleet security.

During his Cadet Cruise, Steve decides that Tyshon catches the eye of his commanding officer due to his professional attitude, high level of skill, and bravery. This results in a Promotion to the rank of Lieutenant (Junior Grade). Tyshon is on his way to great things!

For Tyshon's first Tour of Duty, Steve opts for a Hostile Frontier Defense Mission. Tyshon served on a ship flying patrols to protect the Federation from Klingon attacks. He notes down the new skills and traits. Again faced with overlapping skills, Steve opts to add 1 to Tyshon's Weapons Systems specialization, reasoning that Tyshon has made his name as a hot phaser control officer. He also notes that the package comes with a Promotion to Lieutenant. Since he's already a Lieutenant (JG), one of the points spent on the second Promotion would be wasted. He asks the Narrator if he can apply that point elsewhere—to a Famous Incident—and the Narrator agrees. Steve decides that during a Klingon raid in which most of the bridge crew was injured, Tyshon took over the weapons systems, destroyed the Klingon ship, and saved hundreds of Federation citizens. For his selfless act of heroism, he was promoted to Lieutenant.

All Steve has to do now is put the finishing touches on Tyshon, and he's ready to go. He notes Tyshon's three Courage Points on his character sheet. For his Renown, he puts his starting point into the Skill Aspect, and also puts the two points gained from his Famous Incident there as well, reflecting the fact that Tyshon has become known for his abilities under fire. Lastly, he calculates Tyshon's Resistance (Fitness+Vitality), which is 3.

ANTIQUATED OR UNFAMILIAR TECHNOLOGY

Characters often find themselves working with strange equipment (such as the control panels on a captured Klingon ship) or, if they accidentally travel through time, with equipment which is so antiquated and obsolete to them that they don't know much about using it. As a rule of thumb, Tests with Computer, Engineering, Shipboard Systems, Personal Equipment, and other technology-oriented skills are one category of Difficulty harder when a character works with unfamiliar or antiquated equipment, and two categories of Difficulty harder for very strange or highly obsolete equipment. These penalties do not apply if the character has an appropriate specialization (for example, Shipboard Systems (20th Century Radar Systems)).

The Narrator determines just how antiquated or unusual a technological item seems to a particular character, taking into account his life experiences, specializations, and so forth. As a general guideline, anything more than 100 years old typically qualifies as "highly obsolete."

Lieutenant Tyshon is now ready for adventure!

ATTRIBUTES

Fitness 3 [5]
Coordination 3 [5]
    Reaction +1
Intellect 2 [5]
    Perception +1
Presence 2 [5]
    Empathy +1
Psi 0 [5]
  SKILLS
Athletics (Running, Lifting) 2 (3) and (3)
Computer (Research) 1 (2)
Culture (Tiburonian) 2 (3)
Dodge 1
Energy Weapon (Phaser) 2 (4)
Gaming (Three-Dimensional Chess) 1 (2)
History (Federation) 1 (2)
History (Tiburonian) 1 (2)
Language
    Federation Standard 1
    Tiburonian 2
Law (Starfleet Regulations) 1 (2)
Personal Equipment (Communicator) 1 (2)
Physical Science (Physics) 1 (2)
Planetary Tactics (Shipboard) 1 (2)
Planetside Survival (Forest) 1 (2)
Security (Security Systems, Law Enforcement) 3 (3) and (3)
Shipboard Systems (Weapons Systems; Sensors) 1 (3) and (2)
Starship Tactics (Klingon; Romulan) 1 (2) and (2)
Systems Engineering (Security) 2 (2)
Unarmed Combat: Starfleet Martial Arts (Punch) 1 (2)
Vehicle Operations (Shuttlecraft) 1 (2)
World Knowledge (Tiburon) 1 (2)

TRAITS

Curious +1, Promotion (Lieutenant) +3; Hedonist -1, Vengeful -1

COURAGE POINTS: 3

RENOWN: 3
Aggression: 0, Discipline: 0, Initiative: 0, Openness: 0, Skill: 3

RESISTANCE: 3
Wound Levels: 3/3/3/3/3/3/0

CHARACTERISTICS

The *Star Trek Roleplaying Game* measures characters with characteristics. There are four types of characteristics—attributes (and edges), skills, advantages, and disadvantages—which your character obtains from his Template, Overlay, Background History, and any other expenditure of Development Points you make during character creation. Characteristics quantify a Starfleet hero (or a dastardly Klingon villain) in game terms, telling you whether he can do something: His chances of hitting the Romulan with a phaser shot, his ability to operate a tricorder properly, how fast he runs.

Characteristics link with the game's rules, allowing you, for example, to determine if a character succeeds with a Test. But it's important to see beyond that aspect and view characteristics as the building blocks which help you breathe life into your character. Don't just think of your character as someone with Energy Weapon (Phaser) 2 (3), think of him as someone who learned all about phasers from grizzled old Chief Cullen back at the Academy and who's trying to become the best shot on the ship. Characteristics tell you what your Crew member can do, but more important than that, they help you define who he is and how you want to play him.

ATTRIBUTES

Attributes are the most basic game element. They tell you how fit, intelligent, and quick your character is. Attribute scores normally range from 1 to 5, though some species can have higher scores. Your character's Template provides his basic attributes; you can alter them during character creation if you prefer. There are five attributes:

Fitness: Your character's physical makeup. Fitness tells you how strong he is (see Athletics (Lifting), page 76), his ability to withstand injury, and his overall athletic ability.

Coordination: Your character's gross and fine motor skills. Coordination governs his ability to shoot, fight, dodge attacks, perform acrobatics, etc.

Intellect: Your character's overall intelligence, deductive reasoning capability, technical acumen and perception. A very important attribute in the high-tech society of the *Star Trek Roleplaying Game*, it governs engineering, the use of computers, many command and tactical abilities, medical skills, and many other useful abilities.

Presence: Your character's personal magnetism and force of personality. Presence represents, among other things, your character's skill at negotiating with alien diplomats, bluffing your way out of the clutches of an immensely powerful enemy, or charming an extradimensional beauty into releasing you from confinement.

Psi: Your character's innate talent or capacity for extrasensory mental abilities—mind melding, telepathy, empathy and the like. Most lifeforms have Psi 0, meaning they have no innate capacity for psionic abilities (they can't buy Psionic skills or raise or lower their Psi edges, but if the Narrator allows may spend Experience Points on Psi so that they can develop such powers). Of course, members of some species, like Vulcans, possess natural psionic abilities.

EDGES

Each attribute has two edges that represent its important aspects or facets. They help to differentiate characters. For example, even though two characters have the same Intellect, one is a little more perceptive, the other a little more logical. The Icon System expresses edges in terms of plus or minus values, indicating a bonus or penalty which modifies the number of dice players roll in appropriate situations. For example, a security officer might have a high Fitness, but he's a little bit of a weakling (-1 Strength), whereas his friend the engineer prides himself on his systematic approach to problem-solving (+1 Logic). Typically, edges range from -2 to +2. (For more about Tests, see the Action chapter, page 97.)

FITNESS EDGES

Strength. The Strength edge applies whenever a character tries to lift heavy objects, punch or kick an enemy, smash open a door, or otherwise exert physical force.

Vitality. The Vitality edge represents a character's general health and stamina. It applies whenever he tries to resist the effects of injury, disease, poison, fatigue, or the like.

COORDINATION EDGES

Dexterity. The Dexterity edge applies whenever a character tries to move agilely, quickly, or gracefully, such as when he's trying to move stealthily, perform acrobatic feats, or hit a target in combat.

Reaction. The Reaction edge represents a character's reflexes, and applies to situations where he has to react suddenly, like attacking first in combat, dodging or parrying attacks, or reacting to changing battlefield conditions.

INTELLECT EDGES

Logic. The quintessential Vulcan characteristic, the Logic edge applies to any Test in which the character must call upon his talents for problem-solving or deduction.

Perception. The Perception edge reflects a character's awareness of his local environment; it applies to Tests to perceive events or conditions (such as the Klingons sneaking up on his position).

PRESENCE EDGES

Empathy. The Empathy edge applies whenever a character has to sympathize with someone, read body language, determine what a person is really feeling, and so forth.

Willpower. The Willpower edge represents as character's strength of will. It helps him withstand and overcome the effects of pain, illness, psionic powers, and manipulation.

PSI EDGES

Focus. The Focus edge applies to situations where a Psi-talented character tries to use his mental powers with a degree of precision.

Range. The Range edge applies whenever where a Psi-talented character tries to use his mental powers effectively over a distance.

Skills

Skills represent a character's learned talents, abilities, and knowledges. Like attributes, they range from 1 to 5 (and, rarely, can rise above 5)—the higher the skill level, the greater the character's degree of competence with the skill. A Science Officer with Space Sciences (Astrogation) 3 (4) knows more and can do more than one with the same skill at 2 (3).

Each skill is linked to an attribute (listed in its description); you use them together when making Skill Tests (see the Action chapter, pages 98-105). Most Tests will, and should, include both skills and attributes.

Since there's often more than one way to skin a cat (or outwit a Klingon), the Narrator should be flexible when determining which skill(s) apply to a particular situation. If a character wants to use a skill which is not the most directly applicable one, the Narrator can increase the Difficulty of the Skill Test to represent how much harder the task is with that skill.

Ensign Sam Decker needs to fire some phaser artillery. However, that requires the Heavy Weapons (Phaser Artillery) Skill, which Decker doesn't know—and it cannot be used untrained. But he does know Shipboard Systems (Weapon Systems), so his player asks if that Skill could be used to fire the weapon. The Narrator decides that Decker can use Shipboard Systems (Weapon Systems) to fire the phaser artillery, but since that Skill relates to Heavy Weapons only marginally, he will increase the Difficulty Number by 3—what would have been a Moderate (7) Heavy Weapons (Phaser Artillery) Test to fire at a target at medium range becomes a Challenging (10) Shipboard Systems (Weapons Systems) Test.

Many skills require extensive training—you can't just start speaking Andorian, for example, you have to study it a long time to develop fluency. But characters can use some skills without formal training, albeit poorly. The Icon System calls this "untrained skill use." Characters cannot use skills marked with this icon (▶) untrained; they can attempt all others even if they haven't had proper training. (See page 105 in the *Action* chapter for more information on untrained skill use.)

Not every skill on the Skills Table is appropriate for characters who belong to Starfleet, either. (Such skills may or may not be appropriate for non-Starfleet characters, depending on character conception and background). An icon (❖) marks these skills. If you want to play a Starfleet character who knows one of these skills, you need to develop an interesting explanation or background story to explain how he learned it, and get your Narrator's approval. (For more information, see the *Characters* chapter, page 40.)

SPECIALIZATION

Some skills require *specialization*. Since skills in the Icon System represent broad areas of learning and ability, it's usually not possible for a character to be thoroughly versed in every aspect of any given subject—hence, the need to specialize, to develop expertise in a particular facet of that skill. Examples include Energy Weapons (Phaser), Charm (Seduction), and Command (Starship Command). On your character sheet, write the specializations in parentheses following the base level of the skill. For example, Lt. Thorev, an Andorian communications officer, knows Shipboard Systems (Communications) 2 (3), meaning that he has the Shipboard Systems skill at level 2, but can use Starfleet communications systems at level 3.

Skills that require specialization get one specialization "for free"—the character automatically receives the specialization of his choice when he learns the skill; it costs no Development Points. Additional specializations after the first cost 1 Development Point each.

Specializations start at one level higher than the base skill. Thorev, who knows Shipboard Systems at level 2, has his specialization, Communications, at level 3. The character gets to add the number indicated by his specialization, not his base skill, to the dice rolled when making Tests to which that specialization applies. For example, when Thorev makes a Test using his Shipboard Systems (Communications) specialization to send a coded message to Starfleet Command, he rolls his Intellect dice and adds 3, not 2, to the highest die result.

Of course, just because a character specializes in a particular subject does not mean he knows nothing about related subjects in his field. A character with a skill knows the basics of that subject regardless of what specialization(s) he takes, and can attempt to use other specializations of his skill at the skill's base level. For example, Thorev can make a Shipboard Systems (Navigation) or (Sensors) Test using his base Shipboard Systems skill of 2, even though he hasn't learned those specific specializations—he knows enough about his ship's systems, in general, to know what to do, he's just not as good at working with them as he is with communications systems.

During character creation, or with the Experience Points he earns, a character can increase a specialization. This represents the fact that he learned even more about the subject by using his training in the field—practical experience reinforcing and augmenting theoretical knowledge and training. For example, Thorev could spend points to increase his specialization to Shipboard Systems (Communications) 2 (5).

Each skill in the Skill List includes suggested specializations. These suggestions are not exclusive; they're just the most prominent or common examples for that skill. Feel free to develop other specializations suitable to your characters and series (subject, of course, to Narrator approval).

Remember, edges, advantages, and disadvantages can affect Skill Tests. See the *Action* (page 97) chapter for information regarding Tests and assigning modifiers. The (▶) icon indicates a skill which characters cannot use untrained; the (❖) icon skills that generally are inappropriate for Starfleet characters.

SKILL LIST

COMMAND

Administration (Intellect)
Bureaucratic Manipulation, Logistics, Specific Planetary Government, Starship Administration

❖▶ Behavior Modification (Intellect)
Brainwashing, Hypnotism, Resistance

Command (Presence)
Combat Leadership, Military Training, Starship Command

Diplomacy (Presence)
Commercial Treaties, Federation Law, Intergalactic Affairs, Intergalactic Law, Planetary Affairs (Earth, Vulcan, and so forth)

▶ Espionage (Intellect)
Counterintelligence, Covert Communications, Cryptography, Forgery, Species-Specific Intelligence Techniques (Romulan, Andorian, etc.), Traffic Analysis

Persuasion (Presence)
Debate, Oratory, Storytelling

Planetary Tactics (Intellect)
Guerrilla Warfare, Mechanized Ground, Shipboard, Small-Unit

▶ Starship Tactics (Intellect)
Planetary Support Tactics, Specific Naval Tactics (Federation, Klingon, Romulan)

▶ Strategic Operations (Intellect)
Defense-in-Depth, Invasion Strategies, Neutral Zone Strategies, Specific Strategies (Core, Frontier, Sector)

ENGINEERING AND SECURITY

▶ Demolitions (Intellect)
Bomb Disposal, Booby Traps, Land Mines, Nuclear Demolitions, Primitive Demolitions, Shipboard Demolitions

Energy Weapon (Coordination)
Disruptor, Disruptor Rifle, Phaser, Phaser Rifle

▶ Engineering, Material (Intellect)
Aeronautical/Aerodynamic, Civil, Mechanical, Metallurgical, Personal Equipment, Structural/Spaceframe, Vehicular

▶ Engineering, Propulsion (Intellect)
Fusion, Impulse, Ion, Rocketry, Warp Drive

▶ Engineering, Systems (Intellect)
Cloaking Device, Communications Systems, Computer Systems, Life Support, Phaser Systems, Power Systems, Sensor Systems, Shields, Torpedo/Probe Systems, Transporter Systems

First Aid (Intellect)
Chemical-Biological First Aid, Species-Specific First Aid, Wound/Combat Trauma

▶ Heavy Weapons (Intellect)
Individual Weapon Type

▶ Personal Equipment (Intellect)
Communicator, Environmental Suit, Medical Tricorder, Tricorder, Universal Translator

▶ Projectile Weapon (Coordination)
Gunpowder Pistol, Gunpowder Rifle, Submachine Gun, Needle Weapons, Gauss Weapons

▶ Security (Intellect)
Law Enforcement, Patrolling, Security Systems

▶ Shipboard Systems (Intellect)
Cloaking Device, Communications, Helm, Library Computer, Life Support, Navigation, Sensors, Shields, Transporter, Weapons Systems

▶ Unarmed Combat (Coordination)

▶ Vehicle Operation (Intellect)
Atmospheric Craft, Close Orbital Craft, Ground Vehicles, Shuttlecraft

SCIENCES

▶ Computer (Intellect)
Computer Simulation/Modeling, Data Alteration/Hacking, Programming, Research

▶ Life Sciences (Intellect)
Agronomy, Bioengineering, Biology, Bionics, Biotechnology, Botany, Ecology, Exobiology, Genetics, Microbiology, Paleontology, Zoology

▶ Medical Sciences (Intellect)
Exoanatomy, Forensics, General Medicine, Pathology, Psychology, Specific Species Medicine (Vulcan, Klingon, etc.), Surgical Specializations, Toxicology

▶ Physical Sciences (Intellect)
Chemistry, Computer Science, Mathematics, Physics

▶ Planetary Sciences (Intellect)
Climatology, Geology, Hydrology, Mineralogy, Oceanography, Planetology, Volcanology

▶ Social Sciences (Intellect)
Anthropology, Archaeology, Economics, Geography, Paleoanthropology, Political Science, Sociology

▶ Space Sciences (Intellect)
Astrogation, Astronomy, Astrophysics, Stellar Cartography, Warp Field Theory

World Knowledge (Intellect)
Specific Planet

GENERAL

Acrobatics (Coordination)
Balance Walking, Gymnastics, Mid-Air Dodge, Rope Swinging

Animal Handling (Presence)
Specific Animal

▶ Artistic Expression (Intellect)
Dance, Drawing, Painting, Poetry, Singing, Specific Musical Instrument

Athletics (Fitness)
Climbing, Jumping, Lifting, Specific Sport/Game, Running

Bargain (Presence)
Artwork, Bribery, Dilithium Crystals, Marketplace Haggling, Weapons

Charm (Presence)
  Influence, Seduction
Culture (Intellect)
  Specific Culture
Disguise (Presence)
  Specific Species
Dodge (Coordination)
Fast Talk (Intellect)
Gaming (Intellect)
  Specific Game
History (Intellect)
  Specific Organization, Specific Planet, Specific Species
❖ Intimidation (Presence)
  Bluster, Torture
◗ Languages (Intellect) (each Language is a separate Skill)
◗ Law (Intellect)
  Federation Law, Specific Planetary/Government Laws, Starfleet Regulations
Merchant (Intellect)
  Specific Business Type, Specific Market, Specific Product
Planetside Survival (Intellect)
  Arctic, Desert, Forest, Jungle, Mountain, Ocean, Specific World, Urban
Primitive Weaponry (Coordination)
  Chaka, D'k tagh, Lirpa, Longbow, *Mek'leth,* Rapier, Sword
Search (Intellect)
◗ Sleight of Hand
  Conceal Weapons, Magic Tricks, Pick Pocket
Stealth (Coordination)
  Hide, Stealthy Movement
Streetwise (Intellect)
  Locate Contraband, Underworld of Specific Planet or Species

PSIONIC
  ◗ Mind Control (Psi)
  ◗ Mind Meld (Psi)
  Mind Shield (Psi)
  ◗ Projective Empathy (Psi)
  ◗ Projective Telepathy (Psi)
  ◗ Receptive Empathy (Psi)
  ◗ Receptive Telepathy (Psi)

Skill Descriptions

COMMAND

ADMINISTRATION (INTELLECT)

The Administration skill represents a character's ability to organize personnel, work within bureaucratic systems, manage datawork, plan missions, and generally run an organization or group of people. He ensures that his ship's crew works well, that the ship itself is properly supplied with food and equipment, chooses people who work together well for landing parties, and so forth.

Administration allows a character to improve the efficiency of a group of people attempting to accomplish a task. If he "takes the lead" during certain Combined or Extended Tests, and succeeds with an Administration Skill Test, the Narrator may lower the target cumulative Test Result by an amount equal to his Administration skill level or Specialization. Alternately, the Narrator may lower the Difficulty of the Test by one (or two if the character achieves a Dramatic Success).

  Routine: Managing a disciplined, professional group (*i.e.,* a Starfleet
    starship crew, a hospital staff) under noncrisis conditions
  Moderate: Planning a landing party mission to a known planet
  Challenging: Planning a landing party mission to a strange planet;
    managing a disciplined, professional group under crisis conditions
  Difficult: Running a planetary government
  Nearly Impossible: Planning an interstellar economy
  Specializations: Bureaucratic Manipulation, Logistics, Specific
    Planetary Government, Starship Administration

BEHAVIOR MODIFICATION (INTELLECT)

Behavior Modification allows a character to change the behavior of other persons, typically against their will. It's not appropriate for Starfleet officers—it violates many principles on which the Federation was founded. However, the Klingons and Romulans aren't so squeamish. Starfleet Officers can only learn Behavior Modification (Resistance), and should not use the skill to modify another's behavior.

Behavior Modification requires an Opposed Test against an unwilling target's Behavior Modification skill (if he has it) or the higher of his Intellect or

Presence (if he doesn't), modified by Perception or Willpower, to resist. Targets who "break" (lose the Opposed Test) may receive additional Tests to regain the ability to resist if ordered to betray principles or secrets they hold dear.

> *Routine:* Generally, there is no routine use of Behavior
>   Modification.
> *Moderate:* Hypnotizing a willing subject
> *Challenging:* Brainwashing an untrained draftee
> *Difficult:* Hypnotizing an unwilling, but untrained, subject
> *Nearly Impossible:* Brainwashing an elite subject
> *Specializations:* Brainwashing, Hypnotism, Resistance

COMMAND (PRESENCE)

Command measures a character's ability to convince other characters—particularly subordinates—to follow instructions. Of course, Crew members shouldn't use it to order other Crew members around, even if they are of lesser rank; such situations require roleplaying, not dice-rolling.

Command allows a character to coordinate projects with many workers, such as overseeing a large landing party, or the actions of several people working together—in game terms, Combined or Extended Tests. A successful Command Test allows the character to subtract his skill level (or specialization level) from the cumulative Test Result needed to complete the task. Alternately, the Narrator may reduce the Difficulty of a Test by one (two for a Dramatic Success). Command also lets a character convince others to follow orders during times of emergency or crisis.

> *Routine:* Starfleet officer leading Starfleet Academy cadets
> *Moderate:* Starfleet commander leading trained Starfleet officers
> *Challenging:* Starfleet officer leading random civilians in a crisis
> *Difficult:* Starfleet officer leading allied personnel
> *Nearly Impossible:* Starfleet officer leading enemy personnel
> *Specializations:* Combat Leadership, Military Training, Starship
>   Command

DIPLOMACY (PRESENCE)

Diplomacy simulates a character's skill at conducting negotiations between governments, planets, societies, or corporations. A character with Diplomacy also knows about the state of intergalactic politics and alliances.

When involved in a negotiation or similar situation, a character can attempt a Diplomacy Test. Success indicates that the participants come to view his position more favorably. In game terms, reduce the Difficulty of any Tests involving the target's responses or reactions. If, at a critical juncture, you need a quick and easy way to determine the outcome of a negotiation you can use an Opposed Diplomacy Test. Success indicates a meaningful resolution of the problem; failure that the talks have broken down (and Dramatic Failure may mean the character unwittingly starts a war!).

Diplomacy, Persuasion, and Charm, though related, have significant differences. Diplomacy represents a character's negotiating skills—his ability to work with others to reach a mutual solution to some problem by obtaining concessions from all concerned or finding innovative solutions. Persuasion represents his ability to argue skillfully and forcefully, and thus convince others to agree with him. Charm is similar to persuasion, but involves the use of personal charisma and emotional appeals to win people to your side.

> *Routine:* Keeping an allied ambassador friendly
> *Moderate:* Bringing a willing planet into the Federation
> *Challenging:* Negotiating a boundary with a new, but not
>   unfriendly, species
> *Difficult:* Negotiating a peace with an enemy species
> *Nearly Impossible:* Building a long-lasting alliance with an enemy
>   species
> *Specializations:* Commercial Treaties, Federation Law, Intergalactic
>   Affairs, Intergalactic Law, Planetary (Earth, Vulcan, and so forth)
>   Affairs

ESPIONAGE (INTELLECT)

A character with this skill possesses knowledge of intelligence agencies, espionage operations, and intelligence-gathering techniques. He knows what kind of information to gather, how to gather it for best results, and how to analyze it once he's got it (*i.e.*, to separate true information from disinformation, and useful information from ordinary information). Espionage also gives him the ability to use the skills of undercover agents, such as establishing covert communications systems, encoding and decrypting codes and ciphers, and forgery.

> *Routine:* Using a computerized encryption/decryption system
> *Moderate:* Identifying a foreign code or item of covert equipment
> *Challenging:* Establishing a network of informants on a foreign
>   planet
> *Difficult:* Using traffic analysis to determine the course plots of the
>   Romulan fleet
> *Nearly Impossible:* Turning a Klingon official into a Federation
>   double agent
> *Specializations:* Counterintelligence, Covert Communications,
>   Cryptography, Forgery, Species-Specific Intelligence Techniques
>   (Federation, Klingon, Romulan, and the like), Traffic Analysis

PERSUASION (PRESENCE)

Persuasion simulates a character's ability to make arguments which sway people to his point of view. Depending on who he's debating with, those arguments may be plausible and reasonable, impassioned and sincere, based on sheer force of personality and will, or all three at once. Narrators should make players roleplay Persuasion attempts whenever possible, applying positive or negative modifiers based on good or bad roleplaying. Persuasion attempts require an Opposed Test against an unwilling target's Persuasion skill (if he has it or wishes to use it untrained) or Intellect (if not), modified by Willpower or Logic (depending on the types of arguments being put forward).

Persuasion, Fast Talk, and Charm have similarities, but also some crucial differences. Fast Talk typically involves lying or trickery; Persuasion does not. Charm allows a character to persuade someone to do something, but relies on emotional connections, subconscious cues and the like. It allows a character to influence a target favorably by making the character and his opinions seem attractive; in contrast, Persuasion combines elements of reason and personal appeal. A character can use Persuasion to influence a target negatively (against someone or something else) without making the target view the character himself in a positive light.

> *Routine:* Persuading a friend, fellow crewman, or relative who has similar views
> *Moderate:* Persuading a neutral target to a position bolstered by obvious or well-documented facts
> *Challenging:* Persuading a neutral target to a position the character does not actually believe in; persuading an opposing target to a position bolstered by obvious or well- documented facts
> *Difficult:* Persuading a hostile target to a position supported only by strong logic
> *Nearly Impossible:* Persuading an irrational, hostile target during combat
> *Specializations:* Debate, Oratory, Storytelling

PLANETARY TACTICS (INTELLECT)

A character with Planetary Tactics (as opposed to Starship Tactics) can plan and lead any type of military operations on a planet or in an atmosphere. If a commander succeeds with this skill, he can give his forces a -1 Difficulty modifier (for movement, attack, and defense actions) for one round.

> *Routine:* Defending a well supplied strongpoint against technologically inferior attackers
> *Moderate:* Defeating an outnumbered force in a single battle
> *Challenging:* Defeating an outnumbered army in a single campaign
> *Difficult:* Defeating a superior force
> *Nearly Impossible:* Defeating a superior force at odds greater than ten to one

Sample Specializations:

Guerrilla Warfare:
Enables a character to plan and lead low-intensity operations such as hit-and-run raids, ambushes, and sabotage. Guerrilla warfare is usually fought by natives against an invading or occupying force; Starfleet advisers might assist species fighting against Klingon occupation.

Shipboard Tactics:
Enables a character to plan combats that take place on board a single starship, such as boarding actions (whether leading them or defending against them), security emergencies, searching for infiltrators or saboteurs, etc.

Other Specializations:
Grand Strategy, Guerrilla Warfare, Mechanized Ground Warfare, Sea Combat, Small-Unit Tactics

STARSHIP TACTICS (INTELLECT)

A character's skill at the organizing and operation starships in space combat or in support of ground forces is represented by Starship Tactics. This skill is important during full scale space combat; among other things, it determines starship initiative (see the *Starship Combat* chapter, page 154).

> *Routine:* Defeating a technologically backward ship in a straight firefight
> *Moderate:* Defeating an outnumbered force in a straight firefight
> *Challenging:* Defeating a slightly superior force in a straight firefight
> *Difficult:* Defeating a superior force while surprised
> *Nearly Impossible:* Defeating a superior force at odds greater than five to one
> *Specializations:* Planetary Support Tactics, Specific Naval (Federation, Klingon, Romulan) Tactics

STRATEGIC OPERATIONS (INTELLECT)

Strategic Operations represents a character's skill at waging large-scale interstellar and intragalactic warfare. Specifically, he can plan fleet operations, select targets, and manage force deployments. The Narrator can allow him to make Strategic Operations Tests as a quick and easy way to determine the general outcome of theater-wide actions in specific regions of space.

> *Routine:* Maintaining a patrol along the Neutral Zone
> *Moderate:* Defending against pinprick raids by an inferior enemy
> *Challenging:* Defending against an in-depth attack by an equal enemy
> *Difficult:* Mounting an in-depth attack against an equal enemy
> *Nearly Impossible:* Successfully invading the territory of and conquering a superior enemy
> *Specializations:* Defense-in-Depth, Invasion Strategies, Neutral Zone Strategies, Specific Naval (Federation, Klingon, Romulan) Strategies

ENGINEERING AND SECURITY

DEMOLITIONS (INTELLECT)

Demolitions represents a character's skill at setting, triggering, and defusing explosives. He can create explosions for specific purposes and effects, such as destroying a building without damaging nearby structures, making a fake explosion look real, or blowing through an armored door.

Demolitions allows a character to either cause additional damage with an explosion, or use it to create a specific effect, such as setting an exploding booby trap. At the Narrator's option, an explosive may do an extra one to two dice for every point by which the character makes his Demolitions Test.

Routine: Setting off standard modern demolitions
Moderate: Destroying a specific target; setting a bomb to activate when a vehicle starts; setting off primitive (*e.g.*, 20th-century) demolitions
Challenging: Destroying an armored door; blowing open a bomb-proof container
Difficult: Defusing a complex or unfamiliar bomb or explosive
Nearly Impossible: Blowing a ship airlock without depressurizing the inner chambers
Specializations: Bomb Disposal, Booby Traps, Land Mines, Nuclear Demolitions, Primitive Demolitions (such as gunpowder, plastique and thermite), Shipboard Demolitions

ENERGY WEAPON (COORDINATION)

The character knows how to properly fire energy weapons, and how to repair, modify, or adjust them as necessary. His skill concentrates on a particular type of weapon (for Starfleet characters, the phaser or phaser rifle; for Klingons and Romulans, disruptors).

Routine: Firing at a target at Point Blank or Short range
Moderate: Firing at a target at Medium range, repairing a weapon out of combat
Challenging: Firing at a target at Long range
Difficult: Repairing a weapon in combat
Nearly Impossible: Repairing a weapon which is going to explode in a few seconds during combat
Specializations: Disruptor, Disruptor Rifle, Phaser, Phaser Rifle

ENGINEERING SKILLS

This suite of skills and specializations allow a character to build, analyze, maintain, modify, and repair various technological systems and devices—everything from a starbase's computers, to a ship's life support plant or warp engines, to a transporter. With the right tools and materials, a sufficiently skilled engineer can build the item or system from scratch. Characters must choose a specific type of Engineering to learn, and a Specialization within that field.

In addition to their practical benefits, Engineering skills provide a character with a high degree of theoretical knowledge about the subject. For example, a character with Propulsion Engineering could make a Test to determine whether the radiation from a nearby nebula would make it dangerous to enter the nebula at warp speed.

Routine: Maintenance of well designed equipment (such as Starfleet equipment)
Moderate: Repair of moderate damage with and to familiar equipment
Challenging: Jury-rigging an item or repair from related parts
Difficult: Significantly improving the design of a standard piece of equipment
Nearly Impossible: Creating a space-time transponder using stone knives and bearskins

MATERIAL ENGINEERING (INTELLECT)

Material Engineering primarily involves the manipulation and alteration of physical and material objects and components.

Sample Specializations:
Structural/Spaceframe Engineering: This specialization covers the design and construction of starships. Characters trained in this field deal with issues relating to ship design, construction of orbital stations, and appropriate hull materials.

Other Specializations: Aeronautical/Aerodynamic, Civil, Mechanical, Metallurgical, Personal Equipment, Vehicular

PROPULSION ENGINEERING (INTELLECT)

Characters with Propulsion Engineering know how to design, modify, build, and repair starship propulsion systems—anything from primitive action/reaction drives to impulse and other sublight drives, to modern antimatter warp engines.

Sample Specializations:
Warp Drive Engineering: This specialization covers both the technical components (such as the Bussard collectors and the warp coils) and the general theory (matter-antimatter interaction, dilithium crystallization) of warp drive propulsion.

Other Specializations: Fusion, Impulse, Ion, Rocketry, Shuttlecraft Propulsion Systems

SYSTEMS ENGINEERING (INTELLECT)

This broad skill allows a character to build, maintain, modify, and repair the various computer, electronic, and other systems within the modern starship. Most personnel have some familiarity with this skill, so that they can repair and maintain their own stations, but a systems engineer knows about all of the ship's systems and how they interrelate.

Sample Specializations:
Computer Systems: Most starships wouldn't get far without their advanced computer systems and memory banks. A character with this Specialization can modify and maintain such systems to keep the ship functioning properly–or perhaps make the ship's computer's voice that of a sultry alien female.
Transporter Systems: A character with this Specialization is the man to call when the landing party is trapped down on the planet and you need to figure out why the transporters aren't functioning. He knows all about them, from their components and subsystems to the matter/energy conversion theories on which they're based.

Other Specializations: Cloaking Device, Communications Systems, Diagnostics, Life Support, Phaser Systems, Power Systems, Sensor Systems, Shields, Torpedo/Probe Systems

FIRST AID (INTELLECT)

A character with First Aid can perform emergency medical procedures in order to stabilize a wounded character's injuries or administer short-term treatments for other maladies. If he hasn't specialized in the species of the character he's treating, all Tests are one category of Difficulty harder (for example, a Moderate task becomes Challenging). (For more information, see *Damage And Healing* on page 114.)

Routine: Halting minor bleeding or mitigating shock
Moderate: CPR
Challenging: Stopping arterial bleeding, setting a broken bone
Difficult: Minor surgery
Nearly Impossible: Stopping major internal bleeding, major surgery
Specializations: Chemical-Biological First Aid, Species-Specific First Aid (Andorian, Human, Klingon, Romulan/Vulcan), Wound/Combat Trauma

HEAVY WEAPONS (INTELLECT)

This skill, a relatively unusual one among Starfleet officers, allows characters to use military-grade weapons properly–to plot target coordinates, manipulate the weapon's controls and fire the weapon. It does not apply to starship weapons; that requires Shipboard Systems (Weapons Systems).

Routine: Firing a weapon at a preset target
Moderate: Indirect fire using grid coordinates
Challenging: Laying down covering or opportunity fire on moving targets
Difficult: Targeting and firing at Long range
Nearly Impossible: Targeting and firing at extreme range or in conditions where there is no visibility
Specializations: Individual Weapon Type (Phaser Artillery, Plasma Mortar, and so on).

PERSONAL EQUIPMENT (INTELLECT)

In the highly technological society of Starfleet, many devices–tricorders, environmental suits, communicators, and the like–are used on board a ship every day. This skill represents the ability to use, maintain, and make minor modifications and "field" repairs to such equipment. (In some cases, such as with communicators, the Narrator may allow characters to use this skill untrained; with more advanced equipment, like tricorders or environmental suits, training is required.)

Routine: Communicating with a ship
Moderate: Communicating with a ship through mild interference
Challenging: Communicating with a ship through strong interference
Difficult: Communicating with a ship through extremely strong interference
Nearly Impossible: Making field repairs to a damaged environmental suit in combat with almost no materials
Specializations: Communicator, Environmental Suit, Medical Tricorder, Tricorder (any of these may be limited by species, *e.g.,* Klingon Tricorders), Universal Translator

PROJECTILE WEAPON (COORDINATION)

A character with Projectile Weapon knows how to fire primitive projectile weapons–gunpowder pistols or rifles from industrial-era Earth, for example. He can also make minor repairs or modifications to such weapons (for example, field-stripping a rifle or clearing a jammed submachine gun). Advanced alien weapons such as needlers and Gauss guns also fall under the Projectile Weapon skill.

Routine: Firing at a target at Point Blank or Short range.
Moderate: Firing at a target at Medium range; repairing a weapon out of combat
Challenging: Firing at a target at Long range
Difficult: Repairing a weapon in combat
Nearly Impossible: Firing at a target at extremely long range with no visibility
Specializations: Gauss Weapon, Gunpowder Pistol, Gunpowder Rifle, Needler, Submachine Gun

SECURITY (INTELLECT)

This skill represents a character's knowledge of, and ability to implement or follow, security techniques and procedures, and the laws and law enforcement procedures on his ship or in his locale. He can build, install and disable (or avoid) various types of locks, alarms, security systems, and security lockout codes. Obviously, this is a Starfleet Security officer's primary skill.

Routine: Standing guard; finding a relevant law in a legal database
Moderate: Disarming or penetrating a simple security system; picking a simple mechanical lock
Challenging: Disarming or penetrating a complex security system; picking a complex mechanical lock
Difficult: Disarming or penetrating a very complex security system; "picking" an electronic lock
Nearly Impossible: Disarming or penetrating a devilishly complex security system set up by a paranoid recluse
Specializations: Law Enforcement, Patrolling, Security Systems

SHIPBOARD SYSTEMS (INTELLECT)

This broad and extremely useful skill represents a character's familiarity and expertise with a specific system on a starship, such as the helm, navigation, weapons systems, transporters, or sensors. He can operate the equipment associated with a particular system, and, to a lesser extent, other systems on the ship. Because all control panels within a given organization or species (or even from species to species) share certain similarities, a character can usually operate a station other than his own—the navigator might man the helm, or the transporter operator run the sensors using their base Shipboard Systems skill level. However, a character can perform more advanced tasks in the fields he has specialized in (for example, a transporter specialist can try to beam someone through interference.)

Routine: Firing ship's phasers at a target at Point Blank or Short range; plotting a course for Earth; beaming down to a planet without preset coordinates
Moderate: Firing ship's phasers at a target at Medium range; following a plasma trail; beaming up a specific individual using sensor data only
Challenging: Firing ship's phasers at a target at Long range; navigating an asteroid field; intership beaming
Difficult: Navigating through a nebula; beaming to another ship under full impulse
Nearly Impossible: Using the phasers to sculpt an asteroid; escaping a black hole; beaming to another ship under warp

Sample Specializations
Communications: A Communications specialist knows how to interpret signals received by a communications device, encode and decode transmissions, eliminate static and background noise, and enhance weak signals. Shipboard Systems (Communications) Tests are often fairly easy (and unnecessary for routine operations like answering a hail or opening a channel); only when interference, static, and similar phenomena occur do they become more difficult.

Helm: This specialization measures a character's ability to pilot a starship. The helmsman does not plot the course (that requires Navigation; see below), he just steers the ship. Helm Tests are normally reserved for combat situations, emergencies, or unusual circumstances (plasma or ion storms, dense nebulae, and the like). Failure to make a successful Helm Test can lead to maneuvering problems, or even a collision.

Library Computer: This specialization represents a character's ability to use the ship's library computer system. Most uses—looking up simple or easy to find information, for example—require no Test. Looking for obscure or hidden information, or trying to find routine information quickly while under pressure, would require a Test. Cross-correlating widely dispersed data, or building theoretical models using the computer, generally falls under the Computer skill, although characters may use Shipboard Systems (Library Computer) at higher degrees of Difficulty.

Navigation: This specialization represents a character's ability to plot a desired course, and to determine the ship's present direction, velocity and location. Under ordinary circumstances, Navigation requires no Test, or at most a Routine test; only when interference, a lack of navigational beacons or "landmarks," or other difficulties arise is a Test necessary.

Sensors: This specialization determines how well a character can operate sensing devices to detect various phenomena—everything from lifeforms, to energy readings, to the conditions on a planet. Base the Difficulty Numbers for Shipboard Systems (Sensors) Tests partly on range, partly on what the character tries to detect with the sensors (the less of it there is to detect, the higher the Difficulty) and partly on the amount of interference caused by strange energy patterns, nebulae, unusual mineral formations, or shielding. Thus, using the sensors to locate something near the ship when no interference exists requires, at the worst, a Routine (3) Test, but trying to locate the same thing near the limits of the sensors' range in the middle of a plasma storm requires a Difficult (13) Test.

Shields: This specialization represents a character's ability to handle a ship's defensive deflector shields, meteor deflectors, and similar systems. Normally operating shields requires no Test, but a Test may be necessary to transfer power between shields or modulate a shield's frequency.

Transporter: A character with this specialization knows how to operate a transporter. He usually only has to make Tests when there's a problem; routine transporter operation does not require a Test.

Weapons Systems: This measures a character's ability to operate a ship's various weapons systems, such as phasers and photon torpedoes.

Other Specializations: Cloaking Device, Life Support

UNARMED COMBAT (COORDINATION)

A character with this skill knows how to fight well with his fists. Any character can use various kinds of untrained brawling or fistfighting attacks (see *Universal Combat Maneuvers* on page 111)—essentially, these are nonformulaic fighting maneuvers ranging from wild punches to flailing kicks. Characters with Unarmed Combat are much better at fighting. They might know an advanced style of martial arts (such as Boxing, Karate, the Vulcan Nerve Pinch, Wrestling, or Aikido), or they might just be especially good at mixing it up. Unarmed Combat skill maximizes a character's ability to use his body as a weapon or shield and to attack with great power and precision. Characters cannot use any Unarmed Combat specialization untrained except for Brawling.

See *Combat*, page 107, for more information on unarmed attacks.

Routine: Hitting an opponent whose Dodge roll was 2-4
Moderate: Hitting an opponent whose Dodge roll was 5-7
Challenging: Hitting an opponent whose Dodge roll was 8-10
Difficult: Hitting an opponent whose Dodge roll was 11-13
Nearly Impossible: Hitting an opponent whose Dodge roll was 14+
Specializations: Boxing, Brawling, Karate, Starfleet Martial Arts, Vulcan Nerve Pinch, Wrestling

VEHICLE OPERATION (INTELLECT)

Vehicle Operations allows a character to operate various types of small vehicles—from aircraft and groundcars to work bees and shuttles. The Difficulty depends on the operation being performed; everyday tasks, like piloting a shuttle from a starbase out to a nearby starship, usually don't require a Test at all.

Routine: Towing a small object with a work bee near a ship's hull; driving a car on snowy/icy roads
Moderate: Landing a plane smoothly and safely; piloting a shuttlecraft through an atmosphere at high speed
Challenging: Piloting a shuttlecraft through a sparse asteroid field
Difficult: Piloting a shuttlecraft through a heavy asteroid field
Nearly Impossible: Piloting a shuttlecraft through a heavy asteroid field while an ion storm interferes with instrumentation and steering
Specializations: Atmospheric Craft, Close Orbital Craft, Ground Vehicles, Shuttlecraft

SCIENCES

COMPUTER (INTELLECT)

This skill reflects a character's ability to use, program and retrieve information from a computer—everything from creating a new program for the computer, to finding a specific piece of information in a computer system, to breaking into an enemy's computers.

Computers in the 23rd century are much more sophisticated and easy to use than 20th-century ones. They typically respond to spoken commands and verbal cues—"Computer, locate Mr. Spock"—instead of requiring elaborate commands or input routines. Performing routine tasks doesn't require a Computer Test; save those for situations where the character is under pressure, attempts an unusually difficult task, tries to retrieve a specific, important piece of data, or tries to use a strange new computer system, for example. Unfamiliar computers (such as Romulan or Klingon systems) increase the Difficulty of a task by one category—a Moderate Test becomes a Challenging Test, at the lowest level for a Challenging task, or 9.

Routine: Obtaining complex information from a computer
Moderate: Running a complex computer simulation
Challenging: Retrieving classified or hidden data from a starship computer
Difficult: Planting a secret computer program in a starship computer system
Nearly Impossible: Analyzing all the code in a station's computer system to find a single logic error
Specializations: Computer Simulation/Modeling, Data Alteration/Hacking, Programming, Research

SCIENCE SKILLS

Characters with Science skills are well-versed in the scientific method. They can identify scientific phenomena, extrapolate from observed data and make conjectures based on known facts. They also have the ability to devise solutions for science-related problems (for example, a geologist can come up with ways to prevent, or lessen the severity of, earthquakes). Science skills also convey competence at the use of scientific laboratory equipment for research, tests, and experiments, where applicable.

Science skills often involve making comparisons to known facts. When observing a new biosphere, for example, a biologist might compare a particular spider-like species with arachnids he knows about, and thus be able to make an educated guess about the creature's habits.

The player must choose a specific Science skill (and, of course, a specialization representing expertise within that field) for his character. A character can make a Skill Test for subjects related to his field at his base skill level using standard specialization rules, but can't make Tests for Science skills he doesn't have. A science officer with Life Sciences (Biology) 2 (3) can roll a Zoology Skill Test at 2, but couldn't make a Planetary Sciences Skill Test.

Routine: Performing a simple experiment; remembering a basic fact

Moderate: Performing a complex experiment; remembering a theory

Challenging: Extrapolating from known data to solve a new, complex problem; remembering an obscure or complex concept

Difficult: Performing a new experiment; developing a cutting-edge theory

Nearly Impossible: Performing a sensitive experiment with no equipment

LIFE SCIENCES (INTELLECT)

Life Sciences primarily involves the study of various types of organisms, from Botany (the study of plants) to Genetics (the study of genomes).

Sample Specializations:

Ecology: The study of ecological systems—the interrelationships between organisms and various natural phenomena (weather, water supply, and so forth).

Exobiology: This covers the study of alien biology, both animal and sentient. The character studies alien reproductive systems, circulatory systems, respiratory systems, and the like.

Other Specializations: Agronomy, Bioengineering, Biology, Bionics, Biotechnology, Botany, Genetics, Microbiology, Paleontology, Zoology

MEDICAL SCIENCES (INTELLECT)

This skill covers the practice of various forms of medicine. Characters with Medical Sciences can diagnose diseases or medical conditions and prescribe treatments. The specializations focus on particular aspects of medicine, such as the medical needs of a specific species (Vulcan Medicine), specific bodily systems, organs, or functions (Cardiology, Neurosurgery), specific ailments (Toxicology, Oncology), or specific types of analysis (Forensics, Pathology).

A character who knows medical skills can also assist with healing characters. See *Damage And Healing*, page 114.

Routine: Diagnosing the common cold

Moderate: Simple surgery on one's own species (a Human doctor performing a tonsillectomy on a Human)

Challenging: Complex surgery on one's own species; simple surgery on an alien lifeform (a Human doctor performing a tonsillectomy on a Vulcan)

Difficult: Experimental surgery on one's own species; complex surgery on an alien lifeform; simple surgery on an unknown lifeform

Nearly Impossible: Surgery on a non-carbon-based lifeform (energy beings, silicon-based lifeforms, dimensional beings); bringing back the dead

Note: General practitioners can perform a variety of functions, but a specialist trains in a more narrow field. Most doctors can identify a poison, for example, but a toxicologist specializes in how toxins react in the body and can more easily identify a poisonous substance.

Sample Specializations:

Surgery: Cardiology: The character specializes in the heart and its associated diseases. He can perform open-heart surgery, bypass surgery and heart transplants.

Vulcan Medicine: The character specializes in Vulcan physiology and can prescribe treatments for maladies that afflict Vulcans.

Other Specializations: Exoanatomy, Forensics, General Medicine, Pathology, Psychology, Specific Species Medicine (Axanari Medicine, Vulcan Medicine and so on), Surgical Specializations (Cardiology, Neurology, Obstetrics and the like), Toxicology

PHYSICAL SCIENCES (INTELLECT)

A character with Physical Sciences has training and expertise in a particular physical science, such as chemistry or physics.

Specializations: Chemistry, Computer Science, Mathematics, Physics

PLANETARY SCIENCES (INTELLECT)

Characters with Planetary Sciences study planets and their various systems, such as climate, minerals, and volcanism.

Specializations: Climatology, Geology, Hydrology, Mineralogy, Oceanography, Planetology, Volcanology

SOCIAL SCIENCES (INTELLECT)

Characters with Social Sciences know about a particular subject relating to societies and how they interact, such as archaeology, geography, or political science.

Sample Specializations:

Anthropology: The study of different cultures, typically through direct observation. The character can form hypotheses about a culture's social mores, customs, and beliefs.

Archaeology: The study of ancient civilizations through the artifacts and records they left behind. The character can make intelligent guesses about a culture, as well as identify particular objects.

Political Science: The character studies how political systems operate and their relationship to a civilization's culture and history.

Other Specializations: Economics, Geography, Paleoanthropology, Sociology

SPACE SCIENCES (INTELLECT)

A character with this skill is an expert in astronomy, astrophysics, thermodynamic physics, or some other space science.

Sample Specializations:
Astrogation: This specialization governs the art of navigation in space, including finding "guide stars," plotting shorter or faster courses, and the impact of warp travel on dimensional orienteering.
Astronomy: Characters with this specialization study space—from stars, to nebulae, to comets, to dark matter.
Warp Field Theory: The study of warp fields and their effects.

Other Specializations: Astrophysics, Stellar Cartography, Subspace Field Dynamics

WORLD KNOWLEDGE (INTELLECT)

A character with this skill knows about the dominant lifeforms, cultures, governments, animals, climate, geography, and ecology of a particular planet. With a successful Test, he can recall a particular fact about that world. The character can also make intelligent comparisons between world data. For example, if confronted with a strange, bear-like creature, a science officer could roll World Knowledge (Vulcan) to compare it to a Vulcan *sehlat*.

Routine: Recalling a fact about your homeworld
Moderate: Recalling a fact about a world you've visited often or studied intently
Challenging: Recalling a fact about a world you've visited a few times or studied
Difficult: Recalling a fact about a world you've visited once or studied casually
Nearly Impossible: Deducing a fact about a world you've never visited or studied
Specializations: Specific Planet (Earth, Vulcan, Axanar and so on)

GENERAL

ACROBATICS (COORDINATION)

A character with this Skill is proficient at tumbling, leaping, rolling, avoiding damage from falls, and similar feats. He can even entertain people who watch his antics.
Routine: Walking along a balance beam
Moderate: Running along a balance beam; avoiding damage from a short fall (up to 3m)
Challenging: Doing a backflip on a balance beam; avoiding damage from a medium fall (up to 6m)
Difficult: Doing a double backflip on a balance beam; avoiding damage from a long fall (up to 12m)
Nearly Impossible: Doing a quintuple somersault; avoiding damage from a very long fall (up to 25m)
Specializations: Balance Walking, Gymnastics, Mid-Air Dodge, Rope Swinging

ANIMAL HANDLING (PRESENCE)

A character with Animal Handling can train and ride many different kinds of animals. Of course, some animals—fiercer or more shy ones—will resist this treatment; part of the character's skill is the ability to work with the animal, and defeat him in a contest of wills, so that he can be properly trained. This requires an Opposed Test against the animal's Instinct, modified by its Ferocity edge (see *The Menagerie*, page 215, for animal characteristics).

Routine: Training or riding a docile animal
Moderate: Training or riding an animal whose Instinct Test result is 3-5
Challenging: Training or riding an animal whose Instinct Test result is 6-8
Difficult: Training or riding an animal whose Instinct Test result is 9-11
Nearly Impossible: Training or riding an animal whose Instinct Test result is 12+
Specializations: Specific Animal (Camel, Horse, Sehlat)

ARTISTIC EXPRESSION (INTELLECT)

Artistic Expression reflects a character's ability to express himself creatively—to draw, compose poetry, sing, dance, write plays, or play a musical instrument, for example.

Routine: Playing a scale, doodling
Moderate: Playing a very simple song; sketching a geometric design
Challenging: Playing a moderately complex song; accurate figure drawing
Difficult: Playing a very complex sonata; composing and painting a moving artwork
Nearly Impossible: Playing an extremely elaborate symphony beautifully in a formal meter on traditional instruments; composing and painting an elaborate, symbolically meaningful masterpiece on an enormous scale
Specializations: Dance, Drawing, Painting, Poetry, Singing, Specific Musical Instrument (Violin, Vulcan Lute and so on)

ATHLETICS (FITNESS)

A character with this skill is proficient at athletic activities like running, climbing, and playing sports or physical games.

If a character wishes to move faster when using a particular form of movement, a successful Moderate (6) Athletics Test allows him to move an additional number of meters per round equal to his Athletics skill level (see *Movement*, page 109.)

Routine: Walking (10m/round) on slick/icy ground; running on
    paved ground
Moderate: Running (15m/round) on ordinary ground; sprinting on
    paved ground
Challenging: Sprinting (20m per round) on ordinary ground; run-
    ning on slick/icy ground
Difficult: Sprinting on slick/icy ground
Nearly Impossible: Sprinting in a swamp

Sample Specializations:

Climbing

Climbing allows characters to scale steep inclines, climb trees, free-climb large rocks, or engage in similar activities. A climbing character moves at a rate in meters equal to his Fitness per minute, or a maximum of 2m per round during combat; successful Tests allow him to move more quickly (see *Movement*, page 109).

Jumping

Characters use Jumping to leap over obstacles (a low wall, a large piece of furniture) or across them (a chasm, a stream). All characters can jump 2m forward or 1m upward without making a Test (see *Movement*, page 109). If a character succeeds with a Moderate (7) Athletics (Jumping) or Fitness Test, he can add up to his skill level (or Fitness) in meters to his forward jump, or half that to his upward jump. If he makes a Challenging (10) roll, he can add up to twice his skill level (or Fitness); if a Difficult (13) roll, three times his skill level (or Fitness); if a Nearly Impossible roll, four times his skill level (or Fitness).

If there's an obstacle in the way, a jump's Difficulty increases by +1 to +3 (or even by one or more categories). If the purpose of the jump is to clear or avoid the obstacle, the object's size determines the Difficulty. If the obstacle is one quarter the character's size (or smaller), the Difficulty is Routine (4); if one half the character's size, Moderate (7); if three quarters the character's size, Challenging (10); if equal to the character's size, Difficult (13); if greater than the character's size, Nearly Impossible (15).

Lifting

Lifting measures a character's ability to lift and carry objects. When a character first lifts an object, he must make a Lifting Test (or a Fitness Test if he does not have this skill) (modified by Strength) with a Difficulty determined by the amount of weight lifted (see accompanying table). At appropriate intervals,

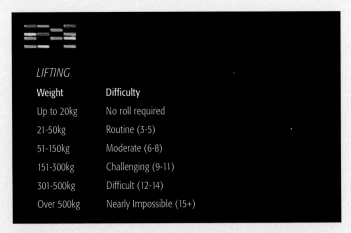

LIFTING	
Weight	Difficulty
Up to 20kg	No roll required
21-50kg	Routine (3-5)
51-150kg	Moderate (6-8)
151-300kg	Challenging (9-11)
301-500kg	Difficult (12-14)
Over 500kg	Nearly Impossible (15+)

the Narrator may have him make another Test to see if he continues to hold on to the object. If he fails a Test, he immediately drops the object. If he matches (but does not beat) the Difficulty, he manages to hang onto the object but can take no other actions.

Running

Running measures a character's ability to run quickly and to keep his balance while running, particularly over unsafe terrain. The Difficulty for a Running Test depends on the type of terrain and the speed at which the character moves (if a Test is required at all); see *Movement*, page 109.

Other Specializations: Specific Sport/Game (Bowling, Skiing, Tennis)

BARGAIN (PRESENCE)

Characters use this skill for haggling—determining the price of goods for sale. Specializations represent a character's expertise in valuing a particular commodity or working a particular market.

The Narrator determines the value of goods prior to play. The type of good, its quality, and the place where a character tries to buy it determine the price of an item. A seller may inflate the prices because he has a monopoly in the area, due to local tariffs or taxes, or just to get the haggling started on a high note.

Bargain requires an Opposed Test against the target's Bargain skill (or Presence if he lacks that skill) (modified by the target's Willpower). However, you should roleplay most situations involving the Bargain skill, rather than resorting to the dice to resolve matters. The dice result should simply reflect a target's reaction to the bargaining attempt. For example, Lt. Graves attempts to bargain with itinerant merchant Cyrano Jones. The die result indicates a failure; Jones thinks Graves is suspiciously stiff and refuses to sell his contraband.

Note: Crew members or NPCs who don't like a deal (perhaps because the other person has made an absurd offer, or rolled extremely well) can always choose to walk away from a deal. Characters can't use Bargain to force another character to accept bad sales terms.

Routine: Bargaining with an average merchant of one's own species
Moderate: Bargaining with an above-average merchant of one's

own species, or an average merchant of another species

Challenging: Bargaining with an above-average member of another species

Difficult: Bargaining with a cagey merchant

Nearly Impossible: Bargaining with a cagey merchant for something you desperately need (and he knows it)

Specializations: Artwork, Bribery, Dilithium Crystals, Marketplace Haggling, Orion Animal Women, Spican Flame Gems, Weapons

CHARM (PRESENCE)

Charm allows a character to persuade a target to do something he may otherwise be unwilling to do, based on the character's personal charisma and appeal. He's literally "turning on the charm," using his sense of humor, physical attractiveness, and similar traits to make the other character agreeable to what he wants. Among other uses, Charm often makes it easier to get information or favors from the target character. Charm requires an Opposed Test against the target's Charm skill (or Presence, if the target doesn't have Charm), modified by the target's Willpower.

Routine: Influencing a relative

Moderate: Influencing a friend

Challenging: Influencing a stranger

Difficult: Influencing someone hostile to you

Nearly Impossible: Influencing someone who hates you, influencing an alien from another galaxy or dimension

Specializations: Influence, Seduction

CONCEALMENT (INTELLECT)

Characters with the Concealment skill are adept at hiding objects on their persons or elsewhere. They can also find hidden objects, though the Search skill can be used for that as well. Of course, the larger the object in comparison to the potential hiding place, the greater the Difficulty to hide it—and the Narrator may rule that it is impossible to hide some objects in some places. Characters do not use Concealment to hide themselves; that requires the Stealth skill.

Routine: Hiding a knife underneath a jacket

Moderate: Hiding a disruptor underneath a jacket

Challenging: Hiding a disruptor underneath a tight shirt

Difficult: Hiding a Type III Phaser Rifle underneath a jacket

Nearly Impossible: Hiding a Type III Phaser Rifle up your sleeve

Specializations: Conceal Weapon, Cache Supplies, Conceal Smuggled Objects

CULTURE (INTELLECT)

A character with Culture knows about the aspects of social, artistic, and religious life common to a nation, planet, or species. Unlike World Knowledge, it doesn't focus on geography or biology except where such factors impinge on society.

Routine: Recall a general fact (Milton was an Earth poet)

Moderate: Recall a more detailed series of facts (John Milton was an English poet who wrote in the 17th century; his greatest work was Paradise Lost)

Challenging: Apply knowledge across fields (discuss Milton's influence on English political development)

Difficult: Recall an obscure fact (Milton's genealogy; the address where he lived)

Nearly Impossible: Near-complete knowledge of the subject (recite Paradise Lost from memory; know where Milton was during any given month of his life)

Specializations: Specific Culture (Earth, Tellarite, Vulcan and so on)

DISGUISE (PRESENCE)

A character with Disguise can alter his physical appearance—hairstyle, skin color, hair color, eye color, and other cosmetic factors—with cosmetics and prosthetics. Disguise requires an Opposed Test against either a target's Disguise skill or his Intellect, modified by his Perception. (In some cases, the Narrator may let a character make a Disguise Test before venturing out in public, so that he can check how good his disguise is; in this case, the character's Test Result sets the Difficulty for anyone trying to detect the disguise.) Of course, if an observer knows the person whom the character disguised himself as, he'll have an easier time detecting the deception; the Narrator should make the character easier to recognize by reducing the Difficulty for detecting the impersonation. A failed Test indicates the disguise doesn't fool the observer.

Routine: Disguise is intended to fool others for a short amount of time at a moderate distance away.

Moderate: Disguise is intended to mask the character's facial features, even at short range.

Challenging: Disguise is intended to alter the character's bodily appearance.

Difficult: Disguise impersonates someone specific.

Nearly Impossible: Impersonating an alien species (a Human trying to impersonate an Andorian, Klingon, Romulan, or the like)

Note: 23rd-century medical science can alter a character's appearance surgically to match a specific person or alien species. This requires a Medical Science (Plastic Surgery) Test, but makes a character even harder to recognize than Disguise.

Specializations: Specific Species (Human, Vulcan, Tiburonian, and so on)

DODGE (COORDINATION)

Characters use Dodge to avoid all types of attacks. Dodging an attack requires a Dodge Test; the Test Result becomes the Difficulty Number for the attack against him (although if the result is lower than the normal Difficulty for the attacker's weapon, use the weapon Difficulty instead). For example, Lt. Grell has Coordination 3, Dodge 4. He decides to dodge a phaser shot at Medium Range. The highest result on his player's three Coordination dice is a 4, so the Difficulty to hit him is 8 (4+4). If he had only rolled a 2, his Test Result of 6 would be less than the attacker's normal Difficulty of 7 at Medium Range. In this case, the attacker would make his attack at a Difficulty 7.

Specializations: None

FAST TALK (INTELLECT)

A character with Fast Talk can convince another person to do or agree to something not in his best interests. It's the classic skill of the con man, the grifter, and the snake-oil salesman—all of whom make their appearances on the final frontier from time to time.

If the target has some reason to suspect the character's intentions, Fast Talk attempts require an Opposed Test against the target's Fast Talk skill or Intellect (modified by the target's Perception or Logic, whichever is higher).

Routine: Target is gullible; something the target would agree to any-way.
Moderate: Target is a close friend or relative; something that will inconvenience the target.
Challenging: Target is a security guard; something that will cause the target trouble (a reprimand).
Difficult: Target should know better; something that will cause the target serious trouble (a review board).
Nearly Impossible: The captain of a starship; something that will get the target jailed or killed
Specializations: None

GAMING (INTELLECT)

A character with Gaming can play games such as games of chance, three-dimensional chess, poker or maybe even fizzbin well (not athletic games, though—that's Athletics). All characters competing in a game make Gaming Tests, and the highest Test Result wins.

Gaming also allows a character to cheat, or determine if other players are cheating. To cheat, the character and the other persons involved in the game each make an Opposed Gaming Test once per round of cheating (to see which of them spots the cheat). If no other characters beats his Test Result, he has successfully cheated. Cheating should involve some roleplaying, too; the character cheating describes how he cheats, and the Skill Test determines how well he succeeds.

Routine: Playing go-fish or tic-tac-toe
Moderate: Playing poker or billiards
Challenging: Playing chess
Difficult: Playing three-dimensional chess
Nearly Impossible: Playing three-dimensional chess against a Vulcan grandmaster
Specializations: Specific Game (Chess, Three-Dimensional Chess, Double-Jack, Poker and so on)

HISTORY (INTELLECT)

A character with this skill possesses knowledge of a historical era—knowledge which very well may save his life when he gets thrust back in time by the Guardian of Forever, encounters immortal aliens like Flint, or slingshots around a star and travels into the past. Any character with access to a computer can look up most historical data, but records from some time periods (Earth's 21st century, Vulcan's Age of Antiquity) are spotty at best.

Routine: Recalling a major fact (Earth fought three World Wars)
Moderate: Recalling a more specific fact (the Second Earth World War pitted Germany against America, England, and Russia; Germany lost; the German leader was Hitler)
Challenging: Recalling a fairly obscure fact (Germany used the first strategic rocket weapons during Earth's Second World War; they were invented by Wernher von Braun)
Difficult: Recalling a linked set of obscure facts (recognizing the design of a V-2; knowing the details of its production and deployment history; discussing its strategic effect on the war)
Nearly Impossible: Near-total mastery of the topic (constructing a day-by-day chronology of the German rocket program, including all relevant scientific, technical, and military personnel and their roles)
Specializations: Specific Organization (the Federation, Starfleet), Specific Planet (Earth, Axanar), Specific Species (Vulcan, Tiburonian)

INTIMIDATION (PRESENCE)

Intimidation represents a character's ability to inspire fear in another person—fear which he can use to coerce information or obedience out of the subject. Intimidation requires an Opposed Test against a target's Intimidation skill or Presence (sometimes Intellect) (modified by Willpower).

This skill is rarely appropriate for Starfleet characters; Starfleet frowns on such methods. Still, there are a few captains out there who can bluster with the best of them.

Routine: Trying to get information out of an average human
Moderate: Trying to get information out of a stubborn human

Challenging: Trying to get information out of most Klingons or Vulcans

Difficult: Trying to get information out of most Romulans

Nearly Impossible: Trying to get information out of a Federation, Klingon, or Romulan captain

Specializations: Bluster, Torture

LANGUAGE (INTELLECT)

The character can speak, read, write, and understand another language without using a Universal Translator. All characters can automatically speak their native tongue.

Routine: Asking simple directions

Moderate: Holding a simple conversation

Challenging: Holding a complex conversation

Difficult: Conveying complex ideas or subtle nuances (discussing formal logic with a Vulcan)

Nearly Impossible: Writing great and meaningful poetry or prose

Specializations: Every language is its own skill; the ability to speak Vulcan does not convey any skill with Centauran, for instance. However, characters can specialize in dialects such as English (20th century slang) or Vulcan (Archaic) if they so desire.

LAW (INTELLECT)

A character with this skill knows about the laws, legal customs, and regulations of a specific organized society.

Routine: Recalling the details of a simple law or regulation

Moderate: Recalling the details of a complex law or regulation

Challenging: Recalling the details of a very complex law or regulation

Difficult: Discerning and exploiting loopholes in legal systems; discovering the relationships of two complex laws

Nearly Impossible: Discerning and exploiting loopholes in Tellarite engineering codes

Specializations: Federation Law, Specific Planetary/Government Laws (Earth, Vulcan, Tellar and so forth), Starfleet Regulations

MERCHANT (INTELLECT)

A character with Merchant knows how to sell goods and operate a sales business. This includes maximizing one's profit, tracking the supply of and demand for goods, knowing the best trade routes, and so forth.

Although Merchant and Bargain relate to each other, they have important differences. Bargain deals with setting and negotiating prices. Merchant covers most other aspects of running a business, including knowing about

the markets for a particular commodity, working the distribution network, or managing a store. Likewise, the art of selling and personal salesmanship generally falls under Persuasion or (in some shady cases) Fast Talk.

Routine: Running a small, single-product sales business

Moderate: Running a large, single-product sales business, such as a typical free freighter's business/trade route

Challenging: Running a small, multi-product sales business or engaging in free trade throughout many sectors or along many trade routes

Difficult: Running a large, multi-product sales business; a chain of orbital bars throughout the entire Arcturus Sector

Nearly Impossible: Running an interstellar trading conglomerate

Specializations: Specific Business Type, Specific Market (for example, Dilithium Market, Flowering Plants Trade Routes, Rigelian Gold Market), Specific Product

PLANETSIDE SURVIVAL (INTELLECT)

Because they spend so much time exploring strange new worlds, all Academy graduates learn how to survive on their own in a hostile environment. Planetside Survival represents that knowledge. Characters make Planetside Survival Tests when they need to find water, food, or shelter; to determine whether something is edible or drinkable, and to find herbs or roots with medicinal value. Many inhabitants of primitive, dangerous, or colony worlds have Planetary Survival for their own habitat.

Routine: Determining whether a particular plant is safe to eat

Moderate: Finding water or edible food in a temperate environment

Challenging: Finding edible food in a desert environment

Difficult: Finding water in a desert environment, surviving below freezing temperatures with little or no shelter

Nearly Impossible: Finding edible food in an arctic environment

Specializations: Arctic, Desert, Forest, Jungle, Mountain, Ocean, Specific World (*e.g.*, Vulcan, Alfa 117, M-113), Urban

PRIMITIVE WEAPONRY (COORDINATION)

This represents the character's ability to use primitive hand weapons (such as clubs, swords, and knives) and ranged weapons (such as bows and crossbows) for the purpose of attack or defense.

Routine: Hitting an opponent whose Dodge roll was 3-5; firing at a target at Point Blank or Short range

Moderate: Hitting an opponent whose Dodge roll was 6-8; firing at a target at Medium range; repairing a weapon out of combat

MASTER ADVANTAGES/DISADVANTAGES LIST

ADVANTAGES

Alertness (+2)

Alien Upbringing (+1)

Ally (+2 to +5)

Ambidexterity (+2)

Athletic Ability (+2)

Bold (+1)

Commendation (+1 to +3)

Contact (+1 to +3)

Curious (+1)

Department Head (+1 to +4)

Double-Jointed (+2)

Eidetic Memory (+3)

Enhanced Vision (+2)

Engineering Aptitude (+3)

Excellent Balance (+1)

Excellent Chemoreception (+1)

Excellent Hearing (+2)

Excellent Metabolism (+1)

Excellent Sight (+2)

Famous Incident (varies)

Favor Owed (+1)

High Pain Threshold (+2)

Indomitable (+2)

Innovative (+1)

Language Ability (+2)

Mathematical Ability (+3)

Medical Remedy (varies)

Mixed Species Heritage (+6)

Multitasking (+2)

Night Vision (+2)

Patron (+2 to +4)

Pattern Recognition (+3)

Peripheral Vision (+1)

Promotion (+0 to +6)

Quick-Draw (+2)

Species Friend (+2 to +5)

Radiation Resistance (+1)

Rapid Healing (+1)

Resolute (+3)

Sense Of Direction (+1)

Sense Of Time (+1)

Sexy (+2)

Shrewd (+1)

Strong Will (+2)

Synergy (+3)

Tactical Genius (+3)

Telepathic Resistance (+4)

Toughness (+1)

Weapon Master (+2 or +4)

Zero-G Training (+2)

DISDVANTAGES

Argumentative (-1)

Arrogant (-1)

Bloodlust (-2)

Chronic Pain (-2)

Code of Honor (-2 to -5)

Compulsion (-1 to -3)

Dark Secret (-1 to -3)

Dependent (-2)

Fanatic (-2 to -3)

Greedy (-1)

Hedonist (-1)

Hides Emotions (-2)

Hypochondria (-1)

Impulsive (-1)

Intolerant (-1 to -3)

Low Pain Threshold (-2)

Medical Problem (-1 or -3)

Obligation (-1 to -3)

Obsessive Tendencies (-1, -3)

Pacifism (-1 to -5)

Phobia (-2 to -5)

Physically Impaired (-1 to -3)

Poor Chemoreception (-1)

Poor Hearing (-1)

Poor Sight (-2)

Rival (-1 to -3)

Slow Healing (-2)

Species Enemy (-3 to -5)

Stubborn (-1)

Sworn Enemy (-1 to -3)

Vengeful (-1 to -2)

Weak Will (-2)

Weakness (-2)

Zero-G Intolerance (-2)

Challenging: Hitting an opponent whose Dodge roll was 9-11; firing at a target at Long range

Difficult: Hitting an opponent whose Dodge roll was 12-14; repairing a weapon in combat

Nearly Impossible: Hitting an opponent whose Dodge roll was 15+

Specializations: Chaka, D'k tagh, Lirpa, Longbow, *Mek'leth,* Rapier, Sword

SEARCH (INTELLECT)

Characters use Search to locate or detect hidden objects (concealed weapons on someone's person) or people (camouflaged soldiers or people trying to sneak past them using Stealth). If an object or target is hidden, the character attempting the search makes an Opposed Test against the target's Concealment or Stealth (or Coordination, if the target doesn't possess those skills), or against the Concealment or Stealth Test Result of the person who hid the object. If an object hasn't been hidden, the character simply makes a roll against a base Difficulty.

Routine: Target is hiding in plain sight.

Moderate: Finding a disruptor hidden under a jacket

Challenging: Finding the right duotronic circuit in a box of them; locating a concealed door or access panel

Difficult: Finding one person in a crowd; locating a very well-concealed door or access panel

Nearly Impossible: The proverbial needle in a haystack

Specializations: None

SLEIGHT OF HAND (COORDINATION)

A character can use Sleight of Hand to palm small objects, making them seem to disappear, and to pick pockets without alerting the target. The palmed object is considered hidden, requiring a searching character to make an Opposed Search Test (or Intellect Test) against the character's Sleight of Hand. Hiding anything larger than the Human hand requires the Concealment skill.

Routine: Palming a computer tape

Moderate: Simple magic tricks; palming a phaser-1

Challenging: Complex magic tricks; palming a phaser-2; picking an unsuspecting person's pocket

Difficult: Extremely complex magic tricks; picking a suspicious person's pocket

Nearly Impossible: Picking a highly suspicious person's pocket

Specializations: Magic Tricks, Pick Pocket

STEALTH (COORDINATION)

Stealth represents a character's ability to hide and move quietly. It's used to hide the character himself; hiding weapons or small items on one's person requires the Concealment skill. Successful use of Stealth requires sufficient cover; hiding in, or sneaking across, open, well-lit, observed areas is not possible. To locate a stealthy person, a character makes an Opposed Search (or Intellect) Test (modified by Perception) against the hiding character's Stealth Test Result

Routine: Hiding around a corner

Moderate: Sneaking across gravel

Challenging: Hiding behind a plant

Difficult: Sneaking across a well-lit area

Nearly Impossible: Hiding in plain sight

Specializations: Hide, Stealthy Movement

STREETWISE (INTELLECT)

A character with Streetwise knows about underworld organizations and how they operate, life on the street, buy or sell goods on the gray and black markets, and so forth. He can also locate individual criminals, make contact with larger underworld organizations, or find someone who's willing to commit a crime. He knows who's who on the street—who runs which gangs, where to find the best smuggler on the planet, and the like.

Routine: Finding an item or service common under most circumstances

Moderate: The item or service is easy to find, but requires some discretion (finding an Orion slave dealer).

Challenging: The item or service involves risk or is well-regulated (Romulan Ale)

Difficult: Finding an item or service rare in Federation space (Klingon disruptor)

Nearly Impossible: Finding an illegal item or service on a Federation starship

Specializations: Locate Contraband, Orion Slavers, Underworld of Specific Planet or Species (Tiburonian, Andorian)

PSIONIC

Psionic Skills represent the mental powers and abilities possessed by certain species (such as Vulcans) and characters. The *Psi* attribute governs all Psionic skills. The *Range* edge reflects a character's ability to use Psionic skills at better than average range (it adds to all Psionic Skill Tests made at range); the *Focus* edge represents the degree of precision with which the character can employ his Psionic skills (it adds to most Psionic Skill Tests other than those made at range).

Each Psionic skill lists basic Difficulties for sample tasks. Resisting a psionic power requires an Opposed Test with the attacking character's Psionic skill (modified by Focus) versus the resisting character's Mind Shield (also modified by Focus); the resisting character may substitute Presence (modified, in this case, by Willpower) for Psi in this case if he wishes. This Opposed Test may be

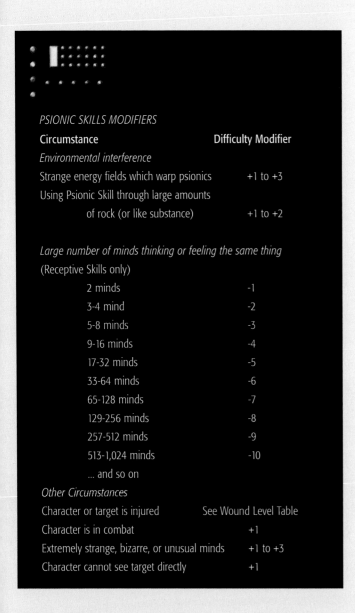

PSIONIC SKILLS MODIFIERS

Circumstance	Difficulty Modifier
Environmental interference	
Strange energy fields which warp psionics	+1 to +3
Using Psionic Skill through large amounts	
of rock (or like substance)	+1 to +2
Large number of minds thinking or feeling the same thing	
(Receptive Skills only)	
2 minds	-1
3-4 mind	-2
5-8 minds	-3
9-16 minds	-4
17-32 minds	-5
33-64 minds	-6
65-128 minds	-7
129-256 minds	-8
257-512 minds	-9
513-1,024 minds	-10
... and so on	
Other Circumstances	
Character or target is injured	See Wound Level Table
Character is in combat	+1
Extremely strange, bizarre, or unusual minds	+1 to +3
Character cannot see target directly	+1

PSIONIC SKILLS RANGE TABLE

Range	Difficulty Modifier
Touch	-1
Point Blank (5m or less)	+0
Short (5.1-20m)	+1
Medium (20.1-50m)	+2
Long (50.1-100m)	+3
Extreme (over 100m)	+4

MIND CONTROL (PSI)

A character with this skill can alter a target's perceptions and actions—he can make the target do things he wouldn't otherwise do (even things directly harmful to himself), see things which aren't really there, reach erroneous conclusions, act contrary to his nature, and so forth. Mind Control can only be used against one target at a time.

A character using Mind Control must explain the overall effect of a particular use of the skill. The more complex the mind control attempt, the higher the Difficulty.

> *Routine:* Something the target would attempt anyway
> *Moderate:* Something that will inconvenience the target
> *Challenging:* Something that will get the target into trouble (a reprimand)
> *Difficult:* Something that violates the target's principles or would get him into serious trouble (a review board)
> *Nearly Impossible:* Forcing the target to commit suicide
> *Specializations:* None

MIND MELD (PSI)

This skill allows a character to read another character's memories, or share memories and thoughts with him. Although closely associated with the Vulcan people, the skill actually includes various methods of memory exchange. Both participants remember the experience afterwards, though they both know the memories belong to someone else.

Using Mind Meld at range is very difficult; add +2 to all Difficulty Numbers if the character is not touching the target.

> *Routine:* Sharing memories with a willing target of one's own species
> *Moderate:* Sharing memories with an unwilling target of one's own species

made once per round (as an Immediate Action; see page 108) during each round that the Psionic Skill affects the target.

Psionic powers work best on targets of the character's own species; using them on other races usually increases the Difficulty (see individual skill descriptions).

Characters can use Psionic abilities at range, but generally find them easier to use when the psionic touches his subject. Employing them at range increases the Difficulty of accomplishing any task (see the Psionic Skills Range Table).

The Range edge modifies the number of dice rolled when making a Psionic Skill Test at range. Characters may not use their Focus edge when using Psionic skills at range.

Many other factors influence the ease with which a character can use a Psionic skill at range. The Psionic Skills Modifiers Table lists some of these factors; Narrators should use these as guidelines for creating modifiers for factors not listed here.

Challenging: Sharing memories with a willing target of another
  species
Difficult: Sharing memories with an unwilling target of another
  species
Nearly Impossible: Sharing memories with a completely alien being
Specializations: None

MIND SHIELD (PSI)

The character can withstand psionic attack or influence. Characters use Mind Shield to make Opposed Tests when resisting Psionic skills such as Projective Empathy or Receptive Telepathy.

Specializations: None

PROJECTIVE EMPATHY (PSI)

The character can project his emotions and feelings into a recipient. The target character feels whatever the character experiences—fear, happiness or trust, for example. At skill level 4 and higher, the character is proficient enough to make the target feel emotions he (the character) is not experiencing.

Routine: Target of one's own species receptive to the empathy
Moderate: Target of one's own species unreceptive to the empathy
Challenging: Target of another species receptive to the empathy
Difficult: Target of another species unreceptive to the empathy
Nearly Impossible: Target is a completely alien being.
Specializations: None

PROJECTIVE TELEPATHY (PSI)

The character can send his thoughts directly into the mind of another person. Projective Telepathy (sometimes called the "Vulcan mind touch") usually serves just as a form of communication, but sometimes it helps to distract or confuse another character.

Routine: Target of one's own species receptive to the telepathy
Moderate: Target of one's own species unreceptive to the telepathy
Challenging: Target of another species receptive to the telepathy
Difficult: Target of another species unreceptive to the telepathy;
  erasing or altering a character's memories
Nearly Impossible: Target is a completely alien being.
Specializations: None

RECEPTIVE EMPATHY (PSI)

Receptive Empathy allows a character to sense the emotional states of others near him. This usually comes across as a general sense of the other person's broad feelings—anger, hostility, peace, happiness and so on.

Routine: Target of one's own species receptive to the empathy
Moderate: Target of one's own species unreceptive to the empathy
Challenging: Target of another species receptive to the empathy
Difficult: Target of another species unreceptive to the empathy
Nearly Impossible: Target is a completely alien being.
Specializations: None

RECEPTIVE TELEPATHY (PSI)

The character can read the surface thoughts of a target. He can, if he wishes, probe the target's thoughts more deeply, but any such attempt is at least one Difficulty category higher (and in some cases runs the risk of getting the character sucked into the target's twisted or alien mindscape). Receptive Telepathy cannot read a target's memories; that requires Mind Meld.

Routine: Target of one's own species receptive to the telepathy
Moderate: Target of one's own species unreceptive to the telepathy
Challenging: Target of another species receptive to the telepathy
Difficult: Target of another species unreceptive to the telepathy;
  erasing or altering a character's memories
Nearly Impossible: Target is a completely alien being.
Specializations: None

Traits

Players can customize their characters with advantages and disadvantages, which describe various traits or abilities—physical, mental, psychological and social—which aren't represented by attributes and skills. These range from the character's curiosity, to his refusal to quit even in the face of long odds, to his blood feud with an old enemy, to important people he knows. Many advantages and disadvantages often modify the number of dice you roll for particular types of Tests, thus increasing or decreasing a character's chance to successfully perform specific actions or types of actions in the game.

Advantages represent special abilities or assets that *Star Trek Roleplaying Game* characters can call on during game play. Each one costs a number of Development Points (indicated in parentheses after the advantage's name). Characters can only purchase most advantages once (particularly those which grant bonus dice or similar benefits), but a few (like Ally or Contact) can be bought more than once.

Disadvantages, on the other hand, represent various restrictions, limitations, losses, or hindrances which afflict a character—anything from physical maladies like poor eyesight or having a chronic illness, to mental vulnerabilities like bloodlust or arrogance. Instead of costing Development Points, they give a character points back to spend on other things (the points received are indicated by a "negative" number in parentheses after the disadvantage's title).

Unlike skills, characters don't "learn" advantages and disadvantages—typically they're born with them, or develop them during their Background History. They help you develop your character's history. For example, *Alien Upbringing* or *Mixed Species Heritage* tell you a lot about a character's past (where he grew up, what his basic instincts are probably like, and so forth). Taking a *Contact* during the Academy stage means your character met someone while he was in school who now helps him out from time to time. Choose the advantages and disadvantages which help to illustrate your vision of your character and give you insight into his personal development, social relationships, and the like.

ADVANTAGES

ALERTNESS (+2)

The character possesses a natural sense for danger, a heightened awareness of his surroundings which alerts him to threats. When he makes Tests in potentially dangerous situations, he rolls an extra die. Additionally, in some situations, the Narrator secretly rolls Search Tests for him and tells him what he perceives.

Alertness is *not* a psychic power; it represents the character's subconscious powers of perception. Typically, the information the character learns from the Narrator because of this advantage is vague—"You feel like someone's watching you," or "Something doesn't feel right."

ALIEN UPBRINGING (+1)

A character with this advantage grew up on an alien planet, raised by members of a species other than his own. When taking this advantage, the player must decide why this happened to the character and how it affected him, thus creating a significant part of his background.

In game terms, the character should replace his Template's skills with the skills from the Template for the species which raised him (he can always learn the skills from his own Template by spending Development Points on them). An Andorian raised on Vulcan, for instance, would possess the skills listed on

ALLY	
Cost	Sample Ally
2	Fellow officer, local constable, or midlevel bureaucrat.
3	Starbase commander, starship captain, judge
5	A Starfleet Admiral, a Federation Commissioner, the Vulcan Ambassador.

the Vulcan Template, since he learned to use the *lirpa* and speak Vulcan with the other children, but he retains the attributes listed for Andorians. He can learn Andorian skills, but he must purchase them with Development Points.

ALLY (+1 TO +5)

A friend, relative, comrade, classmate, or other person with whom the character has a close relationship holds a position of power. For the sake of their relationship, this person will go out of his way to help the character. The more powerful the Ally is, and thus the more helpful he can be, the more this advantage costs. The player and Narrator should develop the Ally, making him a distinctive NPC who contributes to the campaign.

AMBIDEXTERITY (+2)

The character can use either hand to perform actions (firing a weapon, operating machinery and so on) without suffering the standard +1 Difficulty penalty for using the "off hand." Multiple Action Penalties (see page 109) still apply.

ATHLETIC ABILITY (+2)

The character has a natural talent for athletics. He gets to roll an additional die when making Tests to perform physical activities (such as Athletics, Acrobatics, Primitive Weaponry, and Unarmed Combat).

BOLD (+1)

The character is bold; he goes where others fear to go, and dares what the more timid only dream of. Whenever he takes the initiative, and roleplays this advantage properly, he receives a free Courage Point to spend to help him in that situation.

COMMENDATION (+1 TO +3)

Due to his devotion to duty, valor, and/or actions above and beyond the call of duty, the character has received a commendation (a medal, ribbon, or

COMMENDATION

Cost	Commendation
1	Commendation (Preantares Ribbon of Commendation, Second Class; Grankite Order of Tactics; Kragite Order of Heroism; Starfleet Citation for Conspicuous Gallantry)
2	Minor Award (Service Award; Preantares Ribbon of Commendation, First Class; Palm Leaf of Axanar Peace Mission)
3	Major Award (Federation Cluster, UFP Medal of Valor, Medal of Honor [with Clusters], Silver Palm with Cluster)

similar form of recognition). In most campaigns, Starfleet or the Federation awards a Commendation, but it could come from any planetary government, such as the Vulcan Council, or even from a non-Federation government such as the Presidency of Altair VI. A Commendation may also involve the award of Renown Points, but receiving a Commendation does not automatically mean that a character also receives Renown (see *Renown*, page 124). The number of Development Points spent on this advantage determines the type and nature of the Commendation received (see accompanying chart).

CONTACT (+1 TO +3)

The character has some connections with a person of influence and power. The Contact uses his power to perform small favors for the character (like getting him into a diplomatic reception, or arranging a meeting with the Tiburonian ambassador). Said favors must be within his power and not expose him to any sort of harm or danger (including, for example, a judicial inquiry or the loss of his position).

The player and the Narrator should work together to develop this person's identity, position, and exact relationship with the character before the game begins. The more Development Points spent on the Contact, the more powerful and useful he is (see accompanying table).

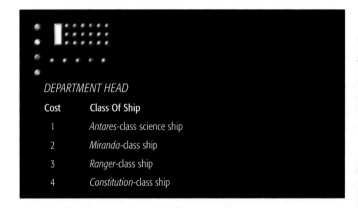

CONTACT

Cost	Sample Contact
1	Fellow officer, local constable or middle-level bureaucrat.
2	Starbase commander, starship captain, judge
3	A Starfleet Admiral, a Federation Commissioner, the Vulcan Ambassador to the UFP

CURIOUS (+1)

Curiosity may have killed the *le-matya*, but that doesn't stop this character from investigating puzzles and mysteries, applying his skills to find the answers to stubborn questions, opening locked doors to see what's behind them, and poking his nose in where it doesn't belong. When he confronts the unknown, he receives a free Courage Point to spend.

DEPARTMENT HEAD (+1 TO +4)

The character commands a department on his starship (for example, Security, Science, Medical, or Engineering). The cost of this advantage depends on the class of ship the character serves on (see accompanying table). Besides this advantage, sufficient rank is a prerequisite to being a department head; typically the character must be a full lieutenant, though a Lieutenant (j.g.) might possibly serve as department head on a *Miranda*-class or *Antares*-class ship.

DEPARTMENT HEAD

Cost	Class Of Ship
1	*Antares*-class science ship
2	*Miranda*-class ship
3	*Ranger*-class ship
4	*Constitution*-class ship

DOUBLE-JOINTED (+2)

The character has an extremely flexible body. He may roll an additional die when making Tests to fit into cramped spaces (like Jefferies tubes or phaser coolant vents), escape from restraints, and similar situations.

EIDETIC MEMORY (+3)

The character has a "photographic memory"—he can recall perfectly everything he directly experiences, including anything he sees, hears, or reads. However, he can't pick up physical or social skills, like commanding a ship or fighting with a *lirpa*, just by watching someone do it: This advantage's benefits generally only apply to learned information. At best, relying on this ability to use a skill your character lacks might, with the Narrator's approval, count as untrained skill use (even for skills which cannot be used untrained).

ENHANCED VISION (+2)

The character can see in wavelengths not normally visible to Humans. Tellarites possess this advantage because of their racial ability to see deep into

the infrared. Note that in many cases, this advantage gives the equivalent of Night Vision.

ENGINEERING APTITUDE (+3)

The character has a natural talent for skills related to mechanics and engineering. He comprehends the principles behind such skills thoroughly (perhaps intuitively), and can easily understand, operate or repair machinery (everything from the warp drive to the doctor's tricorder). When making any Engineering Skill Test, he rolls one extra die.

EXCELLENT BALANCE (+1)

The character has a superb sense of balance; he rarely stumbles or falls, and walks very gracefully. Whenever he makes Athletics or Acrobatics Skill Tests, or any other Test involving balance, he rolls one extra die.

EXCELLENT CHEMORECEPTION (+1)

The character has a well developed sense of smell, and can distinguish between similar smells, determine the direction and source of a smell, and smell things the average person might miss. When he makes Tests based on scent or taste (such as some Search Tests), he rolls one extra die.

EXCELLENT HEARING (+2)

The character hears exceptionally well; he can distinguish between similar sounds, determine the direction and source of those sounds, and perceive distant whispers. When making Tests involving sound or hearing (such as some Search Tests), he rolls one extra die. Tiburonians have this Advantage thanks to their large, parabolically-shaped ears.

EXCELLENT METABOLISM (+1)

The character is very fit. When making Tests to resist the effects of disease, age or poison, he rolls one extra die.

EXCELLENT SIGHT (+2)

The character's eyesight is extremely acute; he notices things other people might miss, such as a Klingon hiding behind a distant rock outcropping. When he makes Tests based on Sight (such as some Search Tests), he rolls one extra die.

FAMOUS INCIDENT (VARIES)

The character was involved in an event of great significance and importance, one known throughout the Federation. James Kirk's participation in the Axanar Peace Mission, his involvement with the tragic events on Tarsus IV, and his defeat of the Romulan incursion of 2266 are good examples of Famous Incidents. The player and Narrator should decide what sort of incident the character participated in, what happened, and what he did (preferably creating something that provides the Narrator with some episode seeds to develop). In game terms, the character receives 2 Renown Points for every Development Point spent. In some cases, a character can combine Famous Incident with the Promotion Advantage—he earned a higher rank because of his actions.

FAVOR OWED (+1)

A highly-placed person—a Starfleet officer, a high-ranking government official or the like—owes the character a favor (usually a pretty big one). Once the character calls in the Favor, the relationship ends (the character owes him no further favors), though the two characters may remain friends (the Narrator may want to take the opportunity to develop the friend as a useful NPC).

HIGH PAIN THRESHOLD (+2)

The character can withstand more pain than most people. Any Test penalties he would suffer due to injury are reduced by 1 (for example, if he was Injured, he would only have a +1 Difficulty to Skill Tests, not the standard +2). Add this bonus to the total penalty as a result of wounds; do not apply it per injury (a character who is Stunned and then Injured would suffer a +1 Difficulty, not 0) (see *Effects of Injuries*, page 116). Furthermore, when making Skill Tests to resist physical torture or pain, he rolls one extra die.

INDOMITABLE (+2)

The character refuses to give up or give in to despair, regardless of how badly the odds are stacked against him—and somehow, because of his courage and strength of spirit, he always manages to triumph in the end. Whenever the situation looks hopeless and he's the underdog, he receives an extra Courage Point to spend overcoming adversity.

INNOVATIVE (+1)

The character often seems to take an innovative perspective towards problems. His solutions for just about any problem, from settling a dispute between

his crewmates to repairing the transporters, are fresh and original. In situations calling for this sort of original thinking, he receives a free Courage Point to spend.

LANGUAGE ABILITY (+2)

The character has an intuitive ability to understand how languages are constructed and used. When making any Tests related to languages, he rolls one extra die. However, he must have at least one skill level in a language to receive this bonus.

MATHEMATICAL ABILITY (+3)

The character has a natural talent for mathematics. When making all computer, science (life, physical and space) and mathematical Skill Tests, he rolls one extra die. However, he must have at least one skill level in the skill to receive this bonus—knowing math doesn't help him program a computer unless he already knows how to program.

MEDICAL REMEDY (VARIES)

The character suffers from blindness, paralysis, muteness or some other condition represented by the *Medical Problem* or *Physically Impaired* disadvantage, but thanks to 23rd-century science (or some other means) also has a remedy. This can range from genetic replacements to bionic prosthetics. For example, a blind character might receive new eyes or a sensor web garment (such as that worn by Dr. Miranda Jones).

The cost of this advantage depends on several factors. If the replacement part or remedy simply substitutes for the character's normal abilities (for example, his sensor web duplicate normal eyesight), the cost of the Medical Remedy equals the cost of the corresponding disadvantage (for example, if Lt. Kelly takes the disadvantage *Physically Impaired: Blind* (-3), he would spend 3 Development Points to buy his Medical Remedy). However, points gained from taking the *Medical Problem* or *Physically Impaired* disadvantage don't count towards the total number of points the character can gain from disadvantages or spend on advantages (for example, if the Narrator rules that

characters cannot have more than 8 points of disadvantages, Lt. Kelly could have 8 points *in addition* to the 3 points received for his Medical Problem; he could also buy 8 points' worth of advantages in addition to the 3 points spent on his Medical Remedy).

If the Medical Remedy also augments the character's faculties (for example, the sensor web provides the equivalent of Enhanced Vision, Excellent Sight or Night Vision), the cost for that part of the advantage equals the cost of the game element the Remedy provides (and those points do count against the character's Advantage total).

> *Amanda wants to give her character, Lt. Benchley, a paralyzed leg—the result of an accident suffered at Starfleet Academy. She chooses the Medical Remedy Advantage. She decides Lt. Benchley wears an exobrace which transmits signals from her brain to her leg, allowing it to move normally. If the exobrace simply allows Lt. Benchley to exercise her normal Fitness and Strength, and to run and perform skills without penalty, its cost balances against the cost of her corresponding Physically Impaired disadvantage, but doesn't count against her total Advantages. However, Amanda decides the exobrace allows Lt. Benchley to run faster. This costs +1 point for each level of Running Specialization for her Athletics skill she desires (and these points count against her Advantage total).*

MIXED SPECIES HERITAGE (+6)

The character is a "halfbreed," the child of parents of different species— Human/Axanari, Vulcan/Human, Andorian/Centauran, etc. The player must choose the two species, and determine which is genetically dominant. Pick three attributes from the dominant species' Template, and the other two from the other species' Template. Consider the character's background carefully, and choose appropriate skills from the two Templates and during his Background History development. Usually, the primary influence on the Template skills and traits comes from the character's homeworld. (Spock, raised on Vulcan, behaves like a Vulcan with Vulcan skills.)

> *Ensign Grennis has a Tellarite father and Human mother. Physically, he is mainly Tellarite, but he does possess certain Human characteristics as well. Grennis' player takes Tellarite Fitness, Coordination (and its associated Reaction edge), and Psi; the Human side contributes Intellect and Presence (with Willpower rather than negative Empathy). During Background History development, the Narrator might allow Grennis' player to "buy off" the Argumentative Disadvantage which Tellarites normally have by spending one Development Point. The player might also allocate points to the skill History (Earth) or World Knowledge (Earth) rather than Tellarite ones to simulate his character's knowledge of his mother's homeworld.*

MULTITASKING (+2)

The character can perform an additional Intellect-based action each round without suffering a Multiple Action Penalty (see page 109). Further actions in a round result in standard Multiple Action Penalties (*e.g.*, +1 to all Difficulty Numbers for three actions, +2 for four and so on). Off hand penalties still apply.

Captain Mallory attempts to make a Starship Tactics (Klingon) Test while firing the ship's phasers (using Shipboard Systems (Weapons Systems)). Both are Intellect skills, so he does not incur the Multiple Action Penalty. Later on, Mallory wants to shoot a hand phaser at Klingon boarders while continuing to fire the ship's phasers. Shipboard Systems is an Intellect skill, while shooting a phaser is a Coordination skill, so Mallory doesn't suffer a Multiple Action Penalty (because he's allowed an additional Intellect Skill-based action). Finally, Mallory finds himself attacked by two Klingons, and he wants to punch both. Because both actions are Coordination skills, he suffers a Multiple Action Penalty; Multitasking provides no benefit in this situation.

NIGHT VISION (+2)

The character has better eyesight in the dark than most people. He's able to reduce the Difficulty penalty for darkness, smoke or other phenomena which obscure vision by 2 (see *Visual Cover*, page 113). Thus, in total darkness (a +3 Difficulty penalty), he still suffers a +1 Difficulty penalty, but in most other situations he can see just fine. To receive the bonus from this advantage, the character's eyes must first become used to the darkness, which takes 1d6 rounds.

PATRON (+2 TO +4)

The character has someone helping him out from behind the scenes—someone who, perhaps, sponsored him to the Academy, saw to it that he was considered for promotion or a position on a good ship, or the like. This patron continues to take an interest in the character's career. When the character needs help, his Patron tries to come to his assistance (with much the same restrictions as a Contact, though a Patron is usually even more friendly towards the character, and willing to go further to help him out). The Patron's power, influence, and ability and willingness to help the character determines how many Development Points he costs (see accompanying table).

PATTERN RECOGNITION (+3)

The character is adept at recognizing patterns within data, solving mysteries and puzzles, deducing facts from incomplete data, spotting camouflage, and similar feats. Whenever confronted with a problem, mystery, or puzzle, he receives 1 Courage Point to spend on any Skill Test to help him solve it. Most Axanari have this Advantage.

PATRON

Cost	Example Patron
2	Moderate figure: This person is a government official on a planet in Federation space, a Starfleet officer (no higher than Captain), or an equivalent figure in another galactic civilization.
3	Influential figure: an important figure in the political life of the UFP, such as Ambassador Sarek or the Fleet Admiral of Starfleet
4	Important figure (President of the UFP, T'Pau of Vulcan)

FREQUENCY

The Ally, Contact, and Patron Advantages can be easily abused by players. As Narrator, you shouldn't let them call on such connections more than once every few episodes. Otherwise, they start to dominate the storyline and prevent the Crew from really shining—and what's the point of going "once more unto the breach" if you're just going to call someone to help you out of trouble?

If the character calls on his powerful connections too frequently, have him make a Challenging (10) Charm (Influence) Test. If he succeeds, the connection comes through for the character. If he fails, the connection cannot, or will not, help him at this time. Keep increasing the Difficulty level for succeeding Tests until the character fails.

PERIPHERAL VISION (+1)

The character has an unusually wide field of vision (though he can't see things behind him, of course). When making visual Search Tests, or other Tests depending on perception, he rolls one extra die.

PROMOTION (+0 TO +6)

The character receives a promotion. Increase his rank by one grade—from Lieutenant to Lieutenant Commander, for instance. A character should buy promotions one rank at a time, to simulate his advancement during his early years in Starfleet. The accompanying table indicates the costs for the various Starfleet ranks (these costs are cumulative; after a character spends 2 points for the rank of Lieutenant, he must pay 3 more Development Points, not just an additional +1 point, for the rank of Lieutenant Commander).

To achieve the rank of Commander or better, the character must possess at least one skill level in the primary skill in three departments, such as Engineering, Helm, Security or Science. No beginning character may start with a rank higher than Lieutenant Commander (or equivalent). See pages 125-126 for further information on promotion and advancement.

*Sheila's character, Aileen Decker, graduates from the Academy
with the rank of Ensign. During the Tour of Duty phase of the
Background History, she purchases the rank of Lieutenant (JG) for
1 point. Later on, she decides to purchase another rank, to full
Lieutenant, costing another 2 points.*

QUICK-DRAW (+2)

The character's reflexes are swift and finely honed. When he makes
Initiative Tests in combat (see page 107), he rolls roll one extra die (in addition
to any bonus dice received for his Reaction edge).

RADIATION RESISTANCE (+1)

The character possesses an unusual resistance to damaging radiation
(often as the result of evolving on a world exposed to higher than normal radiation levels, such as Axanar). The character has +2 Fitness only for purposes of
resisting damage from radiation.

RAPID HEALING (+1)

The character has excellent recuperative powers. His natural healing time
is halved; when he makes Tests to determine if he has naturally healed he rolls
an extra die; and the Difficulty of all rolls to determine the effects of medical
attention on him is reduced by 1. (See *Healing*, pages 117-118, for rules about
recovering from injury.)

Rapid Healing differs from Toughness and High Pain Threshold. A character with High Pain Threshold resists pain well, but doesn't necessarily heal any
more quickly than the average person. A character with Toughness may not
suffer injury from a blow or accident that would harm other characters, but
again, doesn't heal from injuries he does suffer any quicker than normal. A
character with Rapid Healing isn't any tougher or more resilient than most
people, but does heal quickly.

RESOLUTE (+3)

A Resolute character doesn't know the meaning of the word "fail." When
the Klingons take over the ship, he refuses to surrender; when disaster threatens a nearby colony, he's determined to find a way to avert it. When making
Skill Tests to follow his goals, he rolls one extra die. Resolute represents the
positive side of the Obsessive Tendencies disadvantage—the character, unlike
someone who's obsessed, can focus on a goal, but "break off" from it at any
time.

Of course, "following goals" can be interpreted very broadly, so it's up to
the Narrator to determine when Resolute affects a situation. Don't let players
get away with "resolutely" phasering Klingons or making it their "goal" to solve
every problem that comes along.

SENSE OF DIRECTION (+1)

After the character visits an area, he always remembers how to return to
it—he can't get lost in a place he has visited before. This ability functions automatically and requires no Tests.

SENSE OF TIME (+1)

The character's "internal clock" functions very well. He's always aware of
the time, though there's a +/-10% margin of error, since his clock isn't precise.
For example, if he gets knocked out, he knows how long he was unconscious.
This ability functions automatically and requires no Tests.

SEXY (+2)

The character possesses a high degree of personal charisma, charm, and
"sex appeal." Whenever he makes making Presence-based Skill Tests on members of the opposite gender, he rolls one extra die. As Captain Kirk proves, the
persons affected by this advantage don't necessarily have to be of the same
species—or even from the same galaxy—as the character.

SHREWD (+1)

The character is insightful and not easily tricked, able to detect deception
and attempts to persuade him (anything from a merchant's wheedling to sly
Romulan manipulation). Whenever anyone attempts to bluff, Fast Talk, or lie to
him, he receives a free Courage Point to spend to counteract the attempt.

SPECIES FRIEND (+2 TO +5)

The character's past actions, family history, background, or other circumstances have made him known as a friend to a particular species. When
members of that species make Renown Tests (see page 106) to know who he
is, or he makes Charm or Persuasion Tests against such characters, an additional die is rolled. Regarding the Renown Tests, recognition is more likely to

be positive, even if the character's Aspects would normally indicate otherwise. A character may not have this advantage for his own species (or, if he has Mixed Species Heritage, for either of his species).

STRONG WILL (+2)

The character is more willful than most people. Whenever other characters attempt to influence him (for example, with Fast Talk, Intimidation, or Behavior Modification), he rolls one extra die to resist. Strong Will also offers protection against Telepathy—it allows the character to protect certain thoughts or memories from telepathic probing.

SYNERGY (+3)

The character works well in groups. He's skilled at distilling the best suggestions from his co-workers to develop the best plan of action, organizing and managing tasks in the most efficient manner, and working in conjunction with others. When participating in Combined Tests, he adds +2 per participant for additional successful Tests, rather than the standard +1 (see *Combined Tests* in the *Action* Chapter, page 105).

TACTICAL GENIUS (+3)

The character has an instinctive grasp of tactics in all its forms and applications. When making Planetary Tactics, Starship Tactics, Strategic Operations, or Administration (Logistics) Skill Tests, he rolls one extra die.

TELEPATHIC RESISTANCE (+4)

For some reason (physiological or mental), the character is immune to telepathy and empathy. Characters with telepathic abilities (such as Vulcans) may be wary (to say the least) of persons whose minds are closed to them (though they'll only become aware of this when they first attempt to enter the character's mind).

TOUGHNESS (+1)

The character is extremely touch, able to resist injuries better than most people. He has +1 Fitness only for purposes of withstanding damage (see *Effects of Injuries*, pages 116-117, for more information on taking damage). A character cannot have a negative Vitality edge if he takes this advantage. Toughness differs from High Pain Threshold (which indicates a character who suffers less effect from injuries) and Excellent Metabolism (which affects whether a character contracts diseases).

Lt. Volek takes the Toughness advantage—he's spent a rough-and-tumble life and has developed a hardy constitution. His Fitness is 2, but for the purposes of determining how many wounds he can take per Wound Level, he has Fitness 3.

WEAPON MASTER (+2 OR +4)

Thanks to advanced training or some natural aptitude, the character is an expert at the use of a single type of melee weapon (for example, a rapier or *lirpa*). For 2 Development Points, he receives a +1 to all Tests to hit targets in combat with that weapon; for 4 Development Points, he receives a +2 to all such Tests. Characters may buy Weapon Master multiple times for multiple weapons, but cannot buy it for ranged weapons.

ZERO-G TRAINING (+2)

The character has been trained to act in zero-gravity situations. Thanks to this training, he can ignore the standard +1 Difficulty penalty for all Tests performed in zero gravity. (Note that this Advantage is not the same thing as the Personal Equipment (Environmental Suit) skill.)

DISADVANTAGES

Disadvantages represent hindrances, problems, or restrictions that afflict the character from time to time (or, in some cases, at all times). They help you develop your character by giving him challenges and personal limitations to overcome. In game terms, they also provide extra Development Points to offset the hindrances they represent (the points provided by each one are listed after its title in parentheses as a "negative" number). These Development Points may be spent on any game element, not just advantages.

ARGUMENTATIVE (-1)

A characteristic disadvantage for debate-loving Tellarites (who regard it positively, not as a drawback), Argumentative signifies a character who can't resist the chance to argue or play "devil's advocate." Sometimes the character argues for the sake of arguing, even when he actually agrees with his opponent. Whenever an opportunity for argument or debate arises, he must spend

CODES OF HONOR

Value	Code
-2	Prime Directive: May not interfere in a planet's development
-2	Code of Honesty: Never lie; never break your word once given
-2	Code of Fairness: Never take advantage of someone weaker
-2	Hippocratic Oath: May not harm patients under my care; must treat all patients equally to the best of my ability; never harm anyone with poison or false medical treatment
-2	Pledge: Never break your word about a particular subject (player must define the exact nature of the pledge or vow; may be worth more or less than -2, at the Narrator's discretion)
-3	Vulcan Code: Never give in to emotion; solve problems logically; violence breeds emotion
-3	Defender: Must protect the weak and innocent
-4	Starfleet Code: Must uphold the ideals and policies of Starfleet, including the Prime Directive
-4	Klingon Code: Always avenge an insult; never show cowardice

a Courage Point to resist the temptation. If he does not, his behavior temporarily reduces his Presence for making some Tests (or, at the Narrator's option, he rolls one less die when making Tests to influence others).

ARROGANT (-1)

The character thinks that he, or some culture or group he belongs to, is superior to others. Because of this attitude, he rolls one less die for all Command, Fast Talk, Persuasion, and Charm Tests unless he spends a Courage Point to keep from acting gratingly superior.

BLOODLUST (-2)

This disadvantage, which most Klingons possess (though they don't consider it a hindrance), signifies a character who revels in violence, bloodshed, and causing pain. In combat, he becomes so consumed by this passion that he won't stop fighting until there's no on left to fight (he may even turn on his allies after his enemies are dead or defeated!). If he wants to stop before then, he must spend a Courage Point.

CHRONIC PAIN (-2)

Because of some medical condition, like an old war wound or sports

injury, the character suffers from extreme pain almost constantly. At least once every game session, the Narrator should require him to make a Presence Test (modified by the Willpower Edge); if he fails, the pain becomes so bad that, for the rest of the scene, he must roll one less die for all Fitness or Coordination Tests (determined by the Narrator).

CODE OF HONOR (-2 TO -5)

The character lives by a particular moral creed, set of ethical principles, code of honor, or similar rules of personal conduct. This code dictates many important actions, such as whether he can attack an opponent (and if so, how), whether he can surrender, how he acts towards women or certain other members of his species, or the like—and this often requires dangerous behavior on his part. A Code of Honor typically reflects the character's personal honor, not his devotion to duty, though in many cases the two are one and the same.

Violations of one's Code usually earn negative Renown Points (typically equal to the value of the disadvantage, though this varies depending on the circumstances, how many people witness the violation, and the like). Codes of Honor are particularly fun to roleplay when a character has two of them which conflict (such as a vow to take certain actions, but adherence to the Starfleet Code, which runs contrary to the vow).

DARK SECRET (-1 TO -3)

The character knows something, or once did something, which he must keep secret lest dire consequences result. Dark Secrets range from the embarrassing (adultery, committing petty vandalism as a child) to the blatantly illegal (covering up a murder). Because he, rightly or wrongly, feels that revelation of the secret would harm his career and/or personal life, the character will do almost anything to prevent others from learning his secret. If the secret is revealed, the character typically receives a significant amount of negative Renown Points (depending on the nature of the secret), and may also be ostracized, suffer criminal prosecution or other punishments, or the like.

DARK SECRET

Value	Secret
-1	Embarrassing ("You did *what* at the Academy?")
-2	Career-ruining ("You cheated on a test at the Academy?")
-3	Life-threatening ("You *killed* someone at the Academy?")

DEPENDENT (-2)

The character has someone who depends on him—a child, an aging parent, a helpless spouse, or someone similar. The character cannot simply abandon this person (at least not without earning a substantial number of negative Renown Points), and must make every effort to protect and provide for him or her. The player and Narrator should work together to develop this NPC's personality and background, perhaps even bringing him or her into the game on a semi-regular basis.

FANATIC (-2 TO -3)

The character is extremely devoted to some philosophical ideal—a religious creed, patriotism for a particular nation or political viewpoint, or even a person of great appeal (and the beliefs he espouses, of course). The character always defends this ideal, and will even sacrifice his life to preserve or support it. The value of the disadvantage depends on whether the ideal is uncommon, such as an obscure religious doctrine (-2), or common, such as a government or species (-3). If the character is suicidally dedicated to the cause, the –3 value automatically applies. Whenever making Skill Tests related to this ideal or its preservation, the character must spend at least one Courage Point (if he has one to spend at all).

For example, Dr. Sevrin and his followers were fanatically devoted to the idea of escaping a technological lifestyle and finding the planet Eden. They were willing to assault members of Starfleet and hijack a starship to accomplish that goal. Their Fanatic disadvantage is worth -3 points, since they commonly work on its behalf.

GREEDY (-1)

Money talks loudly to the character—whenever there's a profit to be made, he pursues it tenaciously, with every means at his command. If he wants to resist the siren song of wealth, he must spend a Courage Point (otherwise he must pursue the profit, and characters attempting to dissuade him roll one less die for any Tests to do so). Harry Mudd has this disadvantage.

HEDONIST (-1)

The character enjoys luxuries and pleasures of all sorts, from fine food and drink to more earthy delights. Whenever presented with an opportunity to enjoy himself, have fun or take pleasure in something, he must spend 1 Courage Point to resist temptation or indulge himself for at least 1d6 rounds. Tiburonians have this disadvantage, as does Harry Mudd.

HIDES EMOTIONS (-2)

This disadvantage is the stereotypical Vulcan disadvantage, though they don't regard it as such, but as a beneficial thing. The character never expresses his true feelings—he hides his passions behind a blank face or uncooperative attitude, and getting emotional responses out of him is quite difficult. Whenever he makes Tests with Presence skills involving emotion (such as Charm, Persuasion, Fast Talk, and most uses of Command), he rolls one less die.

HYPOCHONDRIA (-1)

The bane of ship's doctors everywhere, the character has a strong tendency to think that he's contracted some awful disease. He pores over medical texts, searching for symptoms which match the way he feels; uses filter masks and disinfectant to protect himself from germs (particularly on strange planets); and bothers the doctor with constant requests for obscure medical tests.

IMPULSIVE (-1)

The character has difficulty curbing his tendency to rush headlong into situations without thinking, planning, or preparing. Whenever confronted with some danger, crisis, or emergency, he must spend a Courage Point to prevent himself from giving in to his impulsiveness—running into battle, entering a radiation-filled chamber, or getting involved in a barfight with Klingon warriors, for example. Other characters roll one less die for Tests made to try to dissuade him from his rash actions.

INTOLERANT (-1 TO -3)

A particular group—from a clique aboard his starship, to an entire species or culture, offends the character in some way (not necessarily a logical one, either). He can't say anything nice about them, and has as little to do with them as possible; when actually interacting with them, he must spend a Courage Point to keep his dislike concealed.

The value of this disadvantage varies based on the scope of the prejudice (see accompanying table).

In the Federation, prejudice of this sort is rare; Starfleet does not tolerate it.

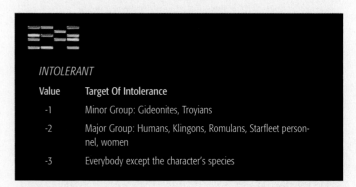

INTOLERANT

Value	Target Of Intolerance
-1	Minor Group: Gideonites, Troyians
-2	Major Group: Humans, Klingons, Romulans, Starfleet personnel, women
-3	Everybody except the character's species

LOW PAIN THRESHOLD (-2)

The character has less resistance to pain than most people. When he suffers a Skill Test modifier due to injury) (see *Effects of Injuries*, page 116), it increases by 1 (for example, if he's Stunned, he has a +2 penalty to Skill Tests, not the usual +1). Add this to the total penalty as a result of wounds; do not apply it per injury (a character who is Stunned and then Injured suffers a +3 penalty, not +4. Furthermore, when making Skill Tests to resist physical torture or pain, or heal wounds, he rolls one less die.

MEDICAL PROBLEM

Value	Extent of Condition
-1	The condition is minor; -1 penalty to one attribute (determined at the time of creation)
-3	The condition is serious; -2 penalty to one attribute

MEDICAL PROBLEM (-1 OR -3)

The character suffers from an ailment which requires daily medical attention to treat. The value of the disadvantage depends on the ailment's severity. In game terms, the ailment is represented by reductions in an attribute (chosen when the character purchases the disadvantage). For every day the character fails to take his medicine or treatment, he suffers the attribute reduction, and this reduction is cumulative. Once the attribute reaches zero, he lapses into a coma and will die in 2-12 hours without appropriate medical attention.

The player and Narrator should work together to develop the specifics of the problem (including which attribute it affects), the appropriate medicines and the ramifications of failing to take the medicine. Figuring out where and how the character got the Medical Problem will help to develop his background, and perhaps lead the player to take other disadvantages or advantages related to the situation.

Amanda elects to take Medical Problem as a disadvantage for her character, Lt. Benchley. She and the Narrator decide that Benchley suffers from a mild, chronic strain of Rigelian fever (-3). If Benchley fails to take ryetalyn every day, she suffers a -2 die penalty to her Fitness. Since Amanda's character is a Human, she could not suffer from a Medical Problem which would reduce her Psi; if she were playing a Vulcan character, she could take such a condition as a disadvantage.

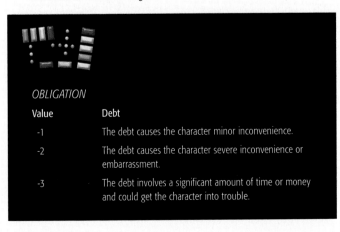

OBLIGATION

Value	Debt
-1	The debt causes the character minor inconvenience.
-2	The debt causes the character severe inconvenience or embarrassment.
-3	The debt involves a significant amount of time or money and could get the character into trouble.

23RD CENTURY MEDICAL CONDITIONS

By the 23rd century, many medical problems endemic in the 20th, such as cardiovascular disease, cancer, and many deadly viruses, have been eradicated by medical science. Medical Problems should involve new, alien conditions such as Rigelian fever, synthococcus novae, xenopolycythemia, and Vegan choriomeningitis.

A character cannot have a Medical Problem unless the disease or condition is incurable (though some conditions may be temporarily "curable" through technology; see *Medical Remedy*, page 87). If and when the Narrator allows a character to "buy off" his condition with Experience Points, the cure should be worked into the series storyline ("In order to make the medicine, first you have to go to Deneb VII for fresh *zalva* berries").

Medical conditions other than diseases or similar conditions are best represented by taking the *Physically Impaired* disadvantage instead of *Medical Problem*.

OBLIGATION (-1 TO -3)

The character owes a debt or similar type of obligation to someone. Since most Obligations involve a time limit, failure to repay the debt in a timely fashion may result in major difficulties for the character (and plenty of episode seeds for the Narrator). The value of the disadvantage depends upon the extravagance or severity of the Obligation; the player and Narrator should work together to come up with a good Obligation which adds drama to the series.

OBSESSIVE TENDENCIES (-1, -3)

Once a character with Obsessive Tendencies decides on a course of action, he focuses on that action completely, ignoring all other issues ("distractions") in his life. Whenever other characters (even his commanding officers) ask him to do something which doesn't further his goal in some way, the fact that he's distracted thinking about his goal means he rolls one less die when making Intellect and Presence Skill and Attribute Tests.

Typically, Obsessive Tendencies is worth –3 points, but at the Narrator's discretion, some characters may have lesser obsessions worth –1 point. The lesser version indicates a strong personality trait or tendency which the character has difficulty resisting (if appropriate, the Narrator may require a Presence Test, modified by Willpower). Examples include Captain Kirk's attraction to women or Ensign Chekov's tendency to attribute anything notable to the Russian people.

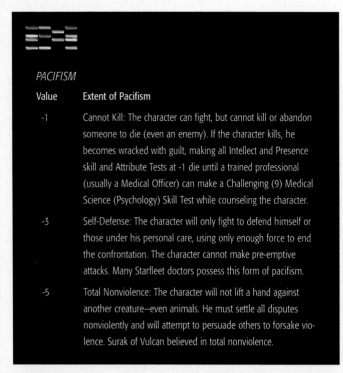

PACIFISM

Value	Extent of Pacifism
-1	Cannot Kill: The character can fight, but cannot kill or abandon someone to die (even an enemy). If the character kills, he becomes wracked with guilt, making all Intellect and Presence skill and Attribute Tests at -1 die until a trained professional (usually a Medical Officer) can make a Challenging (9) Medical Science (Psychology) Skill Test while counseling the character.
-3	Self-Defense: The character will only fight to defend himself or those under his personal care, using only enough force to end the confrontation. The character cannot make pre-emptive attacks. Many Starfleet doctors possess this form of pacifism.
-5	Total Nonviolence: The character will not lift a hand against another creature—even animals. He must settle all disputes nonviolently and will attempt to persuade others to forsake violence. Surak of Vulcan believed in total nonviolence.

PACIFISM (-1 TO -5)

Opposed to violence and bloodshed, and perhaps even willing to die himself rather than take the life of another, the character is a paragon of peace. The value of the disadvantage depends on just how strong his belief in nonviolence is (see accompanying table).

PHOBIA (-2 TO -5)

The character has a morbid fear of a specific item, creature or situation (such as claustrophobia [fear of enclosed spaces], agoraphobia [fear of open spaces], or nictophobia [fear of darkness]). Whenever he encounters that which he fears, he must spend a Courage Point. If he does not, he suffers a Skill Test penalty (the severity of which depends on the value of the disadvantage) until he gets away from the object of his fear or the situation somehow changes.

PHOBIA

Value	Extent of Phobia
-1	Minor phobia (+1 Difficulty to all Tests until situation changes)
-2	Challenging phobia (+3 Difficulty to all Tests until situation changes)
-3	Severe phobia (catatonia; the character freezes up)

The Phobia disadvantage is compounded by its frequency:

Value	Frequency
-1	A rare item or phenomenon (trees onboard a starship, mugatos)
-2	A common item or phenomenon (enclosed spaces, cats, stars)

PHYSICALLY IMPAIRED (-1 TO -3)

Similar in some ways to Medical Problem, this disadvantage means that the character possesses some sort of physical impairment (such as blindness, a missing limb, or paraplegia). The value of the disadvantage depends on the severity of the impairment (see accompanying table); you should determine what your character's handicap is, and how he got it, when he buys this disadvantage; figuring this out can tell you a lot about your character's background.

Thanks to 23rd century medical science, many conditions once considered incurable can be overcome with special medicines, treatments, and equipment (the Federation makes these remedies available to its citizens freely). If applicable and desired, you can take the Medical Remedy advantage for your character, thus compensating for the handicap (essentially, you must choose the impairment before you can choose the remedy). See *Medical Remedy* (page 87) for further information.

Of course, even if a character's impairment cannot be fixed immediately, he can eventually "purchase" a cure by spending Experience Points to "buy off" this disadvantage. This requires the Narrator's permission, and should be worked into the campaign's overall storyline, since it represents a major change in the character's life. Generally, this option should be reserved for non-Federation characters, or special cases.

PHYSICAL IMPAIRMENT

Value	Impairment
0	Missing finger
-1	Mute; paralyzed limb
-2	Missing limb; deaf; unable to function in Earth-normal gravity
-3	Blind; parapalegic

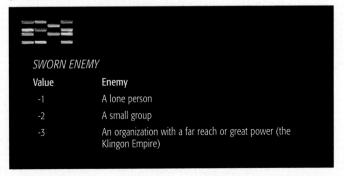

RIVAL	
Value	Rival
-1	Less powerful or influential than the character
-2	A peer (roughly)
-3	More powerful or influential than the character

POOR CHEMORECEPTION (-1)

The character's sense of smell functions poorly. He receives a -1 die penalty to all scent- or taste-based Search Tests.

POOR HEARING (-1)

The character's hearing is suboptimal. He receives a -1 die penalty to all hearing-based Search Tests.

POOR SIGHT (-2)

The character's eyesight is faulty. He receives a -1 die penalty to all sight-based Search Tests.

RIVAL (-1 TO -3)

The character and another character are rivals. They don't get along (at best, they treat each other with frigid courtesy), and want to outdo each other at every turn. It's a zero-sum game—if the rival wins at something, the character loses; there's no middle ground, tie, or room for compromise. Whenever the rival has the opportunity to "show up" the character (by, for example, ingratiating himself with superior officers at the character's expense, being particularly charming to the character's romantic interest, or playing a practical joke on the character), he'll take it. However, he doesn't wish to kill the character or cause him serious injury (that's the Sworn Enemy disadvantage).

The value of this disadvantage depends on how powerful the rival is in relation to the character (see table). At the Narrator's option, a relatively minor or trivial rivalry (such as that between Captain Kirk and his nemesis from his Academy days, Finnegan), or one restricted to a particular activity or subject (such as for the affections of a particular person, or a sports rivalry) is worth a flat -1 point

SLOW HEALING (-2)

The character heals more slowly than most people. It takes him twice as long to heal naturally, and he rolls one less die for all Tests to determine if he has naturally healed; furthermore, the Difficulty of all rolls to determine the effects of medical attention increases by 1. (See *Healing*, pages 117-118, for rules about recovering from injury.)

SPECIES ENEMY	
Value	Enemy
-1	Obscure or unimportant species (Elasians, Troyians)
-3	Lesser or distant species (Medusans, Gorns)
-4	Major or locally important species (Andorians, Tellarites)
-5	Widespread species (Humans, Klingons, Romulans, Vulcans)

SPECIES ENEMY (-1 TO -5)

Because of past events, family history, or some similar circumstance, the character has become known as the enemy of a particular species. Perhaps he cleverly destroyed one of that species' ships and cost them a great victory, or maybe he unforgivably embarrassed its ambassador at a diplomatic function. The value of Species Enemy depends upon the power and scope of the enemy species (see table).

Whenever members of the enemy species make Renown Tests (see page 106) regarding the character, they roll an additional die. Moreover, if they recognize him, it's likely to be in a negative light, even if his Aspects would normally indicate a positive response. Additionally, he rolls one less die when making any Tests with Fast Talk, Charm, Persuasion, or similar skills against the enemy species.

STUBBORN (-1)

Once the character makes up his mind about something, he doesn't change it, even if it becomes glaringly obvious that he's mistaken. Whenever anyone challenges his judgment or decisions, he cannot change them or agree with his challenger unless he spends a Courage Point. (This disadvantage does have one benefit: any Courage Points he spends to resist uses of Persuasion or Intimidation on him have double effect.)

SWORN ENEMY (-1 TO -3)

Somehow, some way, the character's made an enemy out of a person or group (the value of the disadvantage depends on the enemy's power and

SWORN ENEMY	
Value	Enemy
-1	A lone person
-2	A small group
-3	An organization with a far reach or great power (the Klingon Empire)

resources). That person or group wants to ruin him, take his property, hurt him, and eventually kill him. The enemy will expend a lot of time and resources just to make the character's life miserable and "get revenge" on him. The player and Narrator should determine who the enemy is, and why he hates the character so much; this should provide the Narrator with plenty of episode seeds.

VENGEFUL (-1 OR -2)

"Revenge is a dish best served cold." The character has taken this Klingon proverb to heart, and is determined to obtain revenge on a person, group or species which he feels has wronged him. Whenever he encounters the object(s) of his revenge, he must spend a Courage Point to prevent himself from attacking them or plotting against them (assuming he wants to prevent that). The more often the character encounters the object(s) of his revenge, the greater the value of the disadvantage (see accompanying table).

VENGEFUL

Value	Frequency
-1	Uncommon (a person; a remote species like the Gorn or Romulans)
-2	Common (Starfleet, Klingons, Vulcans)

WEAK WILL (-2)

Weak-willed and easily influenced, the character "breaks" quickly when interrogated, and can easily be forced or coerced (with, say, Fast Talk or Intimidation) into doing something he doesn't want to—he rolls one less die to resist such attempts. Furthermore, he's more susceptible to Telepathy than most people; he cannot hide his thoughts, memories, or feelings from even the lightest of mental probes (if he has the Mind Shield skill, he may not raise its level above 3).

WEAKNESS (-2)

Whereas a character with Weak Will has a weak personality, a character with Weakness is physically weak. He cannot have a positive Vitality edge, and has −1 Fitness solely for purposes of resisting damage (see *Effects of Injuries*, pages 116-117, for more information on taking damage).

Ensign Vyradi, a sickly but spunky Tiburonian, takes Weakness to reflect his frail nature. His Fitness is 2, but for purposes of determining how many wounds he can take per Wound Level, his Fitness is only a 1.

ZERO-G INTOLERANCE (-2)

Lack of gravity tends to make the character dizzy, even if he wears magnetic boots or similar gear. Whenever he's in a zero-gravity setting, he must make a Moderate (7) Coordination Test or immediately suffer from a -2 die penalty to all actions undertaken while in zero gravity.

Yes, that's certainly distracting, Diamond thought, as cymbals clattered, drums thundered, and horns bellowed like raucous elephants. The point was surely to provide a decided advantage to the home-team gladiators, who'd have been trained to focus in the midst of this din since they were old enough to pick up a trident. Alas, hand-to-hand combat instruction at Starfleet Academy omitted the pit band. Diamond clenched his jaw and doubled his concentration, as the helmeted warrior began to run towards him.

Diamond had graduated top of his class in unarmed combat, but he would be no match against a Zerebian gladiator bred for the arena. The trick was to out-think the man. Diamond subtly braced himself but stood still as if too frightened to budge. Confidence was etched in every movement of the warrior's powerful muscles. He'd be a superb model for a bronze sculpture, Diamond thought—if he weren't hellbent on separating my head from my shoulders.

Like a leaping cat, the gladiator sprang. Diamond dropped the pretense of terror and rolled toward him, interrupting his momentum and throwing him off-balance. Still, he managed to snag Diamond's tunic with one of the tines of

ACTION

his trident, leaving a big diagonal slash that ran from shoulder to waistline. Diamond looked down to see a red welt rising up on his pectoral muscles.

He feinted to the left, again clearly surprising the gladiator, who'd expected Diamond to capitalize on his advantage, and had braced himself for a rush. The gladiator paused as the music grew more clamorous and the screaming of the crowd increasingly shrill. He set his teeth together and came at Diamond again—more tentatively this time.

Diamond scooped downwards as if to grab a handful of sand and toss it in his opponent's face. The gladiator smiled, as if at an old trick, and charged. But Diamond did not go down for the sand, as the gladiator expected. Instead he dropped his cumbersome broadsword and clunked the warrior full on the chin with a good, honest Federation uppercut. The gladiator shook this off. He did not shake off the subsequent shot to the kidneys. He fell to one knee, and Diamond completed the task with a two-handed swinging smash to the temple.

Diamond studied the gladiator, laid out in the dirt like a rag doll, as the crowd shrieked for the kill. He would deprive them of the pleasure.

The numbers on your character sheet don't just help you conceptualize your character—they provide a means for him to interact with the rest of the *Star Trek* universe, using the rules in this chapter. They'll show you how he solves problems, fights (and hopefully defeats) other characters, and completes the nuts-and-bolts duties that are a part of his missions. The chapter has three sections: Time (the timeframes within which action occurs in the game); Tests (using your Skills to accomplish things); and Combat (rules for fighting).

Time

Actions during an episode or series—from plotting a course to encountering tribesman on a savage planet—occur within discrete periods of time. The *Star Trek Roleplaying Game* uses five abstract divisions to measure the passage of game time.

ROUND

A *round* is the smallest time increment used in the *Star Trek Roleplaying Game*. Rounds usually last five seconds and represent the time it takes to complete a single action (such as making an attack, dodging an attack, or performing certain skills) or group of actions (making several attacks or attacking and dodging).

SCENE

Scenes are the smallest episodic increments used in the game, and are usually confined to a single setting or location. As the name indicates, they're similar to scenes on a television show or film; they blend roleplaying and action together. Action-oriented scenes often last only a few rounds, while narrative-oriented scenes (such as a description of things which happen on a journey between starbases) can last for hours or days of game time.

EPISODE

A series of scenes forms an *episode*. In the *Star Trek Roleplaying Game*, each episode typically involves one or more discrete plots or subplots which

may stand on their own, or may bear some relationship to an ongoing story arc or the overall story told by the series as a whole. Episodes normally include some sort of temporary closure, and often resolve one or more subplots or minor plotlines, and can usually be played out in a single game session.

SERIES

A group of episodes (sometimes closely interconnected or related, sometimes simply featuring the same characters and ship) forms a *series*. Series often feature recurring NPCs and events, as well as an ongoing, larger story arc which links component episodes together (for example, a series might depict an ongoing conflict with the Romulans in a particular sector, with each episode focusing on a specific battle or competition for resources against the Romulans).

DOWNTIME

The best way to think of *downtime* is as "time between"—time between scenes, between episodes, or between series. It's their "off screen" time when they work on their hobbies, train themselves in new skills, get together for parties, and so on. Much of a character's ongoing development occurs during this "time between episodes."

Tests

Star Trek Roleplaying Game stories usually feature a generous dose of action and excitement. The rules describe any task your character attempts—phasering an attacking Klingon, persuading a recalcitrant ruler of the Federation's peaceful intent, or repairing the transporters in the nick of time—in terms of an *Action*. Players must declare specific actions for their characters—what the characters are doing, in other words—in combat or any other situation where the Narrator feels that the need for precise timing or other circumstances warrant it. For more information on actions and how to use them, see *Actions*, page 108.

DIFFICULTY TABLE

Difficulty Number	Description
0	Automatic action—no roll required.
3, **4**, 5	Routine
6, **7**, 8	Moderate
9, **10**, 11	Challenging
12, **13**, 14	Difficult
15+	Nearly Impossible

In many instances, part of the excitement of a scene exists because the outcome is uncertain—will the phaser shot hit the Klingon? Will the lovely alien captor fall for your character's charms? In such situations, the player must make a *Test* to determine whether his character succeeds. Some Tests use attributes alone, but most involve a skill (a *Skill Test*) in addition to an attribute. Whenever it will make the scene more exciting, the Narrator should use Skill Tests to resolve actions.

Most Tests require the character to roll a number of dice equal to the appropriate Attribute, and add the highest die to his skill level. The player compares the total—the *Test Result*—to a *Difficulty Number* set by the Narrator. If the Test Result equals or exceeds the Difficulty Number, the Test succeeds. If the Test Result is less than the Difficulty, the attempt fails. See *Making a Test*, on page 101 below, for more details.

DIFFICULTY

When you go looking for adventure among the stars, you're likely to run into some tricky situations requiring heroic efforts. Of course, some tasks are inherently more difficult than others. The *Star Trek Roleplaying Game* rules reflect this by assigning every task a *Difficulty Number*. The higher the Difficulty Number, the harder the task, and the better your character will have to be to succeed at it. The accompanying table shows the various Difficulty Numbers.

The Icon System organizes possible Difficulty Numbers into categories, such as Routine or Challenging. The Narrator can use these categories as general descriptions when explaining to the players how hard a particular action is. Each category represents a range of numbers, to provide the Narrator with some flexibility when determining the Difficulty for a particular action. For example, a *Challenging* task could have a Difficulty Number of 9, 10, or 11. The typical Difficulty Number for each category is indicated in boldface.

Of course, sometimes various factors make a task easier or harder. It's more difficult to repair a warp engine with 20th-century tools than with modern ones, for example. The Icon System represents such circumstances, called *modifiers*, in two ways. Normally, a Difficulty modifier appears as a simple positive or negative adjustment, which means the actual Difficulty *number* is affected (a +2 modifier increases a Difficulty 4 action to a Difficulty 6 action; a -1 modifier changes a Difficulty 8 action to a Difficulty 7 action). In some cases, modifiers affect an entire Difficulty *category*. Raising the Difficulty by one category would cause a Moderate action to become a Challenging action (the Narrator should still set the exact Difficulty Number).

WHAT DOES DIFFICULTY MEAN?

The Narrator assigns a Difficulty Number whenever a character attempts an action which is not opposed by another character (such as playing a complex melody on the Vulcan lute). (For Tests opposed by another character, see *Opposed Tests*, page 104 below.) Pick a number from within the ranges given, using the category descriptions as a guideline. For example, if a Test is fairly easy, it might be a Routine Test with a Difficulty Number of 3, 4, or 5; a

Moderate action has a 6, 7, or 8 Difficulty. After you get a feel for the game, assigning Difficulty will become second nature. Generally, the minimum Difficulty Number is always 2, regardless of the modifiers applied.

A one-point difference in Difficulty can make a big difference in a tense situation. Since the actual Difficulty Numbers are slightly flexible within each category, the Narrator should know the skill and attribute levels of the Crew members in his game, and set Difficulties they will find appropriately challenging, but not impossible. Unless the player rolls a 6 on his Drama Die (see below), the best result a character can get in a Test is a 6, so the highest roll he can possibly make in most circumstances equals 6 plus his Skill level. Keep this in mind when determining Difficulty Numbers; a character with a skill level of 3 cannot succeed with a Difficulty 10 task unless he gets a 6 on his Drama Die, has some bonus to his Test Result or spends Courage Points. Even if the Drama Die is a 6, the best result a character can obtain on a single roll equals 12 plus his Skill level. In other words, don't say a job is Difficult unless it's *really* Difficult!

Use the following guidelines when assigning Difficulties:

Routine

These tasks are easy; even inexperienced characters can perform them successfully most of the time. Examples include making a standard sensor scan or creating a simple computer program.

Moderate

These tasks require some skill to complete successfully. An average character has a decent chance of failure; an above-average one will usually succeed. Examples include creating a complicated computer program, making a sensor scan for something that is difficult to find, or making routine repairs or adjustments to the warp engines.

Challenging

These tasks are complicated, and often require considerable skill. Average characters will only occasionally succeed at these tasks, and even above-average ones may have some difficulty. Examples include reconfiguring the warp engines under standard conditions or performing a toxicological analysis on a corpse of an unknown humanoid species.

Difficult

These tasks are very hard. Average characters will almost never succeed, and skilled professionals stand a good chance of failure. Examples include bluffing three Romulan ships out of position, or working out a reliable method of cross-universe travel from one data point.

Nearly Impossible

Need we say more? Even legendary characters need a bit of luck to succeed at Nearly Impossible tasks, which often represent not just the difficulty of the job, but the extreme pressure facing the character to complete it quickly and well. Examples include cold-starting the warp engines with uncalibrated dilithium crystals in two minutes, or constructing a time-viewer with twenty dollars' worth of 1930s technology and a ruined tricorder.

WHAT SHOULD I TELL THE PLAYER?

As Narrator, you don't have to tell a player the exact Difficulty Number (or category) you've assigned to a Test. In fact, sometimes keeping the Difficulty a secret heightens the tension during crucial scenes, making the game more fun for everyone. Simply describing tasks as "Routine," "Moderate," "Challenging," and so on gives a player a rough idea of the task's Difficulty without telling him a specific number (which also gives you the opportunity to "fudge" a point or two if necessary). For less critical scenes, of course, you can tell the player the specific Difficulty Number if you want.

DETERMINE THE APPROPRIATE SKILL

In addition to a Difficulty Number, you need to determine which skill governs the action being attempted to obtain a Test Result. For example, if Lt.

OPTIONAL RULE: USING DIFFERENT ATTRIBUTES WITH THE SAME SKILL

Starfleet trains its officers to be ready for anything. That means they need to know a little bit about everything, and be prepared to use their knowledge in unusual or tense situations. To simulate this, sometimes you can use skills with attributes other than those listed under the skills' descriptions. For example, although the Energy Weapon (Phaser) skill relates to Coordination, in the midst of a heated firefight the Narrator might allow a character to use his Intellect in conjunction with his Energy Weapon (Phaser) skill to try to fix a weapon malfunction.

While using a nonstandard attribute with a skill often creates dramatic game effects, it can also lead to rules abuse. Use your best judgment with this rule, and make sure the players justify the variations they request by roleplaying them.

Tyshon, a Starfleet security officer, attempts to shoot a Klingon with a phaser, he would use his Energy Weapon (Phaser) Skill. If Lt. Fitch, a navigation officer, tries to plot a course to Eminiar VII, a Shipboard Systems (Navigation) Test is in order.

Each skill in the game is linked to a particular attribute (for example, Energy Weapon is linked to Coordination, while Shipboard Systems is linked to Intellect). The attribute is important, since it tells you how many dice to roll. (See *Skills*, pages 64-67.)

MAKING A TEST

To make a Test, roll a number of six-sided dice equal to the governing attribute. One of the dice, called a *Drama Die*, should be a different color from the others. If the Drama Die rolls a 6, the character has probably achieved a spectacular success; if it rolls a 1, he may have suffered a noteworthy failure (see below, page 102).

If the Drama Die rolls any other number, it works just like a normal die. The player picks the highest die of all the dice (Drama Die included) and adds that number to the character's Skill level. This total *Test Result* is then compared to the Difficulty Number.

THE DRAMA DIE

As described above, if the Drama Die rolls a 6 or a 1, the result may be more spectacular than normal. If the Drama Die rolls a 6, the character adds both the Drama Die and the next highest die to his skill when determining his Test Result. Since this means the character's Test Result is fairly high (perhaps very high), it usually indicates a great success (especially if the optional "Degree of Success" system is used: see sidebar).

If the player rolls a 1 on the Drama Die, the character may have grievously failed. If all other dice also rolled 1s, then a Dramatic Failure definitely has occurred.

> Lieutenant Garvey scans space around the Theta VII asteroid belt, looking for Klingon ships hiding among the asteroids. The Narrator assigns this fairly specific and involved scan a Difficulty of Moderate (7). Lieutenant Garvey has Shipboard Systems (Sensors) 2 (3) and Intellect 3. Garvey's player rolls her three Attribute dice (one of which, the Drama Die, is a different color), getting a 3, a 5, and another 6 on her Drama Die. Since Garvey got a 6 on her Drama Die, she can add not only that 6, but the next highest die (the 5) to her skill. That gives her a final result of (6+5+3) 14. Since 14 is 6 or more greater than the Difficulty Number of 6, she has achieved a Dramatic Success (see below). The Narrator tells her that her scan was successful, and that she detects two Klingon ships hiding behind a large asteroid 5,000 kilometers away—and that they are powering up their disruptors.

If a character only rolls one die for a Test, that die is automatically the Drama Die. If it rolls a 6, the character may reroll it once, and once only, and add the two rolls to his skill. If it rolls a 1, a Dramatic Failure has occurred. In other words, less skilled characters are more prone to extreme failures, and less prone to achieve great success.

To speed game play and allow the Crew members truly to shine as heroes, the Narrator may wish to not apply the Drama Die rule to most opponents they face. Only the wiliest, strongest, and most skilled foes (such as the captain of a Romulan bird of prey) should use the Drama Die rule; ordinary enemies, such as typical Klingon crewmen, do not get that chance for extreme success.

SUCCESS AND DRAMATIC SUCCESS

If the Test Result equals the Difficulty Number, the character has achieved a *marginal success*—he's succeeded, but just barely, and some minor complication may have arisen. The exact effects of a marginal success depend on the situation, the character, the nature of the Test, and the Narrator's needs and desires; in some cases the Narrator may require additional Tests. For example, a character trying to restore power to the transporters in an emergency manages to fix the problem—but in doing so drains power from the life support systems. It's probably time for another Test....

If the Test Result exceeds the Difficulty Number, the character has succeeded. If the Narrator uses the optional "Degree of Success" system (see sidebar), he can tell you just how well your character succeeded. If Test Result exceeds the Difficulty Number by 6 or more, this always indicates a *Dramatic Success* (see pg. 102).

FAILURE AND DRAMATIC FAILURE

If the total rolled is less than the Difficulty Number, the character has failed. Sometimes this means immediate disaster; other times he may have the chance to make further Tests to salvage the situation. If the Test Result fails to meet the Difficulty Number by 6 or more, or if all dice roll 1s, the character experiences a *Dramatic Failure* (see chart). Dramatic Failures tend to complicate matters, and should always relate directly to the task being attempted. Their effects range from simply embarrassing the character, to putting him in grave danger, exposing him to injury or harm, to a result precisely the reverse of that intended. The Narrator may require (or allow) the failed character to make one or more additional Tests to control or mitigate this new crisis.

IMPROVING YOUR ROLL

There are many ways for players to improve their characters' chances of success. Two of the most common are edges and Courage Points.

EDGES

Edges modify certain Skill Tests—positive edges provide one extra die to roll per point; negative edges subtract one die per point. Thus, a +2 Logic edge allows you to roll two extra dice in applicable situations.

DEGREE OF SUCCESS

The more a Test Result exceeds the assigned Difficulty Number, the better the character performed the task, and the greater the degree of success he enjoys. Exceeding the Difficulty by 1 indicates success; exceeding it by 4 or 5 represents a spectacular result. A Test Result that exceeds the Difficulty Number by 6 or more indicates a *Dramatic Success*, with especially beneficial results (see *Dramatic Success*, page 102). The Dramatic Success rule applies to Opposed Tests, but the Test Result must exceed the opposing Test Result by 6 or more.

Of course, your characters may encounter an infinite variety of situations during their series, so it's not possible to define "degrees of success" specifically or thoroughly—it's up to the Narrator to enhance the game with creative, appropriate descriptions of events. Players like to hear how well their characters have performed, so ham it up! After all, a good *Star Trek Roleplaying Game* session should capture the cinematic "feel" and tension of the shows.

Lt. Garvey uses her Starship Tactics (Klingon) Skill to figure out the best way of approaching the two Klingon ships so that her ship can surprise them. The Narrator declares this a Moderate task (Difficulty 6). Garvey has Starship Tactics (Klingon) 1 (2) and Intellect 2. Her player rolls two attribute dice; the highest result is a 6. Added to Garvey's Skill of 2, that gives her a result of 8 (2 more than she needed to succeed). The Narrator rules that, because she has succeeded by more than 1, she has plotted an approach vector that will surprise the Klingons.

The ship maneuvers into place, alerting the Klingons to its presence as Lt. Garvey planned, but the asteroids block their first shots, giving Garvey the chance to fire! Based on range, hitting the first Klingon ship is a Routine task (Difficulty 4). Garvey has Intellect 2 and Shipboard Systems (Weapon Systems) 3 (3). Fortunately, both of her dice come up 6, giving her a Dramatic Success with a total of 15. The Narrator rules that Garvey's shot hits a weak point in the Klingon ship's shields, penetrating them and blowing a gaping hole in the skulking enemy's engines.

Using each edge's description, and the guidelines presented in the skill descriptions, the Narrator decides whether an edge applies to a particular Test. Use edges whenever possible, but remember that they don't always apply. Not every Intellect-based Test relates to Logic, for example.

Lt. Garvey tries to spot a dangerous predatory cat hiding somewhere in the nearby brush. The Narrator rules that she may make an Intellect Test to spot the cat among the dense foliage, and allows her to add her Perception Edge because she is trying to perceive something. Since she has Perception +1, she gets to roll three dice, not two, for her Intellect Test. On the other hand, when she made that Strategic Operations Test to approach the Klingons in a tactically advantageous manner, she was not really trying to perceive anything out of the ordinary, so the Narrator did not allow Lt. Garvey to apply her Perception Edge to her previous roll.

DRAMATIC SUCCESS

Dramatic Successes occur when a player's roll is six or more above the Difficulty Number. In game terms, this means the attempted action succeeded beyond the player's expectations.

In combat, a Dramatic Success usually indicates that the character hit the target so accurately or so well that he does extra damage (or achieved some other important effect, like breaking an opponent's weapon). As a guideline, the Narrator should consider adding one to two dice to the damage rolled, or creating other useful results. For example:

– Lt. Boyle's shot destroys the weapon in a Romulan centurion's hand.
– Lieutenant Commander Lerok's attack makes the Klingon he's fighting drop his sword.
– The Captain's punch is a lucky shot, rendering the Orion attacking him completely unconscious.
– Lt. Benchley dodges far enough past the Mirakian ape that he gets a clear attack at his foe's furry back.

Dramatic Successes in noncombat situations offer an even broader range of possible results. Here are some samples for the Narrator to use "as-is" or as guidelines for developing other ones. As a good rule of thumb, a Dramatic Success can increase or decrease the Difficulty Number for a related task by 3.

– Dr. Murchison's tricorder determines the exact number, position, and armaments of the Klingons who are planning to ambush him.
– Lieutenant Commander Hertz places her spacecraft in a prime position to avoid sensor detection (there is a +3 Difficulty to any attempt to locate her with sensors).
– Ensign Genchok flirts with Nurse Purvis in the hopes of asking her out on a date, and tells a joke which she finds particularly amusing.
– Chief Engineer O'Toole discovers a technique that will make the emergency repairs more feasible.
– Lieutenant Commander Feldman's hobby just happens to relate to the obscure subject at hand, providing a possible solution to the problem.
– Ensign Ta'thir suddenly has strong a feeling of being watched.
– A character manages to perform a physical feat with particular grace, style, or flamboyance (reducing the Difficulty of any related Charm Tests against anyone who witnessed the feat by -3).
– A character locates a clue, object or item that is particularly useful in the long term.

COURAGE POINTS

Characters can also improve Test Results by spending Courage Points. A player can spend up to 4 Courage Points to improve a single Test Result, with each point adding 1 to the Test Result. This is a good way to turn defeat into victory, failure into triumph, salvage a Dramatic Failure by making it an ordinary failure, or make an ordinary success Dramatic. However, characters

DRAMATIC FAILURE

A Dramatic Failure occurs when a character's roll is six (or more) less than the Difficulty Number—for example, rolling a 4 or less when the Difficulty Number is 10—or when all dice rolled come up 1. The following list provides some suggested descriptions for the effects of a Dramatic Failure; the Narrator can use them "as-is" or as guidelines for creating other effects. As a general guideline, a Dramatic Failure can increase or decrease related Difficulty Numbers by up to 3 points.

– Ensign Genchok has an attack of sneezing or coughing which renders his attempt to charm the lovely Nurse Purvis utterly unsuccessful, despite the clever joke he just told.
– In a highly ambitious attempt to speak an unfamiliar language, Lt. Venak inadvertently says something insulting or humiliating.
– An engineer's failure to recalibrate a system properly causes a deafening explosion, adding +3 to the Difficulty of any of his Search or Intellect rolls based on hearing for several minutes.
– Lt. Tibault's phaser malfunctions severely, requiring several minutes or hours to repair.
– Chief Engineer O'Toole suddenly has a "mental block" and cannot remember something critically important for the next several minutes.
– Ensign Ta'thir accidentally spills a drink on himself, causing extreme embarrassment during a Charm attempt.
– Lieutenant Commander Lerok mistakes the sound of an approaching harmless animal for an enemy.
– Some kind of local interference—primitive radio signals, metal walls, or the like—blocks Dr. Murchison's tricorder until it is recalibrated.
– An animal suddenly cries out at Lt. Boyle's presence, ruining any chances for a stealthy approach.
– The wall Lt. Commander Hammerstein is climbing gives way, sending him falling to the ground.
– Ensign Huntley's foot becomes entrapped by roots, requiring a difficult—and noisy—extraction.
– Local food has caused Lt. Tureth to suffer some kind of allergic reaction—nausea, blurred vision, and other detrimental (but not life-threatening) ill effects—causing her to suffer a +3 Difficulty on all Skill Tests she makes until she is better.

should only spend Courage Points on crucial Tests, those which might lead to catastrophic (or anticlimactic, or worse yet, *boring*) results–the failure of the mission (or an important part of it), the death of the character, or making a valiant and heroic character look inappropriately foolish, for example. A character can decide whether to add Courage Points after he rolls and gets a Test Result he doesn't like; he doesn't have to make the allocation in advance. A character cannot spend more than 4 Courage Points in a single round.

Those Klingons have somehow managed to evade Lt. Garvey's ship in the asteroid belt. If she loses them completely, the mission will be over. She makes a Shipboard Systems (Sensors) Test to locate them; the Narrator rules that the Difficulty is Moderate (8). Her Intellect is 3; unfortunately, her best die roll is a 4. When added to her Shipboard Systems (Sensors) 3 (3), that only gives her a 7. Unwilling to let her quarry get away, she spends a Courage Point to add +1 to her roll, bringing it up to a 8–and success!

GETTING COURAGE POINTS BACK

Courage Points are particularly important for less-experienced characters. However, it's very easy to deplete a character's Courage Points, and his Courage Points normally do not "refresh" until the end of the game session. Characters can regain Courage Points during an episode in several ways, but they cannot exceed their original Courage Point total. Characters can raise their overall Courage Point total by spending Experience Points (see *Rewards,* pages 123-124).

There are three ways for characters to replenish their Courage Pool more quickly:

Dramatically Appropriate Actions

If a character spends Courage Points to accomplish dramatically appropriate feats, the Narrator can elect to reward him by replenishing his Courage Points at the end of the scene. For example, a Starfleet security officer who spends Courage Points at a critical moment to unmask a disguised spy, slip into Klingon military headquarters without being detected, or to disarm a deadly bomb in the force dome moves the plot of the adventure forward, and thus may earn back any Courage Points he spent accomplishing those feats. The more impressive or difficult the task he accomplishes, the more Courage Points he should regain. Use the following as guidelines for recovering Courage Points:

Effective Roleplaying

Players who consistently portray their characters' motivations, personalities, and behavior well should be rewarded and encouraged, and one of the best ways to do this is for the Narrator to give them back Courage Points more quickly than normal. For example, a security officer should recover any Courage Points he spends to accomplish important Energy Weapon, Security, or Shipboard Systems Tests if his player roleplays them well. The rewards should equal the number of Courage Points spent on the roll(s).

Heroic Sacrifice

If a character willingly sacrifices of himself—exposing himself to death, injury, or loss to protect or help his comrades or to further the group's overall mission—he should be rewarded for his valiant efforts with a more rapid recovery of spent Courage Points (and maybe even receive an extra Courage Point or two instead of raw Experience Points; see *Rewards*, pages 123-124).

ATTRIBUTE TESTS

Although skill is paramount in the *Star Trek Roleplaying Game*, sometimes characters have to make Tests based on natural ability alone–*Attribute Tests*. In such cases, simply roll the attribute dice (modified by an applicable edges) normally to obtain the Test Result–you don't add anything from a skill level. The highest die still gives you the Test Result, and Drama Die rules still apply.

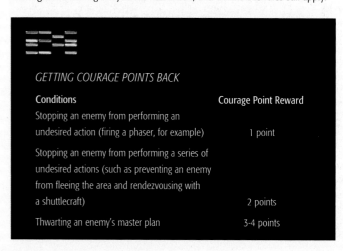

STAR TREK Roleplaying Game

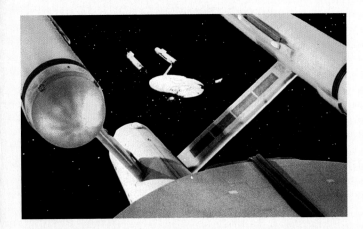

Attribute Tests should be used fairly rarely, since the characters' skill is a crucial element of the *Star Trek Roleplaying Game*. The Narrator should call for Skill Tests to resolve actions whenever possible.

OPPOSED TESTS

When one character directly opposes another character, both characters make appropriate Skill (or Attribute) Tests, and the character with the highest Test Result wins. If the Test Results tie, the character who rolled higher on his Drama Die wins. If the Drama Die rolls also tie, the character who initiated the Test wins. This is referred to as an *Opposed Test*.

Determine the degree of success in an Opposed Test based on the difference between the two Test Results. If the margin is six or more, the winner has achieved a Dramatic Success. However, Dramatic Failure rules don't usually

OPPOSED TEST MODIFIERS

Situation	Modifier
Small Advantage (sun in opponent's eyes)	+1 to Test Result
Moderate Advantage (opponent has very bad footing)	+2 to TR
Significant Advantage (opponent has suffered significant relevant injury)	+3 to TR
Dominating Advantage (opponent is blinded and badly injured)	+4 to TR
Small Disadvantage (a loud noise momentarily distracts character)	-1 to TR
Moderate Disadvantage (character is in poor position to face his opponent, significantly below opponent, on fluctuating terrain, and so forth)	-2 to TR
Significant Disadvantage (character is caught completely off guard; opponent is cheating or possesses important information which character does not, and so forth)	-3 to TR
Dominating Disadvantage (character has suffered a major injury)	-4 to TR

apply during an Opposed Test—just because one character achieved a Dramatic Success doesn't mean the other automatically suffers a Dramatic Failure.

Opposed Tests are common, but they're not *always* appropriate. The Narrator decides when to call for one. Examples of Opposed Tests include:

- *Nurse Purvis uses her own Charm skill to resist Ensign Genchok's romantic overtures (i.e., his attempt to use Charm on her), since they wouldn't make a good couple—his blue skin tone clashes with her uniform.*

- *Lt. Tyshon needs to sneak into a mining facility on Argos VIII to find out if Orion smugglers are hiding inside. He attempts to do so using his Stealth skill, but will be opposed by the guards with their Search skills.*

- *Ambassador Felkis, while at a diplomatic conference on the ship, tries to convince Chief Engineer O'Toole to let him into Main Engineering. He pits his Fast Talk skill against the plain-spoken engineer's Intellect.*

Sometimes a particular situation or environment affects an Opposed Test. If one character is in an advantageous (or disadvantageous) situation, the Narrator can give the player additional (or fewer) dice to roll while making his Test. Note that these modifiers do not reflect superior skill; rather, they represent outside factors or unusual circumstances.

EXTENDED TESTS

Characters can resolve most actions quickly, in just a second or three—the Test Result tells them whether they succeed or fail, and that's the end of it. Did your phaser shot hit the Klingon? Do you spot the hidden panel in the captain's wardroom? One Test attempt and it's over.

But not all situations are so quick and simple. The Icon System uses *Extended Tests* to resolve actions which take a long time or consist of several distinct parts. They typically last for several rounds, but may last several scenes or longer.

Extended Tests are divided into *Turns*. Before a character begins one, the Narrator sets a Difficulty and a Turn length (anything from a round, to a minute, to a day or more, depending on the action being attempted). The player rolls once each Turn and adds his Test Results together. At the end of the Turn sequence, he compares his total cumulative Test Result to a required Test Result established by the Narrator. When he equals or exceeds this cumulative number, his character succeeds at the task. Normal or Dramatic Failures may set him back a Turn or force him to start over (at the Narrator's discretion).

Narrators can also break large, difficult, involved tasks into two or more "pieces" and allow a character to work on each piece as a step in an Extended Test. The character must successfully complete each piece of the larger task in order to succeed at the whole. This is a good way for a character to tackle a task which, because of his low level of skill (or the reality of only being able to roll, at best, a 6 on the dice), he could not otherwise succeed at with a straightforward Test attempt.

Chief Engineer O'Toole needs to repair the extensive damage caused to Engineering by a Klingon attack, and fast. Five subsystems have been damaged, and he must repair each one before he can bring main power back on line. The Narrator makes this an Extended Test, with each Turn representing three minutes of time. The Narrator sets the Difficulty Number at 10, and rules that O'Toole must achieve a total of 45 on his cumulative rolls to get the repairs done properly before the next attack.

O'Toole's first three rolls are successes—10, 12, and 10. However, his fourth roll, a 6, indicates failure and a brief setback. Unfortunately, he has run out of time. The Narrator rules that because of this failure, O'Toole cannot succeed at his task before the Klingons attack again, but may resume work after their next attack, keeping the 32 points already rolled to indicate his progress. If the Klingons cause further damage to Engineering, the Narrator may increase the total that O'Toole must achieve to effect repairs.

Alternately, the Narrator could decide that each subsystem represents a "piece" of the larger whole, and break up the Extended Test that way. While trying to quickly fix all the systems at once might be a Nearly Impossible task—at which O'Toole could not possibly succeed unless he rolled a 6 on his Drama Die and on another die—the Narrator rules that taken individually each repair becomes a Challenging (9) Test. O'Toole will have to make each Test separately and in succession, with each attempt taking one Turn.

Extended Tests don't normally subject characters to a precise time requirement (although your character may be working against the clock—for example, the Narrator might tell you the phaser banks will explode in 5 minutes unless you can prevent it). Instead, the Turn length tells you how long an attempt takes; the faster you reach your cumulative Test Result, the quicker you complete the task. A Dramatic Success or two can accelerate an Extended Test considerably.

COMBINED TESTS

Sometimes several characters work together to accomplish an Extended Test or some particularly difficult or time-consuming task. The Icon System calls this a *Combined Test*. In a Combined Test, each character involved makes a Test with the same skill or attribute. The best Test Result becomes the base result, with each additional successful Test adding 1 to that result (Dramatic Successes add 2). Failures do not add to the total, but Dramatic Failures cause setbacks that may lead to subtractions from the roll or require the group to start again from the beginning.

Five Crew members are trying to build a shelter on an arctic planet, a task which the Narrator rules will take four hours. Each Crew member is using his Material Engineering (Civil) Skill. The Narrator rules that building the shelter is a Moderate (8) task. The Crew members roll, getting results of 14, 12, 12, 7, and 5. This gives them a Combined Test total of 16 (14+1+1; the two failures do not subtract from this total). Since this is 6 more than the Difficulty,

they have achieved a Dramatic Success! The Narrator rules that this Dramatic Success means the work only takes 75% as long as anticipated, so the shelter is completed in plenty of time to protect them from the icy wrath of an incoming storm.

If the last Crew member's roll had resulted in a 1 (a Dramatic Failure), the Narrator might have ruled, for example, that he accidentally caused a minor catastrophe, so finishing the job would now require six hours instead of four.

UNTRAINED SKILL USE

Characters usually stick to the skills they're trained in, but sometimes circumstances force them to make Tests with skills they haven't been formally taught. The Icon System refers to this as *untrained skill use*. Characters cannot use the skills in the *Characters* chapter (page 63) marked with this icon (▶) untrained (in short, if a character doesn't have at least 1 level in the Skill, he can't try to use it at all); all other skills can be used untrained, albeit poorly.

When a character tries to use a skill untrained, he makes an Attribute Test based on the Attribute which governs the skill. For example, if he wants to use Charm untrained, he would make a Presence Test. If he needed to fire a disruptor, but never learned the Energy Weapons skill, he could fire the weapon with a Coordination Test. Drama Die rules apply to untrained Skill Tests.

Commissioner Stelos knows little about medicine. Unfortunately, a Klingon attack cripples his ship's engine, and all of the engineers are injured. The only way to get the engines fixed is to patch up one of the engineers well enough for him to make repairs. Stelos tries an untrained First Aid Test. His Intellect is 4; therefore, he may roll four dice when trying to heal the injured engineer.

TEST MODIFIERS

PREPARATION

Many tasks are easier to perform if the character takes a little time to prepare before getting started. To reflect this, a character may receive an

ACTION

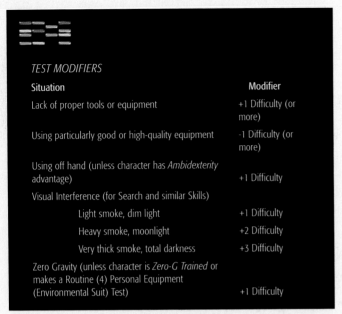

TEST MODIFIERS

Situation	Modifier
Lack of proper tools or equipment	+1 Difficulty (or more)
Using particularly good or high-quality equipment	-1 Difficulty (or more)
Using off hand (unless character has *Ambidexterity* advantage)	+1 Difficulty
Visual Interference (for Search and similar Skills)	
Light smoke, dim light	+1 Difficulty
Heavy smoke, moonlight	+2 Difficulty
Very thick smoke, total darkness	+3 Difficulty
Zero Gravity (unless character is *Zero-G Trained* or makes a Routine (4) Personal Equipment (Environmental Suit) Test)	+1 Difficulty

additional die or a +1 Test Result bonus to Test attempts when he spends time preparing. The amount of time needed to prepare varies, depending on the task. Of course, some actions, such as picking a pocket, may not benefit from preparation; others, like repairing damaged warp engines, automatically take a long time, so preparation doesn't really offer any benefit. The Narrator should use his common sense to evaluate these situations; if necessary, refer to the individual skill descriptions for suggestions.

On the other hand, if a character tries to rush a task which should take a long time, he may make the task harder. "How long will it take you to repair the engines, Mr. O'Toole? Well, Cap'n, for anyone else, two weeks. But for you, I'll see if I can get it done in two days." In these cases, the Narrator should increase the Difficulty of the task sufficiently to reflect the pressure the character is under—the greater the rush, the greater the increase in the Difficulty. Using the example above, if repairing the engines is usually a Moderate (6) repair when it takes two weeks, doing it in two days increases the Difficulty to Difficult (13).

ADDITIONAL ATTEMPTS

Failure isn't always the end of the line—sometimes characters can try again. Each additional attempt adds +1 to the Difficulty of the Test. For example, Lt. Thorev tries to send a message to Starbase 44 through Klingon jamming. The task's base Difficulty is Challenging (9). His first attempt fails, so he tries again, this time at Difficulty 10. If he keeps failing, he can keep trying.

OTHER MODIFIERS

The accompanying table lists a few of the countless other Test modifiers which may occur in your game. The Narrators can use these as guidelines for determining other modifiers.

RENOWN TESTS

Your character's Renown characteristic is used when the Narrator tries to determine whether an NPC has heard of him. The NPC rolls a Renown Test; if he succeeds, he knows of your character by reputation. Renown Tests are like Skill Tests, but relate to a specific aspect of your character's Renown. For example, if your character were facing down hostile aliens, they could roll a Renown Test using his Aggression to find out whether he's the sort of person who backs up his threats. If hostilities break out, his Skill Renown might tell them how dangerous an opponent he can be.

To make a Renown Test, total all of your character's Renown aspects (remember, use the values, positive or negative; don't subtract negative values), and divide by 10 (round up). This tells you the character's *Base Renown*. The NPC rolls a number of dice equal to your character's relevant Aspect (the highest Aspect, if the Test involves no specific Aspect), but in any event not more than 10 dice. The Drama Die rule applies. If the highest die rolled plus your character's Base Renown exceeds the Renown Difficulty (see accompanying chart), the NPC knows or recognizes your character for the Aspect in

DEFAULT RENOWN DIFFICULTIES

Difficulty	Description
3-5	Routine: Your Ship
6-8	Moderate: Starfleet
9-11	Challenging: Your Home Planet, the Sector
12-14	Difficult: The Federation, the Quadrant
15+	Nearly Impossible: Across Known Space

Additional Modifiers

Situation	Modifier to Target's Renown Test
Same species	No modifier
Different friendly species (Humans and Vulcans)	+1 Difficulty
Different hostile species (Humans and Klingons)	+2 Difficulty
Different alien species (Humans and Troyians)	+4 Difficulty
Both characters operate on same planet	-2 Difficulty
Both characters operate in same immediate region of space (system or group of systems)	-1 Difficulty
Both characters operate in same sector	No modifier
Characters normally operate far from one another (across a quadrant)	+1 to +5 Difficulty
Opposing character would probably know target (he has read or studied him, heard stories from his compatriots, and so forth)	-1 to -3 Difficulty
Opposing character would probably not know target (a backwater miner trying to recognize a Starfleet officer, and so forth)	+1 to +5 Difficulty

106

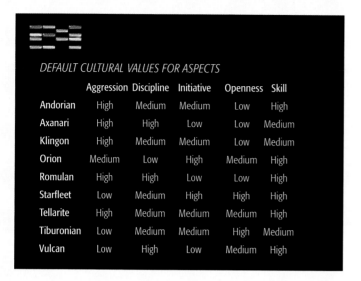

DEFAULT CULTURAL VALUES FOR ASPECTS

	Aggression	Discipline	Initiative	Openness	Skill
Andorian	High	Medium	Medium	Low	High
Axanari	High	High	Low	Low	Medium
Klingon	High	Medium	Medium	Low	Medium
Orion	Medium	Low	High	Medium	High
Romulan	High	High	Low	Low	High
Starfleet	Low	Medium	High	High	High
Tellarite	High	Medium	Medium	Medium	High
Tiburonian	Low	Medium	Medium	High	Medium
Vulcan	Low	High	Low	Medium	High

question. The Narrator might modify the Difficulty if, for example, the stranger has a high World Knowledge or Culture skill related to the character's planet, or if they share Contacts or Allies.

Steve's Tiburonian character Tyshon meets a Klingon on Deep Space Station K-7. Tyshon's Renown Aspects are Initiative 3, Aggression 5, Skill 5, Discipline -3, and Openness -2. Tyshon's overall Renown is 18 (3+5+5+3+2). This gives Tyshon a Base Renown of 2 (18 divided by 10, rounded up). The Narrator rules that the Difficulty Number for determining if the Klingon knows about Tyshon is 6. Since Tyshon's highest Aspect is Aggression, the Narrator rolls five dice for the Klingon, one of which is his Drama Die. His highest die roll is a 4, which he adds to the 2, giving him a 6. The Narrator rules that the Klingon has indeed heard of Tyshon, and specifically that Tyshon is a tough, no-nonsense person. Rolling a second Test against Skill Renown, the Narrator rolls five dice (for his +5 Skill Renown) and again adds 2. Unfortunately, his highest roll is a 2 (+2=4, meaning a failure), so the Narrator rules that the Klingon is not aware of Tyshon's extraordinary skill with a phaser. The Klingon will not back down in the upcoming confrontation.

Each culture (and indeed, each individual) places a different value on the various Renown Aspects. Typically, a member of a culture who values a particular Aspect highly reacts favorably to a character with a positive value in that Aspect, and poorly to one with a negative value in it.

Since Klingons place a High value on Aggression, Tyshon's Aggression Renown causes the Klingon to think highly of Tyshon (relatively speaking). Of course, a high positive Aggression Renown for Tyshon doesn't make Tyshon and the Klingon into friends, but the Klingon respects Tyshon as an enemy and a worthy foe.

Combat

The *Star Trek Roleplaying Game* setting is a rough-and-tumble place where conflicts, up to and including combat, are facts of life. Not everyone shares the Federation's devotion to peace, so Starfleet often has to defend it against aggressors ranging from the Klingons, to the criminal element, to mysterious invaders from other galaxies. Starfleet personnel do their best to find reasonable alternatives to conflict, but when push comes to shove, they'll fight if they must. Characters who are not a part of Starfleet have their own attitudes towards violence—some, such as the likes of Harry Mudd, avoid it whenever possible; others, such as most Klingons, revel in it. As a result, *Star Trek Roleplaying Game* characters often find themselves fighting to preserve their lives or the lives of others.

The Icon System organizes combat (and other scenes involving dramatic or cinematic elements, such as chases or cave-ins) into five-second time periods called *rounds*. The Narrator will use rounds when it's critical to know who acts first—and last—in a particular situation.

ROUND SEQUENCE

Each round is divided into two parts: Initiative and Actions.

INITIATIVE

Your initial step in a combat situation is to determine who acts first in a round—in game terms, who has Initiative. Each character rolls an *Initiative Test*, which is like an Opposed Test between the characters involved in the conflict. Each character makes a Skill Test for the skill he is using—for example, Unarmed Combat if the character is involved in a fistfight; Primitive Weaponry if he is using knives, clubs, a sword, or similar weapons; and Energy Weapon (Phaser) when using that weapon. Characters' *Reaction* edges modify their Initiative Tests.

The character with the highest Initiative Test Result acts first. The rest of the characters act in order of their rolls, from highest to lowest. If two or more results tie, the character who rolls higher on his Drama Die is the victor. If the Drama Die rolls tie as well, the character or side who initiated the conflict wins initiative. A player cannot spend Courage Points to increase his Initiative Test result.

Optional Initiative System

Sometimes Narrators want a less detailed initiative system, to make the game go quicker. If so, they can determine initiative *by side*, rather than by character. Simply choose one character from each side to roll an Initiative Test (often the character with the highest Command skill level). The side with the highest roll acts first (characters on that side act in order of their Coordination attributes, from highest to lowest, modified by their Reaction edges, if applicable). Ties between sides are resolved as in the standard initiative system.

A player cannot spend Courage Points to increase his Initiative Test Result under the optional system.

ACTIONS

After determining initiative, the first player to act tells the Narrator how many actions his character will attempt this round. If he wants to perform more than one action (such as shooting one opponent and punching another), he may incur a *Multiple Action Penalty* (see *Multiple Actions*, below). The Narrator assigns the appropriate penalty (if there is one) and the player makes his first Attribute or Skill Test.

Each character then goes through this same process in order of their Initiative Tests. After all characters perform one action, characters performing multiple actions take their second actions (again in order of initiative). This process continues until each character in the conflict has taken every action declared for the round.

After the round ends, if the conflict has not resolved itself (typically with the defeat of one side), a new round begins. Characters roll initiative and declare actions again. This goes on, round after round, until one side defeats the other.

Immediate Actions; Timed Actions

All actions fall into two categories: *Immediate* actions (actions which take no time, and don't have to be declared at the start of a round) and *Timed* actions (actions which take time and must be declared at the start of a round). Most attacks and other actions in combat are Timed, but not all. The following table provides some guidelines to help Narrators determine whether an action is Immediate or Timed:

Delayed Actions

Sometimes a character would rather wait and see what other characters do, or wait for a particular even to occur, instead of taking his action right away. A character may *delay* his action, "holding" it until later in the round instead of taking it when his Initiative Test says he can. He may act at any later time during the round. If he tries to use his action to stop or interrupt another character's action, he and the other character must make an Opposed Test using their Coordination (modified by their *Reaction edges*). He can only act before his enemy if he wins this contest. The player must tell the Narrator why his character is holding his action (for example, "I wait until I can determine if the Klingons are going to attack with energy weapons or their swords.").

IMMEDIATE ACTIONS (ACTS WHICH TAKE NO TIME IN COMBAT)

– Dropping a weapon.

– Shouting an order; brief communication ("We come in peace!").

– Quickly observing the surroundings.

– Making an Initiative Test.

– Certain Attribute Tests.

TIMED ACTIONS (ACTS WHICH TAKE TIME AND WHICH REQUIRE AN ACTION IN COMBAT)

– Drawing a weapon. It takes an action to draw a weapon. A character can draw a weapon and fire it during the same round, but this counts as a Multiple Action (see below).

– Combat Maneuvers. See the Combat Maneuvers Table.

– Movement Maneuvers. See the Movement Maneuvers Table.

– Reloading. Weapons such as phasers have ammunition supplies that determine how many times a character can fire the weapon before having to reload it. Unless specified otherwise in the weapon's game statistics, reloading such a weapon takes an action. See the *Technology* chapter, pages 177-179.

– Stun setting. Many energy weapons have damage and range settings that characters can adjust for different situations. Switching a weapon's setting doesn't require a Skill Test, but does take an action.

– Taking a tricorder or sensor reading. Taking a basic tricorder or sensor reading requires an action; more detailed or difficult scans may take multiple actions, at the Narrator's discretion.

– First aid. Applying first aid to an injured character takes an action.

– Making a Test. Making most Skill Tests requires an action; Attribute Tests may or may not require an action. However, it is always up to the Narrator to decide whether a particular roll is a Timed action or an Immediate action.

Lieutenant Tyshon is one of several Starfleet officers engaged in a phaser battle with a group of Klingons on the surface of a former Federation colony which the Klingons destroyed. Tyshon has the highest Initiative Test result, so he may act first. Rather than attacking, he delays his action to see what the Klingons do. Later in the round, he notices a Klingon about to shoot Ensign Willingham. Tyshon declares that he will use his delayed action to shoot the Klingon first. Tyshon and the Klingon must make an Opposed Test using their Coordination attributes. If Tyshon wins the Test, he can act before the Klingon and, he hopes, save Ensign Willingham. Otherwise, the Klingon can shoot Willingham first, and Lt. Tyshon may have to satisfy himself with avenging the Ensign's death.

REACTING TO CHANGING CIRCUMSTANCES

Combat is a fluid situation where things often change. When necessary, characters can alter their declared or planned actions to react to changes in a situation. Characters may change their actions to use Dodge (to evade an attack) or Primitive Weaponry or Unarmed Combat (to parry a blow).

If the character has planned to take multiple actions, the Multiple Action Penalty (see below) applies to his effort to dodge or parry. Characters not taking multiple actions may, if they choose, take an *extra* action to dodge or parry (though a Multiple Action Penalty then applies).

When a character changes actions to dodge or parry an incoming attack, his Test Result "sets" the Difficulty for the attack. The attacker must now overcome this new Difficulty in order to succeed. This Test Result remains in effect for the rest of the round (or until the character acts again) and acts as any other dodge or parry roll (see *Difficulty Numbers In Melee Combat*, page 112).

In the next round of his fight against the Klingons, Lt. Tyshon declares he will attempt multiple actions–to wit, shots at three different Klingons, for a total +2 Difficulty penalty to all his shots (see Multiple Actions, next column). After taking his first shot, Tyshon realizes that one of the Klingons is taking aim at him. He declares he will take an extra action and attempt to Dodge the attack. He makes his Dodge roll with -3 to the Test Result, and the Difficulty for any shots he has not yet taken is now +3. After he dodges, the Difficulty Number derived from his Dodge roll becomes the new Difficulty for all attacks against him until he next acts, or the round ends.

In some cases, and if the Narrator permits, characters can change their actions to do things other than dodge or parry an attack, or even to add more actions. For example, if Lt. Tyshon's declared action is to shoot at the Klingon commander, but before he can act, another character shoots and kills the commander, the Narrator might allow Tyshon to change his declared action to shoot a different Klingon (after all, shooting the commander is now pointless). Or, if an attacker disarms Lt. Tyshon, the Narrator might allow him to add an action to draw another weapon.

SURPRISE

Even Starfleet Academy can't teach characters to expect the unexpected all the time. Characters can be *surprised*–startled into immobility by sudden, unexpected occurrences. Ambushes and similar attacks often cause surprise; so do unexpected or startling events (sudden explosions or noises, gravity failure, and the like). The Narrator decides whether one character surprises another. He may, if appropriate, allow a character to make an Opposed Test, pitting his Search roll (or other appropriate skill) against the attacker's Stealth (or other appropriate skill), in an effort to detect an ambush before it occurs.

In game terms, surprise allows an attacker to make an uncontested action before the character can react. A surprised character cannot take any actions—even a dodge, parry, or Immediate action—during this initial attack.

MULTIPLE ACTIONS

Characters aren't limited to just one action in a round; they can try to do several things (like drawing a weapon, firing it, and then diving behind cover) if they want to. However, a character who tries to do too much at one time dramatically reduces his overall chance of success for each task. In short, trying to do too many things at once is a sure-fire guarantee that most or all of them will fail.

The first action in a round is "free"—by itself, it carries no penalty. For each additional action the character wants to take, he incurs a +1 Difficulty penalty *for all actions he takes*, including the first one. For example, a character who declares that he will attempt five actions in a round suffers a +4 Difficulty penalty for *all* Attribute and Skill Tests that round (even the first). In the case of actions which don't involve a Difficulty, such as dodging or parrying, subtract the Difficulty penalty from the Test Result.

MOVEMENT

Roleplaying games aren't boardgames, but there are times when it's important to account for a character's movement in a given situation—sometimes precisely how fast and far a character moves during a round has great significance. (Of course, if you use miniatures, moving them tactically, and even realistically, can add an exciting dimension to your game.)

Humanoid characters normally move 10 meters per round at a brisk walk. They move at different speeds using other types of movement (see accompanying table). A character who wants to move more quickly with a particular mode of movement can make an Athletics Test (or Fitness Test) (using the Difficulties listed in the accompanying tables) to do so; this allows him to move an additional number of meters per round equal to his Athletics Skill level (or Fitness). Normally, characters can move once per round but the Narrator may allow multiple movement actions in a single round. Refer to the *Athletics* skill, page 76, for more information on movement.

Ordinarily, characters don't need to make Skill Test to move successfully, but in some dramatic or pressure-filled situations (like some combats), a misstep can spell disaster. If necessary, the Narrator may require characters to make Athletics (or Fitness) Tests to move quickly without hurting themselves and/or falling. The

MOVEMENT

Type of Movement	Rate	Difficulty
Crawl	5m per action	No roll required
Walk	10m per action	No roll required
Run	15m per action	Routine (5)
Sprint	20m per action	Moderate (7)
Swim	3m per action	Routine (4)
Jump	2m forward, 1m up	Moderate (6)
Climb	2m per action	Moderate (7)

Terrain Modifiers

Terrain Type	Modifier
Swampy	+3
Mountainous/Steep	+2
Wet/Slick/Icy	+2
Water (2' or higher)	+2
Obstacles, many/large	+2
Obstacles, few/small	+1
Sandy	+1
Rocky	+1
Extremely flat or even	-1
Paved	-2

Difficulty of the Tests depends on the terrain and other factors (see accompanying tables). If the character fails the Test, the Narrator should reduce the character's movement (typically by 1m for every point by which he missed the roll), state that he tripped and fell down, or create some other dramatic situation.

MOVEMENT MANEUVERS

Some types of movement count as actions in combat, since they affect combat and take time. The Movement Maneuvers Table indicates which types

MOVEMENT MANEUVERS

Immediate Actions (acts which take no time in combat)

Turning or changing facing

Moving up to 1m walking or running

Movement Maneuvers (Timed actions)

Action*	Difficulty**	Effect***
Dodge	—	Dodge roll becomes the Difficulty Number to hit dodging character
Dropping to prone position	—	A form of Dodge
Getting to one's feet	3	
Moving 2m or more, walk/run	Varies	See Movement Table for Difficulties
Dive for cover	7	A form of Dodge which allows the character to move up to 5m at no penalty; every meter beyond 5 subtracts 1 from the character's dodge roll.
Drop and roll	4	A form of Dodge which allows the character to move up to 1m at no penalty; every meter beyond 1 subtracts 1 from the character's Dodge roll.
Tackle	9	The character moves up to 5m and tackles his opponent; a successful attack means the opponent is knocked down (unless he is substantially larger or stronger than the character), takes 2d6 Stun damage, and, if the character desires, is Grabbed (see the *Combat Maneuvers* chart, below). Tackle requires a Coordination Test or Unarmed Combat Test.

*"Action" is the action the character wishes to take.

**"Difficulty" is the Difficulty Number for the maneuver, if the Narrator requires a Skill Test at all. Most Movement Maneuvers should not require Skill Tests to perform, unless some benefit (such as a Dodge effect or attack) is associated with them.

***"Effect" is how the maneuver affects the character or the combat.

of movement are considered Timed Actions in combat; its entries provide guidelines for handling other forms of movement in combat.

RANGED AND MELEE COMBAT

Ranged combat involves weapons which can inflict damage at a distance—firearms, phasers, bows, thrown spears, *kligats*, and so on.

COMBAT MANEUVERS

Universal Combat Maneuvers (Timed Actions) (usable by any character)

Action	Difficulty	Damage	Notes
Aim	–	–	-1 Difficulty to hit target for each action used to Aim; characters may Aim multiple times
Block	–	–	Parries unarmed hand-to-hand attacks. Character rolls either an appropriate Skill Test (Unarmed Combat) or a Coordination Test and subtracts 3 to establish a Difficulty for hitting him with such attacks.
Grab	9	–	If successful, the character has grabbed his opponent and effectively immobilized him, preventing him from taking any action other than trying to break free. The characters must make an Opposed Test using Fitness (modified by Strength) each round to determine whether the grabbed character can break free. This Opposed Test is an Immediate Action, but may only be attempted once per round. At the Narrator's discretion, a character who has been grabbed can use his Coordination (instead of Fitness+Strength) to attempt to worm free.
Kick	8	4+1d6	
Punch	7	3+1d6	
Roundhouse Punch	8	4+1d6	
Snap Punch/Kick	6	2+1d6	

Boxing (Timed Actions) (usable by characters who know Unarmed Combat: Boxing)

Action	Difficulty	Damage	Notes
Block	–	–	Parries unarmed hand-to-hand attacks. The character rolls a Boxing Test to establish a Difficulty for hitting him with such attacks.
Cross/Jab	7	4+1d6	
Hook/Uppercut	8	5+1d6	

Brawling (Timed Actions) (usable by characters who know Unarmed Combat: Brawling)

Action	Difficulty	Damage	Notes
Flying Smash	8	5+1d6	The brawler jumps into his opponent, hitting him feet-first and knocking him down. However, the character also falls to the ground unless he succeeds with a Moderate (7) Acrobatics (Gymnastics) Test.
Hammer	8	4+1d6	The brawler laces his fingers together to form one large "fist" and uses it to smash or strike his opponent. Miraculously, the brawler's fingers remain unharmed.
Hatchet Chop	8	Special	This is the only "sophisticated" maneuver in the Brawling style; it was adapted from Karate and similar styles. The brawler strikes his opponent in the neck area with the edge of his flattened palm, doing 2+1d6 Stun Damage. This maneuver is best performed from behind; if attempted while standing in front of the target, the Difficulty increases to 9.
Punch	6	2+1d6	
Tackle	8	Special	This maneuver is the same as the Tackle described in the Movement Maneuvers Table, but has a slightly lower Difficulty to reflect the brawler's fighting skill.

Melee combat involves weapons such as knives, clubs, and swords, as well as brawling, wrestling, or martial arts attacks.

You resolve attacks like Skill Tests. To hit a target in combat, a character makes a Skill Test using the appropriate skill (such as Unarmed Combat or Energy Weapon (Phaser)), modified by his *Dexterity* edge. He hits the target if the Test Result equals or exceeds the Difficulty Number.

Ensign Astrose fires his phaser at a target at Long range (Difficulty 10; see Ranged Combat Difficulty Table below). He has

Coordination 4, Dexterity +1, and Energy Weapon (Phaser) 3. He rolls five dice (four for Coordination, +1 for his Dexterity Edge) to make his Skill Test. Luckily, his Drama Die comes up a 6, so he adds it and the next highest die, a 5, to his skill, for a total of 14. He hits!

The biggest difference between ranged and melee combat is how the Narrator determines the Difficulty Number.

 STAR TREK Roleplaying Game

Starfleet Martial Arts (Timed Actions) (usable by characters who know Unarmed Combat: Starfleet Martial Arts)

Action	Difficulty	Damage	Notes
Block	–	–	Parries unarmed hand-to-hand attacks. The character rolls a Starfleet Martial Arts Test to establish a Difficulty for hitting him with such attacks.
Disarm	9	–	This maneuver allows a Starfleet Martial Arts practitioner to disarm an opponent by striking the opponent's weapon from his hand, "locking" the weapon and tearing it out of his grasp, or the like. If the Starfleet Martial Arts Test succeeds, the two characters must engage in Opposed Tests with their Fitness (modified by Strength); the Starfleet Martial Arts practitioner receives a +2 bonus to his Test Result. If the Starfleet Martial Arts practitioner wins the Opposed Roll, his opponent's weapon ends up 1d6 meters away; if he fails, his opponent retains the weapon.
Punch	7	4+1d6	
Strike	8	2+2d6	This maneuver represents the wide variety of kicks, elbow, knee, and palm strikes, and similar maneuvers which Starfleet officers learn.
Throw	8	1+1d6	Target is thrown to the ground and suffers penalties for being prone until he gets to his feet (which takes an action)

Vulcan Nerve Pinch (usable by characters who know Unarmed Combat: Vulcan Nerve Pinch)

Nerve Pinch	8	3+2d6	Stun damage only; Strength does not add to the damage; see rules for Stun Damage, page 117.

"Action" is the action the character wishes to take or combat maneuver he wishes to use.

"Difficulty" is the base Difficulty Number for attacking another character with the maneuver.

"Damage" is the damage done by the maneuver. All damage rolls are modified by a character's *Strength* edge (add or subtract a number of damage points equal to Strength); the Drama Die rule does not apply. The total on the dice is the amount of damage done to the target. At the GM's option, characters can increase the damage a maneuver does by using impromptu weapons such as chair legs, broken bottles and the like.

DIFFICULTY NUMBERS IN MELEE COMBAT

During melee combat, the base Difficulty depends on the weapon or attack used, unless the target attempts to parry or dodge the attack (which involves the Dodge, Primitive Weaponry, or Unarmed Combat skills). If the target tries to parry or dodge (either as a declared action, or as a changed or added action), the Difficulty of the attack becomes the Test Result of the target's parry or Dodge attempt (though this cannot be lower than the base Difficulty to hit with the weapon; if it is, use the base Difficulty instead). The Reaction edge normally modifies dodge attempts, while the Dexterity edge affects parry or blocking attempts.

RANGED COMBAT DIFFICULTY

Range	Difficulty
Point Blank	Routine (3)
Short Range	Routine (4)
Medium Range	Moderate (7)
Long Range	Challenging (10)

Combat maneuvers, including those taught as part of martial arts styles, also have base Difficulties (see the *Combat Maneuvers Table*, pages 111-112). Fighting with fists and swords may seem odd in a world of phasers and disruptors, but it has an important part in the game. Phasers and disruptors are lethal weapons; unless they're always set on stun (and what self-respecting Klingon warrior sets his disruptor on stun all the time?), they'll kill characters frequently.

A good, old-fashioned fistfight, on the other hand, won't. From the formal combats of Triskelion to a bench-clearing brawl on Deep Space Station K-7, hand-to-hand melees are a staple of the *Star Trek* milieu. Who can't picture Kirk and Spock slugging it out with their Klingon adversaries? This rambunctious spirit should run through your episodes, as well. After all, it's easy to nurse a few bruises over a glass of Saurian brandy, but who can bring back Ensign Willingham after he's been disintegrated?

DIFFICULTY NUMBERS IN RANGED COMBAT

In ranged combat, Difficulty Numbers depend on the shooter's distance from the target. This distance—or range—is described as Point Blank, Short Range, Medium Range, or Long Range. Of course, if an opponent attempts to dodge the attack, the Difficulty equals his Dodge Test Result (or the Difficulty based on the distance, whichever is greater), as with melee combat.

OPTIONAL RULE: HIT LOCATIONS

For added realism, Narrators may elect to use this rule, which determines where a successful shot or attack strikes a target. Roll two dice to determine the basic "hit location" and consult the following chart:

Roll	Target Location	Modifier	Effect
2	Upper Arm/Shoulder (Left)	+3	Must make Moderate (7) Coordination roll to hold on to any held items, including weapons.
3	Upper Arm/Shoulder (Right)	+3	Must make Moderate (7) Coordination roll to hold on to any held items, including weapons.
4	Lower Arm/Hand (Left)	+4	Must make Challenging (9) Coordination roll to hold on to any held items, including weapons.
5	Lower Arm/Hand (Right)	+4	Must make Challenging (9) Coordination roll to hold on to any held items, including weapons.
6	Chest (Left or Right Side)	+2	
7	Abdomen/Stomach	+1	x1.5 damage
8	Upper Leg/Thigh (Left)	+2	Reduce all movement to half normal
9	Upper Leg/Thigh (Right)	+2	Reduce all movement to half normal
10	Lower Leg/Foot (Left)	+4	Reduce all movement to one-quarter normal
11	Lower Leg/Foot (Right)	+4	Reduce all movement to one-quarter normal
12	Head	+5	x2 damage

In addition, after a character has determined which location he hit, he can elect to "slide" the result to another hit location based on how proficient he is with the mode of attack. He can "slide" the attack up to one step up or down for each point he has in the Skill he used to make the attack. For example, Ensign Willingham, with an Energy Weapon (Phaser) 2 (3) Skill, can elect to "slide" a hit up to three locations in either direction on the scale when he hits a target with a phaser blast. He rolls a hit location of 6. As a result, he can slide the hit location up to 3 locations in either direction–anywhere from 3-9. Since he does not want to strike the target character in the chest–location 6, a potentially fatal shot–he instead elects to "slide" the hit to the target's right hand (location 5), hoping the target will drop his weapon.

Every weapon that works at range has a Range listing which corresponds to these four categories. For example, a character armed with a phaser-2 pistol has a Range of 5/20/50/80. This means any targets up to 5 meters away are considered to be at Point Blank range; targets from 5.1-20 meters away are at Short Range; targets 20.1-50 meters away are at Medium Range; and targets from 50.1-80 meters away are at Long Range.

For every 10 meters beyond the weapon's listed Long Range, increase the Difficulty by +1.

COMBAT VARIABLES

Many other factors can influence a combat situation. The Icon System represents these factors with various modifiers that increase or decrease the Difficulty of various Tests during a fight. Some of these factors include:

CALLED SHOTS

Characters can aim at a specific target area (such as the arm, leg, hand, head, and so forth). This increases the Difficulty of the attack.

As a general guideline, add +2 to the Difficulty for called shots to hit targets which are from 10 to 75 centimeters long, and +4 to the Difficulty for targets smaller than 10 centimeters long. Narrators desiring more detailed called shot modifiers can use those listed in the optional hit location chart (see

sidebar); those seeking greater simplicity can simply use the Size guidelines provided below.

COVER

It's harder to attack a character who's protected by cover effectively. Cover includes physical barriers between the character and an attacker (such as force fields, walls, rocks, and so on) or factors that make it harder to see a target (smoke, rain, darkness, or other such visual impediments).

Physical cover makes a character harder to hit. If it protects one quarter of his body, increase the Difficulty to hit him by +1; if it protects half of his body, add +2; if it protects three-quarters of his body, add +4. If cover protects a target's entire body, the attacker cannot hit him; the cover must be destroyed before the attacker can hit the target. The accompanying table provides guidelines for the strengths (expressed in terms of armor–see *Resisting Damage: Armor*, page 116) of various materials. Of course, Narrators should use their common sense and dramatic judgment when determining the effects of cover; it's a good way to build tension in a story if handled properly–some types of cover may require multiple shots to destroy before the Crew can attack the real target.

Visual cover makes it harder to see a character, and thus harder to aim shots at him (in game terms, it increases the Difficulty Number to hit him). As a rough guideline, light smoke or dim light increases the Difficulty by +1;

COVER

Cover	Armor
Thin wooden door	6
Wooden door	8
Thin, unarmored metal door	10
Reinforced metal door; large rocks	14
Armored bulkhead, volcanic stone walls	20
Heavily armored security door	24

heavy smoke or moonlight by +2; and thick smoke or total darkness by +3. These penalties also apply to any roll to perceive things visually, including most Search rolls.

OFF HAND

Most characters are either right-handed or left-handed (player's choice). A few have the Ambidexterity advantage, indicating that they're equally adept with both hands. All non-ambidextrous characters suffer a +1 Difficulty to any attacks (or other Skill Tests) made using the character's off hand.

PRONE OR IMMOBILIZED

Prone characters are usually easier to hit (-1 Difficulty), particularly in hand-to-hand combat (being prone may actually make a character harder to hit in some circumstances—+1 Difficulty—with ranged attacks). Immobile characters (ones who are tied up, for example) are much easier to hit (-4 Difficulty).

SIZE

The relative size of object can affect Difficulty Numbers to hit a target—targets larger than the character (such as a starship) are easier to hit, while smaller

ones (insects or small animals, for example) are harder to hit. As a rough guideline, for every doubling of a target's size compared to its attacker, subtract 1 from the Difficulty to hit it. For every halving of a target's size compared to its attacker, add 1 to the Difficulty to hit it.

TARGETING SYSTEMS

Some ranged weapons have built-in targeting systems that make it easier to hit what you're aiming at. Such systems have a Targeting rating (usually ranging from 1 to 3). When a character uses such a weapon, subtract the Targeting rating from the Difficulty Number to hit the target (minimum Difficulty Number of 2, of course).

ZERO GRAVITY

All combat actions and Skill Tests suffer a +1 Difficulty when performed in zero gravity unless a character has the Zero-G Training advantage or makes a Routine (4) Personal Equipment (Environmental Suit) Test.

COURAGE POINTS IN COMBAT

Characters can spend Courage Points at any time during a round. However, they may not use them to improve an Initiative Test or a damage roll.

Damage and Healing

INFLICTING DAMAGE

Attacks which succeed can injure or kill the target. An attack's severity is indicated by the amount of *Damage* it does. Obviously, a punch that does 5 points of damage is far less severe than a disruptor blast that does 23 points.

Some attacks do a set amount of damage (normally based on your Fitness and any Strength edge you possess). Others, such as energy weapons, deliver a variable amount of damage (requiring you to make a die roll). Dramatic Successes typically add 1-2 extra damage dice.

Characters may not spend Courage Points to improve damage rolls. The Drama Die does not apply to damage rolls.

BRAWLING; MARTIAL ARTS

Brawling attacks—untrained, unarmed melee attacks (not the "martial arts" style of the same name)—usually inflict a number of points of damage equal to the attacking character's Fitness+Strength.

Martial arts and other combat maneuvers usually inflict a specific amount of damage, modified by the character's Strength (see *Combat Maneuvers Table*).

Punches and similar attacks typically do Stun Damage (see *Stun Damage*, page 117).

WEAPONS

Weapons have a damage code which describes how much damage they do. For example, a phaser on setting 5 does 15+4d6 damage, meaning a base of 15 points plus the total rolled on four dice.

TAKING DAMAGE

A character can take an amount of damage equal to his Resistance (Fitness+Vitality+applicable armor). Any damage that exceeds the target's Resistance affects him directly.

OTHER FORMS OF DAMAGE

The universe of *Star Trek* can be a dangerous place—combat is often the least of a character's problems. Characters can fall off of cliffs, get trapped in burning shuttlecraft, or experience the joys of explosive decompression. The rules below describe some of the most common ways characters suffer injuries outside of combat; Narrators can use them as guidelines for addressing situations not covered here.

DISEASE

Although many diseases have been conquered by Federation medicine, new plagues such as Rigelian fever, synthococcus novae, xenopolycythemia, and Vegan choriomeningitis have arisen. Some diseases simply do damage, others reduce edges or attributes either permanently or temporarily until cured. In game terms, diseases usually either have some dramatic effects (such as the Psi 2000 virus that supercharges humanoid emotions) or will kill the sufferer in a dramatically suitable period of time.

FALLS

Each 10m of distance fallen causes 1+1d6 damage. Thus, a 70m fall does 7+7d6 damage. This assumes a local gravity roughly equal to Earth's; for environments which involve different gravity, multiply the damage done by the difference between local gravity and Earth gravity. For example, if local gravity is half of Earth's, halve the damage; if it's twice as strong as Earth gravity, double the damage. Note that a fall that breaks a character's leg and traps him in a hostile environment makes far superior drama to one which kills him.

FIRE

Contact with a roughly torch-sized flame causes 3+1d6 damage per round of contact; flammable articles, such as clothing or hair, may catch on fire and do further damage to the character. For larger fires, add +1d6 damage for every doubling of the size of the fire. Immolation causes 3+10d6 damage. Plasma fires or other unusual blazes burn hotter than normal flame, causing double damage.

POISON

Many substances, organic and inorganic, artificial and natural, are poisonous to Humans and their relatives. Different poisons affect different species, and some medicines (like cordrazine) become deadly poisons in larger doses. Poisons range from mild toxins doing 1-2 points of damage to lethal poisons doing 30 or more points at a time. Other toxins can reduce edges or attributes, either automatically or with a failed Fitness+Vitality check. Most venoms take some time to take effect; the loss of points or attributes slowly accumulates over minutes or even hours. For dramatic purposes even a lethal poison should not kill right away; give the characters a chance to treat the victim.

RADIATION

While large doses of radiation can kill a character in seconds, many types of radiation are more insidious. Characters exposed to damaging radiation such as delta rays or celebium poisoning take 1d6 per round for the duration of their exposure. After direct exposure ends, they continue to take 2 points of damage per day (from radiation sickness) until they are treated. For more or less severe types of radiation or exposure, add or subtract damage dice, or lengthen or shorten the time interval. Berthold rays, for example, kill by disintegrating carbon tissue over a period of weeks. Other types of radiation, especially those associated with isolated nebulae or dimensional rifts, can cause anomalous effects. Radiation on Gamma Hydra IV caused accelerated aging, for instance.

DROWNING

Characters can hold their breath underwater for five rounds per point of Fitness+Vitality. For every round after that, a character takes 1 point of damage until Stunned, after which he takes 1d6 damage per round until dead. Resistance offers no protection against drowning damage.

VACUUM

Characters caught in a vacuum (such as that in outer space, or in a medical decompression chamber) without protection die in a number of rounds

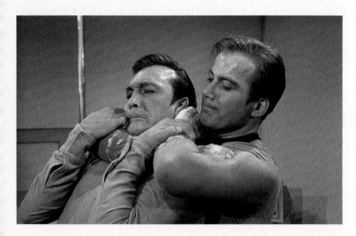

A Klingon (Fitness 3, +1 Vitality) wears battle armor which affords +2 protection against physical attacks and +1 protection against energy attacks. When attacked by a knife, club, sword, or kick, he can resist 6 points of damage (his normal 4 Resistance plus the added protection of the armor). When struck by an energy weapon, he resists 5 points of damage.

Armor rarely covers the wearer's entire body, or covers every area of the body equally well; a character should define which areas of their body are covered, and which aren't protected (or are protected by less armor). If you're using the optional "Hit Locations" rule, this allows you to determine whether the part of the body hit is protected by armor, and if so, by how much.

EFFECTS OF INJURIES

Injuries weaken a character, making it harder for him to exert himself to the fullest. While minor injuries have little or no effect, even little nicks and scrapes can add up to the point where they seriously impair a character's ability to function effectively.

Seven *Wound* Levels describe a character's current injury status, and thus his current degree of impairment. The accompanying Wound Level Table lists each of these levels and their corresponding effects. All characters are *Healthy* until they suffer damage or injury (unless some pre-existing condition worsens their injury status).

Every character can withstand an amount of damage (from one or more attacks) equal to his Resistance (not including armor) before dropping to the next level. For example, an uninjured Starfleet security officer with a Resistance

equal to their Fitness+Vitality. If rescued before death, assume they drop one Wound Level per round of exposure until reaching Near Death.

RESISTING DAMAGE: ARMOR

A character can withstand damage equal to his Resistance, which equals his Fitness+Vitality, augmented by armor. Courage Points may be spent to improve one's Resistance (at the rate of 1 Courage Point per point of Resistance); this effect lasts for one round (or, at the Narrator's option, one scene). Any damage that exceeds a character's Resistance affects the character directly.

Characters can improve their Resistance by wearing armor—Federation security troops often don combat armor before entering a dangerous area, for example. Armor grants protection against both physical and energy damage.

WOUND LEVELS

Wound Level	Effect
Healthy	The character suffers no impairment (this is his normal, uninjured state).
Stunned	The character suffers a +1 Difficulty to all Tests (or -1 to Initiative Tests and dodge or parry rolls) until healed. This penalty is in addition to whatever other penalties already apply.
Injured	The character has been thrown to the ground and is in such pain that further actions this round are impossible. Until he receives first aid or medical attention, he suffers a +1 Difficulty to all Tests (or -1 to Initiative Tests and dodge or parry rolls) until healed. This penalty is in addition to whatever other penalties already apply.
Wounded	The character has been thrown to the ground and is in such pain that further actions this round are impossible. Until he receives first aid or medical attention, he suffers a +2 Difficulty to all Tests (or -2 to Initiative Tests and dodge or parry rolls) until healed. This penalty is in addition to whatever other penalties already apply.
Incapacitated	The character has been thrown to the ground and rendered unconscious for 2d6 minutes. Once awake, the character cannot move or perform actions until first aid or medical attention has been received.
Near Death	The character is so severely wounded that without immediate medical attention, death is inevitable. If a Near Death result is achieved, the character falls prone and unconscious and will die after his Fitness+Vitality in minutes. A successful Routine (4) First Aid Test will stabilize the character, though medical attention—in a sickbay, for example—is required to heal his injuries. If the character does not receive the required medical attention, a new First Aid Test must be made every hour, or the character will fall unconscious and die.
Killed	He's dead, Jim.

3 could take 3 points of damage before being Stunned. It would take an additional 3 points of damage before his status dropped to Injured. All points in a given Wound Level must be lost before a character drops down to the next level. If the security officer had only taken 2 points of damage, he would remain Healthy until he suffered an additional point of damage.

The effects listed on the Wound Level Table are cumulative. Returning to the example above, an uninjured Starfleet security officer takes three points of damage, reducing him to Stunned. He suffers a +1 Difficulty penalty to all Tests. Later on, he is hurt again, this time taking him down to Injured; he now suffers a +2 Difficulty penalty to all Tests.

STUN DAMAGE

Some attacks, such as punches or phasers set on "stun," are not intended to kill or seriously injure a target, just to render him unconscious. These attacks do *Stun Damage*.

Stun Damage From Energy Weapons and Nerve Pinches

Characters can configure some energy weapons—Federation phasers, for example—to inflict nonlethal damage. Starfleet standard operating procedure requires phasers be set on stun, at least initially. For a weapon set on stun, roll damage normally. When the target is reduced to the *Stunned* Wound Level, he is rendered unconscious. This rule also applies to the Vulcan nerve pinch.

The length of time the character remains unconscious depends on the weapon and its settings—refer to the individual weapon descriptions for more details—but at least one to two minutes is typical. For each damage point beyond the *Stunned* Wound Level, a Human character remains unconscious for an additional five minutes. For other species, use the Human figure as a benchmark for modifications. For example, Klingons are more resilient than Humans, so they might remain unconscious for only one-third as long.

DEGREE OF INJURY TABLE

Degree of Injury	Difficulty to Diagnose/Heal
Stunned	Routine (4)
Injured	Moderate (7)
Wounded	Challenging (8)
Incapacitated	Difficult (13)
Near Death	Nearly Impossible (15)

Stun Damage From Punches

Similarly, punches and other unarmed melee attacks usually cause Stun damage. When a character takes enough damage from an unarmed melee attack to drop to the Incapacitated level, he falls unconscious. For each damage point beyond the *Incapacitated* Wound Level, a Human character remains unconscious for an additional five minutes. Again, the Narrator should modify the length of time depending on a character's species.

Effects of Stun Damage

Stun Damage can't kill or seriously injure a character—most of the time. An unconscious character who continues to take Stun Damage may, at the Narrator's discretion, begin to suffer normal damage. Eventually he will die if he keeps taking the damage.

When normal attacks are used together with attacks that only do Stun damage, the Stun damage counts as normal damage for purposes of calculating Wound Levels. For example, suppose a Klingon soldier punches Lt. Tyshon hard enough to reduce him to Injured. If a second Klingon then shoots Tyshon with a disruptor, further wounds will reduce him to Wounded, Incapacitated, Near Death and Killed—the second Klingon does not have to "start over" at Stunned just because his disruptor does a different "type" of damage than the first Klingon's punches.

When characters regain consciousness after being stunned by an energy weapon (such as a Federation phaser), they are considered Healthy. No residual damage remains (unless they were further attacked when they were unconscious). If a character was rendered unconscious by unarmed combat damage (in a fistfight, for example), he regains consciousness at the lowest level of his Stunned Wound Level.

For example, a character who regains consciousness after a brawl has one point remaining in his Stunned Wound Level. If he takes one more point of damage, he will become Injured. It doesn't matter what a character's Resistance is; when characters regain consciousness after being physically knocked out, they have one point remaining in their Stunned Wound Level.

HEALING

Injuries aren't permanent, of course. Characters can heal from them naturally, or receive first aid or advanced medical treatment. Thanks to the wonders

NATURAL HEALING

Fitness Roll	Healing Result
1-3	Character's health worsens; treat as injury of one step worse than injury suffered (for example, as a Wounded injury if character was Injured). This result does not apply to characters who are only Stunned.
4-6	No effect; character suffers from injury at the same level.
7-9	Partial recovery; character still suffers from injury, but at one level better (for example, a Wounded character would become merely Injured, and a Stunned character would be back at full health).
10-12	Partial to full recovery; character still suffers from injury, but at two levels better (for example, an Incapacitated character would become merely Injured; a Wounded character would be completely recovered).
13+	Full recovery. Character regains all Wound Levels and returns to a Healthy state.

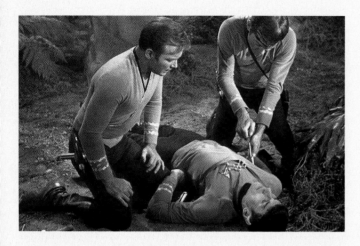

of 23rd-century medicine, wounds that once would have incapacitated a character for days or even killed him can be cured fairly easily.

NATURAL HEALING

Natural healing–without the benefit of medicine or medical attention–is a slow, painful process. In game terms, a character must rest for a certain amount of time, and then attempt to make a Fitness Test (modified by his Vitality edge). Compare the Test Result to the Natural Healing Table for the results. While healing naturally, a character is essentially bedridden–if he exercises or works, the Difficulty of his Fitness Tests during recovery increases by +1.

A Stunned character must rest for 1d6 minutes before attempting a healing roll (or, at the Narrator's option, is automatically healed at the end of that time). An Injured character must rest for 1d3 days before attempting a healing roll; a Wounded character, for 1d6 days; an Incapacitated character, 1d3 weeks; a Near Death character, 1d3 months. Of course, the Narrator might rule that special or unusual circumstances allow a character to make Fitness Tests more quickly.

MEDICAL ATTENTION

The swifter, better route is to receive medical care of some sort (first aid, field dressing from a doctor or medical tech, or treatment in a sickbay). Depending on the nature of the injury, this may be accomplished quickly (a round or two), or may take a lot longer (equivalent to the recuperation periods described under *Natural Healing*).

Characters can use the First Aid Skill and standard medical kits to stabilize or heal wounds in the field. Field medicine of this sort requires the character to have at least a rudimentary knowledge of first aid or medicine, however. (See *Technology*, pages 172-173, for more information on medical equipment.)

Advanced medical care, on the other hand, can't be performed in the field; it requires more than a medkit or medical tricorder. It includes the ongoing attention of doctors and nurses in a sickbay or hospital. Characters who want to administer this sort of care must know an appropriate Medical Sciences skill and have proper facilities.

In general, the following benchmark Difficulties apply to the use of medical tricorders and medical kits to heal wounds. Reduce the Difficulty by 2 if the character is receiving advanced medical care.

If the First Aid or Medical Sciences roll is successful, the character's damage is reduced by one level: Near Death reduces to Incapacitated, Incapacitated reduces to Wounded, and so on.

Example of Combat

Three Klingons (each Fitness 3, Strength +1, Vitality +1, Coordination 2) pick a fight with three Starfleet officers–Lt. Commander Jansen (Fitness 4, Strength +1, Vitality +1, Coordination 3, Reaction +1), Lt. Tavak (Fitness 3, Vitality +1, Coordination 4, Reaction +1, Dexterity +1), and Ensign Willingham (Fitness 2, Coordination 2, Dexterity +1)–in a shop in a Rigellian bazaar. Although the three officers try to leave quietly, the Klingons block the exit. The only way out is to stand and fight.

In the first round of combat, all characters roll Initiative Tests (a Skill Test with the skill to be used, modified by Reaction). Lt. Commander Jansen is going to use his Unarmed Combat (Starfleet Martial Arts) 2 (3), so he rolls four dice (three for his Coordination, plus one for Reaction); his best result is a 5, so his Test Result is 8 (5 + 3 for his skill). Lieutenant Tavak is going to use his Unarmed Combat (Starfleet Martial Arts, Vulcan Nerve Pinch) 2 (3) and (3), so he rolls five dice (for Coordination + Reaction); his Drama Die is a 6, so he adds it and the next highest die, a 3, to his skill level, for a Test Result of 12. Ensign Willingham uses his Unarmed Combat (Starfleet Martial Arts) 1 (2), so he rolls two dice (Coordination + Reaction), getting a 4 as his best result, so his total is 6. The three Klingons (Agrak, Burat, and Chang) plan to use their Unarmed Combat (Brawling) 2 (3) skills; they get Initiative Test Results of 7, 6, and 4, respectively. Burat rolled higher on his Drama Die than Ensign Willingham did, so he will go before Willingham. Therefore, the order of combat during this round is Tavak, Jansen, Agrak, Burat, Willingham, and Chang.

Tavak declares he will only take one action this round. Preferring to use nonviolent methods to end the fight, he opts to apply a Vulcan nerve pinch to Burat. He rolls four dice (from his Coordination, since Unarmed Combat is a Coordination-based skill), and gets a 6 as his best result (but not on his Drama Die, unfortunately). Added to his skill level of 3, this gives him a Test Result of 9. Since the Difficulty for the Vulcan nerve pinch is 8, he grabs the Klingon. The maneuver does (3+2d6) damage. He rolls his two dice and gets a 12, so he does 15 points of Stun damage–the most he can possibly do. Since Burat's Resistance is 4, he resists 4 points of the damage, leaving 11 points. That's enough to reduce Burat to Stunned (and thus, since it is Stun damage from a Vulcan nerve pinch, unconscious), and Burat slumps into a table full of tiny metal ornaments, smashing it under his supine form. Since Tavak did 7 points of damage beyond what was necessary to render Burat Stunned, the Narrator rules that Burat will remain unconscious for an additional 15 minutes (about half the time a Human would remain unconscious).

Lt. Commander Jansen acts next. He declares he will attempt two actions: He wants to punch Agrak and Chang. Therefore he will have a +1 Difficulty modifier to both of his Punch maneuvers (making them Difficulty 8, instead of their usual 7). For his first attack, he rolls four dice (three for Coordination, plus one for Dexterity); his best roll is a 5. Adding this to his Unarmed Combat (Starfleet Martial Arts) 2 (3) yields a Test Result of 8—a hit! The base damage for his Punch is 4+1d6, and he adds +1 point of damage because of his Strength +1. He rolls a 2, so he does 7 points of damage. Agrak's Resistance is 4, so he resists 4 points of damage, taking the remaining 3. Since his Resistance is 4, that is not enough to move him to the Stunned Wound Level.

Agrak attacks next. He bellows "Die, Earther scum!" (bellowing epithets does not require an action) and swings his fist in a mighty jab at Lt. Commander Jansen. His Difficulty Number is 7. He rolls two dice (for his Coordination); his best die is a 2. This is added to his skill level of 3, for a Test Result of 5. He misses, smashing a brightly-painted ceramic bowl instead of Jansen's head.

Ensign Willingham's player has no illusions about Willingham's ability to pummel a Klingon warrior into unconsciousness with his bare hands, so he asks the Narrator if there is any sort of makeshift weapon nearby. The Narrator tells him there is a large wooden sculpture on a nearby counter; he can use his Primitive Weaponry skill to wield it, but its unwieldiness will give Willingham a +1 Difficulty penalty on his attack roll. Willingham grabs the idol and smashes it over Chang's head. He rolls three dice (two for Coordination, plus one for +1 Dexterity); his Drama Die comes up a 6, and his next highest die is a 4. Added to his Primitive Weaponry skill level of 2, that gives him a 12—more than enough to hit with the idol, but not quite enough for a Dramatic Success. Willingham's player rolls two dice for damage (the statue acts just like a club, which does 2+2d6 damage), getting a 7, for a total of 9 points of damage. Chang resists four of those points and takes 5, rendering him Stunned (and thus at a +1 Difficulty for all Tests until he is healed). Because he has yet to reach Incapacitated, Chang is still conscious, and for his action decides to flatten the statue-swinging Willingham with a kick from his hobnailed Klingon boots. The Narrator rolls two dice for Chang (for his Coordination 2), getting a 5 as the highest die. Adding that to Chang's Unarmed Combat skill of 2 produces a 7, not enough for a kick to succeed, especially since Chang is at +1 Difficulty thanks to being knocked groggy. Willingham scampers out of Chang's way, and the Klingon's boot smashes into a delicate glass carafe full of bright blue liquor, spraying everyone.

Since all combatants have acted for the first time (or are unconscious), the combat proceeds to any additional actions in this round. Only Lt. Commander Jansen declared more than one action, so he is the only one left to act. He is concerned about having had so little effect with his first blow, so he asks the Narrator if he can change his second action to attack Agrak again, with a Strike this time. The Narrator agrees. This time Jansen's Test Result with his Unarmed Combat (Starfleet Martial Arts) roll is a 9, indicating another hit. (The Strike's base Difficulty is 8, with a +1 modifier for Jansen's taking two actions.) Even better, when Jansen rolls his two dice for damage (for a Starfleet Martial Arts strike doing 2+2d6), he rolls a total of 11. He does 14 (2+11 plus his extra point for Strength) points of damage this time, of which Agrak takes 10 (after subtracting his Resistance of 4). Combined with the previous 3 points of damage, that's enough to reduce Agrak to Wounded (but only for purposes of

knocking him out, since unarmed melee attacks don't do lethal damage until after the target is knocked out). Agrak is knocked to the ground by the force of Jansen's powerful punches, and will be at +2 Difficulty for all Tests until healed.

Initiative Tests for the next round establish the following order of combat: Chang, Jansen, Tavak, Willingham, Agrak. Chang decides to take three actions this round: draw his sword, attack Willingham, and dodge Willingham's counterattack. This will impose a +2 to the Difficulty of all of his actions (or a -2 to his Dodge Test Result). Pulling his *mek'leth* requires no Skill Test, unfortunately.

Jansen also declares two actions: draw his phaser and fire at Chang. Drawing his phaser requires no Skill Test.

Tavak declares he will move over to Agrak and administer another Vulcan nerve pinch. The Narrator rules that Tavak is only 1m away from Agrak, so getting to him will not require an action. He also rules that because Agrak is prone and Wounded, he will be easier to hit (Difficulty will be at -2). Tavak rolls his five dice (for his Coordination + Reaction), and gets a 5 as his best result. This, plus his skill level of 3, equals 8—enough to hit even without the -2 reduction in Difficulty. The Narrator rules that, given Agrak's current state of injury, the nerve pinch automatically knocks him out for the rest of the fight, so Tavak's player doesn't bother to roll damage.

Willingham declares two actions: block Chang's attack with the wooden statue, and then counterattack. He rolls three dice (two for Coordination, plus one for Dexterity) and gets a 5, which he adds to his Primitive Weaponry skill of 2 for a 7, and the Narrator grants him a +1 to Block for the clubbed statue, for a total of 8. That's the Difficulty for Chang's attack against him.

All characters having taken their first action, second actions begin. Chang slashes at Willingham with his sword. Chang has Primitive Weaponry (*mek'leth*) 3 (4). He rolls his two Coordination dice, and gets a 5 as his best roll. Despite his warrior skill, he still missed (5 plus the skill level of 4 equals 9, less than the Difficulty of hitting Willingham, which is a base of 8 from Willingham's Block Test, +2 because Chang has declared two additional actions, +1 because Chang is Stunned, for a total of 11). The Narrator rules that Willingham deftly blocks the blow, although the sword hacks a chunk out of the statue. (Had Chang rolled lower, the Narrator might have ruled that Willingham's Block knocked the sword out of line, or even that Chang's attack missed Willingham entirely.)

Jansen goes next; he fires his phaser at Chang. They are at Point-Blank range, so his Difficulty to hit is a mere 3. Jansen has Energy Weapon (Phaser) 2 (3). The Narrator is using the optional "Automatic Success" rule, so since Jansen's skill level equals or exceeds the Difficulty (he doesn't have a Dexterity edge), Jansen automatically hits the Klingon. Jansen's phaser was previously set on 2 (Medium Stun), which does 4+2d6 damage. Jansen rolls a 10 on his two dice, for a total of 14 points of damage. Chang resists 4 points of this damage, but takes the remaining 10—enough to take him from Stunned all the way down to Wounded. Because the phaser was set on stun, Chang drops unconscious, and will remain so for 10 minutes. (Remember, even though Chang's Wound Level is Wounded, he is still only unconscious.) The player characters then take the three Klingons prisoner so they can turn them over to the authorities.

COMBAT QUICK REFERENCE SHEET

I. INITIATIVE: WHO ACTS FIRST

A. Initiative Test: Each character in combat rolls an Initiative Test using the relevant skill.
   1. The Reaction edge can modify the Initiative Test.
   2. The character who gets the highest Initiative Test Result acts first; the remaining characters act in order, from highest to lowest roll.
      a. Ties: If two or more results tie, the character who rolled higher on his Drama Die is the victor. If the Drama Die rolls are the same as well, the character or side who began the fight wins Initiative.
   3. A player cannot spend Courage Points to alter his Initiative Test.

II. ACTIONS: WHAT CHARACTERS CAN DO

A. Characters may take one or more actions during each round.
B. After Initiative is determined, each character declares his actions.
   1. Immediate Actions; Timed Actions: There are two types of actions characters can take: Immediate Actions, which take no time in combat and do not have to be declared; and Timed Actions, which take time in combat and must be declared.
   2. Delayed or Changed Actions; Surprise: Characters may delay their actions, but, must engage in an Opposed Coordination Test if they later attempt to "interrupt" another character's action. They may also change a declared action to dodge or parry an attack. Characters who are surprised by an attack can take no action (not even Immediate Actions or dodging/parrying) while surprised.
   3. Multiple Actions: Characters may declare multiple actions in a round. The first action is "free", but every action after the first adds a cumulative +1 Difficulty to all Tests that round (even the first one).
C. Movement: Characters can move up to 10m per round at a brisk walk; moving faster may require a Test with modifiers for terrain.
   1. Movement Maneuvers: Characters may also perform Movement Maneuvers, such as dropping prone or diving for cover.

III. RANGED COMBAT

A. Ranged combat uses ranged weapons such as phasers or arrows.
B. The Difficulty to hit a target depends on how far away it is: Point Blank (3), Short (4), Medium (7) or Long (10).
   1. Dodging: If a target dodges a ranged attack, the Difficulty is not based on range, but on the Test Result of his Dodge roll; however, the minimum Difficulty remains the one indicated by the range.
   2. Combat Variables: There are numerous situations which can modify a character's ability to make a successful ranged attack, including cover, weapon targeting systems, and zero gravity conditions.

C. Hitting a Target: To hit a target, the character rolls his attribute (plus his Dexterity edge, if he has one) and adds the highest die to his skill; Drama Die rules apply.

IV. MELEE COMBAT

A. Melee combat involves punches, martial arts or other combat maneuvers, and weapons such as knives.
B. Difficulty for melee combat depends upon the type of attack or maneuver being used. For example, the Difficulty for a basic Punch is 7.
   1. If a target dodges or parries a melee attack, the Difficulty is based on the Test Result of his Dodge, Block, or Primitive Weaponry roll; however, the minimum Difficulty is still based on the attack type.
   2. Combat Variables: There are numerous situations that can modify a character's ability to make a successful melee attack, including cover and zero gravity.
C. To hit a target, the character rolls his attribute (plus his Dexterity edge, if applicable) and adds the highest die to his skill; Drama Die rules apply.

V. DAMAGE

A. Most weapons and attacks cause normal damage(i.e., damage that can injure or kill someone). Some attacks, including phasers set on stun and punches, only cause Stun damage; stun damage renders a target unconscious once he reaches a certain Wound Level (*Stunned* for energy weapons and Vulcan nerve pinches; *Incapacitated* for punches and similar attacks).
   1. Brawling Attacks: Untrained, unarmed melee attacks cause damage equal to the attacker's Fitness + Strength (Stun damage).
   2. Weapons and combat maneuvers have their own damage codes to indicate how much damage they cause; Strength modifies the damage roll for melee combat. For example, a basic Punch does 3+1d6 damage, modified by the character's Strength.
B. Rolling Damage: Attack damage equals the total rolled on the dice.
   1. The Drama Die rule does not apply to damage rolls.
   2. Courage Points may not be spent to increase damage rolls.
C. Resisting Damage: Characters may resist a number of points of damage equal to their Resistance (plus any Armor) from each attack. All points of damage beyond that apply directly to the character, injuring him.
D. The state of a character's health is measured by *Wound Levels*. There are seven Wound Levels: Healthy, Stunned, Injured, Wounded, Incapacitated, Near Death, and Killed. A character can take his Resistance in damage before dropping to the next level. The worse a character's Wound Level, the more Difficulty penalties he suffers; there may be other ill effects as well.
E. Healing: Characters may heal naturally, or with medical help. Either type of healing requires the character to make Fitness Tests (modified by Vitality, if the character has the edge) to improve his Wound Level. Healing with medical attention is normally quicker and easier.

Diamond admired the Hans Arp bronze in Admiral Donwoods' office. He and Donwoods had crossed swords in the past, but at least the man had impeccable taste when it came to art.

The door swooshed open and Donwoods sauntered in, in his usual mildly disdainful way. He scarcely looked up at Diamond as he crossed behind his desk to his big padded chair. He was reading a briefing, eyes peering out from behind antique spectacles. Diamond once again found himself wishing that his old mentor, Admiral Vaughn, was still shackled to his desk instead of honing his golf game at the expense of his other retired colleagues.

"Good news, Diamond. Saving half the Federation Council from death at the hands of that mitochondrial parasite has done wonders for your career jacket. You've been wanting command of a bigger ship for a long time now, haven't you?"

"Yes, sir."

"It's no secret that I've opposed your transfer requests. Until now. I trust a Constitution-class vessel will give you the leg room you require?"

"Constitution-class? Which one?"

"The Potemkin. Crosbie's joining us in rear echelon."

"Thank you, sir."

"Don't thank me. And one more thing—your last action as commander of the Solzhenitsyn will be to discipline that Lt. Seel of yours. He should have watched his tongue around the Tiburonese ambassador. Bust him down to ensign."

REWARDS

"But, Admiral, Seel was possessed by the parasite when he said those things. You've read my report."

Donwoods smiled tightly. "The ambassador is quite insistent."

"I protest, sir; Seel is a fine officer. Politics be damned."

"The reprimand can go in his jacket or yours, Mr. Diamond. Of course, with a reprimand on your record…"

"The Potemkin goes to someone else. Very well, sir. The Solzhenitsyn needs a refit anyway, and with six months in space dock, perhaps my team can find out how Starfleet Command let security for the Council get so lax. I'm sure Commissioner Dakin will be very interested in my findings."

Donwoods gave Diamond a look far colder than the bronze on his desk. Diamond returned it with glacial calm.

"The Potemkin warps out for the Klingon frontier in forty-eight hours. You and Lieutenant Seel had better be on it, and out of my sight, in twelve."

"With pleasure, sir."

Characters learn, grow, and become better at what they do—just like real people. They're dynamic individuals who learn from their experiences, interact with others, and adapt to new situations. The Icon System simulates this by granting characters Experience Points that they can use to improve existing skills, buy new skills, improve attributes and edges, and sometimes even buy or improve advantages. Thus, the more characters do in the game, the more they learn, and they better they become at their jobs. If appropriate, they may even go up in rank and work their way up the Starfleet ladder.

Awarding Experience Points

At the end of each game session (or sometimes after several game sessions, if it takes several sessions to complete one episode or the episodes are all related), the Narrator will award Experience Points to the characters. The amount of points a character receives depends on three factors: what the characters accomplished; how well they accomplished it; and how well the players roleplayed their characters.

First, did the characters accomplish their goals during the episode? If they did, they deserve Experience Points. The better they did the job, the more Experience Points they should earn. If they barely succeeded, or caused additional problems along the way, they should get a smaller reward (or perhaps no Experience Points at all). On the other hand, if they did an admirable job, showed initiative and cleverness, didn't do anything stupid, and so on, they probably deserve some extra Experience Points.

Second, did the characters do their job well? Since failure often teaches characters as much as victory, simply failing to accomplish a scenario's goals isn't a reason not to award Experience Points. You have to look at the *reasons* for their failure. If they failed because of their own foolishness, aggressiveness, stupidity, greed, destructiveness, or other character flaws, they're to blame for their own failure, and they should receive a minimal amount of Experience Points (if any). However, if they did their best, acted appropriately, made good decisions, and tried with their heart and spirit, but just happened to fail anyway (perhaps because of poor dice rolls), then they still deserve a normal Experience Point award.

Third, did the players roleplay their characters well? In the *Star Trek Roleplaying Game*, players typically take on the role of Starfleet officers. If they "get into character," act as their character would act, and think as their character would think, they deserve extra Experience Points as a reward for contributing to everyone's enjoyment of the game (assuming that their "roleplaying" actually contributed to the game). Players who don't act like Starfleet characters (they use force frequently and brutally, or readily steal others' belongings, for example), don't roleplay their traits well (for example, a Vulcan character who acts emotionally), or who don't make any effort to interact with others, should receive few or no Experience Points.

The accompanying table provides some guidelines for awarding Experience Points. Note that these rewards are fairly small—typically just a point or two. One to three Experience Points per episode is an average award; more than that indicates extremely good performance or roleplaying. Limiting Experience Points awards allows characters to grow in a slow, fairly controlled

EXPERIENCE POINT AWARDS

Points	Circumstance
1 to 2	Characters accomplished the goal(s) of the episode
-1	Characters accomplished the goal(s) of the episode, but did so poorly or caused additional problems
+1	Characters accomplished the goal(s) of the episode in an exemplary and clever fashion
1	Characters failed to accomplish the goals of the episode, but nevertheless did their best and learned from their failures
+0	Characters were roleplayed properly
+1 to +2	Characters were roleplayed well
-1 to -2	Characters were roleplayed poorly
+1 to +2	Characters did or accomplished something that was of extraordinary service or benefit to Starfleet, the Federation or its citizens, or which required great personal sacrifice on the characters' part
+1	Characters triumphed against overwhelming odds or overcame tremendous obstacles

manner (just like real people—people don't learn new skills or become stronger overnight, or learn new abilities every week). It also helps the Narrator keep the characters from becoming too effective or powerful before the series, and the Narrator, is ready.

The minimum experience point award is zero, regardless of the penalties imposed. You can't take previously-earned Experience Points away from a character, despite how poor his current performance may be.

Spending Experience Points

Characters typically spend Experience Points to buy new skills, improve existing skill levels, or buy new specializations. This reflects the new things a character learns and experiences during the course of his adventures. For example, during an episode a character who knows Propulsion Engineering (Warp Drive) might make several difficult Tests to fix the impulse engines under stressful conditions. The player decides that his character learned a lot from this experience, so he spends some of his Experience Points to buy a new specialization (Impulse).

Buying a brand-new skill is a little trickier. The player must justify some in-game reason or way for a character to learn the new skill—characters don't just have new skills spring full-blown from their heads at the end of adventures. It's often more realistic to set aside a point or two over several episodes, then buy the skill when enough points have been saved up; this reflects a more gradual learning process. The Narrator can provide you with an estimate of how long it takes a character to learn a particular skill. Characters may pick some up relatively quickly (after an extended episode on Axanar, a character might justifiably buy one level in Language (Axanari) as a new skill); others (such as most

Item	Cost
Buying a new Skill (level 1)	5
Improving a known Skill...	
to level 2	3
to level 3	3
to level 4	4
to level 5	5
to level 6	6
Buying a new Specialization	
(at one level higher than the governing skill)	3
Improving an existing Specialization...	
to level 3	2
to level 4	3
to level 5	4
to level 6	5
Improving Attributes...	
to level 2	4
to level 3	4
to level 4	5
to level 5	6
to level 6 (if allowed)	7
Improving Edges	4 per point improved
Buying a new Advantage	4 x value of Advantage
Improving an existing Advantage	4 x improvement in value
Reducing or eliminating a Disadvantage	4 x reduction in value
Courage Point	5

process; they don't wake up one morning with Excellent Hearing or a High Pain Threshold. However, other advantages, such as Ally, Species Friend, Promotion or Contact, are excellent places to spend an Experience Point or three. However, the purchase must be justified based on the events of recent episodes. A character can't just plunk down a few Experience Points and earn a Promotion or become a Species Friend; his recent conduct must have drawn the attention of his superiors, or resulted in saving the species in question from some disaster, before he earns those advantages.

If appropriate, characters can also spend Experience Points to reduce or eliminate disadvantages. This isn't always justifiable—you can't make a Dark Secret go away by spending some points. However, a character could overcome a personality flaw (like Argumentative or Obsessive Tendencies) through counseling and willpower, or receive medical care to eliminate his Poor Hearing.

Although characters spend Experience Points just like Development Points, most game elements cost more when bought with Experience. The accompanying _Experience Point Cost Table_ lists the costs for experience-based character improvements.

All costs for improving skills, attributes, and edges are cumulative. Thus, improving a skill from level 3 to level 5 costs a total of 9 Experience Points (4 for rank 4, 5 for rank 5); going from Logic -2 to Logic 0 costs 8 Experience Points (4 points for each point of improvement).

The Narrator must approve all Experience Point expenditures. Characters cannot purchase Renown with Experience Points: Even those advantages that can grant Renown bonuses should only grant Renown if the Famous Incident, say, was actually roleplayed. No Narrator should let players force her to grant them Renown by buying a Commendation, for example, with Experience Points.

Courage Points

In addition to, or in lieu of, Experience Points, Narrators may reward character conduct with additional Courage Points. Every character has at least 3 Courage Points at the start of the game, and they can "refresh" as he spends them (see page 103 for details on recovering spent Courage Points). But characters often find it helpful to have more than three.

Sciences or Engineering skills) would take a long time to learn, even with constant study every week. The longer the time period between adventures, the quicker that characters can learn many skills.

Characters can also improve attributes or edges, but this takes longer and occurs less frequently. Few characters become more dexterous or develop a more forceful personality overnight. Whether a character can increase an attribute or edge, and how long it takes, is up to the Narrator. Increasing Strength or Dexterity through exercise and combat simulations is relatively easy; boosting one's Intelligence or Presence is a much slower, more involved process.

Buying new advantages is even less common. Characters obviously cannot buy some, such as Mixed Species Heritage, after the character creation

Characters may purchase Courage Points with Experience Points, at the rate of 5 Experience Points per Courage Point. The Narrator may award Courage Points directly to characters who perform particularly noble, heroic, or self-sacrificing actions. Examples include a character who puts himself in extreme danger to rescue people or undertakes an especially dangerous mission (as in "The *Enterprise* Incident"), one who overcomes (but still roleplays) a Phobia or other personal disadvantage to accomplish some heroic feat, one who is nearly killed when he stays behind to hold off some menace while his comrades (or those under his care) escape to safety, or one who braves and overcomes incredible obstacles or opposition to warn the Federation of an impending danger.

Don't let characters have too many Courage Points. Since they allow a character to provide direct bonuses to Test Results, they're very powerful, and can skew the game in the character's favor if he has a lot of them to spend. It's not much fun for anyone to play with a character who never fails at anything—even the greatest heroes should have flaws and weaknesses.

Renown

Besides Experience Points, characters can also earn Renown. Renown, after all, reflects a character's reputation, and one earns a reputation because of one's actions. Anything which gets a character noticed should increase his Renown in appropriate aspects. Thus, a character who saves the Axanari Ambassador from

assassination, for example, would earn Renown. The typical Renown award is 1-2 points, but this depends on the nature of the character's actions and the events surrounding them—things which attract galaxy-wide attention to the character could conceivably earn him a dozen Renown points or more.

The Narrator should examine the circumstances in which the character earned Renown to determine which aspect the award applies to. For example, if he disregarded his own prejudice against Axanari and obeyed orders while saving the Ambassador, he would receive Discipline Renown. If, on the other hand, he saw the threat and acted instantly, or disobeyed an order to do what he knew was right, that would imply Initiative Renown, and so on. If no particular Aspect seems entirely appropriate, award Skill Renown.

SUGGESTED RENOWN GUIDELINES

The *Renown Awards Table* provides some rough guidelines for character Renown awards. Of course, almost any action taken in the proper context could garner Renown for a character, so this list should not be considered exhaustive.

COMMENDATIONS AND AWARDS

Commendations, awards, medals, and other such indicia of exceptional valor, bravery, or merit often accompany significant Renown awards. If a char-

RENOWN AWARDS TABLE

Incident	Renown
Saving the life of an important NPC during a secret diplomatic mission	1-2
Saving the life of an important NPC during a public diplomatic mission	2-3
Saving the life of an important NPC during a highly-publicized or well-known diplomatic mission	4-6
NPC who is saved is extremely important (e.g., the Federation President, a member of the Vulcan Council)	+1-4
Uncovering a Romulan spy in Federation space	1-2
Uncovering a Romulan spy in a dangerous position (e.g., a listening post near an important starbase) in Federation space	3-4
Uncovering a Romulan spy in an extremely dangerous position (e.g., secretary to a Starfleet Admiral) in Federation space	5-6
Displaying skill or valor in a skirmish	1-2
Displaying skill or valor in a minor battle	2-3
Displaying skill or valor in a major battle	4-6
Displaying skill or valor in a battle that threatens the very existence of the Federation (e.g., the Battle of Axanar)	7-12
Successfully completing a minor diplomatic mission	1-2
Successfully completing an important diplomatic mission	2-3
Successfully completing an extremely important diplomatic mission	4-6
Successfully completing a diplomatic mission which may affect the course of galactic politics for decades to come	7-12
Making a scientific discovery of minor importance	1-2
Making a scientific discovery of major importance	3-4
Making a scientific discovery which may have a profound effect on Federation technology	5-10
Discovering a new and important use for existing technolog	1-4

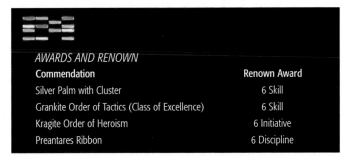

acter earns a large amount of Renown through one action (or series of related actions), he may qualify for a commendation as well. The accompanying table provides a list of common Federation awards, along with suggested Renown awards (for a single incident) which might qualify a character as a recipient (the names of some of the commendations also provide some guidance as to what they should be awarded for). Note that getting the commendation does not mean you automatically get the listed amount of Renown; instead, you have to earn the listed amount of Renown (typically for a single incident, or for valorous conduct over a specific period of time, such as a campaign against the Klingons) to qualify for the commendation.

PROMOTION AND RANK

Unless the Narrator allows it, and the other players don't mind, no beginning character who belongs to Starfleet should start the series with a rank higher than Lieutenant Commander. Part of the fun of the *Star Trek Roleplaying Game* is watching your characters grow and develop from one episode to the next. Earning promotions and peer recognition becomes an important part of such ongoing development.

Characters can't obtain promotions just by spending Experience Points on the necessary skills and advantages and obtaining enough Renown. You've got to roleplay the situation and fit the promotion into the context of the overall series. Among other things, the character needs to have the attention and approval of his superiors (represented, of course, by the Narrator); if he's done something to offend them, he may be stuck at a low rank for a long time, no matter how skilled he is. Even more importantly, if he's not truly worthy of higher rank, Starfleet's not going to give it to him, even if he's the admiral's godson—he's got to deserve the advancement.

Suppose that a character at the Helm decides that he would like to command his own starship one day. Getting there is more than a matter of playing enough games to earn the Experience Points to "buy" his way up the ranks. He needs to talk to his current commander (*i.e.*, the Narrator, in most games) about the requirements, and make arrangements to meet them (which usually takes years). Typically the quest for command involves one or more transfers so that the character can learn all the skills he needs and can familiarize himself with all of the major subsystems of a starship. This presents plenty of roleplaying and storytelling opportunities (not to mention an episode seed or two) which a good Narrator can work into an ongoing series (or many series).

The following section presents some guidelines for Narrators to use when considering player characters for promotion. Keep in mind that these are only

guidelines; the circumstances surrounding any promotion should first and foremost add to the story. In suitably dramatic or important circumstances, a character might receive a promotion even though he hasn't fulfilled all of the criteria listed here. Of course, Starfleet expects the beneficiaries of such informal field promotions to devote much of their time to study and activities intended to bring them up to speed with their peers. Characters should also, at the Narrator's option, purchase the appropriate *Promotion* advantage as soon as possible. See pages 30-31 in the *Starfleet* chapter for details on the Starfleet rank structure and the nature of field or brevet promotions.

Lieutenant (Junior Grade)

2 levels in the primary skill for their department, 1 level in one other departmental skill

Lieutenant

3 levels in the primary skill for their department, 1 level in two or more other departmental skills

Lieutenant Commander

25 Renown, 15 in Starfleet-favored Aspects (Initiative, Skill, Openness); 3 levels in the primary skill for their department, 2 levels in at least two other departmental skills, 1 level in the primary skill of another department

Commander

40 Renown, 25 in Starfleet-favored Aspects; 4 levels in the primary skill for their department, 2 levels in at least three other departmental skills, 1 level in the primary skill of two other departments (Security, Engineering, Helm, Communications, Science, Medical)

Captain

60 Renown, 45 in Starfleet-favored Aspects; Law (Starfleet Regulations) 4(5), Command (any specialization) 4(5), Administration (any specialization) 3 (4), 2 levels in the primary skill of at least two other departments

Commodore

70 Renown, 50 in Starfleet-favored Aspects; Law (Starfleet Regulations) 4(5), Command (any specialization) 4(5), Administration (any specialization) 4 (5), 3 levels in the primary skill of at least two other departments

Admiral

80 Renown, 60 in Starfleet-favored Aspects; Law (Starfleet Regulations) 5 (6), Command (any specialization) 5 (6), Administration (any specialization) 4 (5)

Departmental Skills

The Narrator has a bit of latitude when determining a character's "departmental Skills." Characters must *always* have the appropriate primary skills (such as Command, Security, or the various types of Engineering). But depending on a character's assignment or mission, Espionage could be more important for a Security officer than Persuasion (if he were stationed on a ship containing new technology that the Romulans might want to obtain). Remember that when a rank calls for "2 levels in other departmental Skills," this only represents a general guideline for Narrators and players. Specifics always depend on the character and the series.

TRANSFERRING DEPARTMENTS

Starfleet characters may wish to transfer from one department to another during their careers. Perhaps they want to study new subjects or work their way up to command of a starship. In either case, a character who wishes to transfer must put in a request for transfer with his captain.

A good captain won't approve transfer requests blindly. The character must deserve the transfer, and that means he has to meet several requirements. These include:

Satisfactory Reason

The character must offer a satisfactory explanation for his request. "I want to buy more skills!" is not usually a valid explanation. The character's request should reflect a good *in-game* reason why he wants to transfer, not a reason primarily motivated by game rules.

Good Renown

The character should have positive totals in Renown for Skill, Initiative, and Openness (other organizations and cultures will require positive totals in other Aspects). Negative Renown in any of these aspects means that the captain will almost certainly deny the transfer (unless he feels it would improve the character's performance, and thus Renown).

Satisfactory Performance

The character's performance in his present job must be satisfactory—no demotions, demerits, reprimands, or other negative notes in his personnel record (or, at the very least, they must have occurred a long time ago). Few

RULES-DRIVEN PROMOTIONS

The following optional guidelines are for Narrators who prefer a mechanical method of promotion over a purely event-driven one. The Narrator can either have the character's superior officer (or other Starfleet official) roll a Challenging (10) Renown Test (to simulate the character coming to the attention of Starfleet) either after a Challenging (9) Administration (Starfleet Bureaucracy) Test or after a suitably dramatic increase in character Renown. No character should be promoted using this method until they qualify at least at the minimum levels given above; the Narrator is encouraged to come up with other, additional qualifications if she wishes. Characters receiving field or brevet promotions should not be considered for further promotion until they meet the minimum standards of their field or brevet rank.

captains will transfer a problem character (unless, perhaps, to let someone else deal with him).

Replacement

Another crewmember must be available to take over the character's current position, and, if necessary, the character must train his replacement before transferring.

Assuming the character meets these requirements, the captain will probably grant his request. If necessary, the character can improve his chances by roleplaying, and succeeding in, an Opposed Test of his Persuasion+Presence versus the captain's Persuasion+Intellect.

TRANSFERRING TO A BETTER SHIP

Besides being promoted, characters who do their duty well may also be transferred to a better ship. Usually this means a bigger, better-equipped ship, but "better" can vary from character to character; one character might want a transfer to a ship closer to, say, a front in the ongoing conflict with the Klingons, while another might value a posting to a science vessel exploring intriguing astronomical phenomena. Obviously, if the characters start out on the biggest, best ship the Federation maintains, few places exist for them to go, but they could still be transferred to a ship commanded by a more prestigious captain or which has a more "glamorous" purpose.

To merit consideration for transfer to a better ship, characters typically need at least 20 Renown, 12 points of it in Starfleet-favored Aspects. Beyond that, they've got to get themselves noticed as "up-and-comers" by Starfleet Command or the captain (or first officer) of the new ship. A Patron, Ally, or Favor Owed may help; so will a commendation or large Renown award for a single incident.

Of course, the transfer should be part of the game; the Narrator may even use it as the seed for an entire episode (or series of episodes). It's not just game mechanics and dice-rolling; it's a chance to roleplay. Moving the characters to a better ship, with perhaps a different mission, is sometimes a good way to re-focus a *Star Trek Roleplaying Game* series, or to change the current series' direction and tone.

For example, suppose that, over the course of several episodes, the characters' ship has to work together with a better ship (and perhaps personnel from several other ships) in a major space battle against Romulan aggression, or to defeat some dangerous force threatening the Federation. This allows the Crew to strut its stuff and impress the other captain, or her first officer. The Narrator should make sure that the Crew gets the chance to work with these NPCs—perhaps their captain posts them as liaisons to the better ship, for example. If some crewmembers on the better ship suffer injuries or death during the incident depicted in the episode, the captain of that ship can then request that the Crew be permanently transferred to his ship.

Another good way to engineer a ship transfer is to give the Crew a new ship, a reconstructed ship, or even an experimental ship as their own. Being the ones to put a newer, bigger, shinier ship through its paces should be enough to excite any Crew.

Pearlstein mournfully surveyed the engine room of the U.S.S. Fraser. "You can practically smell the mothballs, eh, Captain?"

Duffy couldn't help but laugh. Like most engineers, Pearlstein treated his ship like a member of the family. To leave the Indomitable behind and fly a mission on this other ship–why, it was like stepping out on your wife.

"Josh, you know better than anyone that the Indomitable isn't spaceworthy yet. It'll be in space dock for another month, minimum."

"I just can't help feeling I should be there with her, that's all. I'm not saying Goloth isn't a good builder, you understand. It's just that nobody understands that ship like I do."

"True, but I need you with me. I need someone I can trust to get this bucket into shape within forty-eight hours. Can you do it?"

Pearlstein made a face. "Forty-eight hours? Our best is the best we can do, sir."

STARSHIPS

Duffy slapped him on the back. "That's the old Josh Pearlstein can-do attitude coming back. After all, we don't want those colonists to spend an hour more than they have to in Klingon custody, do we?"

"Of course not, sir. And of course we'll do it. But, sir–A Cook-class vessel? On what might turn out to be a combat mission? This hunk of rust must be fifty years old! Why don't they just give us a Boeing 797 and ask us to fly that to Satara III?"

"Nobody said life in Starfleet was easy, Josh."

"All I ask is for some kind of middle ground between easy and impossible." Pearlstein set his kit down on the engine room floor and withdrew a tricorder to scan for structural flaws. His eyes landed on a small dull-grayish spot on a console. He reached out and pulled the spot loose, holding it up to the captain for inspection.

"Would you believe it? Who worked here last? They ought to be court-martialed, except they're probably dead in a shipwreck, or of old age and stupidity! Look at it! Solder, Captain! Solder!"

What Is a Starship?

Starships are interstellar craft which uses warp propulsion to enable it to achieve faster-than-light speeds. It's a broad term, encompassing everything from Zefram Cochrane's first *Phoenix* to the powerful *Constitution*-class ships to the enormous, awesome vessels of the First Federation. The starships of the Federation's Starfleet project UFP influence throughout the galaxy and capably handle a variety of missions—military, exploration, diplomatic, and humanitarian, to name but a few. Starfleet classifies sublight ships like shuttles as craft, while usually referring to generation ships like the worldship *Yonada* or sleeper ships like the *S.S. Botany Bay* as spaceships.

SHIP TYPES

Starfleet builds vessels for specific functions (some of which, like "exploration," are quite broad), as do most starfaring civilizations. Some cultures emphasize the construction of certain types of ships (Klingons, for example, have several warship designs but few trading ships); other cultures use fewer designs and a few use very generalized ships. The peaceful, scientific culture of the Federation means that Starfleet starships traditionally focus on exploration.

Starfleet uses the following general classifications for ships:

Couriers

Light transport vessels used to deliver special cargoes—diplomats; rare, precious, or valuable objects; sensitive documents; and vital perishables such as medicines. Fast and heavily shielded, couriers have small crews, light weapons, and relatively limited storage space.

Cruisers

Medium- to large-sized starships primarily used mainly for quasi-military duties (patrol, interdiction, and the like). However, they are capable of many other missions, such as escort duty or colony support. The *Miranda*-class ships currently on the Utopia Planitia drawing boards are cruisers, scheduled to replace the older *Comanche*-class patrol ships by 2274.

Escorts

Small, heavily armed and shielded, combat-oriented ships. Starfleet builds relatively few escorts, not being a military organization; the Klingons, on the other hand, build many of them. Escorts are usually assigned to a starbase (or even a large starship), since they're not equipped for extended missions. Watching a galactic power's escort production and maintenance often provides information about whether it expects hostilities in the near future.

Explorers

Multipurpose starships suited for many different duties—exploration, defense, diplomacy, and many others. Ever since the *Daedalus*, explorers have been Starfleet's primary vessels. Among the largest and most heavily armed ships built by Starfleet, explorers often cruise on multi-year missions. The *Constitution* class is the best-known example of an explorer.

Fighters

Tiny, short-range starships with limited warp capability, relatively powerful weapons, and small crews (often only one pilot). Fighters are more common in planetary systems, where they can receive regular refueling and maintenance.

Freighters

Transport vessels used to move cargo throughout the galaxy. They are the lifeblood of the Federation's economy, and a crucial link to colonies that aren't yet self-sufficient. Most carriers are slow and not well-equipped for fighting. Freighters which carry deuterium fuel are called tankers, those which carry large numbers of personnel are called transports (for colonial and Starfleet use) or liners (for civilian use).

Frigates

Small- to medium-sized starships used mostly for patrol, defense, and interdiction. Frigates are well armed for their size and generally well equipped for a long service life. Frigate-sized ships are sometimes the most powerful ships that smaller spacefaring civilizations can construct; such frigates are sometimes more heavily armed, or fitted out like explorers.

Scouts

Small ships intended for short-range expeditions into unknown territory—they fly out, look around, and then fly back to a starbase to report. Starfleet scouts are built for up to a year's self-sufficiency; well armed for their size, but no match for a dedicated warship. They come equipped with sophisticated sensor bays and plenty of long-range probes for exploration missions, paving the way for future scouting missions.

Shuttlecraft

Shuttlecraft are short-range transports with few weapons systems and relatively low speeds. Starfleet issues shuttles to starships to be used, for example, to carry personnel down to planets when transporters don't work. Shuttles can carry a variety of scientific instrumentation, and often see duty as "piloted probes" into interstellar anomalies.

Surveyors

These ships, which can vary wildly in size, perform long-term scientific or cultural study missions. Like characters, they tend to be specialized for studying a particular subject. Cosmophysical surveyors collect data on space-time anomalies, energy fields, and strange radiation; stellar surveyors study astronomical phenomena, map the reaches of space, and update astrogational charts; anthropological surveyors observe prewar civilizations, etc. Surveyors are equipped for learning, not war; they have excellent sensor suites, weak weapons and shields, and so forth. *Antares*-class science vessels are surveyors.

NAVIGATION

To travel around the galaxy, you have to know how to get from point A to point B without getting lost—in short, how to navigate in space. This is the ship's Navigator's job, and there are roughly three ways he can do it.

The first is *relative heading and bearing*. Starships are considered to be at the center of two 360 degree circles: the azimuth (horizontal to the ship's gravity plane) and the elevation. The ship's relative heading equals 000 on the azimuth and 0 on elevation, referred as a heading of 000 mark 0. Another object's bearing is defined on these planes: an object exactly 90 degrees port and 45 degrees "above" is bearing 90 mark 45. Relative bearing can also be used to determine flight path by ordering a heading of, for example, 290 mark 35. Once the ship has been turned and is proceeding on the new course, the ship's computers reorient the relative heading, making the current direction 000.0.

In some instances, starships use *absolute heading*, meaning a heading determined in comparison to astronomical charts that orient the ship to galactic center. A ship moving on absolute heading 000 mark 0 is traveling directly toward the Galactic Core. This navigational method is useful for communicating galactic coordinates, especially to civilizations using alien navigation protocols.

Lastly, Navigators can use *analog* navigational methods, involving proceeding towards a previously catalogued destination or landmark. Of course, this requires the ship's navigational computer and database, since the Navigator can't keep track of literally trillions of stellar objects (such as planets, stars, sectors, artificial objects like starbases, or galactopolitical boundaries like the Neutral Zone) in his head. Navigational computers are programmed with billions of these destinations, so the Navigator need only tell the ship to proceed to "Tarsus IV" and it sets the course there automatically.

Due to galactic rotation and the constant changes taking place in space—everything from stars exploding to planets being moved around by beings like the Metrons—astrogation can be difficult. All spacefaring species maintain enormous astrogational databases to assist them with this task, and constantly update them with information from exploratory craft, powerful subspace observatories, and scientific exchange treaties.

ARTIFICIAL NAVIGATION AIDS

Artificial navigation devices include navigation buoys and subspace radio relays placed by Starfleet for use by Federation ships. Other species and pow-

ers construct similar devices. These aids transmit navigational datafeeds to starships via subspace radio. Each Federation sector has at least one navigation buoy; hazardous sectors have many more. Loss of contact with these navigation aids increases the navigation Difficulty by +1 or +2. This is not crucial, as any starship should be able to navigate by celestial phenomena alone.

STELLAR NAVIGATION AIDS

Known celestial reference points (such as guide stars like Canopus, Archanis, and Sirius) help a good Navigator do his job even in the absence of artificial aids. Since the pattern of the stars changes constantly as a ship moves, typically the Navigator uses the ship's sensors to home in on relatively stable objects, such as stellar pairs, black holes, pulsars, nebulae, and distant quasars, and then moves the ship in relation to them. Starship navigation databases include information on many thousand known celestial objects. As long as a starship maintains sensor contact with these phenomena, the Navigator probably can't get lost. Navigating without artificial or natural navigation references (or without the computer) increases the Difficulty by +6.

MAKING SKILL TESTS

Normally, characters don't have to make Tests to navigate properly; the Narrator can assume that, as long as a ship's sensors are functioning, most Starship Systems (Navigation) Tests are at a Routine (3) Difficulty. In more difficult situations—such as during a sensor failure, plotting a course across an unknown area, when an unexpected phenomenon appears (an uncharted asteroid crosses the ship's path, a plasma storm occurs, a subspace rift opens in front of the ship), or when traveling through or near potentially dangerous stellar phenomena like nebulae or gravity wells—a Shipboard Systems (Navigation) Test is necessary. The Narrator determines the Test's Difficulty, based on the situation.

Starship Locations

Most Federation starships follow the standard pattern created by Gnarr of Tellar when he designed the *U.S.S. Daedalus* and its sister ships in the mid-22nd century. Large ships have a primary hull and a secondary, engineering, hull fitted with two warp nacelles. In some models both hulls are adjacent; in others, they are joined by pylons or dorsals. Each ship has a bridge, the central control room and command post for the ship. The primary hull can separate from the engineering hull in emergencies, although the maneuver is a tricky and desperate one.

BRIDGE

The main bridge controls the ship. It contains the command module and at least two other workstations: the science station and communications station. All but the smallest starship bridges also contain additional workstations. On some ships (more often on a ship under yellow or red alert), security personnel may

be stationed on the bridge either as guards on the turbolift or manning a peripheral station (either communications, engineering, or life support) as a security command post.

Command Module

On most starships, the command, navigation, and helm stations are located in the center of the bridge on a small raised dais known as the command module. The command module contains all of the most vital bridge functions.

Captain's Chair

The primary command station is the captain's chair. This station features armrests incorporating an intercom that can contact all critical areas of the ship, as well as performing general broadcasts. In addition, the command station contains a direct voice link to the ship's computer, override controls for most vital ship functions, and readouts to display any on-board emergencies.

Helm

The helm station controls the actual piloting of the ship. The helmsman monitors automatic flight operations and manually pilots the ship, if necessary. Manual control seldom occurs outside of emergencies or other precise and difficult situations. The helmsman is also responsible for adjusting the ship's course to compensate for navigational hazards and for monitoring the navigational deflectors and the navigational and long-range astronomical sensors.

In combat, the helmsman is responsible for the deflector shields and other defensive systems as well as for targeting and firing the ship's weapons, subject to the captain's orders. When the captain places the ship at red alert status due to an external threat a tactical viewer automatically deploys from the helm console. This viewer provides detailed information on the position, bearing, and identity of all other ships within range. It can be used to help maintain targeting locks on rapidly moving vessels, and to focus phaser banks and photon torpedoes on localized targets like an enemy ship's weapons ports or engines, or on a single ground vehicle on the surface of a nearby planet.

Navigation

The navigation station is responsible for plotting the ship's course. In addition, this station is used to determine the ship's exact position, velocity, and

direction. The navigator plots all courses, records the ship's position, and determines any possible spatial anomalies or other dangers on the ship's projected course. To this end, the navigation station is linked to the science station's sensor and computer systems. The navigation station also has control of the main viewscreen. In an emergency, the navigation station can also control the firing of the ship's weapons and operating the deflector screens.

Peripheral Bridge Stations

The remainder of these workstations rings the periphery of the ship's bridge. Starship bridges are usually circular rooms with a large main viewscreen located at the front of the room.

Communications

The communications station controls both internal and external communications. The communication station handles all encryption and decryption routines for Starfleet codes as well as monitoring and controlling the ship's Universal Translator. The communications officer is responsible for refining the Universal Translator's search routines. In addition, the communications station controls internal broadcasts to the rest of the ship's crew and compiles damage reports and other communications from elsewhere in the ship.

Science

The science station controls and oversees the operation of all sensors and probes; it also contains equipment for interpreting the data from these sources and for rapidly accessing related data from the ship's library computer. In addition, the science officer coordinates the activities of the technicians in the ship's various laboratories. To aid in the interpretation of the data gathered by the sensors, the science station also contains a specially designed viewer dis-

CONTROL PANELS

Every crew station on a starship has a specialized control panel. Each of these panels contains a large number of specialized readouts and controls. The vast majority of these controls consist of large, simple, easy-to-operate switches, buttons, and dials. Most of the readouts utilize clearly labeled lines of display lights which indicate the status of various shipboard functions.

Starfleet has found that in crisis situations most humanoids are able to operate large, obvious controls like these considerably more rapidly and with less possible confusion than other, more complex controls. Every control panel features a speaker and microphone to communicate with the ship's computer or with other locations throughout the ship. Each panel also has at least one input slot for standard reader tapes and a small viewscreen or other device for observing visual data. Any control panel on the ship contains circuits for a manual override of computer control; depending on the instructions given the computer, a technician can bypass these circuits.

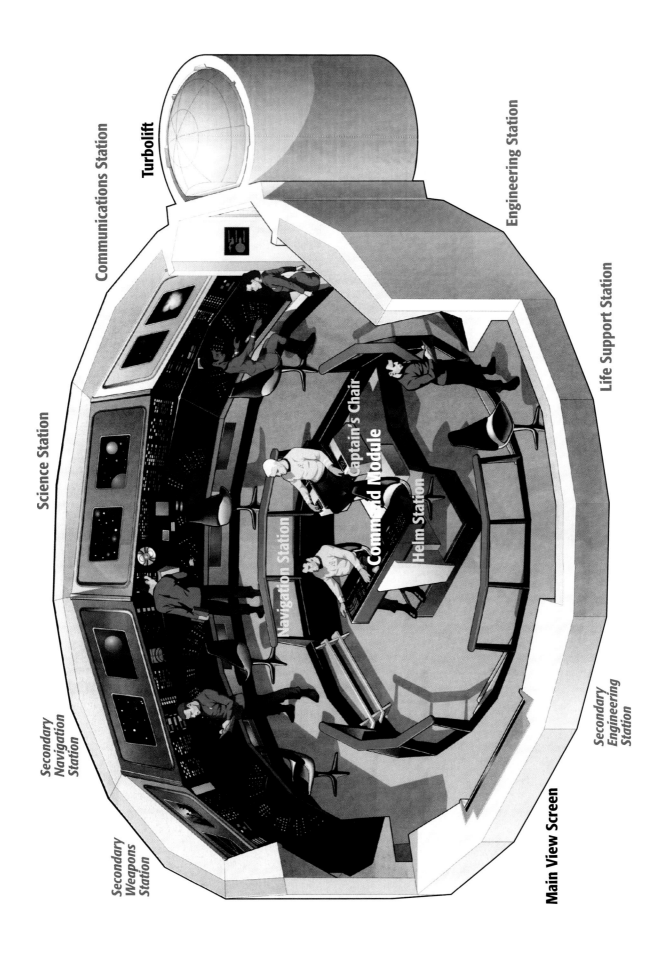

Communications Station

Turbolift

Science Station

Secondary
Navigation
Station

Secondary
Weapons
Station

Navigation Station

Captain's Chair

Command Module

Helm Station

Engineering Station

Life Support Station

Secondary
Engineering
Station

Main View Screen

playing highly detailed holographic sensor images which the Science Officer can manipulate to provide the maximum information content.

The science officer's station is also the primary link to the ship's computer. Commands given at this station can override commands given to the computer from anywhere else. If necessary, the science officer can use the computer to determine instantly detailed information on the ship's condition and to take control of any other function on the ship. (Such control is cumbersome and slow; add at least two levels of Difficulty to any Shipboard Systems task run through the computer station.) While it is possible for critical areas like engineering to lock out such computer overrides, the ship's computer immediately reports such actions to the bridge.

Other Bridge Stations

The majority of starships also contain both a bridge engineering station and a life support station. The engineering station allows the ship's engineer to oversee and control engineering operations while on the bridge. The life support station allows the operators to oversee and control the life support system of the entire ship.

Since the ship's life support systems are highly automated, this station is generally manned only in emergencies. Larger starships also contain several secondary bridge stations, including a secondary weapons station, a secondary engineering systems station, and a secondary navigation station. All of these stations contain somewhat more sophisticated, but also more difficult to use, control panels than those found at the main helm and navigation stations. They are most often used as backups or in unusual situations like piloting near dangerous spatial anomalies or going into combat against opponents using unknown weapon technologies.

PRIMARY HULL

The primary hull, or "saucer section", of a starship contains key facilities for ship operations. Larger and more complex versions of these facilities can often be found duplicated in the engineering hulls of capital ships.

Armory

Near the office of the Chief Security Officer, the armory holds the personal weapons needed for security troops and for military operations planetside. Larger weapons are stored disassembled near the fabricators if needed. The main armory usually contains several hundred hand and pistol phasers (types 1 and 2), and fifty or so phaser-3 rifles. Larger ships hold smaller arms lockers elsewhere.

Auxiliary Control

Also called the "emergency bridge", this station can assume or override any of the functions of the main bridge when needed. Auxiliary control has a main viewscreen and all the main stations found on the primary bridge, although in simpler and less flexible configurations. This station is usually unmanned, although some starships post security guards here in potential crisis situations. Auxiliary control is usually several decks below the primary bridge, and often near the impulse engineering station.

Briefing Room

This large room serves as a conference area for the ship's department heads and senior staff. It is outfitted with a large viewscreen, a direct library computer link, and a conference table. If needed, it can accommodate hearings, courts-martial, or other formal events with the addition of extra seating.

Corridors

Corridors on a starship are relatively wide, if low-ceilinged. Within eyeshot of anywhere in a corridor is a communication panel which opens channels on voice command; thus, any point in the ship can communicate with any other point. Niches contain access ladders to other levels to save congestion in the turbolift, and in many cases to allow access to internal systems. Outer corridors have ejection slots for disposal of immediately dangerous materials such as overloading phasers.

Quarters

Officers on a starship have two-room cabins containing a work area and a sleeping area. Ship's personnel are at liberty to decorate their cabins as they see fit.

Recreation Facilities

Starships are frequently away on missions which last for many months. To maintain the health and morale of the crew, ships contain a variety of recreational facilities. Most Starfleet vessels contain several small gymnasiums where crew members can play games like handball or jai alai, fence, spar, or lift weights. Starships also hold one or more small theaters where the crew can either watch a variety of stored video or holographic movies or perform amateur concerts and theatrical productions. In addition, there are a variety of small lounges where ship's personnel can talk, drink, and play cards, chess, or other games. On larger ships, one of those small lounges serves as the ship's chapel. Larger starships also contain swimming pools and large aesthetically designed hydroponic gardens where the ship's complement can enjoy the beauty of growing plants and the sounds of running water. However, everyone in Starfleet recognizes that the recreational facilities on board a starship are quite limited. Therefore, commanding officers usually grant crew members several days of shore leave when a starship visits a starbase, Federation outpost, or friendly planet.

Sickbay

Sickbay contains a clinic, a medical research laboratory (linked to the library computer), the office of the Chief Medical Officer, and an intensive care unit. The majority of actual medical treatment occurs in the intensive care unit or in the attached examination and operating room. Each ICU has several medical diagnostic beds, which continuously monitor patients, perform all of the functions of a medical tricorder, and notify the physician immediately if the patient experiences any problems. Larger ships have multiple ICUs, labs, and clinics, spaced throughout the ship. A starship sickbay maintains a large staff of highly trained doctors (including specialists), nurses, and technicians to ensure that starship crews receive the best medical care possible. (For more details, see *Technology*, page 167.)

Transporter Room

The primary transporter room usually holds a standard personal transporter (for more details, see *Technology*, pages 167-169) and the main transporter control circuit and setting boards for all other transporter stations. A transporter engineer or tech is on duty in every transporter room at all times, with the best officer on each shift in command in the primary transporter room. Transporter rooms often have associated security teams nearby for rapid deployment to a planet or for containment of any threat unexpectedly beamed aboard. The main transporter room usually holds a sensor station with a viewscreen, and some transporter rooms have food synthesizers for the benefit of officers standing long watches.

Turbolifts

Many starships are relatively large, and transporter technology does not allow for safe beaming throughout the interior of a starship. Turbolifts are the normal method of getting around inside a starship. Unlike 20th-century elevators, turbolifts are capable of both horizontal and vertical movement. Starships generally possess several turbolift tubes running from the top deck to the bottom and from the front of the ship to the back. *Constitution*-class starships also have four radially arranged turbolift tubes in their primary hull to allow rapid access to all sections. Capable of moving at speeds of up to 50 kph, the gravitically powered turbolifts can speed crew members to within 40 meters of any point of the ship in under thirty seconds.

Weapons Control Stations

The phaser control station, located adjacent to the actual phaser banks, is responsible for firing and maintaining these weapons systems. Powerful recirculators pump toxic phaser coolant gas into the phaser banks on the other side of the phaser control bulkhead; although this makes the station livable, it presents a grave risk should the bulkhead breach or the access vents not be secured. The photon torpedo launchers are controlled from the torpedo room. While the ship's weapons are normally fired from the bridge, if a ship is damaged it may be necessary to fire them from the relevant weapons control station. Each weapons control station also has access panels and diagnostic equipment to allow trained crew members to access and repair the weapons directly.

SECONDARY HULL

The secondary (engineering) hull, or "cylinder section," of a starship serves as the primary engineering center of the ship. It also holds the necessities for long voyages such as cargo, fabricators and synthesizers, water tanks, and so forth. The engineering hull duplicates many rooms found in the primary hull.

Brig

This confinement area exists to detain individuals suspected of serious criminal offenses or others who may pose a danger to the ship, such as enemy prisoners. The brig has a force-field door. The main brig is usually in a remote

section of the secondary hull with at least one security station between it and either the hangar deck or engineering. Some ships place their main brig in the saucer section, or have secondary brigs there.

Hangar Deck

All starships too large to land on a planet carry at least one shuttlecraft. Normally located at the rear of the starship, the hangar deck is where the ship's shuttlecraft are launched and retrieved. The hangar deck contains large duranium doors that open when a shuttlecraft is landing or being launched. In addition, the hangar deck has a specialized tractor beam to help guide shuttlecraft in to land, and a force field that keeps the air inside the compartment when the doors are opened. A *Constitution*-class starship normally carries six shuttlecraft.

Jefferies Tubes

A network of access tubes, known as Jefferies tubes, runs from engineering to various power systems on the ship. Using the Jefferies tubes other components, including the exterior of the warp coils, the plasma flow systems, or even the antimatter control circuits can be accessed without taking the warp engines off-line. In an emergency, technicians can tap, redirect, or interrupt power to a ship's systems here, as well.

Main Engineering

Engineering is the section responsible for operating and maintaining the fusion reactors which generate power for the ship, the impulse engines, the warp drive, the artificial gravity, and gravitic compensators. Main engineering is normally located in a starship's secondary hull. The matter/antimatter integrator, where the dilithium crystals control and moderate the matter-antimatter interaction, is also located in main engineering, near the intermix chamber. However, the warp coils used to maintain and direct the warp field are located in the warp nacelles. Impulse engineering (in the primary hull) closely resembles main engineering, and bypass circuits exist between both to allow the Chief Engineer to monitor and adjust the engines from either station regardless of the drive currently in operation. A skilled technician can use these bypass circuits to cut power to any ship function, or to any deck or area of a ship.

Ship Templates

The *Star Trek Roleplaying Game* describes all starships with a Starship Template. This gives Narrators and players a sense of the relative power and capabilities of each vessel, and allows them to relate different ships to each other along a common reference scale.

All starships, like all Crew members, have certain characteristics or "attributes." These rate the ship's capabilities for moving, sensing things, attacking, and defending itself.

EXPLANATION OF TEMPLATE ELEMENTS

VITAL STATISTICS

These characteristics contain basic information about the ship:

Name or Name of Class

The designation of the ship and/or ship class.

Class and Type

This is the ship's class name and designation according to Federation standard protocols, such as "*Constitution*-class Explorer."

Commissioning Date

Date of prototype launch, if available.

HULL CHARACTERISTICS

Each ship's hull has three qualities: Size, Resistance, and Structural Points. Hull Characteristics do not require Power.

Size

The ship's overall size. Size is a function of not only its dimensions

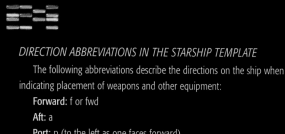

DIRECTION ABBREVIATIONS IN THE STARSHIP TEMPLATE

The following abbreviations describe the directions on the ship when indicating placement of weapons and other equipment:

Forward: f or fwd
Aft: a
Port: p (to the left as one faces forward)
Starboard: s or stbd (to the right as one faces forward)
Dorsal: d or dsl (the "top" of the ship)
Ventral: v or vnl (the "bottom" of the ship)

These directions combine as necessary: forward dorsal is fd, aft ventral is av, and so on.

STARSHIP SIZE

Size	Example
7	Klingon D-9 "Devil" class battlecruiser
6	*Constitution*-class starship (*U.S.S. Enterprise*); Klingon D-7 "Deadly" class battlecruiser
5	Klingon D-5 "Devastator" class battlecruiser
4	*Ranger*-class starship; *Antares*-class science vessel; Romulan bird of prey
3	*Daedalus*-class starship; Tholian webship, Vulcan *T'Pari*-class surveyor
2	DY-500 class ship, Class J cargo ship
1	Shuttlecraft, any class of probe

The First Federation ship *Fesarius*, commanded by Balok, transcends this scale. Grant any ship which fits this scale a +20 bonus to hit the *Fesarius* or any similar ship.

(approximate length, beam [width at its widest point], and height in meters), but its tonnes of weight and number of decks in thickness. Ship sizes can vary from ship to ship within a class, since each one is constructed individually and contains various small modifications and changes unique to it.

In game terms, ships are ranked in Size from 1 to 10, indicating rough relationships in size. As of 2269, Starfleet has not built or encountered any ships above Size 7. Size affects how easy it is to hit another ship in combat. The Starship Size Table provides guidelines for ship size ratings.

Resistance

A measure of the durability of the ship's hull—its capacity to protect those inside it from outside attack. Deflector shields are a ship's main defense, but the hull does offer some "armor" which protects the ship's interior. Typically ships have 1-4 points of Resistance; smaller ships may have no Resistance at all.

Structural Points

An overall rating of a ship's physical integrity. Weapons damage subtracts from the ship's Structural Points; when they're all gone, the ship is completely destroyed.

Every ship's Structural Points equal its (Size x 20). Thus, a Constitution-class starship (Size 6) has 120 Structural Points. For objects larger or smaller than the Size scale, the Narrator should assign a proportional number of Structural Points; for example, Balok's ship, the Fesarius, would have at least 8,000 Structural Points!

OPERATIONS CHARACTERISTICS

The Operations Characteristics reflect the capabilities of a ship's crew and some of its less combat-useful equipment.

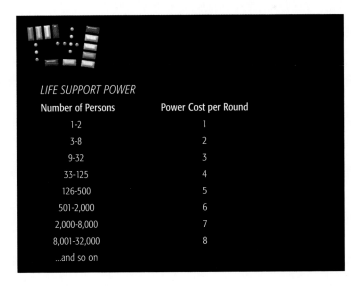

LIFE SUPPORT POWER

Number of Persons	Power Cost per Round
1-2	1
3-8	2
9-32	3
33-125	4
126-500	5
501-2,000	6
2,000-8,000	7
8,001-32,000	8
...and so on	

Crew/Passengers/Evac

"Crew" represents the ship's normal crew complement. Crew levels can change; different missions require slightly different crew sizes, and in fact, thanks to modern automation, it takes as few as 20 crewmen to operate most starships (at least for short periods in non-crisis situations). "Passengers" represents the standard number of passengers that the ship can comfortably carry in addition to its crew. "Evac" represents the maximum number of persons that can be carried on the ship in an emergency situation; this number includes the Passengers.

Crew and passengers cost Power—power to maintain the ship's life support and other environmental systems. The Power cost per round depends on the number of people that the ship can carry.

If power to the life support systems is reduced for any reason (such as damage or diverting it to other systems), the reduced oxygen level makes it harder for the crew to function effectively (increase the Difficulty of Fitness Tests, or impose other penalties or problems for the characters as appropriate).

Computers

This is the number of core computers a starship possesses which are able to support all computer functions. A starship has one core computer for every 2 points in this category. A ship's computer control can only be compromised if all core computers are disabled, and even then, Engineering may be able to link subprocessors throughout a ship to form a primitive computer to keep the ship operating. For technical details on starship computers, see page 165 of the *Technology* chapter.

Computers cost 1 Power per point of Computers. Thus, a *Constitution*-class starship, which has 4 points' worth of Computers, must spend 4 points of Power per round to keep all of them operating at peak efficiency.

Transporters

The number of personnel, cargo and emergency transporters on the ship. Emergency transporters have no receivers and can only beam out. Personnel and cargo transporters have ranges of about 40,000 kilometers, emergency transporters a range of about 15,000 kilometers. A ship cannot use its transporters while its shields or cloak are up, nor can personnel transport into any area protected by shields. For further information on the potential and limitations of the transporter, see pages 167-169 of the *Technology* chapter.

The Power cost for Transporters varies by ship, depending upon the number and type of transporters it has. Typically the cost is 1 Power for every two transporters. If Transporters are operated on less than full power, the transporters' range and ability to "punch" through interference is proportionally reduced. Further technical information on transporters appears on pages 167-169 of the *Technology* chapter.

Tractor Beams

The number, type and location of the ship's main tractor beams (shuttle bay and Reaction Control System tractor beams are not included). Tractor beams can latch on to very large masses; towing ability is a function of engine power available. More details appear in *Technology*, page 170.

The Tractor Beam Table provides rough guidelines for how much mass a tractor beam can move at what ranges.

PROPULSION AND POWER CHARACTERISTICS

Warp System

If a ship has warp capability, this attribute describes it. Listed in order and separated by slashes are the ship's Standard speed (the speed it typically uses to cruise through space), its Sustainable speed (the highest speed it can maintain without stressing the ship or its engines), and its Maximum speed (the highest speed it can attain, including the amount of time it can maintain that speed). Running at Maximum speed beyond that time risks damage to the engines. The Narrator should roll two dice; on a result of 2, 3, or 4, the engines are damaged and lose 25% of their speed and ability to produce Power.)

The Warp System costs 2 Power per round for every warp factor being maintained. Thus, a ship moving at warp 6 would have to spend 12 Power per round to maintain that speed. However, since combat rarely takes place at warp speed, this cost usually does not come into consideration during play.

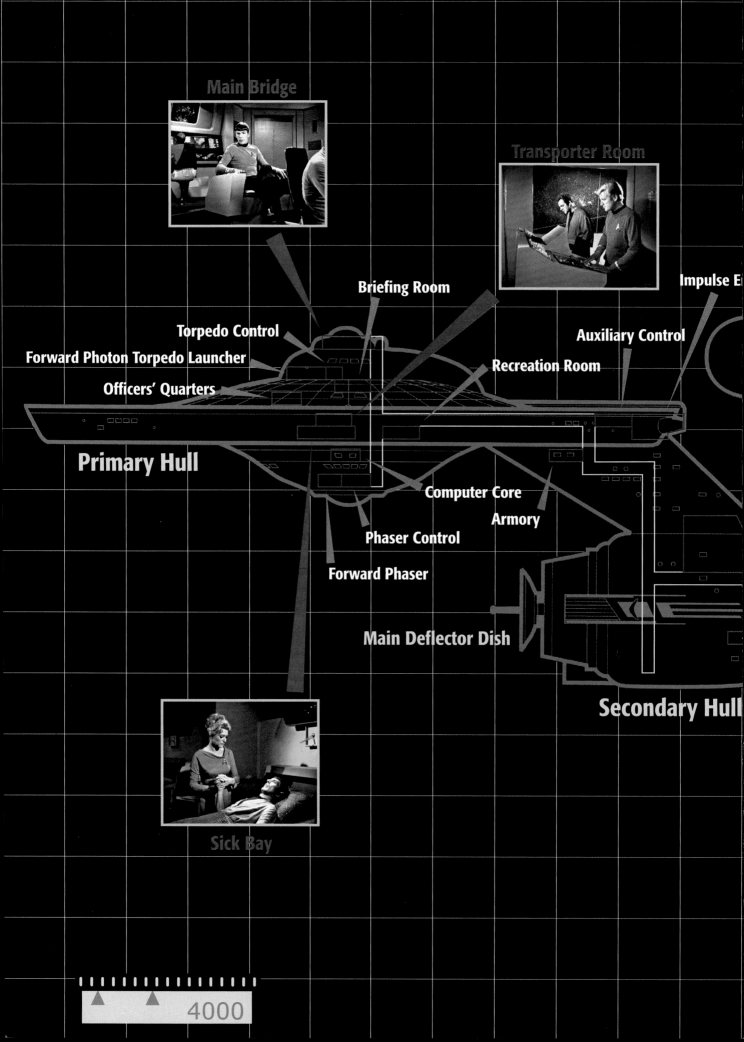

Main Bridge

Transporter Room

Impulse E[

Briefing Room

Torpedo Control

Auxiliary Control

Forward Photon Torpedo Launcher

Recreation Room

Officers' Quarters

Primary Hull

Computer Core

Armory

Phaser Control

Forward Phaser

Main Deflector Dish

Secondary Hull

Sick Bay

4000

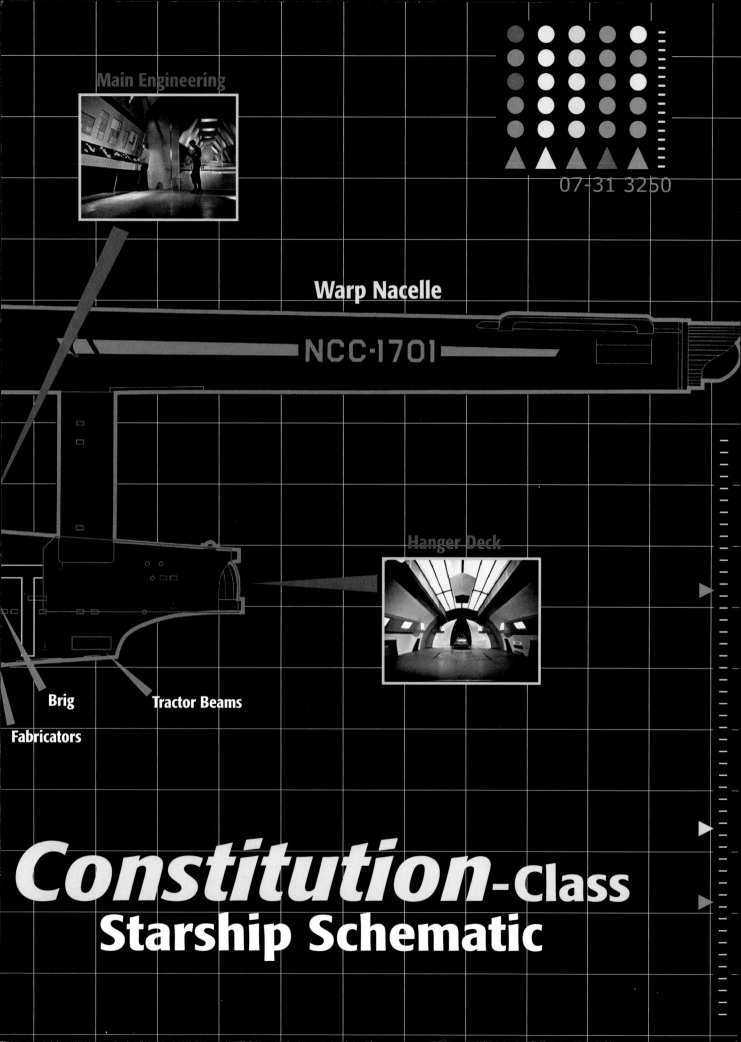

Main Engineering

Warp Nacelle

NCC·1701

Hanger Deck

Brig

Tractor Beams

Fabricators

07-31 3250

Constitution-Class
Starship Schematic

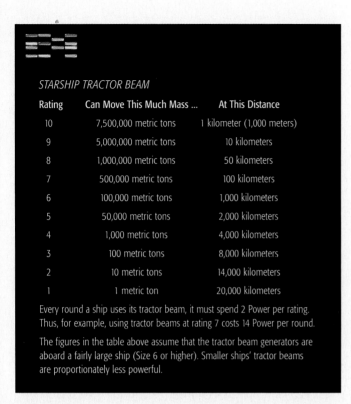

STARSHIP TRACTOR BEAM

Rating	Can Move This Much Mass ...	At This Distance
10	7,500,000 metric tons	1 kilometer (1,000 meters)
9	5,000,000 metric tons	10 kilometers
8	1,000,000 metric tons	50 kilometers
7	500,000 metric tons	100 kilometers
6	100,000 metric tons	1,000 kilometers
5	50,000 metric tons	2,000 kilometers
4	1,000 metric tons	4,000 kilometers
3	100 metric tons	8,000 kilometers
2	10 metric tons	14,000 kilometers
1	1 metric ton	20,000 kilometers

Every round a ship uses its tractor beam, it must spend 2 Power per rating. Thus, for example, using tractor beams at rating 7 costs 14 Power per round.

The figures in the table above assume that the tractor beam generators are aboard a fairly large ship (Size 6 or higher). Smaller ships' tractor beams are proportionately less powerful.

Warp Theory

Starships employ warp propulsion as their primary mode of travel. Whether through matter/antimatter annihilation or some other process, this propels the ship at speeds faster than light. Without warp drive, ships would be unable to traverse the vast interstellar distances between planets. The Narrator should understand the principles behind warp travel so that she can accurately portray faster-than-light travel and understand how it affects her game.

The warp drive employs controlled matter/antimatter annihilation to provide the energy needed to travel faster-than-light. The problems of time dilation, mass, and travel time are solved by the creation of asymmetrical spatial distortion fields known as the warp field. Warp drives produce a series of nested layers of warp-field energy (through the nacelles). Each layer exerts a controlled amount of force forward. This produces the necessary transition into subspace, where the laws of normal relativistic space do not apply.

For the technical details behind the warp drive, see page 169 of the *Technology* chapter.

Travel Times

In most episodes, the captain, or other commanding officer, simply gives the Helm and Navigator flight instructions, including speed. While the players will often want to know exactly how long it takes to get from Point A to Point B, the dramatic needs of the story should determine the length of the journey. If the episode requires the characters to be on Rigel IV, having them take three weeks to get there isn't any fun (they'll lose sight of their objective, become distracted, and so forth). Sometimes it's better for the dramatic needs of the game to gloss over reality and just get the Crew where it needs to be (even if

you simply say, "You arrive three weeks later"). Set the warp speed for the ship at whatever level you need to get the Crew to their destination within the desired timeframe. If you need the Crew to fly across a sector in seven days, they travel at warp factor 6; if you need them there in four days, they can travel at warp 8.

If you establish a definitive distance between two planets—Earth and Vulcan, for example—you may want to stick with it, since players often demand consistency ("Hey, last week it took us 57 days at warp 6 to travel 60 light-years.") even though it may limit your storytelling ability. If you find such demands overly constraining, fudge widely and often. The story should rule, not the math. Generally, it's better simply to state distance in terms of travel time at "standard warp" speed; if the Crew wants to go faster, you can always increase the speed.

If travel times are important, consult the Warp Factor Chart (page 139) and estimate the distance between the ship and its destination. For example, you might assume Chondag II orbits a "nearby star" in the Rodlican sector; thus a trip from Rodlican to Chondag II would take five days at warp factor 6. Try to think of distances in multiples of the defined categories. Veltandis might be farther away from Rodlican than Chondag II—say three times the distance of a nearby star—thus requiring a trip of fifteen days at warp 6. You can keep track of these estimated distances, should you wish to refer to them later.

Note: Starfleet reconfigures the values for warp factors, using an asymptotic curve going to infinity at Warp 10, by the 24th century.

Impulse System

This characteristic represents a ship's impulse speed, expressed in terms of the percent of *c* (the speed of light) it can reach. Both the Sustainable and Maximum speeds are listed. See page 166 in the *Technology* chapter for more information on impulse engines.

The Impulse System costs 1 point of Power per round for every 10 percent of lightspeed the ship maintains. For example, a ship flying at .75 Impulse would spend 7 Power per round.

Although most ships can exceed .25*c* during combat or in emergency situations, .25*c* remains the Starfleet standard for "full impulse." Beyond this speed, it's usually more efficient to travel at warp speeds (however, high impulse speeds are often necessary during battle).

Speed	km/hr	Multiple of c	Earth to Moon	Across Sol system	To nearby star	Across sector	Across UFP	To Andromeda	Notes
Full impulse	270 mil	0.25	5.38 sec	44 hrs	20 yrs	80 yrs	20,000 yrs	8.8 million yrs	See page 138
Warp 1	1 bil	1	1.34 sec	11 hrs	5 yrs	20 yrs	5,000 yrs	2.2 million yrs	Warp 1 = LIGHT SPEED
Warp 2	8 bil	8	0.16 sec	1.37 hrs	7.5 mo	2.5 yrs	625 yrs	275,000 yrs	
Warp 3	27 bil	27	49.6 ms	24 min	2.2 mo	8.8 mo	185 yrs	81,500 yrs	
Warp 4	64 bil	64	21 ms	10 min	28.5 days	4 mo	78 yrs	34,400 yrs	
Warp 5	125 bil	125	11 ms	5 min	2 weeks	2 mo	40 yrs	17,600 yrs	
Warp 6	216 bil	216	6 ms	2.9 min	8.4 days	34 days	23 yrs	10,185 yrs	Normal maximum warp speed
Warp 7	343 bil	343	3 ms	109 sec	5.3 days	21 days	14.5 yrs	6,400 yrs	
Warp 8	512 bil	512	1.25 ms	73 sec	3.5 days	14 days	9.7 yrs	4,300 yrs	Maximum safe warp
Warp 10	1 tril	1,000	0.64 ms	37 sec	1.8 days	7 days	5 yrs	2,200 yrs	
Warp 14	2.74 tril	2,744	0.23 ms	13 sec	16 hrs	2.5 days	1.8 yrs	800 yrs	Speed if matter-antimatter integrator flows wide open; will destroy a ship in minutes
Warp 19	6.86 tril	6,859	0.09 ms	5 sec	6.4 hrs	1 day	8.6 months	320 yrs	Kelvan-modified warp engine potential

Power

On a starship, the warp core and main impulse engines provide power to all ship systems, everything from life support and computers to weapons and shields. If those systems are down or damaged, the ship runs on battery power sufficient to power life support, navigational systems (including the navigational deflector), and half-impulse drive only for about a week. Batteries cannot be drained rapidly enough to power a phaser burst, for example, although a sufficiently gifted engineer might be able to cross-circuit battery power to operate the transporters. Every system on a starship requires a certain amount of power each round to function. This is expressed as a number of points. For example, to maintain life support on a ship which carries four people costs 2 Power per round of battle (see the Life Support Power Table, page 135).

Power represents the amount of power the warp core and related systems produce per round. A ship produces a number of Power points per round equal to its Power characteristic. Power can be rerouted between systems to give some systems more power; see *Starship Combat*, pages 154-155, for details.

SENSOR SYSTEMS

These characteristics detail a ship's sensors—its eyes and ears in space. Sensors are rated for their gain (represented by a bonus to any Shipboard Systems (Sensors) Test Results made with the sensor) and range. More detailed data on ship's sensors appears on page 167 of the *Technology* chapter.

Long-range Sensors

The long-range sensor array, located behind the main deflector in most starships, is a set of subspace devices that can detect things at faster than the speed of light. Its range is rated in light-years. Long-range sensors cost 6 Power per round to use. For every +5 Power devoted to them, they provide an additional +1 to Shipboard Systems (Sensors) Tests.

Lateral Sensors

The lateral sensor arrays are smaller sensors which usually can sense only at the speed of light (or less); their range tends to be limited to one light-year or so. Lateral sensors cost 4 Power per round to use. For every +5 Power devoted to them, they provide an additional +1 to Shipboard Systems (Sensors) Tests.

Navigational Sensors

These sensors collect and process the data needed to keep a ship on the proper course. They are tied into the long-range and lateral sensors; their range is based on those sensors' range. They cost 5 Power per round to use; however, they are rarely used during combat situations, so this cost usually does not come into consideration during play.

Cloak

A cloaking device is a sophisticated energy field which prevents a ship from being detected with sensors (or normal Human senses, either). Cloaking devices require enormous amounts of power—so much so that a cloaked ship can't use weapons, shields or transporters. Romulan and Klingon ships often have cloaking devices; Starfleet ships never have them.

Cloaks are rated in terms of a number of points of effectiveness. Each point represents a +1 Difficulty to all Tests to detect the cloaked ship with sensors or senses. Cloaks cost 4 Power per point of effectiveness per round they

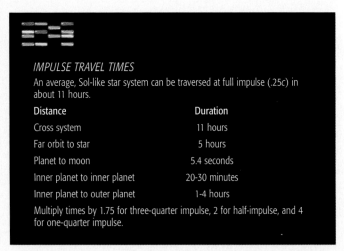

are in use; no ship's weapons, shields, or transporters may be used while a cloak is activated.

Sensors Skill

For situations when the Narrator does not know the Shipboard Systems (Sensors) skill rank of the persons operating a starship's sensors, use this characteristic as a general indicator of the competence level of the sensor operator. Consider it the equivalent of a Shipboard Systems (Sensors) Skill (assume an Intellect of 2). When using the Sensors Skill characteristic, bonuses for the gain of a sensor should not normally be applied.

WEAPON SYSTEMS

Starships typically carry two types of weapons: beam weapons and missile weapons. The crew fires them with the Shipboard Systems (Weapons Systems) skill. For further information, see the *Starship Combat* (page 158) and *Technology* (pages 169-170) chapters.

Beam Weapons

Beam weapons (such as phasers or disruptors) have five characteristics: Range (the point-blank, short, medium, and long ranges for the weapon, expressed in kilometers), Arc (the combined arcs of fire for the ship's beam

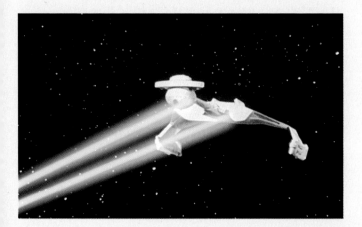

weapons; most vessels have a firing arc in all bearings, 720 degrees around the ship), Accuracy (the Difficulty to hit a target with the beam weapon at the various ranges), Damage (the amount of damage the weapon does), and Power (the amount of Power required for each shot).

Beam weapons cost 1 Power per point of damage done up to their maximum listed damage. They can be made to do more than maximum damage if the crew feeds more Power—3 Power per additional point of damage up to 125% of the maximum listed damage. This requires a Moderate (6) Systems Engineering (Phaser Systems) or Shipboard Systems (Weapons Systems) Test. See *Starship Combat*, pages 156-158, for details.

Missile Weapons

Missile weapons (such as photon torpedoes) have eight characteristics: Number (the typical number of torpedoes carried), Launchers (the number and location of the ship's launching systems), Spread (the maximum number of torpedoes that can be launched simultaneously from a single launcher), Arc (the arcs of fire for the ship's missile weapons), Range (the point-blank, short, medium, and long ranges for the weapon, expressed in kilometers), Accuracy (the Difficulty to hit a target with the missile weapon at the various ranges), Damage (the amount of damage the weapon does), and Power (the amount of Power required to arm and fire one or more missiles from a single launcher). Typically self-guided, missile weapons can correct course to follow a moving target.

Missile weapons cost 5 Power to arm and launch the torpedoes from a single launcher, regardless of how many missiles are launched by that launcher.

Weapons Skill

This characteristic is a general representation of the skill of a ship's personnel at operating weapons (assume Intellect 2) for use by the Narrator when she doesn't know an NPC's exact level of skill. It could also represent automated military systems which attack targets without the help of living operators.

DEFENSIVE SYSTEMS

Defensive systems protect the ship. Most ships have only one—deflector shields. (See page 169 in *Technology* for details.) Shields have two characteristics: Protection (the standard and maximum levels of protection the shields provide, rated in terms of a number of points), and Power cost. Deflector shields protect a starship as long as they have power, by deflecting the damage caused by weapons. When they are damaged, additional Power can be diverted to the shields to keep them functioning. This requires a Moderate (6) Systems Engineering (Shields) or Shipboard Systems (Shields) Test. See *Starship Combat*, page 160, for details.

Shields typically cost 1 Power per point of Protection provided per round, up to their standard level (the ship pays the full cost for the Protection even if it's been diminished by incoming fire). Beyond their standard level, they cost 3 Power per round per point of Protection provided up to their maximum level. This cost must be paid per shield; most ships have two shields (forward and aft). A ship cannot increase its shields' Protection beyond their maximum level.

A Note On Power Costs

Whenever a Template element has a Power requirement, the requirement appears in brackets. For example, [6 power/round] means that the system requires 6 points of Power per round to operate at maximum efficiency.

UFP Ships

CONSTITUTION-CLASS STARSHIP

Class and Type: *Constitution*-class Explorer
Commissioning Date: 2245
HULL CHARACTERISTICS
> **Size:** 6
> **Resistance:** 3
> **Structural Points:** 120

OPERATIONS CHARACTERISTICS
> **Crew/Passengers/Evac:** 435/235/3,500 [7 Power/round]
> **Computers:** 4 [2 Power/round]
> **Transporters:** 4 personnel, 6 cargo, 4 emergency [7 Power/round]
> **Tractor Beams:** 1 fv, 1 av [2 Power/rating/round]

PROPULSION AND POWER CHARACTERISTICS
> **Warp System:** 4.0/6.0/8.0 (12 hours) [2/warp factor]
> **Impulse System:** .5 c/.75 c [5/7 Power/round]
> **Power:** 135

SENSOR SYSTEMS
> **Long-range Sensors:** +1/15 light-years [6 Power/round]
> **Lateral Sensors:** +1/1 light-year [4 Power/round]
> **Navigational Sensors:** +1 [5 Power/round]
> **Sensors Skill:** 4

WEAPONS SYSTEMS
> *Type VII Phaser*
> **Range:** 10/30,000/100,000/300,000
> **Arc:** Forward (120 degrees)
> **Accuracy:** 4/5/7/10
> **Damage:** 14
> **Power:** [14]
> *Photon Torpedoes*
> **Number:** 100
> **Launchers:** 1 fv
> **Spread:** 4
> **Arc:** Forward (120 degrees)
> **Range:** 15/300,000/1,000,000/3,000,000
> **Accuracy:** 4/5/7/10
> **Damage:** 18
> **Power:** [5]
> **Weapons Skill:** 4

DEFENSIVE SYSTEMS

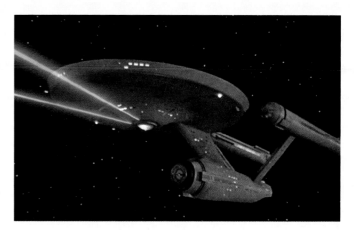

Starfleet Deflector Shield
> **Protection:** 40/60 [40 Power/shield/round]

DESCRIPTION AND NOTES

Fleet data: The most powerful ship produced by Starfleet, the *Constitution*–class explorer incorporates all of the latest technological advancements of the Federation. Intended for long-term missions ranging from exploration to scientific surveys, defense, deep-space patrol, and/or expeditionary support, it features Type VII phasers, photon torpedo launchers, fourteen laboratories, and the most powerful engines available, based on the revolutionary designs of Dr. Lawrence Marvick. The ship's computer is a versatile duotronic model designed by the brilliant Dr. Richard Daystrom in 2243. Most *Constitution*-class ships underwent refits between 2258 and 2265 to expand crew capacity from 203 to 435 following the invention of the improved food synthesizer, and to replace the original *Tesla*-class laser cannons with phasers, following the development of that weapon in 2256.

Noteworthy vessels/service records/encounters: *U.S.S. Constitution*, class prototype, flagship of Fleet Captain Garth of Izar during Axanar crisis and afterward; *U.S.S. Asimov* (scientific refit of the *U.S.S. Valiant* to field-test the duotronic sensor-library computer array, 2254), mostly Centauran crew under Capt. Gan Laikan, after first two missions (2255–2265) holds record for most Class M planets discovered, in fourth year of third five-year mission; *U.S.S. Constellation*, commanded by Commodore Matt Decker, destroyed by "planet killer" weapon near planet L-374 (2267); *U.S.S. Defiant*, disappeared into a spatial interphase near Tholian space (2268); *U.S.S. Eagle*, crewed entirely by Andorians, under Capt. Igrilan it has the most-decorated crew in Starfleet; *U.S.S. Endeavour*; *U.S.S. Enterprise*, commanded by Capt. Robert M. April (2245–2250) and Capt. Christopher Pike (2251–2261), in last year of five-year mission under Capt. James T. Kirk (2264–2269); *U.S.S. Essex*; *U.S.S. Excalibur*, commanded by Capt. Harris, severely damaged during a war games drill with the M-5 computer (2268); *U.S.S. Exeter*, all members of crew but Capt. Ronald Tracey killed by bacteriological warfare agent on Omega IV, ship later recovered by the crew of the *Enterprise* (2268); *U.S.S. Farragut*, 200 crewmen and Capt. Thomas Garrovick killed by dikironium cloud creature at Tycho IV (2257); *U.S.S. Hood*, participated in war games trials of M-5 computer (2268); *U.S.S. Intrepid*, crewed entirely by Vulcans, was destroyed by a spaceborne amoeba creature near the Gamma 7A System (2268); *U.S.S. Lexington*, commanded by Commodore Robert Wesley, lost 53 crewmen during disastrous war games trials of the M-5 computer (2268); *U.S.S. Potemkin*, participated in war games trials of M-5 computer (2268); *U.S.S. Republic*; *U.S.S. Yorktown*, commanded by Captain Evan Foster (2254–2269), currently patrolling between the Klingon frontier and Theta VII.

RANGER-CLASS STARSHIP

Class and Type: *Ranger*-class Explorer
Commissioning Date: 2215
HULL CHARACTERISTICS
  Size: 4
  Resistance: 3
  Structural Points: 80
OPERATIONS CHARACTERISTICS
  Crew/Passengers/Evac: 287/112/2,200 [7 Power/round]
  Computers: 2 [1 Power/round]
  Transporters: 3 personnel, 5 cargo, 3 emergency [5 Power/round]
  Tractor Beams: 1 fv, 1 av [2 Power/rating/round]
PROPULSION AND POWER CHARACTERISTICS
  Warp System: 3.0/4.0/6.0 (12 hours) [2/warp factor]
  Impulse System: .5 c/.75 c [5/7 Power/round]
  Power: 115
SENSOR SYSTEMS
  Long-range Sensors: +1/12 light-years [6 Power/round]
  Lateral Sensors: +1/1 light-year [4 Power/round]
  Navigational Sensors: +1 [5 Power/round]
  Sensors Skill: 3
WEAPONS SYSTEMS
  Tesla-class Laser Cannon
  Range: 9/27,000/80,000/250,000
  Arc: Forward (120 degrees)
  Accuracy: 5/6/8/11
  Damage: 10

  Power: [10]
  Photon Torpedoes
  Number: 75
  Launchers: 1 fv
  Spread: not capable
  Arc: Forward (120 degrees)
  Range: 15/300,000/1,000,000/3,000,000
  Accuracy: 4/5/7/10
  Damage: 18
  Power: [5]
  Weapons Skill: 3
DEFENSIVE SYSTEMS
  Starfleet Deflector Shield
  Protection: 35/45 [35 Power/shield/round]

DESCRIPTION AND NOTES

Fleet data: Now considered slightly obsolete, though still quite functional, the *Ranger*-class ship served as Starfleet's top of the line from 2215 until the commissioning of the *Constitution* class in 2245. The class suffers from relatively low computing power (and thus relatively poorer sensors and targeting systems). However, its pioneering use of tritanium hull construction and innovative interior design (both developed by Mark Chausser, the brilliant Human artist-engineer, at the University of Oreas on Alpha Centauri IV) and its full implementation of the M-2196 impulse engine mounts made it the strongest, most maneuverable ship of its era.

Noteworthy vessels/service records/encounters: *U.S.S. Ranger*, prototype, captured by Klingons shortly after first contact (2218); *U.S.S. Bastion*, destroyed five Klingon ships in battle near the Mutara Nebula before being herself destroyed (2228); *U.S.S. Carolina*, on detached duty patrolling Romulan Neutral Zone; *U.S.S. Explorer*, failed to return from deep space exploratory mission to Theta Reticula system (2233); *U.S.S. Orleans*, served as testbed for prototype phaser weapon (2256); *U.S.S. Sal'koth*, captured I.K.S. Dit'kra (2239); *U.S.S. Valiant*, declared a "casualty" of the "war" between Eminiar VII and Vendikar and destroyed by the inhabitants of those planets (2217).

DAEDALUS-CLASS STARSHIP

Class and Type: *Daedalus*-class Explorer
Commissioning Date: 2162
HULL CHARACTERISTICS
  Size: 3
  Resistance: 2
  Structural Points: 60
OPERATIONS CHARACTERISTICS
  Crew/Passengers/Evac: 165/85/1,550 [6 Power/round]
  Computers: 2 [1 Power/round]
  Transporters: None

Tractor Beams: 1 fv, 1 av [2 Power/rating/round]

PROPULSION AND POWER CHARACTERISTICS

Warp System: 3.0/4.0/6.0 (12 hours) [2/warp factor]

Impulse System: .4 c/.66 c [4/7 Power/round]

Power: 100

SENSOR SYSTEMS

Long-range Sensors: +0/10 light-years [6 Power/round]

Lateral Sensors: +0/1 light-year [4 Power/round]

Navigational Sensors: +0 [5 Power/round]

Sensors Skill: 3

WEAPONS SYSTEMS

Magnusson-class Laser Cannon

Range: 8/25,000/75,000/200,000

Arc: Forward (120 degrees)

Accuracy: 5/6/8/11

Damage: 10

Power: [10]

Photon Torpedoes

Number: 40

Launchers: 1 fv

Spread: not capable

Arc: Forward (120 degrees)

Range: 10/250,000/750,000/2,500,000

Accuracy: 5/6/8/11

Damage: 16

Power: [5]

Weapons Skill: 3

Defensive Systems

Starfleet Deflector Shield

Protection: 30/30 [30 Power/shield/round; no emergency strength]

DESCRIPTION AND NOTES

Fleet data: The *Daedalus*-class ship was the first of the great multifunction explorer vessels created by Starfleet. The *Daedalus* married the spaceframe designs of Gnarr of Tellar to the UESPA components used in the Earth-

Romulan War fleets. Although remembered fondly by the few surviving veterans who served on one, the *Daedalus*-class vessels were remarkably primitive by modern standards. They lacked transporters (except for a few ships who received them during the upgrading process later in their service lives), subspace radio (meaning they would be out of contact with Starfleet for as long as years at a time), advanced impulse engines (although some of the M-2169 models were installed in later refits), and most of the creature comforts available today (few veterans reminisce kindly about the nutrient paste-based "food" prepared in *Daedalus*-class galleys). The last of these vessels were withdrawn from service in 2196.

Noteworthy vessels/service records/encounters: *U.S.S. Daedalus*, prototype; *U.S.S. Archon*, visited Beta III, a planet in the C-111 star system, where it was destroyed by the planet's powerful computer, Landru, and its surviving crew absorbed into the Betan population (2167); *U.S.S. Essex*, destroyed with all hands, including Capt. Bryce Shumar and First Officer Steven Mullen, above the Class M moon of Mab-Bu IV by an electromagnetic storm (2167); *U.S.S. Horizon*, visited planet Sigma Iotia II and left behind a copy of Chicago Mobs of the Twenties, thereby changing the entire Iotian culture, only to be destroyed in an unexplained catastrophe very shortly thereafter (its radio distress call was received 100 years later and responded to by the *U.S.S. Enterprise*) (2168).

CLASS F SHUTTLECRAFT

Class and Type: Class F Shuttlecraft

Commissioning Date: 2245

HULL CHARACTERISTICS

Size: 1

Resistance: 2

Structural Points: 20

OPERATIONS CHARACTERISTICS

Crew/Passengers/Evac: 2/6/20 [2 Power/round]

Computers: 2 [1 Power/round]

Transporters: None

Tractor Beams: 1 fv [2 Power/rating/round]

PROPULSION AND POWER CHARACTERISTICS

Warp System: None

Impulse System: .4 c/.66 c [4/7 Power/round]

Power: 70

SENSOR SYSTEMS

Long-range Sensors: +0/10 light-years [6 Power/round]

Lateral Sensors: +0/1 light-year [4 Power/round]

Navigational Sensors: +0 [5 Power/round]

Sensors Skill: 3

WEAPONS SYSTEMS

None

Weapons Skill: N/A

DEFENSIVE SYSTEMS

Starfleet Deflector Shield
Protection: 25/30 [25 Power/shield/round]

DESCRIPTION AND NOTES

Fleet data: The Class F shuttlecraft is commonly found on *Constitution*-class starships and other Starfleet vessels. It serves as a personnel and cargo transportation vehicle. It carries no armaments, has no transporter, and cannot attain warp speeds with its ion impulse engines.

Noteworthy vessels/service records/encounters: *Copernicus*, destroyed along with the *U.S.S. Constellation* (2267); *Galileo*, shuttlecraft attached to the *U.S.S. Enterprise*, lost near planet Taurus II while its crew was investigating the Murasaki Effect (2267); *Kepler*, lost along with the *U.S.S. Defiant* (2268).

ANTARES-CLASS SCIENCE VESSEL

Class and Type: *Antares*-class Surveyor
Commissioning Date: 2250
HULL CHARACTERISTICS
   Size: 4
   Resistance: 3
   Structural Points: 80
OPERATIONS CHARACTERISTICS
   Crew/Passengers/Evac: 225/75/1,400 [6 Power/round]
   Computers: 4 [2 Power/round]
   Transporters: 2 personnel, 4 cargo, 2 emergency [4 Power/round]
   Tractor Beams: 1 fv, 1 av [2 Power/rating/round]
PROPULSION AND POWER CHARACTERISTICS
   Warp System: 4.0/5.0/7.0 (12 hours) [2/warp factor]
   Impulse System: .5 c/.75 c [5/7 Power/round]
   Power: 90
SENSOR SYSTEMS
   Long-range Sensors: +1/12 light-years [6 Power/round]
   Lateral Sensors: +1/1 light-year [4 Power/round]

   Navigational Sensors: +1 [5 Power/round]
   Sensors Skill: 3
WEAPONS SYSTEMS
   Type IV Phaser
   Range: 10/30,000/100,000/300,000
   Arc: Forward (120 degrees)
   Accuracy: 4/5/7/10
   Damage: 8
   Power: [8]
   Weapons Skill: 3
DEFENSIVE SYSTEMS
   Starfleet Deflector Shield
   Protection: 30/40 [30 Power/shield/round]

DESCRIPTION AND NOTES

Fleet data: *Antares*-class ships replaced the old *Cook*-class deep-space surveyors in 2250. They serve the Federation and Starfleet as science vessels. Their primary missions include conducting exploratory surveys, monitoring unusual stellar phenomena, collecting and analyzing samples from newly discovered planets, and performing a wide range of experiments in outer space. Their crews usually include specialists from many varied scientific fields.

Noteworthy vessels/service records/encounters: *U.S.S. Antares*, prototype, destroyed by Charles Evans when he caused the baffle plate on the ship's energy pile to disappear (2266); *U.S.S. Algol*, mixed Vulcan-Centauran crew under Capt. Jen Weman engaged in long-term charting of Perseus Arm; *U.S.S. Betelgeuse*, studied Ostrogoth Nebula (2258–2260); *U.S.S. John Ross* (Diplomatic Service refit of the *U.S.S. Zeta Reticulum* for first contact missions, 2263), under Capt. Sandra Earle, made first contact with intelligent long-chain polymer creatures in the Timrek Nebula (2268).

T'PARI-CLASS SURVEYOR

Class and Type: *T'Pari*-class Surveyor
Commissioning Date: 2250
HULL CHARACTERISTICS
   Size: 4
   Resistance: 2
   Structural Points: 80
OPERATIONS CHARACTERISTICS
   Crew/Passengers/Evac: 45/80/200 [5 Power/round]
   Computers: 4 [2 Power/round]
   Transporters: 2 personnel, 2 cargo, 2 emergency [3 Power/round]
   Tractor Beams: 1 fv, 1 av [2 Power/rating/round]
PROPULSION AND POWER CHARACTERISTICS
   Warp System: 5.0/6.0/7.5 (12 hours) [2/warp factor]
   Impulse System: .5 c/.75 c [5/7 Power/round]
   Power: 90

SENSOR SYSTEMS

    Long-range Sensors: +1/14 light-years [6 Power/round]

    Lateral Sensors: +1/1 light-year [4 Power/round]

    Navigational Sensors: +1 [5 Power/round]

    Sensors Skill: 3

WEAPONS SYSTEMS

    Type IV Phaser

    Range: 10/30,000/100,000/300,000

    Arc: Forward (120 degrees)

    Accuracy: 4/5/7/10

    Damage: 8

    Power: [8]

    Weapons Skill: 3

DEFENSIVE SYSTEMS

    Starfleet Deflector Shield

    Protection: 30/40 [30 Power/shield/round]

DESCRIPTION AND NOTES

Fleet data: The successor to the *Voroth*-class ship (one of which, the *Vesaya*, made first contact with Earth in 2063), the *T'Pari*-class surveyor is a Vulcan vessel designed for exploration and scientific surveys. Although somewhat cramped and spartan by Human or Tiburonese standards, the ship's design serves its Vulcan crew quite well and maximizes their efficiency.

Noteworthy vessels/service records/encounters: *V.S.S. T'Pari*, prototype; *V.S.S. Kal'cheroth*, surveyed the Class M moons of Capella III (2262); *V.S.S. T'Neran*, conducted comparative study of stellar and planetary evolution across multiple systems (2255–2267); *V.S.S. T'Plana-Hath*, on deep space mission to the Great Barrier at the core of the galaxy (begun 2259).

Civilian Ships

DY-500-CLASS SHIP

    Class and Type: DY-500 Freighter

    Commissioning Date: 2090

    Hull Characteristics

        Size: 2

        Resistance: 1

        Structural Points: 40

    OPERATIONS CHARACTERISTICS

        Crew/Passengers/Evac: 8/40/110 [4 Power/round]

        Computers: 2 [1 Power/round]

        Transporters: None

        Tractor Beams: None

    PROPULSION AND POWER CHARACTERISTICS

        Warp System: None

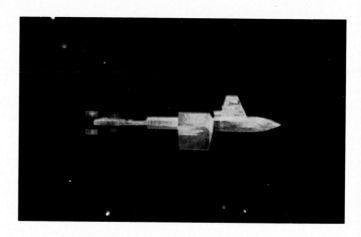

    Impulse System: .1 c/.2 c [1/2 Power/round]

    Power: 90

SENSOR SYSTEMS

    Long-range Sensors: +0/5 light-years [6 Power/round]

    Lateral Sensors: +0/.5 light-year [4 Power/round]

    Navigational Sensors: +0 [5 Power/round]

    Sensors Skill: 2

WEAPONS SYSTEMS

    None

    Weapons Skill: N/A

DEFENSIVE SYSTEMS

    Deflector Shield

    Protection: 15/15 [15 Power/shield/round; no emergency shield strength]

DESCRIPTION AND NOTES

Fleet data: An antiquated form of interplanetary transport, DY-500-class vessels can still be found in less advanced systems or in the hands of less affluent merchants and traders who stay within a particular system. Some DY-500 ships are completely automated, robotically piloting cargoes of ore or grain from planet to planet. The DY-500 is an improved version of the DY-100-class nuclear-powered vessel originally developed on Earth in the late 20th century (such as the *S.S. Botany Bay*, encountered by the *U.S.S. Enterprise* in 2267).

CLASS J STARSHIP

    Class and Type: Class J Freighter

    Commissioning Date: 2230

    HULL CHARACTERISTICS

        Size: 2

        Resistance: 1

       Structural Points: 40

    OPERATIONS CHARACTERISTICS

        Crew/Passengers/Evac: 12/20/150 [5 Power/round]

        Computers: 2 [1 Power/round]

Transporters: 1 personnel, 2 cargo, 1 emergency [2 Power/round]
Tractor Beams: 1 fv, 1 av [2 Power/rating/round]
PROPULSION AND POWER CHARACTERISTICS
    Warp System: 3.0/4.0/5.5 (6 hours) [2/warp factor]
    Impulse System: .4 c/.66 c [4/7 Power/round]
    Power: 50
SENSOR SYSTEMS
    Long-range Sensors: +0/8 light-years [6 Power/round]
    Lateral Sensors: +0/1 light-year [4 Power/round]
    Navigational Sensors: +0 [5 Power/round]
    Sensors Skill: 2
WEAPONS SYSTEMS
    None
    Weapons Skill: N/A
DEFENSIVE SYSTEMS
    Deflector Shield
      Protection: 15/18 [15 Power/shield/round]

DESCRIPTION AND NOTES

Fleet data: This small cargo vessel plies the major trade routes between the various planets of the Federation and beyond. Its size makes it affordable, but allows the pilot to carry only relatively small amounts of cargo. Therefore, the items carried on a Class J ship often are often very valuable, making such ships prime targets for Orion pirates and their ilk. Starfleet uses older Class J ships as cadet training vessels.

CLASS B FREIGHTER

    Class and Type: Freighter
    Commissioning Date: 2220
    HULL CHARACTERISTICS
      Size: 4
      Resistance: 2
      Structural Points: 80
    OPERATIONS CHARACTERISTICS

Crew/Passengers/Evac: 20/50/200 [5 Power/round]
Computers: 2 [1 Power/round]
Transporters: 2 personnel, 4 cargo, 2 emergency [4 Power/round]
Tractor Beams: 1 fv, 1 av [2 Power/rating/round]
PROPULSION AND POWER CHARACTERISTICS
    Warp System: 3.0/4.0/5.5 (6 hours) [2/warp factor]
    Impulse System: .4 c/.66 c [4/7 Power/round]
    Power: 60
SENSOR SYSTEMS
    Long-range Sensors: +0/10 light-years [6 Power/round]
    Lateral Sensors: +0/1 light-year [4 Power/round]
    Navigational Sensors: +0 [5 Power/round]
    Sensors Skill: 3
Weapons Systems
    None
    Weapons Skill: N/A
Defensive Systems
    Deflector Shield
      Protection: 18/22
      [18 Power/shield/round]

Description and Notes

Fleet data: A cargo ship much larger and more powerful than the Class J, this civilian freighter comes in a wide variety of models, styles, and configurations. While most serve to carry bulk cargoes from colonies to core worlds and back again, some are designed as transports (in varying degrees of luxury—the *Astral Queen* is one of the most luxurious ships in space), tankers, or the like. Larger models also exist.

SPACE CRUISER

    Class and Type: Freighter
    Commissioning Date: 2240
    HULL CHARACTERISTICS
      Size: 3

Resistance: 2
Structural Points: 60

Operations Characteristics
    Crew/Passengers/Evac: 14/40/300 [5 Power/round]
    Computers: 2 [1 Power/round]
    Transporters: 2 personnel, 2 cargo, 2 emergency [3 Power/round]
    Tractor Beams: 1 fv, 1 av [2 Power/rating/round]

PROPULSION AND POWER CHARACTERISTICS
    Warp System: 4.0/5.0/5.0 (6 hours) [2/warp factor]
    Impulse System: .4 c/.66 c [4/7 Power/round]
    Power: 60

SENSOR SYSTEMS
    Long-range Sensors: +0/8 light-years [6 Power/round]
    Lateral Sensors: +0/1 light-year [4 Power/round]
    Navigational Sensors: +0 [5 Power/round]
    Sensors Skill: 3

WEAPONS SYSTEMS
    None
    Weapons Skill: N/A

DEFENSIVE SYSTEMS
    Deflector Shield
    Protection: 20/25 [20 Power/shield/round]

DESCRIPTION AND NOTES

Fleet data: This generic classification of ship includes countless different types and styles of civilian transports owned by governments, organizations, and individuals. A few owners equip their cruisers with weapons or upgraded systems.

Klingon Ships

D-9 *"DEVIL"*-CLASS BATTLECRUISER

Class and Type: D-9-class warship
Commissioning Date: 2265 (Starfleet Intelligence estimate)

HULL CHARACTERISTICS
    Size: 7
    Resistance: 3
    Structural Points: 140

OPERATIONS CHARACTERISTICS
    Crew/Passengers/Evac: 460/175/5,000 [7 Power/round]
    Computers: 4 [2 Power/round]
    Transporters: 10 personnel, 6 cargo, 4 emergency [10 Power/round]
    Tractor Beams: 1 fv, 1 av [2 Power/rating/round]

PROPULSION AND POWER CHARACTERISTICS
    Warp System: 5.0/6.0/8.0 (12 hours) [2/warp factor]
    Impulse System: .5 c/.75 c [5/7 Power/round]
    Power: 150

SENSOR SYSTEMS
    Long-range Sensors: +1/15 light-years [6 Power/round]
    Lateral Sensors: +1/1 light-year [4 Power/round]
    Navigational Sensors: +1 [5 Power/round]
    Cloak: 2 [8 Power/round]
    Sensors Skill: 4

WEAPONS SYSTEMS
    Type VI Disruptor
    Range: 10/30,000/100,000/300,000
    Arc: Forward (120 degrees)
    Accuracy: 4/5/7/10
    Damage: 16
    Power: [16]
    Torpedoes
    Number: 800
    Launchers: 4 fv

Spread: 4
Arc: Forward (120 degrees)
Range: 15/300,000/1,000,000/3,000,000
Accuracy: 4/5/7/10
Damage: 18
Power: [5]
Weapons Skill: 4
Defensive Systems
IKAF Deflector Shield
Protection: 45/55 [45 Power/shield/round]

DESCRIPTION AND NOTES

Fleet data: Arguably the most advanced ship possessed by the Federation or any of its primary enemies, the D-9 "Devil" battlecruiser is thought to have recently been introduced into the Klingon fleet. Starfleet Intelligence believes that its role is as a "power projection" ship, capable of landing up to 5,000 troops on a planet using armored shuttles or large transporter grids. Armed with powerful disruptors and a heavy torpedo load for planetary bombardment, and possessing a primitive cloaking device which obscures it to sensors (but not normal sight), it can take on and defeat a *Constitution*-class vessel.

D-7 *"DEADLY"*-CLASS BATTLECRUISER

Class and Type: D-7-class warship
Commissioning Date: 2250 (Starfleet Intelligence estimate)
HULL CHARACTERISTICS
Size: 6
Resistance: 3
Structural Points: 120
OPERATIONS CHARACTERISTICS
Crew/Passengers/Evac: 400/135/2,900 [7 Power/round]
Computers: 4 [2 Power/round]
Transporters: 4 personnel, 6 cargo, 4 emergency [7 Power/round]
Tractor Beams: 1 fv, 1 av [2 Power/rating/round]

PROPULSION AND POWER CHARACTERISTICS
Warp System: 5.0/6.0/7.5 (12 hours) [2/warp factor]
Impulse System: .5 c/.75 c [5/7 Power/round]
Power: 125
SENSOR SYSTEMS
Long-range Sensors: +1/15 light-years [6 Power/round]
Lateral Sensors: +1/1 light-year [4 Power/round]
Navigational Sensors: +1 [5 Power/round]
Sensors Skill: 4
WEAPONS SYSTEMS
Type V Disruptor
Range: 10/30,000/100,000/300,000
Arc: Forward (120 degrees)
Accuracy: 4/5/7/10
Damage: 14
Power: [14]
Torpedoes
Number: 175
Launchers: 1 fv
Spread: 3
Arc: Forward (120 degrees)
Range: 15/300,000/1,000,000/3,000,000
Accuracy: 4/5/7/10
Damage: 18
Power: [5]
Weapons Skill: 4
DEFENSIVE SYSTEMS
IKAF Deflector Shield
Protection: 35/45 [35 Power/shield/round]

DESCRIPTION AND NOTES

Fleet data: The D-7 is the main combat vessel of the Imperial Klingon Defense Force. First encountered by Starfleet toward the end of the Federation-Klingon war, when it replaced the D-5 as the Klingons' top-of-the-line vessel, it has proven to be a powerful ship capable of putting up a tough fight against even the strongest Starfleet vessels.

Pursuant to the terms of an agreement between the Klingon Empire and the Romulan Star Empire, the Romulans have received and begun using an unknown number of D-7 class ships. These ships are functionally identical to the Klingon ships, although they possess a Cloak 7.

D-5 *"DEVASTATOR"*-CLASS BATTLECRUISER

Class and Type: D-5-class warship
Commissioning Date: Early-mid-23rdcentury
HULL CHARACTERISTICS
Size: 5
Resistance: 3

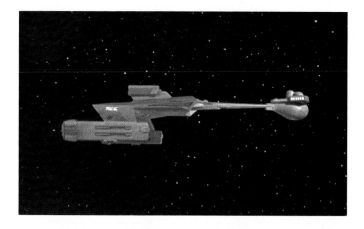

Structural Points: 100

OPERATIONS CHARACTERISTICS

Crew/Passengers/Evac: 350/100/1,400 [6 Power/round]

Computers: 2 [1 Power/round]

Transporters: 2 personnel, 2 cargo, 2 emergency [3 Power/round]

Tractor Beams: 1 fv, 1 av [2 Power/rating/round]

PROPULSION AND POWER CHARACTERISTICS

Warp System: 4.0/5.0/7.0 (12 hours) [2/warp factor]

Impulse System: .4 c/.66 c [6/7 Power/round]

Power: 100

SENSOR SYSTEMS

Long-range Sensors: +1/12 light-years [6 Power/round]

Lateral Sensors: +1/1 light-year [4 Power/round]

Navigational Sensors: +1 [5 Power/round]

Sensors Skill: 4

WEAPONS SYSTEMS

Type IV Disruptor

Range: 10/30,000/100,000/300,000

Arc: Forward (120 degrees)

Accuracy: 4/5/7/10

Damage: 12

Power: [12]

Torpedoes

Number: 150

Launchers: 1 fv

Spread: 3

Arc: Forward (120 degrees)

Range: 15/300,000/1,000,000/3,000,000

Accuracy: 4/5/7/10

Damage: 16

Power: [5]

Weapons Skill: 4

DEFENSIVE SYSTEMS

IKAF Deflector Shield

Protection: 28/35 [28 Power/shield/round]

DESCRIPTION AND NOTES

Fleet data: Now considered outmoded, the D-5 served as the primary Klingon vessel during the Federation-Klingon War until the introduction of the D-7, and for many years thereafter continued to be commonly encountered by Starfleet vessels. Since 2267, however, it has presumably been relegated to secondary roles within the Empire, for almost none have been seen.

Romulan Ships

ROMULAN BIRD OF PREY

Class and Type: Romulan warship

Commissioning Date: Mid-23rd century

HULL CHARACTERISTICS

Size: 4

Resistance: 3

Structural Points: 80

OPERATIONS CHARACTERISTICS

Crew/Passengers/Evac: 205/50/1,800 [6 Power/round]

Computers: 4 [2 Power/round]

Transporters: 4 personnel, 4 cargo, 2 emergency [5 Power/round]

Tractor Beams: 1 fv, 1 av [2 Power/rating/round]

PROPULSION AND POWER CHARACTERISTICS

Warp System: None

Impulse System: .5 c/.9 c [5/9 Power/round]

Power: 125

SENSOR SYSTEMS

Long-range Sensors: +1/15 light-years [6 Power/round]

Lateral Sensors: +1/1 light-year [4 Power/round]

Navigational Sensors: +1 [5 Power/round]

Cloak: 7 [28 Power/round]

Sensors Skill: 4

WEAPONS SYSTEMS

Type H Disruptor

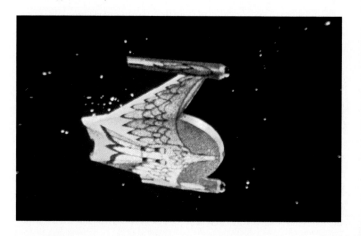

Range: 10/30,000/100,000/300,000

Arc: Forward (120 degrees)

Accuracy: 4/5/7/10

Damage: 15

Power: [15]

Plasma Torpedoes

Number: 75

Launchers: 1 fv

Spread: not capable

Arc: Forward (120 degrees)

Range: 30,000/250,000/900,000/1,500,000

Accuracy: 4/5/7/10

Damage: See text

Power: [5]

Weapons Skill: 4

DEFENSIVE SYSTEMS

Romulan Deflector Shield

Protection: 35/40 [35 Power/shield/round]

DESCRIPTION AND NOTES

Fleet data: First encountered by Starfleet in 2266, when one of these ships crossed the Neutral Zone to test Federation response and was destroyed by the *U.S.S. Enterprise*, this ship has given Starfleet Command many sleepless nights. Birds of prey have single-use magnetic bottles that propel them at warp speed to their tactical target areas. By now, unknown numbers of birds of prey could be stationed within a short flight of the Federation border. Equipped with a cloaking device and powerful weapons such as plasma torpedoes, Romulan birds of prey could wreak extensive devastation on Federation targets should the Romulans choose to attack the Federation.

Plasma Torpedoes

Plasma torpedoes work slightly differently from photon torpedoes, in that they are very powerful against nearby targets, but lose power the further they travel. When fired at a target within one Movement Unit of the firing ship, a plasma torpedo does 30 points of damage. For each three Movement Units thereafter, it loses 1 point of damage, until it reaches 0 points and dissipates.

Miscellaneous Ships

ORION PIRATE SHIP

Class and Type: Orion warship

Commissioning Date: Early to mid-23rd century

HULL CHARACTERISTICS

Size: 4

Resistance: 3

Structural Points: 80

OPERATIONS CHARACTERISTICS

Crew/Passengers/Evac: 70/50/500 [6 Power/round]

Computers: 2 [1 Power/round]

Transporters: 2 personnel, 2 cargo, 2 emergency [3 Power/round]

Tractor Beams: 1 fv, 1 av [2 Power/rating/round]

PROPULSION AND POWER CHARACTERISTICS

Warp System: 4.0/5.0/6.5 (12 hours) [2/warp factor]

Impulse System: .5 c/.75 c [5/7 Power/round]

Power: 95

SENSOR SYSTEMS

Long-range Sensors: +1/12 light-years [6 Power/round]

Lateral Sensors: +1/1 light-year [4 Power/round]

Navigational Sensors: +0 [5 Power/round]

Sensors Skill: 3

WEAPONS SYSTEMS

Type Epsilon Disruptor

Range: 10/30,000/100,000/300,000

Arc: Forward (120 degrees)

Accuracy: 4/5/7/10

Damage: 12

Power: [12]

Weapons Skill: 4

DEFENSIVE SYSTEMS

Orion Deflector Shield

Protection: 28/35 [28 Power/shield/round]

DESCRIPTION AND NOTES

Fleet data: This ship template represents the typical raiding vessel used by Orion pirates (and, for that matter, many other pirates). Equipped with better sensors than most trading vessels, it can detect targets at long range and then swoop in for the kill using its better engines.

The Narrator should make minor changes to the template as necessary to reflect different pirate captains' preferences. For example, some want stronger weapons at the expense of slower engines, or better sensors and shields at the expense of the weapons systems. Some even have torpedo launchers salvaged from derelict military ships. Some Orion ships have been adjusted for suicide missions, allowing effectively doubled power output—until they destroy themselves.

THOLIAN WEBSHIP

Class and Type: Tholian warship
Commissioning Date: Early-mid-23rd century

HULL CHARACTERISTICS
Size: 3
Resistance: 3
Structural Points: 60

OPERATIONS CHARACTERISTICS
Crew/Passengers/Evac: 20/40/300 [5 Power/round]
Computers: 2 [1 Power/round]
Transporters: 1 personnel, 1 cargo, 1 emergency [1 Power/round]
Tractor Beams: 1 fv [2 Power/rating/round]

PROPULSION AND POWER CHARACTERISTICS
Warp System: 3.0/4.0/5.0 (12 hours) [2/warp factor]
Impulse System: .5 c/.75 c [5/7 Power/round]
Power: 100

SENSOR SYSTEMS
Long-range Sensors: +1/12 light-years [6 Power/round]
Lateral Sensors: +1/1 light-year [4 Power/round]
Navigational Sensors: +0 [5 Power/round]
Sensors Skill: 4

WEAPONS SYSTEMS
Tholian Web Generator (see text)
[10 Power/round]
Weapons Skill: N/A

DEFENSIVE SYSTEMS
Tholian Deflector Shield
Protection: 30/37 [30 Power/shield/round]

DESCRIPTION AND NOTES

Fleet data: The Federation encountered a fleet of these ships in 2268 when the *U.S.S. Defiant* was lost and the *U.S.S. Enterprise* nearly so. Its primary purpose seems to be to "spin" a Tholian web.

Tholian Web
A Tholian web is a powerful energy field capable of destroying starships. It takes time to prepare the web, however, so it can only be used on ships which are already stranded or disabled. Since the borders of Tholian space are sprinkled with pockets of interspace (which can disable even a *Constitution*-class ship), this weapon often proves quite useful to the Tholians, since it can be activated beyond the target ship's weapon range and thus destroy that ship without risking any Tholian lives.

A Tholian webship begins "spinning" a web (it's actually more of a net than a web) at a point beyond the weapons range of the target ship. It takes 100 rounds to spin fully; each round 1% more of the web is completed. When the web is completed the Tholians activate it, making it contract and destroy the ship captured within it. Neither shields, nor a cloak, nor a strong hull can save a ship from being completely destroyed by the web. The only known escape is to restore mobility to the target before the web has been completed; however, it may be possible to disrupt the web with some energy pulses in some instances.

GORN BATTLECRUISER

Class and Type: Gorn warship; exact class designation unknown
Commissioning Date: Early-mid-23rd century
HULL CHARACTERISTICS
Size: 6
Resistance: 4
Structural Points: 120
OPERATIONS CHARACTERISTICS
Crew/Passengers/Evac: 375/100/1,850 [7 Power/round]
Computers: 4 [2 Power/round]
Transporters: 3 personnel, 4 cargo, 3 emergency [5 Power/round]
Tractor Beams: 1 fv, 1 av [2 Power/rating/round]
PROPULSION AND POWER CHARACTERISTICS
Warp System: 6.0/7.0/8.0 (12 hours) [2/warp factor]
Impulse System: .5 c/.75 c [5/7 Power/round]
Power: 130
SENSOR SYSTEMS
Long-range Sensors: +1/14 light-years [6 Power/round]
Lateral Sensors: +1/1 light-year [4 Power/round]
Navigational Sensors: +1 [5 Power/round]
Sensors Skill: 4
WEAPONS SYSTEMS
Narrow-wave Disruptor Cannon
Range: 10/30,000/100,000/300,000
Arc: Forward (180 degrees)

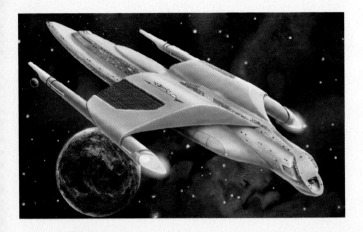

Accuracy: 4/5/7/10

Damage: 14

Power: [14]

Torpedoes

Number: 50

Launchers: 1 fv

Spread: 3

Arc: Forward (120 degrees)

Range: 15/300,000/1,000,000/3,000,000

Accuracy: 4/5/7/10

Damage: 18

Power: [5]

Weapons Skill: 4

DEFENSIVE SYSTEMS

Gorn Deflector Shield

Protection: 40/50 [40 Power/shield/round]

DESCRIPTION AND NOTES

Fleet data: This ship has been encountered only once by the Federation, by the *U.S.S. Enterprise* near Cestus III (2267), and even that encounter was from a great distance. Based on Starfleet analyses of the available data, the ship seems to be powerful, heavily defended, and at least as well armed as a *Constitution*-class ship.

The Gorn ship encountered in 2267 was more maneuverable than the *Enterprise*. Gorn ships perform all feats of Maneuver at one Difficulty lower than Federation ships do.

The ship rocked with the impact, throwing the bridge crew first to the left and to the right. A shower of sparks erupted from a console; the ensign manning that station fell backwards into the railing.

"That was a direct photon torpedo hit," said Mr. Eleb, his antennae taut with tension. "Shield integrity down to 28%."

The voice of Pearlstein, the chief engineer, rang through the comm system. "We can't take another one like that, Captain."

Captain Duffy clutched the arms of his chair and gritted his teeth. "Helmsman," he said to Lt. Bruni, "We could use those evasive maneuvers any time now."

Bruni would have been offended if the two of them hadn't been through so much together. "I'm trying every trick in the book, Captain. Problem is, they got the same book."

STARSHIP COMBAT

Duffy looked grimly at the viewscreen. Here he was, Captain of the U.S.S. Indomitable, *losing badly to*... *the* U.S.S. Indomitable, *no doubt commanded by his own doppelganger. When those blasted god-like aliens said he'd be given an even chance, he never figured they meant it literally. They'd duplicated his entire ship and crew and sent it to hunt them down and destroy him. Dammit, how does a man go about outmaneuvering himself?*

"We've got to do something they can't anticipate," he thought aloud. "Something I would never think of in a million years. I've got it! We know their deck layout exactly, so we can get a transporter lock on their impulse engine."

"We'll need to get through their shields to do that, sir," Eleb reminded him.

"All we need is a second, if we time it right. Target the soft spot between the aft and forward shields. Lock onto their engine and beam it into space."

The ship pitched again.

"Shields are down," Eleb reported. "And ... they've got a transporter lock on our impulse engine."

Although its primary purpose is exploration and discovery, Starfleet also serves to defend the Federation and safeguard the peace within its territory. Conflicts are all too frequent, so Starfleet is always ready for just about anything. The UFP's adversaries, such as the Klingons and Romulans, often have weapons of awesome destructive power, and they're all too willing to use their power for unjust and oppressive ends. Although Starfleet prefers to resolve conflicts without force, and trains its personnel accordingly, when push comes to shove sometimes it has to fight to protect all that the Federation holds dear. Accordingly, gifted tacticians such as Garth of Izar command the well-armed, well-defended Starfleet ships. If it must fight, Starfleet is both ready and able to defend itself with every resource at its command.

Much like personal combat depends on characters' attributes and skills, starship combat depends on two things: the equipment a ship has, and the abilities of its crew. You can find information on ship characteristics in the *Starships* chapter, pages 134-140. Please review that information before proceeding with this chapter or running a starship combat. You should also familiarize yourself with the basic rules of the *Star Trek Roleplaying Game* (see the *Action* chapter, pages 97-120), since there are many parallels and similarities between the those rules and starship combat rules.

Time

Starship combat is organized into five-second-long rounds, just like personal combat. During a round, a starship can take one or more actions without suffering a Multiple Action Penalty. (However, the crewmen operating the starship do incur Multiple Action Penalties if they, for example, make a sensor check and fire phasers in the same round.)

Initiative

Initiative in starship combat is determined with the Starship Tactics skill of each ship's commanding officer. If, for whatever reason, a ship's commander does not have that skill, he may make an Intellect Test instead.

Character Roles

Starship combat is really just interpersonal combat between characters in a different venue; starships don't fight battles on their own. Everyone on the bridge plays an important role in battle. The helmsman maneuvers the ship and fires weapons, the navigator assists the helmsman, the engineers allocate power and so on. As Narrator, it's important that you make starship combat a group endeavor and give every player character something to do. Each character's role should help see the ship to victory; if only the character firing the phasers has any fun, your group will soon shy away from starship combats.

MULTIPLE ACTIONS IN STARSHIP COMBAT

Characters aboard a starship who perform multiple actions in a single round (for example, establishing several sensor locks, firing two weapons, or

establishing a sensor lock and then firing a weapon) are subject to a Multiple Action Penalty, just like in personal combat (see page 109). This is why starships assign specific individuals to particular tasks in combat; doubling up on duties makes characters inefficient.

Helmsman Ensign Barnes wants to fire twice in one round (one phaser attack, one torpedo launch). Because he performs more than one action this round, he suffers a +1 Difficulty on both of his Shipboard Systems (Weapons Systems) rolls to hit the targets.

OPERATIONS

Even a *Constitution*-class starship only has so much power to go around. Everything a ship does, from using sensors and communications systems, to raising shields, to firing weapons, consumes some of that power. In combat, the Engineer's job is to allocate power to the appropriate systems and keep them running efficiently.

POWER ALLOCATION

In game terms, a ship's power-generating ability is represented by its Power characteristic. Power indicates how much energy a ship generates each round. A *Constitution*-class ship, for example, can generate 135 points of Power each round.

Similarly, the Icon System rules indicate how much Power it costs to run each system on a ship per round. If you look at the ships in the *Starships* chapter, you'll see that each one has enough Power to run its systems (including shields and weapons) at their normal levels without significant Power concerns. However, when the Crew starts to redirect power to improve weapon or shield performance, Power usage can become a balancing game. Engineering must allocate Power in the most efficient ways possible.

During battle, at the beginning of every round, the Engineer (or character manning the Engineering station) allocates Power to each shipboard system. He usually consults with the Helm, to ensure he has enough Power. For example, if the Helm fires the phasers at half power, the Engineer has some "spare" Power he can allocate elsewhere—the shields or sensors, for example. Conversely, if the Helm wants to fire the phasers at maximum power, the Engineer has to give him the Power to do so. If necessary, some systems can be shut down or run on decreased Power (and thus decreased effectiveness) so that other systems can receive more Power.

Simply reallocating Power doesn't normally require any Skill Tests; the Engineer just makes the change. However, coaxing more strength or effectiveness from specific systems may require Tests (see elsewhere in this chapter and specific systems descriptions in the Starships chapter). If the Narrator feels that a Test is necessary (perhaps because of damage to the Engineering section), the base Difficulty for any Power transfer is Moderate (7).

Of course, ship safeguards prevent a character from taking Power from some systems (such as life support) without a high-ranking officer's permission. Taking power from these systems requires a Systems Engineering (Power Systems) Skill Test to override their failsafes, or the proper authorization codes.

Freeform Power System

Allocating Power makes starship combat pretty complex, and requires a lot of record-keeping. If you'd rather not get caught up in such complications, you can simply ignore the question of Power altogether. Let the Narrator to keep rough track of such matters so that she can determine a ship's capabilities from round to round, or limit what the Crew can do with their ship based on the circumstances. If necessary, she can simply declare that certain systems are working at some percentage of their peak efficiency; this can reflect damage to the systems, draining Power to use elsewhere, and the like.

IMPULSE SPEEDS

The standard Starfleet designation for "Full Impulse speed" is .25c. Vessels may travel faster than this, but such speeds are generally inefficient (it's more efficient just to go to warp speed). Starship combat is one of the few situations where ships move at high impulse speeds.

FLYING THE SHIP

Starship combat occurs in a gravity-free, three-dimensional environment, so a starship's ability to maneuver is limited only by its physical tolerances and capacities and the skill of its Helm officer. The Helmsman maneuvers the ship, making Shipboard Systems (Helm) Tests to position the ship in battle—to dodge an attack, avoid a collision or set up a perfect spread for the torpedoes. The number of possible maneuvers that a starship could make in combat is virtually limitless. The *Starship Maneuvers* table lists just a few, broadly described, possible maneuvers, with a Difficulty for each when making Shipboard Systems (Helm) Tests. If a ship simply tries to dodge attacks (see *Evasive Action*, page 156), use a flat Difficulty of Moderate (8) for all maneu-

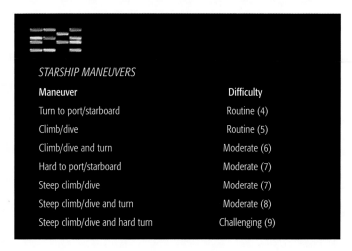

STARSHIP MANEUVERS

Maneuver	Difficulty
Turn to port/starboard	Routine (4)
Climb/dive	Routine (5)
Climb/dive and turn	Moderate (6)
Hard to port/starboard	Moderate (7)
Steep climb/dive	Moderate (7)
Steep climb/dive and turn	Moderate (8)
Steep climb/dive and hard turn	Challenging (9)

vers. For maneuvers not listed here, the Narrator should determine the Difficulty by using the listed examples as guidelines.

MOVEMENT

Starship combat almost always occurs at impulse speeds; only when starships have more or less the same warp velocity and flight path can they engage in warp-speed combat, and even then they're limited to using missile weapons like photon torpedoes.

For purposes of starship combat, starship movement is broken down into Movement Units, each approximately 30,000 kilometers long. Each round, a ship may move one Movement Unit for each 10 percent of lightspeed (rounding down) it uses to move and maneuver. For example, a ship moving at .25c moves 2 Movement Units per round; one moving at .50c moves 5 Movement Units per round.

In battle, a starship can accelerate at one half of its maximum impulse speed per round, or decelerate all of its impulse movement (*i.e.*, come to a "full stop") in one round. For example, suppose the *U.S.S. Essex* (a *Constitution*-class starship which can move at .75c/.9c) moves through a battle at .25c. The captain realizes it must get to the far side of the battlefield as soon as possible to prevent a sneak attack on several other ships. She orders the Helm to accelerate by .45c (half its maximum impulse speed) this round, bringing its speed up to .70c.

THE PLAYING SURFACE

When running starship combat, sometimes it helps to have a physical representation of the battlefield. This makes it easier for the Narrator and player to keep close track of where all the ships are, determine their locations in relation to enemy vessels, and calculate weapon ranges.

Although space is three-dimensional, typically you'll have to use a large, flat area–like a tabletop–for your space battle playing surface, with lead, pewter, or plastic miniatures (such as those manufactured by Last Unicorn) to represent the ships. Of course, you can always use coins, counters, small pieces of paper, or anything similar to represent ships if you don't have miniatures. You can even add a little three-dimensionality to the battlefield if you have some small stands for the ships, or make notations like "+2" or "-3" to indicate how many Movement Units above or below the playing surface a ship is.

On the playing surface, one inch represents one Movement Unit (30,000 km). You can use a surface with inches marked on it by hexes or squares (available at many hobby and game shops), or simply measure ranges and movement with a ruler.

Although maneuverable, starships can't turn on a dime. If the Helm needs to turn a ship around, he has two options. First, he can come to a full stop, turn the ship around with the impulse thrusters, and head in the direction he wants to go. This requires a round, and is considered "being immobile" for purposes of targeting the ship. Alternately, he can keep the ship moving and turn in a broad arc. This requires a round, a Moderate (7) Shipboard Systems (Helm) Test ("hard to port") and for the ship to use all of its Movement Units for the current round. At the end of the round the ship faces the opposite direction from its original heading, and is also a number of Movement Units away from its original position, in the direction of the turn, equal to half the Movement Units used to make the arc.

> While moving at .9c, the Essex needs to head back in the opposite direction. Her captain orders a broad arc to starboard. It takes 9 Movement Units and an entire round to make this arc. At the end of the arc the Essex faces the desired direction, but is 4.5 Movement Units to starboard of its starting position.

EVASIVE ACTION

A skilled Helm can make his ship harder to hit through clever maneuvering–dodging, in effect. The base Difficulty to "dodge" is Moderate (8) using Shipboard Systems (Helm). For every two points by which the Test Result exceeds this number, opponents have a +1 Difficulty to hit the ship with any attacks that round. For example, if the Shipboard Systems (Helm) Test Result was a 12, the ship increases the Difficulty of any attempt to hit it that round by +2.

WEAPONS SYSTEMS

The Helmsman stays busy in ship combat, because he has primary responsibility for firing weapons. The Navigator typically helps him with this duty, and Narrators with both a Helmsman and a Navigator in the Crew can consider firing weapons to be a Combined Test (see page 105), or simply assign weapons to the Navigator while giving the Helm the sole task of maneuvering the ship. The character firing the weapons uses Shipboard Systems (Weapons Systems) to determine if he hits the target ship. He rolls a Skill Test against a Difficulty determined by the type of weapon he's firing and the range to the target. (See the ship templates in the Starships chapter for details regarding ships' weapons.)

TARGETING MODIFIERS

As with personal combat, many different circumstances modify an attack during battle. These include:

Aiming

The Helm may spend time aiming at a specific target. Aiming requires an entire round, during which the starship can make no attacks (with any weapon) nor any maneuvers which would require a Shipboard Systems (Helm) roll. For each round spent aiming at a target, reduce the Difficulty to hit that target by 1.

Called Shots

Characters may attempt to target specific locations on a starship. Doing so increases the Difficulty of the attack, but if the attempt penetrates the target's shields, may allow the ship to disable its target's vital systems, thus ending the battle quicker. The accompanying Starship Hit Location Table lists the Difficulty modifiers for, and effects of, targeting various sections of a ship. Narrators can use these as guidelines to determine modifiers and effects for areas not listed here (or, optionally, roll randomly on the chart to see where a given shot hits when it penetrates a ship's shields). The damage levels given are for a *Constitution*-class (Size 6) ship; the Narrator should feel free to prorate these levels up or down for larger or smaller vessels, or for dramatic necessity.

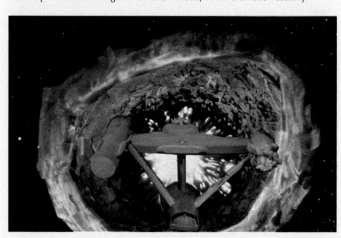

STARSHIP HIT LOCATION TABLE

Roll	Location	Difficulty Modifier	Effect
2	Bridge	+10	A hit to the Bridge which does 7 points of damage or less damages equipment, imposing a +2 Difficulty on all Tests made using Bridge equipment. Two such hits, or one hit that does 12 or more points of damage, destroy the Bridge. Destruction of the Bridge typically kills all characters on the Bridge, but some may be able to get to escape pods in time to be saved.
3	Communications	+6	The first hit which does any damage to Communications increases the Difficulty of all Tests made with Communications equipment by +3; the second hit, or any hit that does 12 or more points of damage, destroys the ship's communications capabilities.
4	Engineering	+8	Each 12 points of damage to Engineering increases the Difficulty of all Engineering Skill Tests which involve the damaged equipment (including Tests to repair the damage) by +2. It also decreases the maximum speed of the impulse and warp engines by 20%. After taking 60 points of damage, Engineering is completely destroyed.
5	Impulse Engines	+7	The Impulse Engines' maximum speed is reduced by 25% for each 4 points of damage they take. When they take 18 or more points of damage, the ship cannot travel at impulse speeds.
6	Life Support	+8	Life Support's effectiveness is reduced 25% for each 9 points of damage it takes. When Life Support is completely destroyed (36 points' worth of damage), the ship cannot support life; anyone remaining on the ship dies as soon as ambient oxygen is depleted.
7	Main Deflector Dish	+6	The Main Deflector Dish can take 30 points of damage before ceasing to function. At that point, all of the ship's shields are reduced to half power and its navigational deflectors are completely inoperable (rendering warp travel dangerous).
8	Sensors	+6	The effectiveness of the Sensors is reduced by 25% for each 6 points of damage they take. Each loss of 25% reduces the sensor's gain modifier by -1 (maximum reduction is to -2), and increases the Difficulty Numbers for all Tests made using the equipment by +2. After Sensors take 24 or more points of damage, the ship can no longer use them at all, rendering it effectively "blind."
9	Shield Generators	+7	Each hit against the Shield Generators which does 7 points of damage or more reduces the effectiveness of all shields by 10%, to a maximum loss of 50% effectiveness.
10	Transporters	+6	Each 4 points of damage destroys one of the ship's transporters (Narrator determines which one).
11	Warp Nacelle	+7	Each Warp Nacelle can take 24 points of damage before being rendered inoperable. If a Warp Nacelle becomes inoperable, the ship's maximum warp speed is reduced by 50%.
12	Weapons System	+8	Each Weapon System (phaser bank, photon torpedo launcher) can take 8 points of damage before being destroyed. The Narrator should determine which weapon system the attack hits (for example, a forward phaser bank or aft torpedo launcher).

Cloak

Romulan ships, and certain Klingon vessel designs as well, use cloaking devices to render themselves invisible to both sensors and the naked eye, preventing effective attacks against them (though a starship can always fire randomly into an area where its crew thinks there's a cloaked ship). If the ship happens to fire in the proper direction, it hits the cloaked ship if the Helmsman makes a Difficult (13) Shipboard Systems (Weapons Systems) Test; bonuses from the sensors, Command skill, and the like do not apply to this roll.

Since a ship cannot use its shields (or transporters) while it's cloaked, there's typically a brief delay between when a ship decloaks and when it activates its shields. This delay affords a tiny chance for a starship to attack the decloaking ship while it's still vulnerable. The crew of the attacking ship must make a Challenging (11) Shipboard Systems (Sensors) Test to detect the decloaking/shield activation as it occurs. If successful, an attack on the decloaking ship before it raises shields is possible, but add +3 to the Difficulty of the Shipboard Systems (Weapons Systems) Test to reflect the brief period of opportunity. If the crew fails the Shipboard Systems (Sensors) Test, the ship cannot attack during this interval—the crew failed to react in time.

Cover

Sometimes starships, like personal combatants, can hide behind cover—say, in a crowded asteroid field, a nebula which interferes with sensors, or behind a small moon. Depending upon the circumstances, including the extent of the cover, this increases the Difficulty of attempts to hit the ship by +1 to +3.

Immobility

It's easier to hit a stationary (either on purpose, or because it's been damaged) ship. Reduce the Difficulty to hit immobile targets by 2.

Multifire

Ship weapons such as torpedo launchers and phasers can launch more than one attack at a time. The effects depend on the type of weapon fired:

Torpedoes

The Helmsman decides how many torpedoes to fire (up to the launcher's Spread rating; see the *Starships* chapter). He makes a Test to hit the target normally. If the Test Result indicates a success, one attack hits; for every 2 points by which the attacker's Test Result exceeds the Difficulty, an additional attack hits. For purposes of determining the damage to shields (but not to the structure of the ship itself), the multifire burst does its base damage, +1 point per shot that hits the target. If the target's shields are penetrated, it is assumed that the first torpedo caused the shields to drop; each remaining torpedo damages the structure of the ship separately.

The Essex fires a spread of three photon torpedoes at another ship at a range of 200,000 kilometers (Difficulty 5). The Helm rolls a 9 on his Test. This means that all three torpedoes hit (one for making the roll, and one for every 2 points by which the Test Result exceeded the Difficulty). For purposes of damaging the shields, this spread of torpedoes did 21 points of damage; if the torpedoes get through the shields, the second and third torpedoes' 18 points of damage will each be applied to the ship separately, for a total of 36.

Beam Weapons

Ships can also multifire beam weapons, such as phasers, using slightly different rules. The Helm first decides how many shots to fire (to a maximum of three). The shots fired can only be at 75% of maximum power, and must pay the Power cost (75% of the standard Power cost) for each shot. Make a Test to hit the target normally. For purposes of determining the damage to shields (but not to the structure of the ship itself), the multifire burst does its base damage, +1 point per shot that hits the target. If a multifire beam weapon attack pene-

trates a ship's shields, it is assumed that the first beam caused the shields to drop; each remaining beam damages the structure of the ship separately.

The Helm of the Essex fires a volley of three phaser shots at the enemy ship. Each shot will do 10 points of damage (75% of the Type VII Phaser's normal maximum of 14) and cost 10 Power. If all three shots hit, the damage for purposes of breaching the target's shields is 13. If that's enough to breach the shields, the first shot goes to dropping the shields; the other two shots' 10 points of damage each apply separately to the ship's Resistance and Structural Points, for a total of 20.

Size

It's easier to hit larger targets, harder to hit smaller ones. If the target is larger than the attacker, for every point of difference between two starships on the Starship Size Table (page 134), subtract 1 from the Difficulty of hitting the target. For every point of difference that the target is smaller, add 1 to the Difficulty. For example, a Constitution-class ship (Size 6) has a -1 Difficulty to hit a Klingon D-9 battlecruiser (Size 7), but +2 Difficulty to hit a Romulan bird of prey (Size 4). The Narrator may rule that certain Tests, targeting systems, or modifiers negate (or further modify) the size difference.

Targeting Systems

On most starships, the Helmsman has access to advanced tactical systems, which aid him in combat. The basic starship combat rules assume such systems are functioning properly at all times. If they are damaged in battle, or incapacitated (for example, by the energy discharges in a nebula), increase the Difficulty of Tests to hit targets. For example, the lack of a targeting system might increase the Difficulty of all Tests to hit targets by 2.

Tractor Beams

Tractor beams technically aren't "weapons," but ships can use them during battle (to immobilize a target, for example). A ship can use its tractor beam

OPTIONAL POWER LOSS FROM DAMAGE

Starships draw power from their engines, auxiliary power systems, and (as a last resort) stored battery power. Although the ship's power systems shunt power from one or another source to where it is needed during battle, enough damage to the power generators will weaken the ship's performance. Narrators using the Hit Location System may rule that every point of damage done to the Warp Nacelles, Engineering, or Impulse Engines reduces available Power by one point. Engineers may make a Moderate (7) Systems Engineering (Power Systems) Test to compensate for this damage by rerouting power from undamaged systems. As with any other rule in the game, the Narrator is free to modify or discard it to promote better drama.

In times of crisis, a starship can use its phasers to attack the population of a planet. The phasers can affect an area with a radius of 10 meters per point of damage the phasers can cause. The beam can be broadened beyond that, but doing so reduces its power–for every additional 3 meters of radius, reduce the damage the beam causes by 1 point.

Typically starships use phasers in this fashion to stun a population, stepping the phasers to their lowest possible output and attenuating as much as possible of the beam through the planet's atmosphere. In this case, every living thing in the affected area takes a number of points of Stun Damage equal to the phaser's damage rating (for example, 14 points of Stun Damage from a Type VII phaser, assuming no reduction in power for increased area). Usually this suffices to render anyone in the area unconscious for a long time.

However, if necessary, a starship captain can invoke General Order 24 and order an attack on a planet's surface with full phasers. If so, the phasers do their normal damage plus their normal damage in dice to everything within the affected area (for example, a Type VII phaser fired from orbit will do 14+14d6 damage to its target region). Narrators should assign Resistance and Structural Points ratings to buildings, vehicles, and other objects to determine how much damage they suffer (see the values for Cover on page 114 of the *Action* chapter), but a General Order 24 bombardment is usually enough to destroy most structures. Photon torpedoes have similar effects, but obviously cannot be fired on Stun.

(see page 170 of the *Technology* chapter for details on tractors) to manipulate objects at a short distance. A starship caught in a tractor beam is trapped and helpless; it cannot go to warp or move at impulse power. To break out of a tractor beam, a starship can attempt to overload it by physically pulling free at impulse power or destroying the tractor beam generator (a Called Shot).

To capture another ship with a tractor beam, the Helm must make a Shipboard Systems (Weapons Systems) Skill Test (use the Difficulty for range for the ship's primary beam weapon) and spends the Power to use the tractor beam that round. If the attack succeeds, consult the *Tractor Beam Table* (page 138) to determine the rating needed to hold the target immobile at that range. If the attacking ship cannot generate that rating at the range between itself and the ship, the tractor beam attack automatically fails. If the tractor beam does capture the target, the attacking ship must continue to pay the Power cost to run its tractor beam every round.

An immobilized ship can attempt to escape using its impulse engines. Each .10c worth of impulse power counteracts 1 point of tractor rating. If the ship's impulse power exceeds the tractor beam's rating, the ship breaks free. Otherwise it remains trapped. Double the Power cost of the impulse engines for purposes of breaking out of a tractor beam.

The Narrator may allow a Difficult (13) Propulsion Engineering (Impulse) Test to increase the output of the impulse engines slightly (by no more than

+.20c, with a maximum impulse speed of .90c). This "extra" impulse speed costs four times as much Power as normal impulse speed.

DAMAGE

Each starship weapon has a *Damage* characteristic indicating how much damage it inflicts on targets (see individual ship templates in the *Starships* chapter, pages 141-152, for this information). For example, a Type VII Phaser causes up to 14 points of damage. Some weapons (like phasers) can cause a variable amount of damage, depending on their current setting.

Beam weapons' Power cost equals the amount of damage the weapon does. A Type VIII phaser normally does 14 points of damage and costs 14 Power; if set at half power, it would cause 7 points of damage and cost 7 Power to fire. The Helm (or other appropriate officer) can increase a beam weapon's damage to a maximum of 125% of its normal listed damage. For example, a Type VII Phaser can be made to generate up to 18 points of damage. This costs 3 Power per additional point of damage over the weapon's maximum, and requires a successful Moderate (6) Systems Engineering (Phasers) or Shipboard Systems (Weapons Systems) Test.

Missile weapons cost a set amount of Power to fire (typically 5 Power), regardless of the damage they cause. The crew cannot increase their Damage rating, but can reduce it if necessary. This requires a Moderate (6) Systems Engineering (Torpedo/Probe Systems) Test. For example, a photon torpedo (18 points of damage normally) could be set to do only 10, but not 30.

Subtract any damage which penetrates a ship's shields and Resistance from its Structural Points. A ship which loses all of its Structural Points is completely destroyed; one which loses half of them is half destroyed, and so forth. At the Narrator's option, a ship which loses a percentage of its Structural Points (say, 50%) also suffers a proportionate decrease in the strength or efficiency of some or all systems and other functions (in this example, by half). However, it is often preferable to use the Ship Hit Location Table to determine more precisely when various systems are damaged by attacks.

Ramming

In extreme circumstances, a starship can ram its opponent–pilot directly into it, forcing a collision which typically destroys both vessels. Ramming a tar-

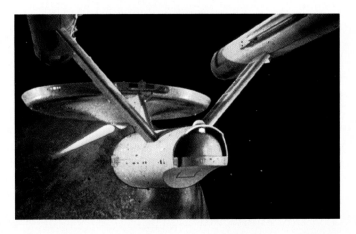

get requires a Moderate (7) Shipboard Systems (Helm) Test. The Narrator may decrease the Difficulty when a ship tries to collide with an extremely large ships, such as the planet-killing "doomsday machine" encountered by the *U.S.S. Enterprise* in 2267, or increase it for small ones, such as shuttlecraft. If the target tries to dodge the ramming vessel, the Test Result of the dodge sets the Difficulty for the ramming attempt.

A successful ramming attempt causes damage equal to the number of Movement Units moved by the attacker that round, times the ship's Size, times 2. Both ships suffer this amount of damage. Thus a *Constitution*-class ship which rams a Klingon attack cruiser at full impulse power (.92*c*) causes 108 points of damage to itself and its target ((9 x 6) x 2 = 108).

RESISTING DAMAGE

Shields

A starship's primary defense against damage is its deflector shields, which "deflect" or ablate an attack's energy. Every ship has two shields—a forward shield and an aft shield—rated in terms of the number of points of protection they provide. The forward and aft shields of a *Constitution*-class starship, for instance, normally provide 40 points of protection, and 60 points of protection at their absolute maximum. (See the individual ship templates for information on a ship's shield strength.)

When a shield is hit by an attack, it takes a number of points of damage equal to the attack. Its ability to protect is reduced by that many points. For example, if a 40-point shield is hit by a photon torpedo and takes 16 points of damage, the shield now only provides 24 points of defense.

When a shield is reduced to 0 points, it buckles and collapses. This leaves the ship with only its Resistance to protect it. A collapsed shield cannot be re-established until the ship's crew succeeds with a Challenging (11) Systems Engineering (Weapons) Test; this usually takes a long time (more time than the average starship combat lasts). If an engineer manages to make temporary repairs during combat, the shield comes back online at 10% of its normal strength (or 20%, if the Test Result for the repair is a Dramatic Success). Depending on the situation and the extent of the damage, the Narrator may decide that such field repairs take more than one round (or are an Extended

Test). Of course, if the Narrator rules that the shield generators have been completely destroyed, the shield cannot be brought online again at all (it requires significant repairs; see *Repairing Damage* on page 162).

At normal strength, each shield costs Power per round equal to the number of points of protection it provides. Powering a 40-point shield costs 40 Power per round, even if the shield has been damaged so that it provides less than full protection. A 40-point shield reduced to 20 points by damage still costs 40 Power per round, for example.

If a shield has been damaged and the Crew wishes to reduce that shield's strength, the reduction equals the appropriate percentage of the shield's full strength. If the ship decides to cut the power to a 40-point shield by a fourth (so that it only costs 30 Power to maintain), then the shield loses 10 points of protection. To continue the previous example, a ship with damaged 40-point shields producing 20 points of protection reduces the power by one-fourth; now it provides a scant 10 points of protection, at a cost of 30 Power. If the ship cuts power to a shield altogether, that shield can be re-activated in subsequent rounds, but only at the same strength and Power cost it was at when it was turned off.

If a ship wishes to strengthen a shield so that it offers the maximum protection it can (60 points on a *Constitution*-class ship, for example), then all points of protection above the normal strength cost 3 Power per point. Thus, for a *Constitution*-class starship to use a shield at full strength costs 100 Power (40 + 60) per round.

Resistance

A starship's hull also provides a limited amount of resistance against attacks—1 to 4 points on most ships. Unlike shields, attacks do not reduce hull resistance; all attacks that penetrate a ship's shields must then cut through the Resistance of the hull before affecting things inside the ship.

Strengthening Damaged Shields

Although starships lose deflector shield integrity as the result of damage, engineers can often strengthen or "repair" shields before they collapse.

First, if a ship is using a shield at less than its full normal strength, it can increase its protection to the listed normal strength for the usual Power cost. This requires an action by the Helm. For example, if a ship's 40-point shields currently operate at 30 (to save on Power) and are hit by an attack reducing their strength to 25, the ship can increase shield strength by 10 points (the difference between 30 and 40). This costs an additional 10 Power per round.

Second, if the ship operates its shields at normal strength, it can increase the shields' protection up to their listed maximum at a cost of 3 Power per point of defense. For example, if a *Constitution*-class ship's 40-point shields are reduced to 30 points, the Crew can increase their protection to 50 by increasing the strength up to the maximum the shield can provide (60 points, 20 more than 40). However, those extra 20 points of protection cost 60 Power.

Third, with a Moderate (7) Systems Engineering (Shields) Test, an Engineer can transfer Power from one shield to another, at the rate of 1 point of protection gained per 2 points transferred. However, the crew cannot reduce a shield below 10 points of protection this way. For example, if a

Constitution-class ship's forward shields are damaged down to 30 points, it could transfer 30 Power points (at most) from its rear shields, thus boosting its forward shield's strength by 15 points (to 45). Transferring points of protection this way does not cost extra Power.

Optional Rule: Automatic Defense

As an optional rule, the Narrator may decide that attacks equal to or less than a certain power level (typically 20% of a shield's normal full strength) cannot do any damage at all. Thus, attacking a *Constitution*-class ship (40-point normal strength shields) with a Type III Phaser (6 points of damage) results in no damage whatsoever to the shields, since 6 is less than or equal to 8 (20% of 40).

The Automatic Defense rule always applies to attacks by hand-held weapons against shields; personal phasers and the like can do no damage to starship shields at all.

SENSORS

Starships can't attack without "seeing" the targets on the battlefield. They need to know where the other ships are, their heading and speed, what types of weapons they are using, where a target's shields might be weakest, and so forth. The character operating the ship's sensors can increase or decrease the likelihood an attack succeeds by providing this kind of information to the Helm (or other weapons officer). This may be the Navigator, a Science Officer, or some other character, depending on the situation.

In each round of starship combat, the Crew member manning the sensors should make a Shipboard Systems (Sensors) Skill Test to obtain a proper sensor lock for the weapons. The Difficulty for obtaining a good sensor lock depends on the circumstances, but is usually Moderate (7). This may increase due to range, interference, the opposing ship's countermeasures and similar factors. For every 2 points by which the Test Result exceeds the Difficulty Number, the Helm gets +1 die to roll when making his Shipboard Systems (Weapons Systems) roll against the target ship. Conversely, for every 2 points by which the character fails his Shipboard Systems (Sensors) roll, the Helm suffers a -1 die penalty.

Lieutenant Calloway operates her ship's sensors during a combat. She has Shipboard Systems (Sensors) 3 (4) and uses the lateral sensors (providing +1 to her roll). The Narrator rules the Difficulty to obtain a sensor lock this round is Moderate (7). Calloway's player rolls the dice; the best result is a 5. Four (the roll) + 4 (her Skill level) +1 (sensors) =9. This is 2 above the Difficulty Number. The Helm receives +1 die for his Tests to hit the opposing ship this round.

Each sensor lock (or failure to obtain a lock) only modifies Shipboard Systems (Weapons Systems) Tests made during that round. Next round, the crew must make another Shipboard Systems (Sensors) Test. If confronted by several ships, the character operating the sensors must make a separate Shipboard Systems (Sensors) Test to affect the Helm's Skill Tests for each ship which the Helm wishes to attack; this will incur a Multiple Action Penalty. Alternately, several characters may use different sensor systems to establish target locks for multiple targets, or the character may switch his attention from one target to another each round.

Lieutenant Calloway directs the sensors to focus on one Romulan bird of prey. She rolls a Shipboard Systems (Sensors) Test against a Moderate (7) Difficulty. Her Test Result is 11, four above the Difficulty Number, providing the Helm with a +2 dice bonus to hit the bird of prey this round. Suddenly, a second bird of prey decloaks to starboard. If Calloway wishes to obtain sensor information about both opponents this round, she would incur a Multiple Action Penalty, increasing the Difficulty of both her Shipboard Systems (Sensors) Tests by one. Instead, Calloway waits until the next round to focus the sensors on the second bird of prey. Not wanting to incur a Multiple Action Penalty, she waits until the following round to attempt a second sensor lock on the first bird of prey.

COMMAND

During battle, commanders (either the captain or the first officer) coordinate the activities of each station and make tactical decisions. The Narrator may grant a bonus to attacks for a ship based on the skill of its commander. If appropriate, the Narrator may allow the Captain (or other commander) to make a Starship Tactics Test. For every 2 points by which the Starship Tactics Test Result exceeds the Difficulty Number, the Helm receives +1 die to roll when making Shipboard Systems (Weapons Systems) rolls against a single ship. However, for every 2 points below the Difficulty Number, the Helm suffers a -1 die penalty. As with the use of sensors, this bonus or penalty applies to all rolls made against a target ship during the current round.

Commanders may attempt multiple rolls to assist attacks against several targets, but incur the Multiple Action Penalty (see page 109). Only one character on a ship (usually the captain or other person in overall command) can

make a Starship Tactics roll to assist the Helm. In some situations, Opposed Starship Tactics Tests (attacking commander versus target commander) may be appropriate.

ENGINEERING

Inevitably, starships get damaged when they go into battle. This ranges from minor phaser scoring on the hull, to shorted-out systems, to exploded instrument panels, to warp core breaches, to smashed sensor arrays. The Chief Engineer and his crew are tasked with repairing this damage as quickly as they can, to prevent the ship's destruction or to keep it in the battle. During a space battle, engineer characters will make many Engineering Skill Tests.

In some situations, a good engineer can temporarily make the engines run more efficiently, providing more Power for a brief period. If the Narrator allows this, it requires a Challenging (10) Systems Engineering (Power Systems) or Propulsion Engineering (Warp Drive) Test. If the Test succeeds, the engines produce an additional 3d6 of points of Power each round for the next 1d6 rounds. Narrators should only allow Engineers to do this once per combat; any more tampering is likely to damage the warp engines, with catastrophic consequences.

Repairing Damage

In the heat of battle, an Engineer may have to repair a specific section of the ship, or a specific system. This may require either an Extended (see pages 104-105) or Combined (see page 105) Engineering Skill Test, depending on the nature and extent of the damage. As a good rule of thumb, consult the Ship Hit Location Table (page 157) for guidelines regarding how many points of damage it takes to destroy a particular part of the ship or system. Depending on the system and the damage, it usually takes the engineers anywhere from one hour to one day to repair every four points of damage (this can be done as an Extended Test, with approximate repair times, Turn lengths and cumulative Test Result requirements established by the Narrator).

It may take a long time to repair a badly damaged ship. This generally involves making Extended Tests; the Narrator sets the Turn duration and cumulative Test Result. Assuming good repair facilities (such as those available at a starbase) and plenty of repair parts, repairs should take one day per four Structural Points lost; the Narrator can extend this time for repairs made without sufficient facilities (in deep space for example), supplies or personnel.

Several characters can combine their efforts to make repairs to a given system, or to a ship as a whole. This is a Combined Test (see page 105); their success indicates their progress towards completing repairs. The Narrator may increase the result of the Combined Test to reflect the additional efforts of NPC crew members.

The path to the cave was steep and strewn with jagged rocks. As Doc Mason crept toward the cave mouth, he slipped. Aroumti grabbed his elbow and steadied him, preventing him from falling and twisting his ankle. Doc considered making a curmudgeonly wisecrack about the lengths he was willing to go to for Achilles Diamond, but knew better. The captain might be armed, and considering the state of mind he'd displayed before beaming down onto this godforsaken boulder in space, he might not hesitate to shoot anything that made a sound out here.

Doc and Aroumti were wearing night-vision goggles, so they wouldn't have to risk alerting the patient by shining a light into the cave. They knew they'd find him here; scans from the deck of the *Solzhenitsyn* had pinpointed his precise location.

As one, they stepped over the threshold of the cave mouth. They saw him immediately, huddled up in a corner. He'd wedged himself behind a stalagmite, far from his sidearm. He was making a strange noise that Doc couldn't place at first. Then he realized that Diamond was singing an old nursery song.

TECHNOLOGY

"Achilles, it's Doc Mason. You're not well. We've come to take you home."

His voice was high and strained. "The whippoorwills, Doc, the whippoorwills! You can't see them, but there are extra colors all around us. Colors that I've never heard before. They want me to do things, Doc, terrible things. The colors want it."

Diamond flinched as Mason approached, but couldn't escape from the hypo. He slumped into unconsciousness. Doc scanned him with the medical tricorder. "Good god, Aroumti! He's suffered massive cellular disruption. It's a wonder he's even alive!"

Aroumti performed his own tricorder scan on the molecular level. "Something has definitely affected the bonding of molecules in his nervous system. Only 0.000123% of the molecules are destabilized, but that's enough to cause severe damage to any organism."

"Transporter accident, you figure?"

"Or transporter sabotage," Aroumti replied.

The technology of the 23rd century is very different from our own. People regularly beam themselves across thousands of kilometers, starships travel many times the speed of light, and medicine can heal almost every known disease or injury. However, even here technology still has its limits.

WHAT TECHNOLOGY SHOULD BE IN STAR TREK

It is superscience. It grants the characters great power without making them unstoppable or invulnerable.

It is Human-enabled. Technology expands but does not replace the power of the mind and body. There's no adventure unless you know what to do better than your equipment does.

It is convenient and made to a Human scale. By the 23rd century many personal devices could theoretically be made as small as desired. However, Starfleet has found that humanoids can handle somewhat bulky, highly durable items much more easily in a crisis. Such items cannot be as easily lost, broken, or dropped in an emergency.

Most personal equipment either fits comfortably in the palm of your hand or can be slung conveniently over your shoulder. Similarly, controls on these devices use easy-to-read and -manipulate buttons, dials, and readouts. On starships, far from additional supplies, the rugged, durable Starfleet equipment is far easier to repair and replace.

WHAT TECHNOLOGY SHOULD NOT BE IN STAR TREK

It is not explicable, any more than a modern electronic engineer could explain CD-ROM drives to a Visigothic warrior. After all, it's superscience. If we could understand how it works, we'd be doing it now.

It is not the answer. It gives the Crew great resources with which to solve problems, but it does not solve their problems for them.

It is not infallible. Nothing adds a little spice to a crisis like an equipment malfunction. If the players lean a little too much on technical marvels and not enough on their brains, take the tech away from them for a while.

It is not incomprehensible. While we may not be able to explain why it works, we can always explain what it does. Given that, there is always a way to sabotage it so that it stops.

It does not break the laws of thermodynamics, although it does stretch them a little. There are no perpetual motion machines: Everything needs power, and you never get something for nothing. Fusion and antimatter make power quite cheap, but power and raw materials must still be provided.

In spite of the hopes of the late 20th century, direct interfaces between Human nervous systems and computers have proven difficult, dangerous, and unreliable. While various technologies like the Centauran sensor web can replace vision and other senses with electronic equivalents, attempts to tie humanoid minds, memories, and thoughts directly into a computer have not yet proved safe.

It is not the most advanced possible. There are literally hundreds of species out there whose technology is more advanced than the Federation's. They have technology that defies all of the above.

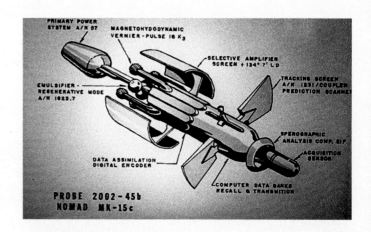

UNUSED TECHNOLOGIES

While the superscience of the 23rd century can do many things, there are also a great number of things it deliberately cannot do. The cultural experiences of Humans and Vulcans, especially, have deeply shaped the technologies developed and used in the Federation.

The Eugenics Wars of the late 20th century left a deep scar upon humanity. The idea of creating a genetically superior master race is deeply repugnant to the vast majority of humans in the Federation. Except for limited medical research designed to cure or prevent genetic defects, all investigation into genetically engineering sentient beings is prohibited by Federation law.

Similarly, Vulcans strongly believe that careful mental training is necessary for a sentient being to develop true intelligence and morality. This belief combined with many humans' fear of creating a computerized master race has greatly slowed research into artificial intelligence. Unlike humanoid genetic engineering, AI research is not illegal or prohibited, but many Federations citizens view it with some distrust. Recent problems with such research have served to reinforce these prejudices. While theoretically possible, fully sentient computers have so far proved to be highly unstable. In some cases such creations can even become dangerously insane. The problems Richard Daystrom experienced when his M-5 computer was tested on the starship *Enterprise* in 2268 are only the most spectacular example of a long series of similar failures.

These same problems have also greatly limited the use of robots in the Federation. While factories and other industrial sites are highly automated, all such complexes relay on Human supervision. Also, most Federation citizens (except the leisure-loving Tiburonians) regard the use of robotic servants in homes, restaurants, and public places as somewhere between needless (and somewhat distasteful) excess and a potential (if highly unlikely) threat.

LIMITING TECHNOLOGY

The players have at their disposal a vast array of incredibly powerful devices. Such devices, if unchecked, could limit many interesting adventure possibilities. As in the various series, sometimes you need to reduce the effectiveness of this technology. A number of planets have electromagnetic or ionic interference in their atmospheres that greatly reduce the range of sensors and communicators and can sometimes render transporters dangerous or unusable. Ion storms (see page 184) can have the same effect and can occur practically anywhere. However, it is best to use these options as infrequently as possible. Not only do tricks get old when repeated too often, but if the players are usually unable to use their vast array of sensors and other devices, they may wonder why anyone bothers with this technology at all.

Other options do exist, however. The force fields used around penal colonies and other high-security installations, as well as the force domes that protect colonies on planets with hostile atmospheres, all limit or prohibit the use of sensors, communicators, and transporters except at designated points. Also, species with technologies significantly more advanced than the Federation can easily defeat most Federation devices. Perhaps the easiest option is simply to have things taken away. If a landing party is captured and taken prisoner, their captors will confiscate its equipment. If they are also out of contact with their ship, they will be left with only their skills and their wits to aid them.

Finally, one of the most enjoyable ways to run an adventure is to allow the characters to use all their vast technological resources while still having to rely upon careful thought and cooperation to complete the adventure. One of the best ways of designing such an adventure is to have them contact something completely unknown. If the new species, disease, or device is not listed in any of the ship's databanks then the players' tech can describe it and help the characters make useful guesses, but these devices cannot solve the problem at hand. The ultimate decisions are still made by Starfleet personnel, not by their devices.

Shipboard Technology

BATTERY POWER

All Federation starships have powerful superconductor-coil batteries in case of total power loss elsewhere. Although systems vary with age, design, and maintenance, a *Constitution*-class starship can generally operate on battery power for a week with life support and gravity. A ship running on battery power can travel only at half-impulse.

COMPUTER SYSTEMS

A starship computer is a marvel of duotronic technology. While fully sentient computers have proved unreliable, starship computers contain sophisticated, although nonsentient, artificial intelligence programs which allow them to understand and respond using ordinary speech. Ship personnel and guests can access the library computer's databanks, containing the equivalent of many trillions of pages of images and text, by using any of the viewers found in every cabin and throughout public areas of the ship.

While many functions can be performed simply by speaking to the computer and listening to its responses, detailed and precise interactions require the user to access a view screen and often a control panel. Crewmen can enter or retrieve additional data from the computer by voice or keyboard; through a

CORBOMITE MANEUVERS AND DOOMSDAY MACHINES: TECHNOLOGY IN YOUR EPISODES

Dilithium crystals, warp speed, transporter devices, phasers, and technological devices or principles lend an unmistakable stamp to *Star Trek*. When Captain Kirk orders his crew to "set phasers on stun" before going into battle or signals Scotty "Beam me up" from the surface of a crumbling planet, you know immediately that you have stepped into the universe of *Star Trek*. One of the pleasures of narrating stories that take place in the far future consists of the ability to indulge in sophisticated (and currently nonexistent) technological gimmickry. The devices of *Star Trek* form an integral element of the series, and should play an equivalent part in your stories.

Just as the series' creators did not stint in their conceptions of how technology makes many aspects of life simpler and more efficient—consider the compact diagnostic instruments used by Dr. McCoy—neither should you limit your own imagination. When devising new technological wonders for your crew to experiment with and, in some cases, battle against, let your creativity run wild. You need not justify your scientific devices by strict adherence to known principles of matter or energy. *Star Trek* takes place in a world of the imagination, not the textbook.

While the science of *Star Trek* does not necessarily agree with the latest knowledge of theoretical physics (or any other kind of physics, for that matter), it does have an internal consistency that guarantees its veracity within the context of the *Star Trek* universe. Make certain you are familiar enough with the standard equipment of Starfleet vessels to avoid mistakes that might undercut the feel of your games.

In many ways, *Star Trek* serves as a paean to the advancement of science, but in other ways, numerous series episodes act as cautionary tales about the potential for misusing technology. Instances of technology run amok or beneficial inventions abused or rendered defective so that they become malevolent entities abound. The two-edged sword of scientific advancement remains one of the most effective weapons for Narrators in the *Star Trek* universe. At least some of your stories should revolve around the use or misuse of technology or the wisdom of creating devices that might fall into irresponsible hands.

signal sent by a tricorder, electronic clipboard, or other remote terminal; or simply by inserting data recorded on standard record tapes (see page 174) into any viewscreen or control panel.

The computer continuously monitors everything inside the ship, including the status of all ship systems. If any emergency inside the ship occurs, the computer will attempt to deal with it on its own while activating warning lights on the relevant control panels.

The heart of all Federation computers is the duotronic circuit. A typical *Constitution*-class starship computer contains more than 900,000 separate duotronic relays, capable of holding up to 8,500 kiloquads of data. On larger

starships the computer is actually distributed throughout the ship. Specialized substations control various critical functions like engineering, life support, and weapons control, but each of these units connects together to form the main computer. In the event of a disaster, each of these substations can act as a separate computer, allowing vital equipment to continue to operate even if the ship has sustained heavy damage and other computers may be damaged.

In spite of its vast resources, the computer is incapable of operating the ship without Human control except during routine maneuvers. The ship requires Human control during emergencies or unknown situations, including ship combat, since the computer is incapable of true creativity. Since the computer is not actually sentient, it is incapable of making complex judgments or anticipating the wants and desires of the crew unless it has been specifically instructed to do something.

For example, the ship's computer will instantly know if a minor system has malfunctioned, but it would not necessarily notify anyone unless asked. If instructed, it will report any occurrence of specific phenomena. All starship computers will instantly respond to and notify the crew about obvious emergencies like life-support failures, but only because they have been programmed to do so. Starship computers also automatically disable dangerously damaged systems and override attempts to use systems in a manner that would be harmful to the ship. However, orders given by any senior officer can instantly bypass these lockouts. The computer also contains a universal translator.

FORCE FIELDS

Based on the same soliton wave technology used in deflector shields, force fields are used throughout Federation starships. All detention and medical isolation cells on starships and other Starfleet facilities use force fields instead of conventional doors. These transparent force fields can be instantly raised and lowered, and they safely absorb any harmful energy discharges or attacks.

Ordinary force fields can safely absorb any single attack that does less than 60 points of damage. However, any attack that does 60 or more points of damage will overload the device and collapse the field. The field will reduce the damage from the attack that knocks it down by 60 points, but will provide no further protection against additional attacks. Only a phaser-3 on maximum setting or a heavier weapon can penetrate a force shield. Force fields can be set

either to allow air to diffuse through normally or to prevent any gas or other matter inside the cell from escaping. The second setting helps contain highly toxic material, contagion, or creatures that exist in poisonous atmospheres.

Some force fields can also be set to allow solid matter to pass through unimpeded while preventing any gases from escaping. The force fields which protect the hangar deck are normally left on this setting, allowing shuttlecraft to enter and exit freely while preventing the atmosphere inside the hangar deck from escaping.

IMPULSE ENGINES

Used to maneuver starships at sublight speeds, the impulse drive uses the onboard fusion reactors to create a helium-deuterium plasma and expel it through directional impulse vents. (The impulse vents close automatically when the impulse engines are not in use.) This drives the ship, by Newtonian reaction, at speeds up to full impulse, or 0.25% of the speed of light. During combat or other emergencies this speed can be temporarily exceeded, but with vastly inefficient expenditures of energy. The impulse engine propulsion packs are normally located aft in the primary hull of a starship.

MANUFACTURING FACILITIES

Fabrication Units
Every large starship carries the facilities to create spare parts, replacement equipment, or other useful tools and devices which the crew might require. These fabrication units use an advanced form of computer-aided design and computer-controlled manufacturing. Anyone with the proper clearance can request that the computer use these facilities to duplicate any part or device with specifications on file in the ship's library computer. In addition, engineers can use these facilities to create almost any unique device they might require. These fabrication technicians utilize a combination of fully automated, computer-controlled manufacturing tools to create the required devices from the stock of raw materials carried on board the starship. If necessary, beaming additional raw materials up from a planet can supplement the ship's stores.

The only practical limit on the fabrication unit is the necessity of having the correct raw materials. For example, a fabrication unit can rapidly shape raw dilithium into a finished crystal, but only if it possesses a stock of dilithium to work with. These units also regularly perform complex chemical synthesis and can create all standard medicines used on a starship. However, certain rare and unusual drugs and other chemicals cannot be synthesized. Such drugs must be acquired in their raw form before the fabrication unit can purify and refine them. In general, making a relatively simple device like a phaser or a flintlock rifle usually takes less than an hour. The facilities on a large starship can produce multiple copies of the same device at the same time.

Food Synthesizers
Storing separate ingredients or prepared meals for the hundreds of crew members on a starship proved impractical. Instead, life support engineers

create meals using a modified fabrication unit. A variety of raw materials grow in nutrient vats. The materials from these vats are then processed and refined into meat, vegetable, and beverage analogs and stored for later use. When a crew member orders a meal these materials are then suitably modified through the addition of flavoring and colorings as well as alterations in texture produced by mechanical manipulation. Any items on the standard menu can be requested from a food delivery unit using voice commands. Special menus and more elaborate requests can be input to these units using standard record tapes. Food synthesizer units are found in the mess halls, recreation areas, and cabins of senior officers.

Given the somewhat limited nature of the food provided by this equipment, all starships engaging in diplomatic missions also carry supplies of high-quality preserved food for use in diplomatic banquets, and larger starships also produce a small supply of fresh fruit and vegetables in their hydroponic gardens. Many crew members also carry along limited supplies of food and drink for personal use.

MEDICAL TECHNOLOGY

In the sickbay, doctors and nurses can rapidly treat almost all wounds which do not instantly kill the patient. Diagnostic sensors built into each bed monitor patients' life signs at all times. Medical personnel repair broken bones and other injuries in a matter of hours, and easily cure most diseases using the vast variety of known drugs and treatments. With the exception of severe neurological damage and unknown diseases or poisons, almost any condition is curable if the patient is still alive when he is brought into sickbay. In the case of especially severe or dangerous injuries the patient is sometimes placed under a cryosurgical suspension hood (a panel folded over his torso) to lower the patient's metabolism drastically, reducing the risk of shock and hemorrhaging during an operation. Similar hoods can create entirely medically sterile areas over a patient's chest, allowing doctors to perform even open-heart surgery without masks or air scrubbers.

When an unknown medical problem is discovered, the medical laboratories use a combination of computer modeling and advanced chemical and biological tests to isolate the problem rapidly and to produce an antidote or cure. Under normal conditions, finding a cure for a new disease rarely takes longer than a few hours.

SENSORS

The sensors aboard a starship are divided into two types. The main sensors are used to examine planets, alien starships, and other objects the ship encounters, and to analyze any unusual energy phenomena. These sensors are tied into the science stations. The navigational sensors are a specialized sensor suite which keep track of the ship's position and velocity. The navigational sensors connect directly to the flight control systems of the helm and navigation stations.

The main sensors provide all of the functions of the tricorder sensors (geological, meteorological, and biological) with a range of 50,000 km. These sensors can perform scans equivalent to both short- and long-range tricorder

scans at this distance, but more detailed scans can take up to an hour to perform and are easily disrupted by interference. The main sensors can provide detailed astronomical and planetary analyses. The astronomical sensors have a range of approximately 4 parsecs, and can easily detect radio signals from planets and primitive spacecraft at that range. In addition, the ship's sensors can perform detailed wide-spectrum electromagnetic scans and detect and analyze gravitational and spatial anomalies. If desired, a ship's sensors can also be used internally to locate crew members and aliens on board the ship. Unfortunately, unless crew members are wearing communicators, the sensors can determine only the location and species of each lifeform it finds. Starship sensors cannot recognize individuals.

Sometimes a closer and more detailed examination of a phenomenon may be needed. If a shuttlecraft or landing party cannot be safely sent, a probe is used. Probes carry sophisticated sensors, allowing detailed examination of phenomena too dangerous or unstable to observe closely otherwise. Unfortunately, the level of detail provided by a probe's automatic sensors is often inferior to that provided by personal observation. All probes are cylindrical and approximately 2 meters long, about the same size as a photon torpedo. Weapons or science officers launch probes using the photon torpedo launcher.

SUBSPACE RADIO

Invented in the last decade of the 22nd century, subspace radio transmits a phased warp pulse which travels rapidly through the fabric of subspace. Today it is used by all starfaring races to maintain contact between distant worlds and starships. Subspace radio travels at approximately 4,000 times the speed of light. While this speed is much faster than normal warp travel, a message still takes over seven hours to travel a single parsec. Starship captains must usually make decisions based on the particular situation and their best understanding of Starfleet policy, since waiting for an answer from a message to the nearest starbase can often take many hours or even days.

TRANSPORTERS

The primary method for entering and leaving the ship, the transporter comes in three separate varieties: standard, emergency, and cargo. Standard

personal transporters can transport six people and their equipment to and from the ship at a range of up to 26,000 km. All but the smallest starships contain multiple personal transporters. A few small ships and research stations contain a smaller version of the standard transporter which can accommodate only two people at a time.

Emergency transporters are larger units capable of beaming up to twenty-two people to or from the ship at a range of up to 13,000 km. Because they are considerably less energy-efficient than standard transporters they are used only in emergencies. Both types of transporters can safely transport any living or nonliving cargoes. Both of these transporters consist of a series of scanning disks each 1.5 meters in diameter. To transport successfully the subject must stand at least partially on one of these scanning disks.

Cargo transporters also have a range of 26,000 km. However, to conserve power and computer time the resolution of their scanning grids is low enough that they can safely transport only nonliving matter. All Federation cargo transporters have safety interlocks which prevent their use on living beings. If a cargo transporter is somehow used to transport a living being, the creature will arrive at its destination dead. Instead of the more accurate individual scanning disks, a cargo transporter has a single large hexagonal scanning platform composed of 96 diamond-shaped segments. Most moderate- and large-sized starships have several examples of each type of transporter on board.

Transporters work by dematerializing the subject from matter into energy, broadcasting that energized matter stream down a narrow-focus subspace carrier wave, then reassembling the energy back into matter. Both dematerialization and rematerialization take approximately ten seconds, but the process may take somewhat longer if there are problems. Transporters are unable to function through deflector shields or heavy ionic interference.

Transporters consist of five primary components:

Control station

Trained engineers use this workstation to monitor and control transporter operation. Ordinary operation of the transporter is extremely routine and can even be preset on a time delay by the person being transported. However, if there are problems in the transport, a highly trained transporter operator is essential to ensure the safety of the individuals being transported. During

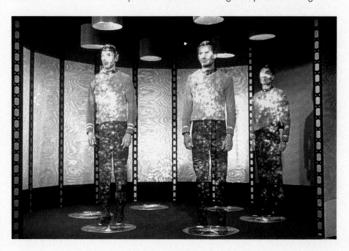

emergencies, the transporter control station can tie into the full power of both the ship's engines and the ship's computer to aid in making difficult transports.

Scanning disks

These disks analyze the subject down to a subatomic level. Other scanners on the outside of the ship control the destination of transport beams and scan subjects for transport to the ship. These scanners can lock onto communicator signals or can be used with other ship sensors to lock onto life signs.

Energizing and transition coils

These coils actually dematerialize and rematerialize the subject.

Pattern Buffer

This magnetic containment tank holds the subject's pattern before the actual transport begins. The pattern buffer stores the matter stream while the Doppler compensators adjust it to cancel any relative motion between the transporter and the target. The buffer can safely store patterns for up to three minutes.

Emitter and receiver arrays

Located on the outside of the ship, they transmit and receive matter streams between the ship and the target.

All transporters are also equipped with decontamination equipment which can kill all known viruses and bacteria and which helps eliminate chemical contamination and excess radiation. This decontamination is separate from the actual transporter mechanism and can be engaged only after a subject has fully materialized. Full decontamination takes at least one minute.

First developed in 2211, transporters are still a relatively new technology in 2269. While most transports are routine and uneventful, even mild ion storms or other high-energy phenomena not severe enough to interfere with either sensor scans or communications can make transport unsafe. Because of the complexity of the process, transporter operation is sometimes a very delicate procedure.

While transport to and from a planet is normally quite reliable, safety protocols specify that subjects should be transported only into large open areas. Transport into small spaces such as tight corridors or accessways is possible, but great care is needed. Even a minor misalignment during rematerialization can result in the subject materializing partially inside solid matter. For this reason, as well as because of the degree of interference produced by operational warp drives and the problem of exactly matching velocity, beaming from one ship to another is exceedingly risky unless passengers are beamed directly from one transporter to another. Intership beaming, within the same ship, carries a significant element of risk if the ship is in warp, and even under impulse only skilled operators should attempt it.

While some outside of Starfleet wonder that many thousands of people regularly use such a potentially life-threatening device, Starfleet engineers are quick to point out that the yearly accident risk from regular transporter use is only one in 5,000 for nonfatal accidents and one in 10,000 for fatal accidents. This is less than half the accident rate from regular motor vehicle use on Earth in the late 20th and early 21st centuries.

In situations where beaming is imperative, command personnel can override normal safety protocols and attempt a risky transport. Doing so risks having the subject's molecules dispersed into deep space or fused to rock deep within a planet's crust. Also, transport during risky conditions can produce numerous unusual problems. On several occasions individuals have been duplicated or divided into two separate beings. Operating transporters near dimensional or temporal rifts can result in the subjects accidentally being transported through time or into another dimension. When attempting hazardous transports, having a skilled engineer perform the transport is best way to assure that the passengers arrive safely.

WARP PROPULSION SYSTEM

Warp drive allows faster-than-light travel, opening the galaxy to a sentient species. Humanity attained the stars when Zefram Cochrane invented the warp drive in 2063. Warp engines are powered by matter/antimatter annihilation. Unconstrained, this reaction would destroy the ship; specially shaped crystals can focus a damping field which allows the intermix to proceed safely. Cochrane's original design used beautiful, carefully grown laboratory lithium crystals, which proved very unstable and have been superseded by dilithium over the last decades. Dilithium is the only naturally occurring substance which can interact with and control this reaction in a nonexplosive fashion. Dilithium is relatively rare on many worlds and cannot yet be synthesized. Starfleet considers worlds like Coridan and Troyius, which posses rich dilithium supplies, exceedingly valuable to the Federation.

The actual reaction occurs in the matter/antimatter integrator (also called the warp core or the intermix chamber) located in main engineering. Here the ship's dilithium crystals safely modulate and control the reaction behind powerful baffle plates. This reaction produces a highly charged plasma, which must maintain a temperature between 4,000° and 4,400° Centigrade; if the intermix temperature rises above 5,500° C, the field could overheat catastrophically. Channeled through the pylons into the two warp nacelles, this plasma energizes the warp coils and generates the warp field in which the ship can travel faster than light. The more efficient warp engines used in the *Constitution*-class ships stem from design innovations by Dr. Lawrence Marvick.

The antimatter is stored in special magnetic pods. In emergencies these antimatter pods can be ejected from the ship, to prevent a failure in the antimatter containment fields from destroying the ship. The ship's supply of antimatter must be periodically replenished. This refueling can be done at any Federation starbase. The matter can also be replenished there. However, since the matter used is deuterium, a common isotope of hydrogen, it can also be collected from interstellar gases or isolated from water collected from a planet.

To repair or service the matter/antimatter integrator, the warp engines must be deactivated for the duration of the repairs. This is normally done at a starbase, but in emergencies may be done in the field. This type of shutdown is necessary to replace the dilithium crystals or to service the matter/antimatter injectors, the antimatter converter assembly, or the interior of the warp coils. Engineers can examine, and in emergencies repair, the interior of the warp coils without shutdown using the Jefferies tubes. The exterior of the antimatter pods can be examined at any time; this is done periodically to make sure that the pod's containment fields remain stable. Any potential leaks in the antimatter pods or conduits could easily destroy the ship and must be repaired at once.

While Federation warp engines are extremely reliable, problems do occasionally occur. The dilithium crystals are the heart of the warp engines and must be replaced immediately if they crack, deteriorate, or become damaged. Because dilithium's crystal structure is necessarily so finely balanced, many types of interstellar energy can degrade, alter, or even decrystallize it.

STARSHIP WEAPON SYSTEMS

DEFLECTOR SHIELDS

These powerful force fields provide protection from interstellar particles and debris as well as from hostile action. The navigational deflector operates continuously. It creates a low-power force field designed specifically to protect starships from low-level radiation and small particles. Navigational deflectors do not affect transporter use. The main deflector shields are only activated when a threat is perceived. The main deflector shields can protect the ship from most forms of matter or energy directed against it. However, enough battering can weaken or even temporarily disrupt shield operation, leaving the ship vulnerable to harm (see *Starship Combat*, page 160).

PHASERS

The standard Starfleet weapons, phasers are found on almost every Federation ship. These powerful and highly versatile weapons can also be used as tools to excavate and reshape terrain, as well as to remove obstacles from the ship's path. Like ordinary hand phasers, starship phaser banks are capable of a wide variety of settings. While orbiting a planet, a ship's phasers can do everything from stunning everyone within a radius of several city blocks (see *Starship Combat*, page 159) to boring deep into the world's crust. The one limit on phasers is that phaser beams travel at the speed of light, so they are not useful in attacking targets capable of warp speed, unless the ships match speeds.

PHOTON TORPEDOES

The primary heavy weapon for Starfleet ship-to-ship combat, these self-propelled torpedoes contain several kilograms of antimatter magnetically bound into a duranium casing. Photon torpedoes are capable of speeds in excess of warp 9, allowing them to be used against all but the fastest vessels.

TRACTOR BEAMS

While not strictly weapons, the Helm operates them in the same manner and from the same control stations as the ship's weapons. Tractor beams use focused gravitic radiation to pull objects to the ship. Standard tractor beams have a maximum range of 150,000 km. The tractor beams on a *Constitution*-class starship can accelerate an object the size of a small freighter at up to 2 G. By reversing the polarity of the tractor beam, this device can also be used to push objects away from the ship with equal speed. By combining beams of mixed polarities it is even possible to manipulate objects carefully at a great distance from the ship. See *Starship Combat*, page 158-159, for more details.

LASER CANNONS

Prior to 2257 Federation starships were fitted with lasers instead of phasers. While a starship's phaser batteries can be tuned to minimize interactions with a planet's atmosphere, firing large lasers from orbit was usually impractical since doing so often produced significant atmospheric heating which could both greatly reduce beam efficiency and unintentionally harm regions well outside the beam's impact point.

When a starship wished to perform finely directed laser attacks the standard procedure was to beam down a laser cannon to the surface using a cargo transporter. Laser cannons were capable of doing everything from tunneling though a mountain to cutting down a square kilometer of forest in less than an hour. The enormous power requirements of this weapon made a self-contained power supply impractical. Instead, the starship would transmit power to the device using a modulated tachyon beam.

On its highest setting this weapon was almost as powerful as modern starship phasers, and remotely powering one could place a significant strain on older ships' engines. Today, laser cannons can be found on obsolete starships, as mining tools and planetary defenses on numerous isolated colony worlds, and on less advanced worlds outside the Federation. In these installations laser cannons are generally connected directly to a large power plant.

Range: 100/5,000/20,000/100,000 meters
Size: 3 m long, 3 kiloliters in volume
Mass: 2 tons
Duration: Powered by starship engines

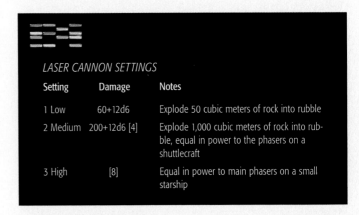

LASER CANNON SETTINGS

Setting	Damage	Notes
1 Low	60+12d6	Explode 50 cubic meters of rock into rubble
2 Medium	200+12d6 [4]	Explode 1,000 cubic meters of rock into rubble, equal in power to the phasers on a shuttlecraft
3 High	[8]	Equal in power to main phasers on a small starship

PERSONAL EQUIPMENT

The following section lists the most widely used devices employed by Starfleet personnel. Most landing parties will carry some or all of these devices.

EQUIPMENT TERMINOLOGY

Every piece of equipment listed here has a short chart at the end giving more useful information about it. In addition to information about the object's size and mass, the chart may include one or more of the following entries:

Range

For missile weapons, range indicates how far the weapon may fire. Weapon ranges are listed as point blank/short range/medium range/long range. For sensors, range describes the useful detection distance of the sensor.

Duration

How long the device can function before it must be recharged. Most devices have a listing in hours; weapons list the number of charges their power pack contains. Unless otherwise specified, most power packs can be recharged. Recharging generally takes no more than one hour.

Armor

How much armor protection the device provides for the user.

Block

How much damage a melee weapon can block when used to parry another melee weapon.

Damage

How much damage the weapon does.

ANTIGRAVITY LIFTER

This device is used for handling heavy or delicate cargo throughout the Federation. When activated, this device completely negates its own weight and the weight of the object it is attached to. In addition, when a operator pulls the antigrav using one of its two handles, the internal microgravity propulsion system effectively negates most of the inertia of the device and its cargo. When the operator releases the handles the device uses its internal propulsion system to remain completely stationary, usually hanging in midair.

Starfleet and the rest of the Federation use numerous models and sizes of antigravity lifters. Such devices range in size from small hand-held units to large, self-propelled floating platforms the size of a 20th-century cargo pallet. The most common type of antigrav used on board a starship is a unit which can be comfortably moved by either one or two people. This antigrav is designed to move objects no larger than 1.5 meters in any dimension with a mass no greater than 1,000 kg. This is the largest size antigrav which can be safely transported using an ordinary personal transporter. Like most antigravs, this device is equipped with a standard Federation molecular adhesion unit. When activated, the antigrav will bond tightly to any object it is attached to, and will release the object only when the molecular adhesion unit is deactivated.

Size: 0.9 m x 35 cm x 20 cm
Mass: 10 kg
Duration: 500 hours

COMMUNICATOR

Crew members carry this whenever they leave the ship and may need to contact it. Military and security forces of most worlds in or near the Federation carry similar devices. Communicators serve several functions. Most importantly, they allow the user to communicate with personnel back on the ship and to access the ship's computer. In addition, even when not in use, the communicator puts out a faint subspace signal which allows the ship's sensors to keep track of the movements of the user. Every communicator broadcasts a unique identification signal, so each individual carrying a communicator can be identified. The signal from a communicator can serve as a beacon for locking a transporter onto the user. Communicators also contain highly sophisticated encryption software to allow them to send and receive coded messages using all standard Starfleet codes. In addition, communicators can be used to translate most known languages. While they don't actually contain universal translators, communicators contain translation algorithms for all known languages in their miniature databanks. Communicators automatically translate both broadcast messages and any speech spoken within a few meters of the unit.

All Starfleet communicators have a maximum range of 26,000 km when communicating with a starship or other large transceiver. Communicators also allow members of a landing party to contact each other directly, but their

range when out of contact with a ship is only 300 km. Communicators can only send and receive audio signals. Video transmission and reception requires the use of a tricorder. Like many other small Federation devices, communicators have a molecular adhesion patch on one side that allows them to adhere tightly to clothing until removed with a slight twist.

Size: 11 cm x 6 cm x 2.5 cm
Mass: 0.2 kg
Duration: 500 hours

EARPIECE TRANSCEIVER

Used primarily by Starfleet communications officers, this device allows the user to send and receive messages on board a starship without disturbing nearby personnel. This unit fits in the ear and is worn much like a 20th-century earring. A miniature speaker broadcasts messages to the user, and a bone conduction microphone can pick up the user's subvocalizations and transmit them to the starship's communications system. In emergencies earpiece transceivers can also be used to communicate discreetly with the ship's computer without the knowledge of mutineers or invaders.

Size: 6 cm x 2.5 cm x 2.5 cm
Mass: negligible
Duration: 50 hours

ENVIRONMENTAL SUITS

In order to visit planets with hostile or thin atmospheres, or to enter the vacuum of space, starship personnel must wear environmental suits. Although far lighter and more comfortable than 20th-century "moon suits," environmental suits still encumber free movement. An individual wearing an environment suit must subtract 1 die from any Skill Tests based on Coordination. Characters with the Personal Equipment (Environment Suit) specialization do not suffer this penalty. An environment suit allows the wearer to safely endure moderate levels of radiation, extremes of pressure from vacuum to 5 atmospheres, and temperatures from −100° C to 120° C. However, they are not heavily armored. Environment suits can be punctured by melee weapons larger than knives, or by phaser or disruptor fire. The self-sealing suits will instantly repair any punc-

tures which do less than 3 points of damage, but larger punctures must be patched. Every suit carries six patches on easy tear-away attachments.

The suit itself consists of a silver radiation-resistant, full-body jumpsuit with removable gloves and a large transparent helmet, as well as gravitic boots allowing the user to walk normally on solid surfaces even in zero gravity. The suit's life-support system is housed in the chest around the attachment for the helmet. Using advanced chemical reprocessing this life-support system can purify the air and recycle drinking water for up to twelve hours. Earlier suit models had only four hours of life support, but they have been largely replaced in Starfleet. Controls mounted on the wrists and chest panel operate the gravitic boots, the built-in communicator, and the helmet-mounted suit lights. The energy signatures produced by the suit are easily detectable by all sensors, making it nearly impossible to hide while wearing one.

Armor: [1] (Damage greater than 1 will puncture the suit)
Size: 15 L (folded) + boots and helmet
Mass: 9 kg
Duration: 12 hours

MEDICAL KIT

Every Starfleet doctor or medic on a landing party going into an unknown or potentially hostile situation carries a standard medical kit in addition to his medical tricorder. This kit, usually carried on a shoulder strap, contains a hypospray, an anabolic protoplaser, a spray applicator, several energy scalpels, a medical scanner, and a moderate supply of most common drugs. This kit allows the doctor to perform most standard and emergency medical procedures on-site. However, patients with severe injuries or serious illnesses will need to be moved to sickbay for full diagnosis and treatment. To the extent possible, Starfleet designs the instruments in the kit to work on all humanoid lifeforms, and even on nonhumanoids with relatively familiar biochemistries.

Starfleet physicians must be ready to render aid and assistance at any time. All on-duty Starfleet physicians carry a smaller version of the medical kit in a pouch on their belts. This emergency kit contains a hypospray, a medical scanner, a spray applicator, and a small supply of commonly used drugs. This smaller medical kit is usually known as a medical pouch. A physician's medical pouch is designed only to enable him to render the most basic form of first aid. A full medical kit or a starship sickbay is necessary to treat any moderate or severe injuries or illnesses fully.

Medical Kit
   Size: 30 cm x 12 cm x 7 cm
   Mass: 1 kg

Medical Pouch
   Size 25 cm x 8 cm x 2.5 cm
   Mass: 0.2 kg

Anabolic Protoplaser

The anabolic protoplaser heals small and moderate wounds almost instantly. It even removes scars. It is extremely easy to use, even by individuals who have received only basic first aid training: Simply run it over the surface of the injury. An anabolic protoplaser will remove one wound level of damage from any injury. No rolls are needed to use this device, unless there are extenuating circumstances. However, this device cannot heal any wound longer or deeper than 6 cm.

A larger, surgical version of the anabolic protoplaser designed specifically to heal serious burns, deep cuts such as surgical incisions, and other severe trauma is sometimes included in medical kits when physicians plan to enter battlefields or disaster areas. This device can reduce the severity of a wound by two levels and can completely heal cuts and gashes which are no more than 10 cm deep.

Basic Anabolic Protoplaser
   Size: 18 cm x 3 cm x 3 cm
   Mass: 0.2 kg
   Duration: 100 hours of use

Surgical Anabolic Protoplaser
   Size: 28 cm x 4.5 cm x 4.5 cm
   Mass: 0.3 kg
   Duration: 25 hours of use

Energy Scalpel

While Federation medicine can solve many problems without the need for surgery, it is still sometimes necessary. Energy scalpels provide a precisely controlled cutting beam. There are two varieties: A linear beam scalpel produces a line of phaserlike energy which cuts everything in its path. Simple controls on the side can vary the length of the beam between 0.5 and 8 cm. A focal point scalpel produces a single pinpoint of cutting energy between 0.5 and 8 cm away from the end of the device. This cutting point allows physicians to cut below a patient's skin without actually making an external incision. A standard medical kit contains both types of scalpel. While energy scalpels cannot cut metal or other resilient materials, their beams can cut flesh, bone, and most organic composites and plastics. Energy scalpels should be used only by trained medical personnel.

Size: 5.5 cm x 3.5 cm x 3.5 cm
Mass: 0.1 kg
Duration: 100 hours

Hypospray

This self-sterilizing instrument is the primary drug delivery device in the Federation. When the hypospray is pressed against the skin and activated, it sprays the drug through the patient's skin. A hypospray can be set to deliver intravenous or intramuscular injections and will work through most garments, including both Starfleet uniforms and standard environmental suits. Each drug ampoule inserted into a hypospray provides up to ten injections. The user can select the desired dosage by using a few simple controls. Changing drug ampoules takes only a few seconds. While anyone can use a hypospray, selecting the proper drugs and dosages takes the skill of a trained doctor or medic. A standard hypospray in a medical pouch comes with ampoules of stimulants, tranquilizers, painkillers, tri-ox compound (a drug allowing easier respiration in low-oxygen atmospheres or at high altitudes), and a broad-spectrum antitoxin. Additional doses, as well as antibiotics, antivirals, and antiradiation drugs, are stored in a full medical kit.

Size: 22 cm x 3 cm x 3 cm
Mass: 0.1 kg
Duration: 10 injections/ampoule

Medical Scanner

While a medical tricorder is superior for detailed diagnosis of complex medical problems, the small, portable medical scanner gives extremely rapid readings of a patient's important vital signs. A medical scanner does not provide information on specific diseases, but it does furnish precise information on the patient's heart rate, blood pressure, temperature, and level of blood oxygen. In addition, it can accurately detect sites of significant infection or internal tissue damage. A series of six readouts on the bottom of the device displays this information to the user. Because of the technical nature of these data, medical scanners are useful only to trained medical practitioners. Using a medical scanner to examine a patient usually requires only a few seconds.

Size: 6 cm x 3.5 cm x 3.5 cm
Mass: negligible
Duration: 100 hours

Spray Applicator

This device is used to treat surface injuries. It is designed to spray on a wide range of antibiotics, healing stimulators, protective dressings, and topical anesthetics. Spray applicators are exceedingly simple to use. The appropriate medicine vial is inserted in the device, the user pushes a button, and the unit sprays a metered dose of the drug. Each drug vial inserted in this unit provides up to 50 sprays.

Size: 6.5 cm x 2 cm x 2 cm
Mass: negligible
Duration: 50 sprays/vial

ELECTRONIC CLIPBOARD

Electronic clipboards act as portable interfaces with the ship's computer, and are especially useful for storing and viewing documents. The majority of the electronic clipboard's surface is a touch-sensitive, high-resolution screen. The electronic clipboard also contains as a speaker and microphone for voice data. A user generally either dictates reports to his clipboard, which then transforms the reports into appropriately formatted text, or he writes on its screen using an included stylus. Each electronic clipboard also has an access port which can hold up to two record tapes. Electronic clipboards can interface with each other as well as with shipboard library banks to send and receive reports or access data.

Although an electronic clipboard can hold several billion pages of text and pictures in its internal duotronic memory (making it potentially a very powerful computer in its own right), most specialists use computer terminals for direct access, leaving electronic clipboards primarily for yeomen and other administrative personnel.

While civilian versions of the electronic clipboard can usually fit in a pocket, Starfleet versions are substantially larger. Efficiency studies by Starfleet indicated that its larger size increased ease of use and made writing on them significantly easier. The latter is especially important since regulations still specify that all reports must be signed by the person making them.

Size: 35 cm x 22 cm x 6 cm
Mass: 0.3 kg
Duration: 100 hours

RECORD TAPES

Record tapes, also known as micro tapes, are the standard recording media in Starfleet. All communications to and from a starship are recorded on record tapes, as are the Captain's logs and all sensor readings made by a starship. Even if a starship's computer is destroyed, the highly durable record tapes are likely to survive and reveal the fate of the ship. Record tapes are relatively large given the limits of Federation technology. However, the majority of the tape is merely an easy-to-handle square, flat casing.

The actual recording medium is a small data disk, identical to those used in both science and medical tricorders. For ease of use, when a data disk is removed from a tricorder, it is inserted into a record tape case. Each record tape or data disk can hold approximately a hundred hours of audiovisual recordings, or around 100 million pages of illustrated text. Every viewer and computer workstation has several slots for inserting record tapes. In an effort to improve efficiency and to promote Federation unity, all record tapes within the Federation conform to a uniform standard and may be used in any computer manufactured in the Federation.

All record tapes may be erased and rerecorded multiple times. For security purposes and to prevent the loss of important data, procedure dictates that all log entries, sensor readings, medical information, and other important data be stored both in the main computer's memory and on individual record tapes.

Size: 7 cm x 7 cm x 0.6 cm (data disks are 3 cm x 3 cm x 0.5 cm)
Mass: negligible
Duration: unlimited

SUBCUTANEOUS TRANSPONDER

The biggest drawback that both universal translators and the translation units found in Starfleet communicators possess is that their use is extremely obvious. For someone wishing to appear to be a native speaker of a language a universal translator is useless. However, in the mid-23rd century advances in cybernetic technology allowed a limited version of the translation unit found in a Starfleet communicator to be tied directly into the user's speech centers. This translation device is incapable of translating or understanding unknown languages. However, it can translate any known language stored in its miniature databank. Because of space limitations, the translator in this tiny device can hold only six languages.

The translator in this device is a smaller version of the one found in a Starfleet communicator. Since it is tied directly into the user's brain, the universal translator effectively allows the user full knowledge both of how to speak and to understand all stored languages. The only exceptions to this ability are languages which the universal translator cannot translate, as well as any languages the user's vocal apparatus cannot physically reproduce. The subcutaneous transponder also contains a miniature locator beacon with a range equal to a standard communicator (26,000 km). This locator allows a starship's sensors to keep track of the exact position of the subject. If desired a starship can keep a continuous transporter lock on the subject.

This device was originally designed to allow Federation anthropologists and first-contact specialists to live discretely among aliens while not giving away the fact that they were from off-world. Today, Federation landing parties, as well as legitimate merchants, spies, and con artists, also make use of this device.

Size: Implanted
Mass: negligible
Duration: 500 hours

TRICORDERS

Tricorders are extremely compact and powerful sensory devices. In addition to containing a wide range of miniature electromagnetic, magnetic, audio, chemical, and subspace sensors, tricorders also include extremely detailed databanks on a wide range of scientific and historical information. The computer in the tricorder can rapidly identify known lifeforms, materials, and energy sources by comparing sensory readings with information in its databanks. Tricorders can also attempt to analyze new lifeforms, materials, or energy sources. This analysis may take up to an hour, but the tricorder can be used normally while the analysis is going on. Each tricorder contains a subspace communicator with a range equal to that of a personal communicator. Tricorders can send and receive data of all types from a starship computer or other distant source.

The tricorder's viewscreen and the speaker beneath it are capable of displaying any audiovisual information recorded by or stored in the tricorder. This screen can also display sensor data from the tricorder, including visual representations of IR, UV, or other invisible radiation. It is possible to use a tricorder to perceive objects and creatures normally invisible to humans. Tricorders can hold up to eight standard data disks. Each data disk may store over 100 hours of high-density audiovisual recording or similarly complex data.

Tricorders can also communicate with other devices. They can link with other tricorders within range to coordinate sensor scans or contact large computers like those found on a starship or starbase, or like a Federation library computer. Tricorders can fully process and analyze data from these remote sources. If necessary, tricorders can also be used in place of communicators to enable landing parties to communicate with their ship or each other. Like communicators, a tricorder can contact a starship up to 26,000 km away and another tricorder or communicator up to 300 km away. Using its built-in sensors, a tricorder can perform the following different scans:

Biological, long-range

The unit can detect the number and position of all lifeforms of a given size within range. Individual lifeforms can also be tracked.

Biological, short-range

The unit can identify the type of lifeform (humanoid, energy being, reptilian), including the exact species if the lifeform is known to Federation science. It will also provide general information about the creature's physical condition.

Geological, long-range

The unit can locate large caves, significant mineral deposits, and important geological features like fault lines. This setting also allows the device to determine the rough chemical composition of any substance within range and to locate large concentrations of any desired material.

Geological, short-range

The unit can detect small caves and concealed features like underground water or small mineral deposits. The unit can also locate small concentrations (even a few grams) of a desired substance. The exact chemical composition of unknown substances can also be determined.

Meteorological, long-range

The unit can analyze local weather patterns, predict the weather up to twenty hours in advance, and detect problems like ionic interference. This setting will also reveal the magnitude, type, and location of any large (like a shuttlecraft) energy sources within range.

Meteorological, short-range

The unit can determine the exact composition of the local atmosphere; it can also detect and locate small energy sources (like a phaser or another tricorder).

Range: 1,500 meters for long-range scans, 20 meters for short-range scans. All long-range scans are omnidirectional, but the user must aim the tricorder at a specific location to perform a short-range scan. Various types of ionic and other interference can greatly reduce the range of all tricorder scans

Size: 17 cm x 11 cm x 4.8 cm
Mass: 0.5 kg
Duration: 800 hours

Medical Tricorder

A medical tricorder is a specialized tricorder designed specifically to aid in medical work. To aid in diagnosis it contains a special medical sensor probe. This probe contains numerous specialized medical sensors. In addition, the tricorder itself contains an enormous database of information on more than 100

humanoid and nonhumanoid aliens, and hundreds of thousands of diseases and medical problems. Because of the limited space in the device it can perform only short range geological and meteorological scans. However, medical tricorders can perform standard long- and short-range biological scans.

The sensors on the medical probe can detect all vital signs at a range of five meters. When this sensor is no more than one meter from its target, these sensors can also analyze the being's internal structure, in a manner similar to a 20th-century CAT scan, which can detect broken bones and other internal injuries or problems. This probe is also capable of extremely detailed observations, including DNA typing, blood chemistry analysis, and detection of all known drugs, poisons, bacteria, viruses, and prions.

Range: 1,500 meters for long-range biological scans; 20 meters for short-range biological, geological and meteorological scans; 1 meter for scans by the medical probe.
Size: 17 cm x 11 cm x 4.8 cm
Mass: 0.5 kg
Duration: 800 hours

UNIVERSAL TRANSLATOR

To interact usefully with any new alien race you first must be able to communicate with it. To solve this problem Starfleet developed advanced computers capable of translating any known language into any other known language. All communicators are programmed to understand hundreds of known languages, and can tap into the ship's computer for access to additional language data. However, a universal translator is necessary when dealing with any previously unknown language. Personnel on or in contact with a starship can use the universal translator connected to the ship's computer. However, landing parties which expect to be out of contact with their ship always carry portable universal translators.

A universal translator analyzes languages and compares them to its linguistic databank. Instant translation is available between any of the many thousands of languages stored in the translator. This translation is fully two-way, so both parties can hear the other's speech in their own language. The universal translator can also analyze unknown languages and usually deliver a reasonable translation within half an hour of exposure to a new language.

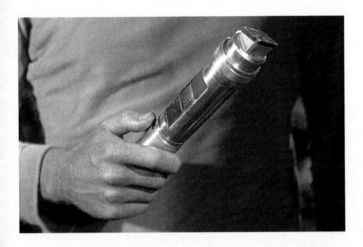

Whenever a universal translator is used, it is obvious that the speech comes from the device and not from the speaker. The only way to pass for a native speaker of a language is actually to learn the language or to use a subcutaneous transponder.

Size: 28 cm x 3.5 cm x 3.5 cm

Mass: 0.2 kg

Duration: 100 hours

MENTAL SCANNING AND ALTERNATION TECHNOLOGY

Using information on humanoid psyches gathered primarily by Vulcan physicians and scientists, the Federation has developed a number of advanced devices which can actually scan and alter thought patterns. In the Federation there are strict laws governing the uses of such technologies. Only seriously ill patients in licensed psychiatric facilities or individuals who give their consent may have such devices used upon them. Unfortunately, these laws apply only to planets which belong to the Federation. In the Klingon Empire a variant of this technology is used as a barbaric, but effective, interrogation technique.

NEURAL NEUTRALIZER

Developed by Dr. Simon Van Gelder in 2264, the neural neutralizer was designed to suppress memories and violent tendencies in the criminally insane. Using a scanner similar to that found in a psychotricorder combined with advanced neural feedback equipment, the device can suppress both emotions and memories. When used by a skilled operator it can also implant mental compulsions similar to posthypnotic suggestions, but considerably more powerful. This device can suppress any memory and implant any compulsion, but individuals with sufficiently strong wills or intensive mental training can resist the device's effects for a considerable time.

Suppressed memories and implanted compulsions can both be uncovered by a Vulcan mind-meld or any similarly powerful telepathic probe. However, memories which have been sufficiently suppressed can require a mind-meld deep enough to place both the subject and the telepath at risk of permanent mental damage. If used improperly this device can easily cause insanity or

even death. Neural neutralizers are currently heavily regulated. Today, variants of this device are only used in the most advanced Federation psychiatric facilities. However, lower-powered versions which merely reduce the insanity of memories and emotions are now commonly in use for treating post-traumatic stress and similar mental disorders.

Size: 1.5 cubic meters; the device resembles a large chair with a moveable headset in addition to a separate control console for operating the device.

Mass: 2 tons (including the control console)

Duration: This device must be connected to an external power supply.

PSYCHOTRICORDER

In appearance the psychotricorder appears identical to an ordinary science tricorder. However, this complex device has only one function. When properly used it can scan, record, and display an individual's memories of any time within the last thirty days. Memories older than this have faded enough that they are too difficult to access unless the subject has the Eidetic Memory Advantage. Using a psychotricorder, a skilled operator can either record all thoughts, memories, and sensory impressions which occurred during a given span of time, or he can record a single incident which the subject is concentrating upon. The memories recorded by this device can then be analyzed by a computer, viewed upon the unit's display screen, or transferred for viewing on a larger viewscreen. Recorded memories contain all audio and visual sensory impression experienced by the subject and all of the subject's subvocalized thoughts.

Often when viewing psychotricorder recordings the memories are played as a movie with the subject's thoughts appearing as subtitles on the screen. Each data disk in a psychotricorder can record up to ten hours of a subject's memories. Standard starship computers have the same capabilities as a psychotricorder. In addition, all starships contain special computer verifier equipment that can detect any lies told by a subject.

Developed in 2262, the psychotricorder is revolutionizing the Federation judicial system. Anyone who pleads innocence can agree to have his memories checked. The only limit on the use of this device is that the subject must be completely willing to have the desired memories recorded. Attempting to use this device to interrogate an unwilling subject merely results in images of solid walls or rude messages telling the user to go away. Also, sufficiently

skilled telepaths can disguise their own memories or alter the memories of another sufficiently that a psychotricorder will produce inaccurate readings. These limits combined with the reluctance of some planetary judiciary departments to trust the results of a criminal trial to a machine have so far limited the acceptance of this device on some worlds.

Size: 17 cm x 11 cm x 4.8 cm
Mass: 0.5 kg
Duration: 100 hours

PERSONAL WEAPONS

PHASERS

Phasers are the standard weapons used by the Federation and its allies. Phasers, short for PHASed Energy Rectifiers, produce beams of rapid nadions (highly energetic, short-lived subatomic particles). These particles can produce a wide variety of effects, depending upon their energy state. At low energy, phasers produce a bioelectric shock which will stun most targets. At moderate settings, the beam heats the target; at the higher settings, this heating is replaced by large-scale subatomic disruption which can cause medium-sized objects to vaporize and larger ones to explode.

A phaser can be fired in pulses or as a continuous beam. The width of this beam can be varied from its normal narrow configuration to a special wide-beam mode. When used on wide-beam setting, phasers have a maximum range of only 10 meters, but the beam affects everything in a swath up to 8 meters wide. Using a phaser on wide beam takes three times as many charges as using it on the normal setting. Also, because of the extremely high power densities in the wide-beam use, it can be used only on settings 1–3.

In addition to being powerful weapons, phasers are useful tools. On narrow-beam setting a phaser can be used as a cutting tool to clear undergrowth in the jungle or to shape wood, metal, or rock. On wide beam, phasers can be used to heat rock and provide warmth in cold climates, as well as to clear away obstacles like snow, ice, or vegetation. If a phaser is set on overload, the unit explodes within 30 seconds. The blast does 1 point of damage for every charge it contains and covers an area with a radius of 30 meters.

Phaser-1

Phaser-1's are small, hand-held weapons which are commonly carried on all missions with any possibility of danger. Local law enforcement on most Federation worlds also carry phaser-1's, as do ordinary civilians on potentially dangerous colony worlds. On some worlds the only allowable weapons are phaser-1's, which are restricted to stun settings (1 and 2). To help comply with such regulations all phasers are fitted with governors which can be used to restrict them to stun settings only.

Phaser-1's contain only a single prefire amplification chamber, so they are capable of firing only on settings 1–5. Like many other small Federation devices, on one side phaser-1's have a molecular adhesion patch which allows them to adhere tightly to clothing or skin until removed with a slight twist.

Range: 5/10/20/30
Size: 11 cm x 6 cm x 2.5 cm
Mass: 0.2 kg
Duration: 100 charges

Phaser-2

The larger, pistol-like phaser-2's are used by Starfleet personnel only. Civilians and planetary security forces are not allowed to use this weapon. They are only issued when there is a significant threat of violence. Phaser-2's consist of a weapon body into which an ordinary phaser-1 is fitted. This weapon body contains a larger power pack and an additional prefire amplification chamber. Phaser-2's have more charges and a longer range, and can be used on settings 1–6.

Range: 5/20/50/80
Size: 22 cm x 3.5 cm x 16 cm
Mass: 0.5 kg
Duration: 250 charges

Phaser-3

Phaser-3's are heavy rifle-like weapons which are used only during wartime and in highly dangerous situations where there is an immediate threat to safety. When Starfleet personnel are carrying phaser-3's they are ready for battle. A substantially larger power pack and a third prefire amplification chamber give this deadly weapon many more charges, a substantially longer range, and the ability to use settings 1–7.

Range: 10/50/150/300
Size: 70 cm long, 2.5 l in volume
Mass: 1.6 kg
Duration: 1,000 charges

LASERS

Lasers are obsolete energy weapons which were used in Starfleet until 2256, when phasers entered widespread use. Lasers, short for Light Amplification by Simulated Emission of Radiation, emit intense coherent beams of visible light. Unlike phasers and disruptors, lasers can neither stun

PHASER, LASER, AND DISRUPTOR DAMAGE

Phaser Damage

Setting	Damage	CHG	Notes
1 Light Stun	(2+2d6)	1	Stun a Human for 5 minutes
2 Heavy Stun	(4+4d6)	2	Stun a Human for 1 hour and a Klingon for 15 minutes
3 Thermal	10+2d6	4	Cut a 1 m hole in 10 cm of steel in 3 minutes
4 Disrupt	12+3d6	6	Cut a 1 m hole in 10 cm of steel or rock in 30 seconds
5 Disintegrate A	16+4d6	10	Vaporize a humanoid-sized target
6 Disintegrate B	24+5d6	15	Vaporize metals, disrupt resistant materials, explode up to 5 cubic meters of rock into rubble
7 Disintegrate C	30+9d6	20	Vaporize almost any substance (energy rebound prior to vaporization common), explode 10 cubic meters of rock into rubble

Laser Damage

1 Low Thermal	10+2d6	1	Cut a 1 m hole in 10 cm of steel in 3 minutes
2 High Thermal	12+3d6	3	Cut a 1 m hole in 10 cm of steel or rock in 30 seconds
3 Disrupt	14+4d6	5	Kill a humanoid, shatter small rocks, cut a 1 m hole in a starship bulkhead in 10 minutes

Disruptor Damage

1 Heavy Stun	(4+2d6)	1	Stun a Human for 15 minutes and a Klingon for 5 minutes
2 Thermal	10+2d6	3	Cut a 1 m hole in 10 cm of steel in 3 minutes
3 Disrupt	24+5d6	10	Vaporize almost anything including humanoids and resilient alloys

subjects nor disintegrate them. Instead, at lower settings lasers produce thermal damage, while at higher settings the intensity of the heat focused on the target causes the area hit to explode. Due to their lack of versatility lasers have been replaced by phasers on all but the most isolated Federation worlds. In general, carrying a laser means the user is either from a remote colony world or is a criminal who cannot legally carry a phaser-1 and who acquired this weapon illegally.

Range: 5/10/25/50
Size: 24 cm x 5 cm x 16 cm
Mass: 0.6 kg
Duration: 50 charges

DISRUPTORS

Disruptors are a common alternative to phasers, used primarily in the Romulan Star Empire and the Klingon Empire. They were originally developed by the Klingons, and were adopted by the Romulans when the Klingons agreed to share technology with them.

Disruptors fire bolts of tightly focused gravitic energy. Disruptors have only three settings: stun, thermal, and disruption. On the stun setting disruptors stun their targets through a combination of concussion and neural shock. On

the thermal setting the energy released by a disruptor bolt can cut through metal or cause lethal damage. On the disruption setting the energy sets up destructive resonance oscillations in the target. Humanoid targets are completely vaporized, and large targets like boulders usually shatter from thermal shock.

In the Federation, disruptors are regarded as crude devices whose only use is as a lethal weapon. They cannot produce the same variety of effects as phasers, and they are incapable of wide-beam settings. The range of power is similar to that found with phasers. While disruptors are incapable of wide-beam shots and continuous beams, they do hold considerably more shots than a comparably sized phaser.

Klingon and Romulan disruptors are functionally identical, but differ greatly in appearance. Unlike phasers, disruptors cannot simply be recharged. A new power cartridge must be physically loaded into the weapon. A disruptor set on overload will explode within 30 seconds. The blast does 1 point of damage for every charge it contains and covers an area with a radius of 50 meters.

Range: 5/10/25/40
Size: 35 cm long, 1.2 L in volume
Mass: 1 kg
Duration: 300 charges

Archaic Missile Weapons

Flintlock Rifle

A primitive muzzle-loading projective weapon which can be manufactured by preindustrial cultures. The Klingon Empire has been known to provide their more primitive allies with flintlock rifles on occasion. This weapon can fire only a single shot before it must be reloaded. Reloading takes three full rounds.

Range: 10/20/50/100
Size: 1.3 m long
Mass: 3 kg
Damage: 10+3d6
Shots: 1

Kligat

A missile weapon first developed by the humanoid inhabitants of Capella IV. The *kligat* is a large ring armed with three blades spaced equally about the circumference. While only beings with a Fitness of 3 or more can use the *kligat*, it is a dangerous weapon in the hands of a skilled user. When thrown the *kligat* whirls like a boomerang or a Frisbee. This spin allows it to be highly accurate and extremely deadly.

Range: 5/20/50/100
Size: 25 cm in diameter
Mass: 0.5 kg
Damage: 7+2d6

Machinegun

Used only by prestarflight industrial cultures, the machinegun is a deadly projectile weapon capable of firing multiple shots every round. Machineguns fire eight shots every action. The success of each shot should be rolled separately.

At the cost of increasing the difficulty of the attack by 2 points, a machinegun can be used to attack a group of targets standing close together. In random order roll attacks on each target in sequence until all eight shots have either hit or missed.

Range: 5/10/25/50
Size: 1 m long
Mass: 2.5 kg
Damage: 8+2d6
Shots: 32

Melee Weapons

Starfleet does not normally employ melee weapons, although civilian police use stunrods when necessary. Since they operate within the narrow corridors of spaceships, Starfleet security personnel prefer to use phasers set on stun. In contrast, many alien races use melee weapons of various sorts. Here are some of the melee weapons a starship crew may encounter.

Knife

Knives are one of the most basic tools and weapons used by humanoids across the galaxy.

Size: 15–30 cm long with a 10-20 blade
Mass: 0.2–0.4 kg
Accuracy: 7
Block: +1
Damage: 3+2d6

Lirpa

The *lirpa* is an ancient Vulcan ritual weapon, essentially a long pole with a weighted club on one end and a razor-sharp blade on the other. Its only common uses today are as a martial arts exercise and during the *pon farr* madness, on those rare occasions when the ancient rites of mating combat are invoked.

Size: 160 cm x 30 cm x 20 cm
Mass: 5.6 kg
Accuracy: 9
Block: +3
Damage: Blade 3+2d6, Club 2+2d6

Rapier

Some humans with an interest in athletics and a sense of history enjoy fencing. Rapiers are long narrow swords which are light and highly accurate. Fencing is a complex and demanding sport. Several Starfleet officers including Hikaru Sulu have won competitive fencing awards.

Size: 90–110 cm long

Mass: 0.7 kg

Accuracy: 6

Block: +2

Damage: 4+d6 (fencing rapiers are usually blunt and do only 1+1d6 damage)

Stunrod

Stunrods are energized melee weapons used by planetary police and security forces across the Federation. A stunrod is a padded club which does minimal physical damage, but which can inflict phaserlike stun effects upon anyone it hits.

Size: 50 cm long, 3 cm in diameter

Mass: 0.5 kg

Block: +2

Damage: 2 + Stun effects equal to phaser settings 1–2; the user can change the setting at will.

Charges: 200

ADVANCED ALIEN TECHNOLOGY

While the Federation possesses extremely advanced technology, the continued exploration of space has proved that other older species have learned a great deal more. When traveling into unexplored space, Starfleet personnel must be ready to encounter technologies vastly superior to their own which easily do things which they had previously imagined to be impossible. In addition to dangers like invulnerable force shields and weapons which can easily pierce starship deflector shields, previous starships have encountered a number of unusual technologies that seem to have been developed repeatedly by numerous different species.

Computers and robots which seem to be fully sentient have been encountered on numerous occasions by Federations starships. While somewhat less able to deal with new and rapidly changing situations than most organic sentient beings, sentient robots and computers are relatively common among species more advanced than the Federation. Currently Federation scientists are carefully examining the recently discovered robots on the planet Mudd.

The ability to transfer consciousness between sentient beings, as well as the ability to store a sentient consciousness in a robotic body or some other inorganic storage receptacle, also seems to be fairly widespread. Due to the inability of Federation scientists to understand such procedures as well as the obvious serious moral and ethical implications Federation researchers are not currently attempting to duplicate such devices.

Time travel is clearly another area in which numerous species have proved superior to the Federation. However, after the recent agreement with the Guardian of Forever and the discovery of the ability of starships to travel backward in time by combining high warp factors with extreme gravitational fields, Federation scientists have recently begun a carefully monitored program of temporal exploration.

Warp drives capable of achieving transwarp velocities, transporterlike devices capable of transmitting matter between different star systems, and medical technology capable of raising the dead have also been encountered on several occasions. While Federation scientists would love to duplicate all of these effects, the technologies involved have proved to be far beyond current scientific understanding.

"It's no use, Captain!" Seel cried. "It's as if there's something sucking us in!"

Duffy's brow crinkled. "I need more to go on than 'something', people! Danna, scans still detect no ships in the vicinity?"

"Just what you see on the viewscreen, Captain: that oddly colored nebula right in front of us, and sector after sector of empty space around us."

"Mr. Eleb, don't tell me the nebula has a tractor beam on us!"

"Improbable as it may seem, that's exactly what my readings suggest, Captain."

"Seel, get us out of here: full reverse impulse."

"I tried that already, Captain."

"Well, try it again!"

Duffy looked over at his Tellarite helmsman and saw a double, then a triple image of the man. He gazed around; no matter where he looked, his vision distorted. Soon he was seeing multiple versions of everyone on the bridge. Then there was a flash of white light.

Suddenly he was somewhere else. Lights shone directly in his face, blinding him. He moved his hands up to shade his eyes. He could dimly make out rows upon rows of red theater seats. He looked down. He was standing on floorboards. A stage. He was on a stage.

A rasping voice issued forth from the seats. Duffy looked down and saw a corpulent man decked out in antique clothing: a shiny windbreaker, ball cap, jeans, and a black silk shirt. Gold chains dangled down into his profuse chest hair.

"Who are you?" Duffy demanded. "Why have you brought me here?"

SPACE... THE FINAL FRONTIER

"I have gone by many names. You have designated me as Nebula A-S12-4664."

"A sentient nebula?"

"I am much more than sentient, Captain Duffy. But never mind that. My scan of your minds reveals that your species possesses a concept previously unfamiliar to me, a concept called humor. You will perform comedy routines for me, and make me laugh, so that my understanding of all things will be enlarged."

"And if I don't?"

A follow-spot illuminated the balcony, where Seel, Eleb, Pearlstein, Basta, and the others sat, mouths taped shut.

"In that case," the nebula intoned, "we instead explore another manifestation of the human desire for entertainment: the concept you call ... horror."

Even in the 23rd century, the Milky Way galaxy is still almost too vast for Human comprehension. It contains a hundred billion stars and stretches across nearly a hundred thousand light-years. The ships of Starfleet have explored barely a thousandth of the galaxy, and even adding together all the territory known to species the Federation has only heard of, less than one percent of the galaxy is known space. The rest is unknown.

Astronomers have mapped out certain large-scale structures in the galaxy. There is the core, with two arms spiraling out toward the rim. Nearby are two small satellite galaxies, the Magellanic Clouds, and on the far side from known space is another small galaxy, the Sagittarius Dwarf galaxy, which our own galaxy is slowly absorbing.

THE CORE

The heart of the galaxy is a spherical region approximately twenty thousand light-years across. Mostly young, hot-burning giants crowd into it, centered on a huge black hole. This makes the core a very dangerous region, with incredibly high radiation levels. The stars are all short-lived types, often with enormous fluctuations in brightness. Ion storms and particle showers are common.

No carbon-based lifeforms survive long in the core region without protection. Starships venturing into the heart of the galaxy need to have their shields at maximum to protect against radiation. If any life exists in the core, it must be very alien—energy beings, or creatures capable of thriving in a constant shower of hard radiation.

THE SPIRAL ARMS

Two bright arms spiral out from the center of the galaxy, separated by dark regions. The arms are bright because they contain lots of young, bright stars; the dark lanes in between have older, dimmer stars. Interestingly, there are about as many stars per cubic parsec inside the spiral arms as in the dark lanes—the lanes are not empty voids, they just aren't as lit up as the arms. The regions of star formation in the spiral arms are almost as hazardous as the core itself, with dense nebulae, ion storms, and occasional exploding stars, but are rich in heavy elements and rare minerals.

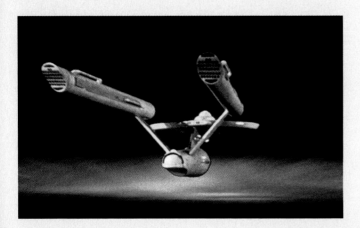

Known space is located between two spiral arms. The Sagittarius Arm is coreward, toward the galaxy's heart, and the Orion Arm is to rimward. The Orion Arm is the closest region of active star formation, full of hot nebulae, bright giant stars, and protostars. The Klingon and Romulan Empires lie to the "antispinward" of the Federation; the opposite frontier, in the direction of galactic spin, is "spinward."

THE ENERGY BARRIER

The galaxy has its own magnetic fields, just like the Earth or Sol. The galactic field traps energetic particles in a region at the galaxy's edge, known as the "Energy Barrier." The Barrier is a zone of very intense radiation; few ships can survive the passage through it. The high radiation levels in the Barrier create all sorts of bizarre effects—astrophysicists theorize that the energy levels cause a partial breakdown of physical laws. The *S.S. Valiant,* the first Earth vessel to penetrate the Barrier, was destroyed after the energies of the Barrier caused an immense increase in the psionic abilities of some individuals on board.

The *U.S.S. Enterprise* encountered a similar phenomenon in 2267 while searching for survivors of the *Valiant.* In 2268 the *Enterprise* again passed through the Barrier, while hijacked by the Kelvans, but this time encountered no psionic phenomena, possibly because the Kelvan modifications protected the ship. Later that year, another passage of the *Enterprise* through the Barrier induced temporal displacement in its crew.

Evidently the Milky Way galaxy has an especially powerful or concentrated Energy Barrier. The Kelvan expedition from Andromeda was severely damaged while passing through the Barrier, which suggests their own galaxy does not generate one.

ASTROGRAPHY

Starfleet has only recently adopted a uniform system of coordinates for navigation and mapping. Most Federation member races use their own charts of nearby space, and it is only in the outer reaches of known space that travelers employ the Starfleet system. Both Earth and Andorian charts use a circular coordinate system centered on the home star, with space divided up into quadrants. The newer Starfleet system is based on the Earth-centered coordinate system and divides space into sectors (each roughly twenty light-years across). Navigators trained in the older systems often use the terms "quadrant" and "sector" interchangeably. (For a sample sector of space, see the *Sicondor Sector,* page 263.)

PERILS AND HAZARDS

Space is a dangerous place. Besides the ordinary perils of cosmic radiation, meteoroids, hard vacuum, and extremes of heat and cold, space travelers must beware other, extraordinary hazards.

BLACK HOLES

A black hole—sometimes more politely called a black star—is an object so dense that its escape velocity is greater than the speed of light. No matter or energy can leave a black hole, and its enormous gravity warps the fabric of space-time. Not even a warp-capable starship can escape a black hole's gravity if it ventures within the "event horizon," as the distorted fabric of space makes it impossible for the engines to work.

Even outside the event horizon, the region around a black hole is very dangerous. The tidal forces created by the black star's immense gravity can tear a ship apart. The black hole's "accretion disk" is like a dense planetary nebula full of meteoroids. Objects falling into the hole's event horizon reach the speed of light and give off energetic X-rays as they fall, flooding the area with deadly radiation.

Time actually moves more slowly around a black hole; the crew of a ship orbiting close to the event horizon will find that weeks have passed elsewhere while only hours have gone by for them. Artifacts of fantastic age can sometimes be found in the vicinity of black holes. Rotating black holes have even weirder effects on space-time. It is possible to plot a course around a spinning black hole which emerges *earlier* in time!

COMETS AND ASTEROIDS

Comets and asteroids are similar objects—small chunks of matter much smaller than planets. Asteroids are made of rock and metal; comets are predominantly ice. When a comet's orbit brings it close to its star, the ice partially vaporizes, creating a long tail of dust and gas.

Asteroids and comets pose little danger to spaceships. Most ships' sensors can detect an approaching body in time for the crew to take evasive action, and an asteroid or comet has minimal gravity to pull in a ship. The main danger posed by asteroids and comets is to planets. Even a modest-sized asteroid a dozen kilometers across can cause tremendous damage if it hits a planet. Though small by planetary standards, an asteroid is still a big object, thousands of times larger than any ship. Diverting or destroying an asteroid is extremely difficult.

In some regions of space, asteroids and comets exist in dense fields, and these areas are natural lurking places for any ship trying to avoid detection. All sensor tasks are at +1 Difficulty in an asteroid field, and ships are limited to one-quarter impulse speed.

FLARE STARS

Certain stars have unstable nuclear fusion reactions at their cores. These flare stars can suddenly increase in brightness at irregular intervals, in some cases becoming more than six times brighter than usual. While most starships can handle the increased radiation, the danger is that flare stars do not follow a predictable pattern and can go off without warning. Ships in the vicinity of a flare star must remain on alert with shields raised at all times.

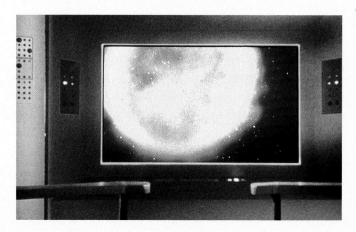

Planets orbiting a flare star have no way to avoid the occasional increases in brightness. The flares make it hard for life to evolve on any planet of a flare star, but some especially hardy lifeforms might develop natural defenses, enabling them to survive being baked every few weeks.

ION STORMS

A common hazard in space travel, an ion storm is a stream of electrically charged dust and gas passing through space. They are usually no more than a few thousand kilometers across and two million kilometers or so in length, but are very hard to detect. Ion storms can wreak havoc with the navigation and control systems of starships.

In game terms, a ship in an ion storm is continually bombarded by energy pulses doing 1d6 x 10 damage points every turn. Ion storms cannot actually destroy anything, but they can render ship systems (especially transporters and computers) inoperable, and can kill crewmen in exposed probes, shuttlecraft, or sensor pods. Ion storms can also fluctuate through subspace, affecting the ship's communications and even opening dimensional or temporal rifts.

METEOROID SHOWERS

Chunks of rock and ice no larger than pebbles can be a lethal hazard in space. At the speeds attained by most spacecraft, a collision with even a tiny piece of solid matter can release tremendous energy. Fortunately, most ships have force shields to deflect stray rocks. But sometimes ships encounter a large shower of meteoroids, containing thousands of tiny pebbles. Assume each meteoroid impact does damage equal to a ship's warp speed; ships under impulse power take 1 point of damage. During a meteoroid shower, the ship takes ten meteoroid hits each turn until it is clear of the shower.

NEBULAE

A nebula is a cloud of gas and dust in space. There are two types. A planetary nebula is the material blown off when a star explodes in a supernova blast. An interstellar nebula is a diffuse cloud of dust and gas in open space.

In general planetary nebulae are denser than interstellar nebulae, and pose more of a threat to ships because they are often still hot and radioactive. Planetary nebulae seldom extend more than a light-year from the remnant of the exploding stars which formed them. Ships cannot travel at more than half impulse speed in a planetary nebula because the dense gas can literally melt the hull at high speeds. The swirls of energetic gas also interfere with sensors— any sensor task is at +2 Difficulty in a dense nebula. In addition, showers of meteoroids are common in planetary nebulae. However, planetary nebulae can be treasure troves of rare heavy elements. Asteroid prospectors are often willing to risk the hazards in search of rich lodes.

Interstellar nebulae, the "nurseries" where new stars are formed, are much bigger than planetary nebulae. They can extend for hundreds of light-years, and are generally found at the leading edge of the galaxy's spiral arms. Interstellar nebulae are fairly thin, so ships can move through them at up to warp 1. The sensor penalty is only +1 Difficulty. The chief hazard in interstellar nebulae are protostars, clumps of denser gas forming into new stars. Treat a protostar as a planetary nebula. Unfortunately, protostars are hard to detect, so a starship can blunder into a dense region with no warning.

PULSARS AND NEUTRON STARS

After a massive star blows apart in a supernova, the remnant becomes a neutron star. Neutron stars are the densest things in the universe next to black holes. Their gravity is so intense that normal matter collapses into a mass of

DYING STARS

As stars get old and use up their nuclear fuel, the outer layers of the star expand, ballooning up into a red giant. Red giants are *huge*, with diameters in the hundreds of millions of kilometers. When Earth's Sol eventually turns red giant, its surface will extend to the orbit of Mars! Of course, this means that red giants are very tenuous. A good description of a red giant is "a red-hot vacuum." Ships can actually fly *inside* a red giant star's outer layers. Shields are a must, of course—within a giant star a ship takes 60 points of damage each round from the glowing plasma. Eventually the giant blows off its outer layers completely, laying bare the dense heart of the star, a white dwarf.

But large stars—those with twice Sol's mass or more—have a more dramatic fate. They explode in a supernova detonation. The supernova blast tears the star apart, leaving only a tiny, superdense remnant of the core, a neutron star.

Red giant stars in Federation space include Alpha Ceti, Antares, and Betelgeuse. Some red giants do have habitable planets; it is assumed these were once frozen ice worlds that have been warmed by the dying star's increased heat. Because red giants do not remain long in that state, intelligent life doesn't usually evolve on planets of giant stars, but the worlds can be colonized and remain habitable for millions of years.

STELLAR CLASSIFICATIONS

Astrophysicists categorize stars by color, brightness, and size. The letter classification system can be remembered by the mnemonic phrase "Only Bad Astronomers Foolishly Get Klingons Mad." A number from 0 to 9 follows the letter code for more detail.

Type O stars are the most massive and brightest stars. They are blue, and put out thousands of times more energy than Earth's Sol. They don't live very long, though—a Type O star is likely to go supernova after only half a billion years. Few Type O stars have life-bearing planets, but they often have very rich asteroid belts full of valuable elements.

Type B stars are blue-white giants, less spectacular than the O stars but still very bright and massive. A few Type B stars, like Rigel, have life-bearing planets, though some planetologists speculate that these were artificially terraformed.

Type A stars are slightly dimmer and less massive. Sirius and Vega are Type A stars. White dwarfs are also Type A stars (although astrophysicists sometimes designate them Type D). Habitable worlds orbiting Type A stars are rare, although Altair and Deneb are both Type A stars.

Type F stars are two or three times brighter than Sol, and good candidates for habitable worlds. Canopus is a Type F star, as is Procyon.

Type G stars are yellow stars like Sol, Capella, or Alpha Centauri A. They are the most likely to have life-bearing planets.

Type K stars are orange stars, smaller and cooler than Sol, but still likely to have habitable planets. Arcturus and Tau Ceti are Type K stars.

Type M stars are red and cool. Red dwarf stars are the most common stars in the galaxy. More than two thirds of all stars are red dwarfs. Small and dim, only a few have habitable planets. Wolf 359 and Barnard's Star are Type M. Red giants are what all stars become in their dying stage.

A further classification is given by Roman numerals, giving the star's size. Type V stars are normal main-sequence stars like Sol. These are the most common. Type IV indicates subgiants, II and III are giants, and Type I stars rank as supergiants. So Earth's Sol is Type G2 V—a yellow, main-sequence star. Vulcan's star, 40 Eridani A, is Type K1 V—an orange star, also on the main sequence. Rigel is Type B8 I—a dazzling, blue-white supergiant.

tightly packed neutrons. Essentially a neutron star is a colossal atomic nucleus. Neutronium, the name for this kind of matter, is the ultimate armor. It is so dense nothing can penetrate it. Of course, the fact that a cubic centimeter of neutronium weights a hundred million tons limits its usefulness somewhat. Only very advanced civilizations, such as the builders of the planet-killing "Doomsday Device," can work neutronium.

The chief danger from a neutron star is its crushing gravity. Like a black hole, a neutron star can damage ships passing nearby with tidal forces. Unlike a black hole, neutron stars cannot capture ships capable of reaching light-speed.

A rapidly rotating neutron star can emit a pulse of intense radiation in a narrow beam, like a lighthouse beacon. The beam flicks around and around several times a second. These "beacons" are known as pulsars, and they can be quite dangerous. The radiation beam is intense enough to damage ships up to a light-year away.

ROGUE WORLDS

Not all planets are content to circle endlessly about a star. Sometimes a supernova explosion or a near encounter of two stars can pull planets loose and send them wandering through interstellar space. Rogue worlds are a fairly minor hazard; the risk of colliding with one is remote. But a rogue planet's gravity can pull starships off course.

A rogue world entering a star system can cause significant damage. Actual collisions are rare, but the gravity of an interloper can disturb the orbits of planets in a star system, causing climate changes and massive quakes. It is impossible to destroy or divert something as big as a rogue planet.

Some rogue worlds may have been home to advanced civilizations before being flung into the depths of space. Such planets may hold ruins of great importance—or possibly survivors.

SPACEBORNE LIFE

One rare but especially dangerous hazard to starships is an encounter with space-dwelling lifeforms. Several such organisms have been encountered, including the giant amoeba creature of Gamma 7A and the noncorporeal entity which destroyed a Klingon ship at Beta XII-A in 2269. The autonomous planet-smashing device known as the "Doomsday Machine" could also be considered a form of spaceborne life.

The chief danger with space-dwelling organisms is their sheer power. Most seem to be at least the equal of a starship in energy output, and they often have extremely potent weapons and defenses. The less intelligent ones, such as the space amoeba, behave in fairly predictable ways, but an intelligent space creature is every bit as dangerous as a hostile starship.

SUPERNOVAS

A supernova occurs when a massive red giant star uses up its hydrogen fuel. The star's core collapses, causing an explosion which literally blows the star apart. Supernovas are lethal to any ship or world in the system, and the pulse of radiation given off by an exploding star can be harmful to lifeforms at a distance of several light-years. A starship capable of reaching warp 1 can outrun the blast wave of a stellar explosion, but nothing can save a planet of a dying sun.

UNSTABLE PLANETS

Fortunately, planets don't explode often, but it is pretty spectacular when they do. The conditions required are very rare and poorly understood. Usually

there is some warning, in the form of progressively more intense tectonic activity. Ultimately the planet tears itself apart, creating a cluster of asteroids. The planet Psi 2000 disintegrated in 2267, and a nearby starship recorded its death.

The main danger from unstable planets is to anyone on the surface when the world blows up. Ships in orbit are at risk from continent-sized fragments, but most starships can easily outrun flying debris. Only if a ship's crew were foolish enough to shut down the warp drive would a vessel be in danger.

TIME WARPS AND TIME TRAVEL

There are four known methods of traveling in time, all of which are highly dangerous. Because of the potential for harm by time travelers meddling in the course of history, Starfleet generally avoids time travel, except when necessary to correct changes made by others. Starfleet assumes that the other starfaring civilizations have similar restrictions.

The first method requires a black hole. A ship passing close to a rotating black hole can follow a course which takes it back in time. This is not for the faint of heart—the ship must withstand the radiation and tidal stress around the black hole, and must follow a precisely-calculated course to arrive at the proper point in the past. Even a tiny error can land the ship centuries off course. Since time moves more slowly around a black hole, travelers can also go to the future by entering the slow time region and then leaving again when a suitable interval has passed in the outside universe. With even more delicate calculations, a time warp is possible using less massive bodies, such as ordinary stars. The *U.S.S. Enterprise* pioneered this "slingshot effect" in 2267.

The second method of time travel is the warp implosion. This is accomplished by altering the intermix formula based on the theoretical relationship between time and antimatter. Nine out of ten times, the result is simply the destruction of the ship, the crew, and everything nearby. If done properly, a warp implosion can catapult a starship back in time. Returning forward can be done by the same method. Since the ship's engines need a complete overhaul and new antimatter afterward, this is not a method recommended for casual visits to the past.

A third way to travel in time is to pass through a time warp. A few natural "time warps" exist in the galaxy. These phenomena are usually short-lived and

RANDOM STAR SYSTEMS

While it is best to create a star system from scratch to fit a role in the story, sometimes an adventure veers off in a direction the Narrator never expected. To generate a star system quickly, use the following system. Obviously, any details which are important to the ongoing adventure shouldn't be randomly rolled.

Name: Make up a name. Combining two Greek letters is a simple method, or see *By Any Other Name* (page 235).

Affiliation: This assumes the system is in or near Federation space. Roll one die. 1–3: Federation territory, 4: Rival Interstellar Power (Klingons, Romulans, etc.), 5: neutral, 6: unclaimed. All systems beyond explored space are of course unclaimed.

System Type: Roll one die. 1–4: single star, 5: binary, 6: trinary. For each star roll two dice to determine the star type. All stars are assumed to be main-sequence stars. 2–7: Type M, 8: Type K, 9: Type G, 10: Type F, 11: Type A, 12: Type B.

Planets: If a habitable world is needed, just put one in. Otherwise roll two dice to determine the number of planets, then roll two dice for each planet's class. 2–3: Class D, 4–5: Class F, 6: Class G, 7: Class H, 8–9: Class J, 10: Class K, 11: Class L, 12: Class M.

Other objects: All systems are assumed to have a number of asteroids, comets, and other small bodies. Anything else, like a space station or a dimensional rift, should be placed by the Narrator.

impossible to chart or predict, but ships stumbling across them can emerge anywhere else in space and time. Getting back requires the crew to find another time warp and hope it leads to the right place, return back through the warp they entered before it shifts parameters or dissipates altogether, or else use one of the other methods.

Finally, some advanced civilizations have developed time portals allowing fairly easy access to the past using technologies unknown to Federation science. The device or being known as the Guardian of Forever is one such portal, and the atavachron developed on the planet Sarpeidon is another. While a top-security Federation science team now studies the Guardian, the atavachron was destroyed when Sarpeidon's sun went nova in 2269.

From the experiences of time travelers, scientists have developed a theory of elastic time. Minor changes do not generally affect the course of history—they are damped out by the random "noise" of events. But some key events can have drastic effects. So when a nameless bum in Earth's Great Depression era incinerated himself with Leonard McCoy's phaser, history was not affected, but when McCoy prevented Edith Keeler from being hit by a truck, the result was a Nazi victory in World War II. Since there is no way to know which changes are important and which ones are not, time travelers should be extremely careful.

When changes do affect history, the time travelers themselves seem to be immune. A person who goes back centuries into the past and does something which prevents his grandparents from being born does not simply wink out of existence. He remains in the past, and his memories are of the history that produced him, not the new continuum. This means that any time voyagers who accidentally alter the course of history do at least have the chance to set things right again.

STARS AND STAR SYSTEMS

Space may be the final frontier, but space itself is pretty empty. Stars and their planets are where intelligent beings live, and where most of the interesting things in the galaxy happen.

About a third of all star systems contain two or more stars; four stars in one system appears to be the upper limit. Systems with two stars are known as binary stars. Triple systems are sometimes called trinary star systems. It is quite possible for a life-bearing world to exist in a multiple star system, as long as the stars are either close enough to one another that the planet can orbit both of them, or else separated widely enough that the planet can circle one star in a stable orbit.

Usually the stars in a multiple system all receive the same name, like Alpha Centauri, with the individual stars denoted by letters—Alpha Centauri A is the brightest of the three stars in the system, B is the next brightest, and so on. Beta Centauri is another star entirely, hundreds of light-years away.

Stars in a multiple system do not have to be the same type—often a dim Type M star circles one of its brighter siblings. Occasionally one partner in a multiple star system is a stellar remnant—a white dwarf, neutron star, or black hole. Usually such systems do not have any habitable worlds, but a sufficiently exotic object might be worth placing a scientific station in orbit to monitor.

THE SYSTEM TEMPLATE

Star systems in the *Star Trek Roleplaying Game* are described using a standard template to present all the basic information. Since this is a roleplaying game and not an astronomy text, the data in the template are those most relevant to game play. Narrators with a scientific bent should feel free to go into more detail if they wish.

SYSTEM NAME

Obviously, this is what the system is called. Many star systems have two names—one assigned by the Federation's scientists and one used by native sentient beings. The Federation uses a standard system based on constellations, with individual stars denoted by Greek letters. Thus, Alpha Centauri is the brightest star (from Earth, anyway) in the constellation Centaurus. The system works well for the region around Earth, but elsewhere star names are a hodgepodge of catalog numbers, local names, or classifications based on Vulcan, Tellarite, and Andorian constellations.

AFFILIATION

Who the system belongs to. A system can be part of the Federation (like the Solar or Andorian systems), a neutral system (like Organia), part of a hostile empire, or unclaimed. It is relatively uncommon for two worlds in a system to have different affiliations, although that has happened a few times where Federation territory overlaps with another starfaring power's space, or where one world in a system opts to join the Federation while another stays neutral. The best-known example of such a divided system is Rigel, with Federation member and colony worlds, neutrals, and an Orion core world among its seventeen planets. If a system is disputed, or claimed by more than one power, that fact should be noted here.

SYSTEM TYPE

This section lists the number and type of stars (see Stellar Classifications, page 185) in the system. The Solar system is simple: a solitary G2 V star. The

PLANETARY CLASSES TABLE

Federation scientists have come up with a classification system for planetary bodies, using letters to denote general types. While most of the categories are of interest only to planetologists, a few are common enough to mention here:

Class D: Small, rocky bodies with no appreciable atmosphere and low gravity. Anything smaller than a Class D world is an asteroid. Regula I is a Class D planet.

Class F: These planets differ from Class D worlds in size and internal structure, but they are also airless and unsuitable for life. Mercury is a good example.

Class G: Class G planets are composed of rock and ice, with atmospheres of methane and carbon dioxide. Saturn's moon Titan is a Class G world. While most are lifeless, a few Class G worlds may have liquid water oceans buried under kilometers of ice, where life might evolve. Class G worlds usually exist only in the outer regions of a star system.

Class H: These are generally somewhat smaller than Earth, with almost no surface water. Oxygen levels in the atmosphere are low, but some Class H planets are marginally habitable by humans. Mars began as an example of a very small, very dry Class H planet with no oxygen at all, although terraforming is altering it toward Class M.

Class J: The biggest planets, Class J worlds are gas giants like Jupiter and Saturn, with masses hundreds of times greater than the Earth's. They have atmospheres of hydrogen and helium. Planetologists have detected life in the upper atmosphere of Class J worlds such as Tau Ceti VII. The upper end of the Class J size scale meets the lower end of brown dwarf stars.

Class K: Class K worlds are roughly Earth-sized but do not have breathable atmospheres or liquid water. Venus and Planet Mudd are Class K.

Class L: These planets are fairly common; they have oxygen-argon atmospheres and liquid water. Humans can live on them quite comfortably. Class L worlds have only plant life.

Class M: The garden spots of the galaxy, Class M planets have liquid water, living things, and oxygen-nitrogen atmospheres. Most are about the same size as Earth. Examples of Class M worlds are Vulcan, Andoria, and of course Earth.

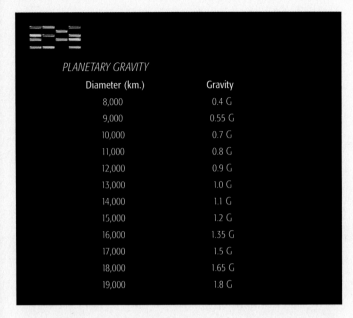

PLANETARY GRAVITY

Diameter (km.)	Gravity
8,000	0.4 G
9,000	0.55 G
10,000	0.7 G
11,000	0.8 G
12,000	0.9 G
13,000	1.0 G
14,000	1.1 G
15,000	1.2 G
16,000	1.35 G
17,000	1.5 G
18,000	1.65 G
19,000	1.8 G

Alpha Centauri system is more complicated—a G2 V star with a K0 V companion, both circled by a distant M5 dwarf companion.

INHABITED PLANETS

For most star travelers, this is the important part. This section should list all the important worlds of the system and give their planetary classes (see chart, page 187). This is also the place to mention inhabited moons and planetoids. If any of the planets are likely to be adventure settings, describe them in more detail with a planetary template (see below).

OTHER PLANETS

If there are other planets in the system, mention that here. Unless one of the uninhabited planets has some notable feature, it isn't really necessary to list their names or anything beyond general types. For the Solar system it would suffice to say that there are eight planets besides Earth and Mars, four of which are Class J gas giants.

OTHER STELLAR OBJECTS

This covers any remaining natural objects of interest in the system—comets, asteroids, etc. This is also the place to list unusual phenomena like dimensional rifts, shattered planets, time warps, or dust clouds.

ARTIFICIAL OBJECTS

Sometimes the most important thing in a system isn't on a planet at all. Often a system's location makes it important for commercial or strategic reasons, but there is no planet suitable for a colony, so an artificial structure is the answer. Starbases and space stations come under this heading, as do things

like derelict starships. A few systems contain "megastructures" of planetary size or larger, like a Dyson sphere or a Niven ring.

SYSTEM IN A SENTENCE (SIS)

This one-sentence summary of the whole system should focus on the most important aspect of the place—the thing characters are likely to remember when they leave.

PLANETS

Humans and other Federation species evolved on planets, and so planets are where they look first when searching for new life and new civilizations. There are a lot of planets in the galaxy—about a trillion. That doesn't include all the moons, asteroids, and other bodies. With so many worlds, there is room for amazing variety. For convenience, star explorers use the shorthand planetary classification system (see sidebar).

THE PLANETARY TEMPLATE

We describe planets in the *Star Trek Roleplaying Game* using a template similar to the one used for star systems. Narrators should write up full template descriptions of any worlds that play important parts in adventures.

NAME

Planets are often referred to simply by their parent star's name, with a number indicating the planet's orbital position. So Earth might be known as Sol III. Obviously, the native inhabitants of a world usually have their own name for the world (like Earth, or Terra), although a colony world may not. For clarity, Starfleet uses the numerical designation for all but the most important planets.

CLASS

The planet's class, as described in the planetary classification table (page 187). Just about all planets with intelligent natives are Class M or possibly Class

H. Humans and other species have colonized a few Class L worlds. A colony on a hostile world must have a sealed environment. Class K or Class F worlds may be home to exotic lifeforms based on silicon or metals.

System Data

This is the place to describe any moons or rings the planet might have, or to mention if the world is itself a moon of a larger planet. Moons up to half the size of the parent planet are possible, though most moons are little more than asteroids. Habitable moons circling habitable planets are very rare indeed, and almost always products of terraforming in the past. A handful of binary planets have been discovered, in which two bodies of about the same size revolve around each other.

Gravity

Gravity is a function of a planet's size and density. Note that humans generally cannot live for long periods in a gravity field greater than 200 percent of standard Earth gravity (2 G) or less than 30 percent of Earth gravity (0.3 G). Since gravity also determines how well a planet holds onto its atmosphere and water, most Class M worlds have roughly standard gravity (1 G). The Planetary Gravity table gives the gravity for a common iron-nickel silica planet like Earth or Mars.

Year and Day

Rather than go into orbital dynamics, the Narrator should just pick a convenient value for a planet's year and leave it at that. List the length of the year in standard (Earth) days, with the length of the local day in standard hours after a slash. In general, planets of bright stars will orbit farther away and so have longer years than planets circling dim ones. As an example, the inhabited worlds of the Rigel system have years nearly a thousand Earth years long! Planets with very long or very short days may have interesting conditions. A long day is likely to create great swings in temperature from day to night, and local lifeforms must have ways to cope with the extremes. Fast-rotating worlds have fairly even temperatures, but the stronger Coriolis effect generates powerful windstorms.

Atmosphere

Class M worlds have oxygen-nitrogen atmospheres, though some planets may have significant amounts of other gases in the mix. The exact proportion of oxygen depends on the planet's atmospheric pressure. Earth has 20 percent oxygen at one standard atmosphere. A thinner atmosphere must have proportionately more oxygen to keep humans from gasping for breath; a thicker one

RANDOM PLANET GENERATOR

This system is intended to create Class M planets, for occasions when an adventure takes the characters to a planet the Narrator has not been able to prepare in advance.

System Data: Roll one die and subtract 3 to get the number of moons. Moons are one die times 1,000 kilometers in diameter, but cannot be larger than half the planet's size. The very biggest moons may be Class H or K, but others are Class D or F.

Gravity: Gravity is based on size. The base diameter for Class M worlds is 13,000 kilometers. Roll one die, multiply by 1,000 kilometers, and add it to the base. Then subtract a second die times 1,000. The result is the planet's diameter. Consult the chart to find the surface gravity.

Year and Day: For the year, assign a value based on the star type. Planets of normal stars have a year length of 1d6 x 100 days; planets of giant stars have years of 1d6 x 1,000 days; planets of supergiants have years 1d6 x 100 standard years long! To determine the day length, roll 2d6 and multiply by 4 to get the rotation period in hours.

Atmosphere: Class M worlds by definition have a breathable atmosphere. The base is 20 percent oxygen. Roll one die, subtract a second die roll from the first, and add the result to 20 to determine the amount of oxygen in the atmosphere. The rest of the atmosphere is nitrogen and trace gases.

Hydrosphere: This is one of the most variable attributes. Roll 2d6 and multiply by 10 percent to determine how much of the planet's surface is covered by water. A result of 10 or 11 indicates the presence of islands, but a roll of 12 means the planet has no dry land at all.

Climate: Roll a die and multiply the result by 10 to determine the basic temperature in degrees Centigrade. The combination of temperature and hydrosphere gives the general climate.

Intelligent Life: Details of life and civilization should be devised by the Narrator. See the chapters *New Life* and *New Civilizations*.

should have proportionately less to prevent hyperoxygenation. On some marginal planets the air pressure means there is only enough oxygen to breathe at certain altitudes—on planets with dense atmospheres humans can only live on mountain plateaus, while on planets with thin air, humans must settle in the lowest possible regions.

HYDROSPHERE

List how much of the surface is covered with water, as a percentage. All life-bearing worlds must have some liquid water. At least one quarter of the surface must be ocean to support life. Note that smaller planets tend to be drier than large ones, though this is not an ironclad rule. Vulcan is both large and dry, for example.

CLIMATE

Climate is the combination of how wet a world is and how much energy it gets from its sun. Naturally, climate varies depending on where you are on a planet—even a "desert world" will have some wet regions. All Class M planets must have an average temperature between 10° and 60° Centigrade, with the "typical" world falling around 30°. This is the average temperature in the middle latitudes. Tropical areas are warmer and polar regions are colder. The temperature coupled with the amount of surface water should give the Narrator a good idea of what the planet's surface will be like. A cold wet world will have icy seas, rugged glacier-carved mountains, and broad expanses of tundra. A cold dry planet will have frozen steppes, cold deserts, and barren mountains. Warm wet worlds may have lots of jungles and swamps, while warm dry worlds will have large desert regions.

INTELLIGENT LIFE

This is the place to list what species calls the planet home, and how many people live there. If the planet has inhabitants of several species, list their populations separately. Using Rigel VII as our example: Orions (740 million), Kaylar (250 million), Chelarians (12 million), Rigelians (7 million), Humans (7 million), and Andorians (2 million).

TECH CLASSIFICATION

List the planet's technology level, and if possible give examples of the current level of achievement, or give a year in Earth's history that matches the planet's technology level. Note any important variations—if the planet has one advanced region amid a sea of primitives, list the technology classifications separately. (See page 231 of *New Civilizations* for more detailed information.)

GOVERNMENT

Give a simple description of the planet's government. If there is no unified government, mention the two or three most powerful states. (See page 232 of *New Civilizations* for more detailed information.)

CULTURE

Obviously a planet can have an amazing diversity of cultures, but for this listing a simplistic "stereotype" will do. Vulcan's culture is "a traditional, scientific, and pacifistic culture based on logic and suppression of emotion," while Earth in 2269 is "an exuberant, pluralistic civilization with a strong interest in galactic exploration and technological progress."

AFFILIATION

As in the star system template, this is what the planet's allegiance is in the great game of galactic power politics. At the planetary level it is possible to go into more detail—is the world a willing ally of the Klingons, is it ruled by a Klingon puppet government, or have the Klingons conquered it outright, making it a subject world? All three are examples of Klingon affiliation.

RESOURCES

Planets are big, and just about any world has nearly everything its people need. This is not necessarily everything they want—many worlds have unique products or natural resources which are in demand elsewhere in the galaxy. This is the place to list Saurian brandy, Orion slave women, dilithium crystals, or ryetalyn. If a planet is noticeably short on a vital resource, that might get mentioned here also.

PLACES OF NOTE

Under this heading, list things like the most important city, places of galactic historical significance, or locations of scientific importance. For Mars, places of note might include the Utopia Planitia Fleet Yards, Olympus Mons, and Mars Colony 3. Places of Note are not necessarily the best tourist destinations—a secret Klingon base is more noteworthy (and gameworthy) than a famous art institute.

SHIP FACILITIES

While the invention of the transporter means that planets no longer need elaborate starports or space stations to handle incoming traffic, ships still need repair facilities. This is the place to list any spacedocks, starbases, or other bases where ships can be serviced.

OTHER DETAILS

This is the place to note anything else of interest about the world, in particular anything which is important to the adventure.

Designing Planets

When designing worlds, Narrators should remember that a planet is only the setting for the story. The story of Little Red Riding Hood takes place in a forest, but the tale doesn't begin "Once upon a time there was a forest."

As a Narrator creating planets for *Star Trek Roleplaying Game* episodes, you should only do as much work as is necessary for the story. There's no need to go overboard. If the adventure is a Starfleet courtroom drama set in a base on Altair IV, then you can simply say "Altair IV is a Class M world" and leave it at that. But if the planet is a major part of the adventure, then it needs to be developed.

Decide what part the planet is to play in the story. Is it an obstacle, a harsh environment the characters must survive? Or is it a paradise threatened by some cataclysm? Pick the conditions to fit the story. Don't be shy about tailoring the planet to play on the emotions of your players. Sure, a harsh desert

RANDOM PLANET GENERATOR: UNUSUAL FEATURES

Unusual Features: Many worlds have unusual features. Select one from the table below, or else roll 2d6.

2. Extreme Axial Tilt: The planet's axis of rotation is tilted more than 45°. This creates a tremendous contrast between the seasons; upper latitudes may have months of darkness in winter and months of continual day in summer.

3. Tidally Locked: The world keeps one face turned toward its sun, the way Earth's Moon always faces the Earth. Half the planet is perpetually dark and frozen, the other side is always sunlit and hot. A band around the edge of the day side may have comfortable temperatures.

4. Rapid Rotation: The planet rotates in only 2d6 hours, so that days and nights are only a few hours long. Such worlds are likely to have extremely violent windstorms, and there may be significantly lower gravity at the equator than at the poles due to centrifugal effects.

5. Slow Rotation: The planet rotates very slowly, with a day length of 2d6 standard days. There may be great swings in temperature from day to night.

6. Thin Atmosphere: The planet's atmosphere is very thin, with a surface pressure less than half of standard. Humans can survive only in deep valleys or with breathing gear. The thin air also means tremendous swings in temperature between day and night.

7. Unusual Climate: The world is excessively hot or excessively cold for most humanoid life. There may be regions of moderate climate—at the poles of a hot world or on the equator of a cold one.

8. Dense Atmosphere: The planet's atmosphere is unusually dense, with a surface pressure of five to ten standard atmospheres. At those pressures, the normal oxygen content is fatal to most starfaring species, so any settlement by humans will be only on high mountain plateaus.

9. Unusual Atmosphere Composition: Though breathable, the atmosphere contains significant amounts of some gases other than nitrogen and oxygen.

10. Unusual Density: The planet is denser than normal for its size. Multiply gravity by 2. Dense planets generally have abundant mineral resources.

11. Orbital Anomaly: The planet has a very eccentric orbit, swinging close to its sun at perihelion and then orbiting far out at aphelion. This can create vast differences in climate and temperature over the course of a year.

12. Moon: The planet is not a planet in its own right, but the moon of a larger body (probably a Class J gas giant like Jupiter or Saturn).

planet is just as likely to be threatened by an approaching asteroid as a green paradise, but it packs more emotional punch if the big rock is going to flatten the Mist Forest instead of the Dunes of Despair.

Since *Star Trek* is a science fiction setting, not fantasy, the Narrator should try to strike a balance between the demands of the story and the need for scientific plausibility. Remember that planets are very big places, with room for lots of variety. Think about all the different places that exist just on Earth. Your worlds should have similar variety.

Let's look at an example: Frank wants to Narrate an episode set on a desert world—a world where water is more precious than dilithium, where desert bandits will kill unwary travelers for the moisture in their flesh. Unfortunately for Frank, he now has to explain how the planet has an oxygen atmosphere. Oxygen comes from plants, and plants need water. If the planet is really all desert, those bandits will be more worried about oxygen to breathe than water to drink.

So Frank decides to add an ocean, small and very salty, at the planet's north pole. The Boreal Sea has a nice sound. Around the Boreal Sea is a narrow belt of forest and grassland, tapering off into the great southern deserts. His planet still has plenty of deserts—more deserts than there is land on all of Earth—but now at least he doesn't have to worry about where the oxygen comes from.

Lots of planets have unusual features. That's often a good thing, as it reminds the players that they aren't in Southern California. It is possible to go overboard, however. A good rule of thumb to follow is to allow one anomaly per planet. If a world has a dense atmosphere, so that human settlers can only survive at high altitude, it shouldn't also have a very long day, and an eccentric orbit, and a belt of deadly radiation making it impossible for ships to approach. Decide which features are important to the story—the isolated mountaintop settlements? The week-long nights? The incredible climate shifts from summer to winter? Or the fact that the planet is cut off from the rest of the galaxy by radiation? Toss out anything that isn't important.

This is not to say that you can't have "local color." You can have plenty of that. Your special effects budget is unlimited. Frank's desert world can have sandboats skimming across the desert under billowing sails, or huge stone heads left by a dead civilization lying half-buried in the sand, or lethal sandstorms. Those are fine—those are things that fit on a world that is half desert, and they don't distract from the story.

A FEW IMPORTANT WORLDS

The Federation has more than a hundred members, and Federation space contains nearly a million planets. It is impossible to describe or even list them all here. Herewith, a sampler of planets visited by Starfleet explorers in the 2260s.

892-IV

A Class M planet completely habitable by humans, 892-IV is either a remarkable instance of Hodgkins' Law or the result of Preserver activity, for it is dominated by a civilization which strongly resembles that of classical Rome on Earth, but with Level Four technology. The planet's rulers know that space explorers have visited their world, and the Federation has advised all vessels to avoid the planet until proper diplomatic contact can be established.

ARDANA

The planet Ardana is a Federation member world, and a major producer of the vital mineral zeinite. Ardana has a severe (and literal) social stratification system—workers live on the planet surface exposed to harmful zeinite fumes, while the ruling elite live in the remarkable flying city Stratos. Recent efforts to improve conditions for the workers progress slowly. The world is a Class M planet, but visitors should use filter masks when visiting the surface.

CESTUS III

The UFP outpost closest to the mysterious Gorn civilization, Cestus III was home to a small colony and science station. A Gorn attack destroyed the colony in 2267, but resettlement plans are underway. Cestus III is a Class M planet with a warm, dry climate.

CORIDAN

The Coridan system contains several worlds with extremely abundant mineral resources, including large deposits of dilithium. The main world, Coridan, is a cold, dry Class M planet. The Coridan government is chronically corrupt and unstable, and the system's admission to the Federation in 2267 was hotly debated at the Babel Conference.

DEEP SPACE STATION K-7

Station K-7 is a Federation outpost just over a parsec from the nearest Klingon world. It orbits a red dwarf star with no planets larger than asteroids.

Because of the Organian treaty, K-7 is not a military base, but is a thriving center of trade and communication. The station itself is of standard Federation design, similar to dozens of other starbases and research facilities.

DENEVA

One of Earth's most successful interstellar colonies (founded in 2165), and a Federation member in its own right, Deneva is a lush and beautiful Class M planet, and an important center of interstellar trade and shipping. In 2267, a species of neural parasite attacked Deneva, causing widespread insanity and death. Quick action by the *U.S.S. Enterprise* crew destroyed the parasites, and the population (over 1 million) is now recovering from the event.

ELBA II

Elba II is a hostile Class K planet with no valuable resources, located far from the main shipping routes. It is therefore the perfect place for the Federation to keep those few individuals who are both incurably insane and dangerous to others. The Elba inmates, led by the legendary Garth of Izar, took control of the facility in 2268 but were eventually recaptured. Security procedures on Elba II have since been upgraded.

EMINIAR

The Eminiar system lies at the edge of Federation space in the cluster NGC 321. The star is a bright Type F sun, with two Class M planets. The inhabitants of Eminiar III, who came there from Eminiar VII centuries ago, call it Vendikar. For the past five hundred years the two planets have waged war, but efforts to limit collateral damage and environmental effects led to a "virtual war" controlled by computers, with casualties destroyed painlessly in disintegration booths. Federation Ambassador Fox was instrumental in negotiating a peace treaty between the two worlds in 2267, along with port-of-call rights for Federation ships.

JANUS VI

A hostile Class K planet, similar in many ways to Venus, Janus VI is a mineral treasure-house, with rich supplies of pergium ore. The mining colony on Janus is completely underground, and has gradually grown into a small town built in tunnels. In 2267 it was discovered that Janus VI is home to a species of intelligent silicon-based life, known as the Horta. After some initial misunderstandings, peaceful contact was made, and the Horta may yet become Federation members.

MEMORY ALPHA

As part of an ambitious plan to collect all the knowledge of the Federation's member civilizations into a single archive, Starfleet hollowed out a Class D planetoid in the center of Federation space and fitted it with vast

computer memory banks. The project suffered a severe blow when alien organisms invaded the computers and erased all the files, but work is now underway to recreate the archive. A back-up facility, Memory Beta, is under construction in a remote system.

RIGEL

The Rigel system is one of the most heavily populated star systems in the galaxy. The star itself is a Type B supergiant, fifty thousand times brighter than Sol. Either by a freak of planetary development or by deliberate meddling by some long-vanished race, Rigel has six habitable worlds. Rigel II is a sultry Class L planet with a hedonistic culture, populated by a mix of species including a large number of Humans. Rigel III, called Chelar by its amphibian inhabitants, is a warm, lush Class M world. Rigel IV is the system capital, an advanced Class M world densely populated by Humans, Orions, and Rigelians. Rigel V, also Class M, is the homeworld of the Vulcanoid Rigelian species. Rigel VII, sometimes called Orion, is thought to be the homeworld of the Orions. It is a dry, cool Class M world with an enormous moon and a barbaric, slave-trading culture. Finally, Rigel XII is a very cold, arid, windswept Class H planet, with only a few hundred inhabitants living in scattered lithium and dilithium mining camps.

SHERMAN'S PLANET

Sherman's Planet is an extremely fertile and rich Class M world, strategically located in the Neutral Zone between the Klingon Empire and the Federation. Since the Organian Treaty grants worlds in the Neutral Zone to whichever power can most efficiently develop them, the Klingons have done everything in their power to halt colonization of Sherman's Planet.

SIGMA DRACONIS

Although the Sigma Draconis system is a mere seven parsecs from Earth, it has been only briefly surveyed. There are nine planets in all, three of which are Class M worlds with intelligent life. Sigma Draconis III is a warm, densely populated world with a preindustrial civilization. Sigma Draconis IV is small and relatively dry, with a civilization just on the verge of developing warp

drive. Sigma Draconis VI is currently in the middle of a severe ice age, with only the tropics warm enough for life. A Federation expedition on a medical rescue mission discovered remains of a highly advanced civilization on Sigma Draconis VI, and it seems likely the other two inhabited planets were settled by refugees from the climate shift.

Sigma Iotia II

A Class M planet located a hundred light-years beyond Federation space, toward the edge of the galaxy. The *U.S.S. Horizon* visited it in 2168, shortly before that ship's mysterious disappearance. The inhabitants, extremely prone to imitation, adopted a bizarre culture based on the history of Chicago gangs in the 1920's. After a follow-up visit in 2268, the planet has formed a unified government, but many in the Federation are afraid of what will happen to the Iotians if they are exposed to other cultures.

Sol

The Sol system is the home of the human species, and one of the most important star systems in the Federation. Sol III, better known as Earth, is a Class M world with a population of several billion. Starfleet Academy is located in the city of San Francisco on Earth. Earth's moon, Luna, is a Class F body but nevertheless has a population in the millions. Sol IV, or Mars, is a marginal Class H world undergoing a massive terraforming project.

Talos IV

The Talos system includes a binary star pair and eleven planets. Talos IV is a Class M world, only marginally habitable due to atomic war. The remaining Talosians live in an underground complex, where they have developed their psionic abilities to an astonishing degree. Talosians can project vivid and utterly convincing mental illusions. Starfleet General Order Number Seven specifically forbids anyone from visiting Talos, on pain of death. The prohibition was established to protect the Federation from the Talosian mental powers, and to protect the Talosians themselves.

Tellun

The Tellun system lies near the border between Federation space and the Klingon Empire, and both sides have claimed it. There are two Class M planets in the Tellun system, both inhabited. Elas (Tellun II) has large dilithium crystal deposits. Troyius (Tellun IV) is more heavily populated. A ceremonial marriage of sovereigns reunited the two planets in 2268, ending centuries of conflict, but Klingon agents still hope to disrupt the peace.

Vulcan

A Class M world circling 40 Eridani A, Vulcan is harsh by Terran standards but supports a thriving array of life. Temperatures on Vulcan are high—50° to 60° Centigrade on average. Vulcan is a leading member world of the Federation, and is home to an ancient and highly advanced civilization. The Vulcan Science Academy, in the capital city of ShirKahr, is renowned as a center of higher education. There is some evidence that the planet was originally seeded by beings from another world.

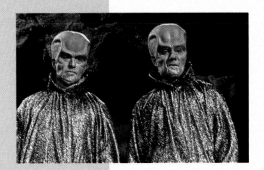

Diamond eyed his captor. She was certainly the most alluring jailer he'd had in a while. Despite the situation, he couldn't help finding her violet hair pleasingly exotic, and her strange scent damnably fascinating. The standard mode of dress on this planet provided no relief from these distracting thoughts. Her thigh-high boots drew the eye irresistibly to the point where her form-fitting metallic outfit was cut to display fully her perfect hip bones.

"You look at me strangely, alien being," she observed.

"Forgive me; on my homeworld, you'd be considered a rare beauty."

She stared at him blankly. "What is this thing called beauty?"

Diamond groped for words. "On my planet, when a man looks at a woman and … is attracted to her, wants to be with her … he says that she is beautiful. And more."

NEW LIFE

She took a single, tentative step toward him. "We know nothing of that here."

"Men and women here, they don't … don't mate, and procreate?"

Her eyes searched him from toe to top, slowly. "Yes. But this being attracted … we do not have that. The Crystal determines all such matters for us."

"That saves a lot of confusion, I suppose.

She took another step in his direction. "So it is said. Yet sometimes I—"

"I'm sure your Crystal knows what's best. On my planet, sometimes we find ourselves ruled by our passions. Love can seize you and turn you inside out. Sometimes a man and a woman can become so enraptured with one another that passion seems to utterly consume them."

A third step. She was now close enough that he could reach through the bars and touch her. "I do not know what it would be like … to be consumed." Her voice had dropped an octave.

Diamond reached out and ran the tips of two fingers along the soft skin of her cheek. She quivered.

Aliens

When the first explorers ventured out among the stars they were astonished to discover that intelligent life is relatively common. There are scores of sentient species in the Federation alone, and hundreds more within known space. The variety of races is staggering. Some have advanced civilizations beyond Human understanding, while others are only learning to tame fire. Some are friends of the Federation. Some are enemies.

THE ALIEN TEMPLATE

We describe intelligent beings in the *Star Trek Roleplaying Game* according to a standard template, which provides a quick way to present all the important information about a species. Obviously, a really detailed description requires more than just the template.

HOMEWORLD

This is the race's planet of origin. Even among starfaring civilizations, the homeworld usually holds the bulk of the race's population. A few species have

DEVILS IN THE DARK? NEW LIFE IN YOUR EPISODES

Besides the exploration of planets, Starfleet's mission includes expanding the United Federation of Planets to encompass new civilizations. Encounters with alien species and cultures provide some of the most satisfying (and often problematic) material for episodes. Although many races, such as the Romulans, Klingons, and Vulcans, resemble Humans in form and thought processes, many others—such as the Horta—have very different metabolisms, thought patterns, and motivations. The theme of life's diversity plays a strong part in many *Star Trek* episodes. The series, in fact, often acts a dramatic forum for exploring the common prejudices and assumptions Humans (or at least 20th-century Humans) hold regarding those even slightly different from them. *Star Trek* takes these differences one step further in its depiction of strange races of intelligent lifeforms. In most cases, the Crew learns to accept these alien creatures for who they are and to base judgments on actions and intentions rather than on skin color, number of eyes, or whether a race possesses a humanoid shape.

Many races encountered in the series consist of divergent Human cultures—lost colonies that have developed their own peculiar class divisions and ethical beliefs or societies that arise from a parallel evolution of the Human species. By interacting with these distant cousins of Earth-centered Humanity, the Crew can discover new insights into its own cultural biases. The message contained within these stories emphasizes the importance of understanding and acceptance over fear and rejection. Whenever you script an episode for your players that introduces a new race or culture, you touch on the infinite diversity that makes up a dominant theme in *Star Trek*.

no homeworld, either because their planet of origin is unknown or because it has been destroyed. Other species have multiple homeworlds. The homeworld of Humans, is of course Earth. The Orion homeworld is thought to be Rigel VII. The Romulan homeworlds are Romulus and Remus, despite the fact that they emigrated from Vulcan.

HOME REGION OR SOVEREIGN TERRITORY

This is the "turf" claimed by the species, or the part of the galaxy in which they are most common. Some species, like the Gorn or the Tholians, are extremely protective of their sovereign space, guarding it against all comers. Others, like the Orions, have no government above the planetary level and claim no sovereign space at all. The Federation falls between those extremes, with a well-defined territory open to trade and peaceful contact. In many cases the sovereign territory of a starfaring power includes large unexplored or undeveloped regions.

SUGGESTED ATTRIBUTE AND EDGE RANGES

The base attributes and edges for the species, with attribute maxima in brackets. While any combination of attributes is possible, Narrators should take a hard look at any species which is too monotonously superior. Attributes are seldom greater than 5 or 6. Extremely large or small races may have a Strength edge based on their size—see the Size Table in the section on designing alien creatures (page 217).

SPECIAL OR UNIQUE ABILITIES

Many alien species have some sort of special abilities. These range from fairly minor talents like Andorian hearing to incredible powers like Antosian cellular metamorphosis or the godlike abilities of the Metrons. Most special abilities derive from the environment in which the species evolved, or else are psionic powers learned through study of the mind. As with attribute ranges, the Narrator should be cautious about giving out special powers. If the story calls for the alien ambassadors to be protected by impenetrable force fields, they could simply wear shield belts rather than have a telekinetic barrier.

SPECIAL OR UNIQUE SKILLS

Some species have skills uncommon among other sentients. These can be specific skills relating to the race's home environment (like Dragon Riding skill for natives of Berengaria VII). Special skills can also reflect the priorities of an alien culture. In a militaristic society everyone might get some combat training, while in a society that values the arts everyone would have some artistic skill.

SIZE

This is simply the average height and weight for adults of the species. No great precision is required. If a race has a great deal of variation, it should be noted here. Most sentient species are between one and three meters in height and between twenty and two hundred kilograms in mass.

TRAITS COMMON TO THE SPECIES

Traits include the range of skin and hair color, the number of fingers, and any features like horns, antennae, or tails. This is also the place to mention if the aliens have scales or feathers, how many eyes they have, and any other identifying characteristics.

STORY NOTES

Under this heading the Narrator should put down a brief summary of the race's "niche" in the series. How are the player characters likely to interact with members of this species? Note that over time a race's role can change, going from an enigma to a potential threat to an ally, or vice versa.

DESCRIPTION

This is the place to give a concise description of the alien species, its civilization, and its history. It isn't necessary to write an encyclopedia, but a couple of paragraphs mentioning all the important details can be very useful. See the sample races below for examples.

DESIGNING ALIENS

The most important task a Narrator faces when designing an alien race isn't the tricky biology questions, or the details of the civilization, or even deciding how the women keep their gauzy costumes from falling off. Those are easy (except for the costumes). The hard part is making aliens who serve their purpose in the story.

That's right—the story comes first, then the aliens. Consider the Klingons, by far the most popular *Star Trek* aliens. When they first appeared in the episode "Errand of Mercy", the writer didn't think, "Hey, I've got a cool idea for these militaristic alien guys. How can I work them into a story?"

Nope. The story idea came first—a conflict between the Federation and a rival power over a seemingly primitive world, which turns out to be inhabited by beings so powerful they can tell everyone to play nice or else. Given that story idea, the Klingons emerged by a fairly logical process. They had to be a technologically advanced race, so that they could pose a legitimate threat to Captain Kirk. Since the Federation is not a conquering power, there had to be a reason why Kirk and company were willing to go to war in order to prevent the Klingons from gaining control of Organia. Obviously they had to be an aggressive, imperialistic culture, a menace to galactic peace. And since they had to be able to interact with Kirk face to face, the Klingons couldn't be any kind of weird lava beings or water-breathers. Everything else was just a question of costumes and make-up.

It's worth noting that the decisions made in creating the Klingons weren't the only possible ones. In *Star Trek*, the Klingons' aggression was

explained as being the result of a need for resources. ("Our worlds are poor, so we must expand outward to survive," says Mara in "Day of the Dove.") But they might also have been motivated by religious fanaticism, a master-race ideology, or even a sense of obligation to uplift and civilize. The conflict in the story would have been the same, but the aliens would have been very different.

You can develop your aliens the same way. Start with the story. Ask yourself what kind of aliens you need. Once you've determined that, then work backward, filling in their planet of origin, their biochemistry, their history, economics, and all the other fun stuff.

For example, Ingrid wants to narrate an episode in which the Starfleet characters are the prey in a brutal hunting game. (It's an old idea, but still a good adventure hook. Old ideas are like that.) All right, what sort of aliens are these hunters going to be?

First of all, they have to be advanced enough to kidnap or capture a group of Starfleet officers. That implies at least Federation-level technology. Since Ingrid doesn't want the characters' starship to just waltz in and rescue them, the aliens have to be powerful enough to make "gunboat diplomacy" impractical. So already a rough outline of the aliens has emerged—they are a minor starfaring power, with a respectable space fleet and perhaps a few colony worlds. They are neutral, so Federation directives have no effect.

Next, Ingrid has to consider why the aliens want to hunt the Starfleet characters. This is the big question, really. If she can't come up with a credible motive, she might as well scrap the episode and try something else.

Again, apply logic: The hunt cannot simply be a lone madman's scheme. If that were true, then the alien government would not prevent a rescue. The manhunt must be at least tolerated by the alien civilization as a whole. Moreover, if they're willing to risk a diplomatic incident, it must be fairly important to them. The hunt must serve some central function in the alien society. What could it be?

Well, if they have starships, they aren't going to be hunting humans just because they're hungry! The hunt is a ritual of some kind, either religious, social, or possibly even for entertainment. Ingrid decides that entertainment isn't a strong enough motive (she might choose otherwise, making her story a commentary on television addicts and the power of the media). That leaves religious or social reasons. Ingrid toys with the idea of making it a religious rite, but then has a clever idea: Suppose the hunt is how the aliens select the best individuals for important positions, and the Starfleet officers are being chased as part of the process of picking an ambassador? Now she even has a surprise ending—the Crew survives the hunt, only to be greeted by the aliens as worthy ambassadors.

It's also important to keep in mind the difference between creating an alien race and creating an alien character. If the story requires a villainous character, that doesn't mean that his entire species has to be pure evil. Again, the Klingons are a good example. Kang, Kor, Korax, and Koloth were all adversaries of Captain Kirk because the Klingon Empire is opposed to the Federation. But Kang is an honorable enemy also driven by love and fear for his wife, Koloth is devious but brazenly debonair, Korax is insulting and crude, and Kor is suspicious and resentful to the point of paranoia. The characters are all Klingons because the episode requires powerful opponents of the Federation, but there is still plenty of room for individual variation in their characters.

THE DETAILS

Once you've determined the role that the aliens will play in the story, then it's time to fill in the details. A species is the product of its history and environment. Remember that you can control those factors, though, so any traits you don't like can be tossed out or changed.

Home Planet

A race's planet of origin shapes it more than anything else. When creating an alien species you should have at least a rough idea of what kind of planet it calls home.

Gravity has a great influence on a creature's physical attributes. A world with high gravity will breed strong beings. Gravity also affects a creature's size—on a planet with high gravity, large creatures will be crippled by their own weight. So heavy-planet beings will be small and compact, possibly with extra legs for support. In surroundings with standard or low gravity they may be capable of amazing feats of leaping and lifting. Low gravity has the opposite effect. Creatures from a light planet can be tall and spindly, fairly weak and frail.

Atmosphere is another important homeworld feature. Most sentient species come from Class-M worlds with oxygen atmospheres; as a result most intelligent species are oxygen-breathers, metabolizing carbon compounds with oxygen to produce energy. They can breathe the same air and eat many of the same foods. But that isn't the only possibility. Chlorine, methane, and cyanide gas can also be the basis for a creature's chemistry. Note that any being who breathes these other gases must use life-support equipment to survive in an environment designed for Humans.

Temperature is another vital factor. Humans are most comfortable at about 20° Centigrade; Vulcans prefer temperatures closer to 40°, but no organism with complex DNA molecules can live long in an environment over 50°. Beings from hot worlds must use some other solvent besides water to keep from boiling. Some Starfleet exobiologists theorize that Tholians may use liquid metal for blood!

Very cold planets pose the opposite problem. Water-based life cannot thrive when all the water is frozen into ice. Beings on cold worlds may use ammonia or even alcohol as the basis for life. Again, any creatures from very cold or hot planets will need life-support gear to survive in the deadly (to them) temperatures found aboard a Federation starship.

Even within the humanoid races there is still plenty of variation at the chemical level. Human blood is red because it is iron-based; Vulcans, Rigelians, Romulans, and Orions have green, copper-based blood; Andorians have blood based on cobalt. Some species may be poisoned by common Human foods, while enjoying delicacies toxic to Earth life.

Since most *Star Trek* episodes take place on Class-M worlds similar to Earth, the Narrator should have a good reason for using aliens with a weird chemistry. Perhaps the story hinges on a scientific puzzle, and the aliens' chemistry is the key to the mystery. Or perhaps the Narrator is trying to make the point that what is habitable to Humans might nevertheless be deadly to others, by showing an alien stranded on a Class-M world, desperately looking for ammonia to drink!

Organisms with a sufficiently unusual chemistry may be hard for Humans even to recognize as alive. The silicon-based Horta are one example. The miners on Janus VI mistook Horta eggs for mineral formations, and ordinary tricorders could not detect the mother Horta. A species based on superfluid liquid helium, or on emotional energy, also might not register as alive.

Environment

The environment in which a species evolved affects it, as well. Creatures native to a desert will prefer dry conditions, even if their home planet also has oceans and tropical jungles. Beings evolved for a very specialized environment may have great difficulty finding suitable places to live. For technological races, the home environment won't be that important—Humans evolved in equatorial grasslands, but live in almost every climate imaginable on Earth. But it may be very important for races with primitive technology.

Moreover, the environment that shaped a species can determine what abilities those beings have. Desert creatures (such as Vulcans) have adaptations to protect against heat and glare. Cold-climate organisms like Andorians specialized for retaining warmth.

Ancestry

Finally, what kind of animal did the species evolve from? Humans evolved from tree-dwelling apes, so we have hands that can grip and binocular vision that can accurately judge distances. When climate change turned the forests into plains, our ancestors became ground-dwelling hunter-gatherers, and so gained the ability to run long distances.

The universe of *Star Trek* assumes that the humanoid body plan is a common one, but that doesn't mean all alien races have to have an evolutionary history exactly like that of Earth humans. Vulcans seem to have evolved in a desert environment, and their ancestors may have been gathering herbivores or scavengers.

Often an intelligent species still shows traits of its animal ancestors. Some scientists believe humans have the persistence to accomplish long tasks and plan ahead because our ancestors caught food by chasing it to exhaustion. Beings descended from pouncing carnivores might be easily frustrated. See the section below on creating animals (page 216) for some ideas on animal lifestyles and how they might affect the way a race would think.

Reproduction and Lifespan

Reproduction and lifespan are buckets in a well. In general, creatures that are long-lived tend to have few offspring, which they tend carefully. Short-lived organisms usually have a lot of children, most of which don't make it to adulthood. Sometimes this strategy is a response to a very hostile environment. Tribbles are perhaps the ultimate expression of the fast-breeding, short-lived strategy. The Vulcans are a good example of the opposite approach—they live tremendously long lives, but mate only once in seven years.

Note that the link between reproduction and lifespan can be severed by technology. Science can artificially extend a race's lifespan or limit its fertility.

Alien Races

Federation explorers have encountered hundreds of sentient species in their voyages through space. Those described below are the most noteworthy or important. Some have unusual powers or abilities, but others are "garden variety" humanoids important in galactic politics.

STARFARING POWERS

Gorn

Homeworld

Starfleet does not know the name and location of the Gorn homeworld, the planet known to its natives as Agornu. It is a large planet with heavy gravity and a warm climate.

Home Region or Sovereign Territory

The Gorn rule a cohesive empire beyond the region explored by Starfleet; Cestus III is the closest Federation outpost to Gorn space. The Gorn are very protective of what they consider "their" territory and react to incursions with overwhelming force. However, they are not expansionist and are not particularly interested in exploration. Until the Gorn raid on Cestus III in 2268, their existence was only a rumor.

Suggested Attribute and Edge Ranges

Fitness 4 [6]
   Strength +2
Coordination 1 [4]
Intellect 2 [5]
Presence 2 [5]
Psi 0 [5]

Special or Unique Abilities

Gorn physiology is amazingly robust. They can resist damage that would kill a Human or Vulcan and are tremendously strong. All Gorn have the advantages of *Excellent Chemoreception, High Pain Threshold, Rapid Healing,* and *Toughness.* Psionic abilities have not been noted among the Gorn.

Special or Unique Skills

None. Because of their isolation, few Gorn have good diplomatic skills or knowledge of other cultures.

Size

Large and massive beings, Gorn stand just over two meters tall and mass about 150 kilograms.

Traits Common to the Species

All Gorn have a saw-tooth ridge running down their spines and a long snout filled with very sharp teeth. Their eyes are segmented, like those of Terran insects, and do not swivel. Their thick hide ranges from green to tan. Female Gorn are slightly smaller than males and have a less prominent spinal ridge. A portion of Gorn communication and interaction is pheromonal.

Story Notes

Despite appearances, the Gorn are not a bunch of clumsy goons. A Gorn ship nearly beat the *U.S.S. Enterprise,* and the Gorn captain Rheuzz'r almost outwitted Captain Kirk during their encounter on the Arena planetoid. They are smart, advanced—and can throw armchair-sized boulders without straining.

The Gorn are good aliens to use for diplomatic or first-contact scenarios. Their empire is powerful, but largely unknown, and could become either a Federation ally or a dangerous foe. Communication is still difficult, and both sides are suspicious and fearful. Starfleet characters visiting Gorn worlds will have to learn everything from scratch—from table manners to politics—and failure could result in war.

Description

The Federation has not yet made formal contact with the species known as the Gorn, and much of the available information relies on second-hand accounts, rumors, and guesses. The Gorn raid on Cestus III and the subsequent encounter between the *Enterprise* and a Gorn vessel provided a wealth of new data.

Some Federation sources have sought comfort in the thought that the Gorn must be as mentally slow as they are physically clumsy, but there is no evidence to support that. Certainly the Gorn vessel encountered by the *Enterprise* was the equal of the Federation ship in speed and defenses, and its weapons were if anything more powerful.

The Gorn do appear to be suspicious and xenophobic, and react to even potential threats with deadly force. They destroyed the colony on Cestus III and tried to ambush the *Enterprise* in order to neutralize Federation defenses along the border.

The following information is for Narrators only, and is unknown to the Federation. The Gorn (the word is both singular and plural, like "fish") have a very old and highly sophisticated civilization. The current Gorn state traces its ancestry back thousands of years to the first empires that arose after the discovery of agriculture. Over the centuries all the barbarian areas of the Gorn homeworld Agornu were conquered and absorbed into the empire.

They colonized several neighboring worlds centuries ago with sublight ships, and with the invention of warp drive Agornu reunited the Gorn worlds into a greater empire. Encounters with some hostile starfaring races led to wars of conquest by the Gorn—they absorbed worlds which accepted Gorn "civilization" into the empire, but those who resisted were utterly wiped out.

For essentially all of Gorn recorded history the universe has been divided into civilization within the empire and barbarism without. There was never a time when the Gorn lived in multiple states roughly equal in power; always there was the empire and the barbarians. Diplomacy was never a process of negotiation between equals, instead being limited to threats or toadying. Their expansion into space has done nothing to change that outlook. The Gorn worlds are the home of the only true civilization in the galaxy, and beyond their space are barbarians like Klingons, Romulans—and the Federation.

Over the centuries the Gorn have learned that the only effective way to deal with barbarians is with force. The Gorn response to incursions into their space is swift and brutal. Barbarians must be stopped before they can raid the homeworlds of civilization, and barbarian outposts within striking distance of Gorn planets must be obliterated. But barbarians who seem willing to accept the superior Gorn civilization can be peacefully integrated into the empire.

Though referred to as an empire, the government of the Gorn could better be described as a "parliamentary theocracy." The head of state is the hereditary Divine Ruler, or Effri'a, descended in unbroken female lineage from the rulers of the first Neolithic city-states. The Effri'a never steps upon bare ground, never touches anything which has not been ritually purified, and is never seen by anyone who has not been initiated into the priesthood.

The actual day-to-day government is in the hands of a parliament, the Agarna, which includes the heads of government bureaus, flag-rank military officers, chief priests, close relatives of the Effri'a, and a few elected members. Terms of office vary—priests, bureaucrats, and military officers serve as long as they are in active service; relatives of the ruler and elected members serve for life. Gorn have an almost fanatical devotion to preserving stability and continuity. The parliament's job is to cope with problems, not to come up with innovations.

KELVANS

Homeworld

The Kelvans are native to the planet Kelva, a world in the Andromeda galaxy, more than two million light years away. It is thought to be a huge Class J gas giant planet with a dense atmosphere.

Home Region or Sovereign Territory

The Kelvan Empire controls a significant fraction of the Andromeda galaxy. If there are other sentient races within Kelvan space they have been either enslaved or eradicated. However, as radiation levels within the Andromeda galaxy increase, the Kelvans may have to abandon their worlds to seek new homes elsewhere.

Suggested Attribute and Edge Ranges

Fitness 3 [6]
Coordination 2 [4]
Intellect 4 [6]
Presence 3 [6]
Psi 3 [6]

Note: These attributes are for Kelvans in their natural form; those who have taken on Human bodies have attributes in the Human range.

Special or Unique Abilities

Kelvans are large, powerful beings and are extremely intelligent but have no special abilities usable in Human form. Their technology is quite advanced.

Special or Unique Skills

Kelvans in their natural form have several skills appropriate for life on a gas giant world, such as Survival (Class J World), and various athletic abilities suitable for floating beings.

Size

An adult Kelvan is enormous, with a flattened balloon-like body ten meters in diameter. Mass is relatively low—only ten or twenty tons!

Traits Common to the Species

Kelvans have a large saucer-shaped body and hundreds of long tentacles. They have no tactile perceptions and emotions as Humans know them.

Story Notes

The Kelvans are a menace to the entire Milky Way galaxy. They are more powerful than the Federation, the Klingons, the Romulans, and the Gorn *combined*! Fortunately, it takes centuries to cross the immense gulfs between the two galaxies, but even a reconnaissance in force by the Kelvans would be a serious threat. Narrators who want to see Starfleet fighting alongside Klingons and Romulans against a common foe can use the Kelvans.

The small party of Kelvans in Human form who have settled in our own galaxy might attempt a little private empire-building. Armed with advanced Kelvan technology, they could certainly carve out a domain of their own. A more ominous possibility might be a deal between the Kelvans and one of the Federation's rivals to conquer the galaxy—just in time to hand it over to the main Kelvan armada.

Description

The first Kelvan expedition to the Milky Way galaxy ran into the energy barrier and was severely damaged. The surviving Kelvan explorers used a life-entity transfer device to take Human form. They attempted to hijack a Federation starship for the long journey back to Andromeda, but in the end were persuaded to abandon the project and settle in our galaxy.

Kelvan technology is impressive. Aside from the achievement of making the intergalactic journey, they have weapons capable of reducing humanoid beings to small crystalline polyhedra. They can create alloys far denser than any known metallurgical theory allows. They also have advanced psionic devices, including the mind-transfer device. Kelvan scouts, at least, are adept at using and improving inferior local technology.

The Kelvan Empire itself is a mighty state; little is known of its society and government. Given that the Kelvan explorers were unfamiliar with any Human emotions like love or anger, presumably Kelvan civilization is very rational and efficient. The casual cruelty displayed by the explorers does not imply a very nice society—unless humanoids are less than insects to the Kelvans.

The Kelvan Empire is threatened by rising radiation levels within the Andromeda galaxy (possibly caused by a runaway chain reaction of supernovas in its galactic core). In about ten thousand years the Kelvans will have to go *somewhere*, and the Milky Way is the closest large galaxy to their own.

KLINGONS

Homeworld

The Klingon homeworld Qo'noS has not been visited by UFP personnel since the disastrous *Ranger* incident of 2218. From remarks made by Klingons, it is poor in resources and can no longer support the Klingon people. The *Ranger* reported the scars of intense surface wars and at least one inhabited moon, Praxis.

Home Region or Sovereign Territory

The Klingons control a sizeable empire, slightly smaller than that of the Federation but more intensively developed and militarized. The Klingon Empire incorporates several worlds with native intelligent species enslaved by the Klingons.

Suggested Attribute and Edge Ranges

Fitness 3 [6]
   Vitality +2
Coordination 3 [5]
Intellect 2 [5]
Presence 2 [6]
   Empathy –2
Psi 0 [3]

Special or Unique Abilities

Klingons are strong and tough, with redundant organs and a rib cage that almost approaches armor, but have no unusual abilities. No Klingons with psionic abilities have yet been encountered.

Special or Unique Skills

Klingons of all ranks receive combat training (including Primitive Weaponry), and officers are schooled extensively in Behavior Modification, Espionage, and Intimidation. Within the heavily monitored society of the Empire, Bureaucratic Manipulation and Forgery are extremely useful.

Size

Klingons are about the same size as Humans or Vulcans—1.5 to 2 meters in height, 50 to 100 kilograms in mass. Most of the Klingons encountered by Starfleet have been on the large side, but presumably their military personnel have to meet certain physical standards. It has been suggested that the Klingons eliminate weaklings with ruthless efficiency.

Traits Common to the Species

Klingons exhibit a wide range of skin and hair tones, slightly darker than Human averages. Facial hair appears to be the rule for Klingon men. Bushy,

A CENTURY OF PROGRESS

Players more familiar with the Klingon Empire in the period of *Star Trek: The Next Generation* may be confused by the description of Klingon culture and society above. It is worth remembering that cultures change in time. Consider the immense changes in Japanese society on ancient Earth between 1860 and 1960–from a xenophobic medieval culture, to a fast-growing military dictatorship, to a beaten and conquered country, to a reborn economic powerhouse. A century is plenty of time for the Klingons to go from a quasifeudal system to a totalitarian state and back again. The hypermilitarism and enforced subordination to authority of the 2260's might be a reaction to the constant civil wars and power struggles of the traditional system of government.

pointed eyebrows are common on both sexes. A medical examination or tricorder scan can quickly spot physiological differences, but externally Klingons can pass for Human.

Story Notes

The Klingons are, of course, the main "bad guys" in the *Star Trek* universe. As the chief astropolitical rivals of the Federation they can turn up almost anywhere. The Organian truce prevents the Klingons and the Federation from going to war directly, but that doesn't mean they can't oppose each other whenever possible. Klingon agents and advisers can turn up on almost any neutral or unexplored planet between the Klingon Empire and Federation space. For an occasional change of pace, the Narrator might want to have Federation personnel and Klingons compelled to join forces.

Description

The Klingon Empire in 2269 is a highly militaristic state controlled by a tyrannical regime. The Internal Security police monitor all levels of society for signs of dissent, and the interests of the state take precedence over all individual rights. Officers maintain discipline through fear, and routinely carry "agonizers" to mete out punishments on the spot to underlings. The penalty

for treason is death. Young Klingons are brought up surrounded by official propaganda, and even history is regularly rewritten to suit the ends of the Klingon leaders.

According to individual Klingons, their worlds are poor in resources, forcing them to expand in order to survive. The Empire is aggressively expansionist, and the Klingons have conquered and enslaved several other races. Klingon governors maintain their rule through terror, killing thousands of hostages at the first sign of resistance. Enslaved planets must export vital minerals and goods to the Klingon homeworlds, and serve as bases for Klingon fleets. Though the Empire's mighty fleets are the chief instrument of expansion, the notorious Klingon Diplomatic Corps is quite adept at subverting planetary governments and gaining control of worlds via brainwashing, propaganda, and treachery.

The Empire appears to be a governed by a junta of military commanders and Internal Security chiefs under a Chancellor. Federation specialists sift Klingon subspace traffic for clues to the Klingon government's specific composition and intentions. If Terran history is any guide, probably very few Klingon rulers die of natural causes.

SAMPLE KLINGON CAPTAIN: KHENG

This Klingon officer might be found in command of a battlecruiser or a planetary garrison. Like all leaders in the Empire he balances absolute loyalty with a healthy dose of personal ambition.

ATTRIBUTES

Fitness 3
    Vitality +2
Coordination 3
Intellect 3
Presence 3
    Empathy –2
    Willpower +2
Psi 0

SKILLS

Administration (Bureaucratic Manipulation) 3 (4)
Behavior Modification (Brainwashing) 2 (3)
Command (Starship Command) 4 (5)
Computer (Data Alteration/Hacking) 1 (2)
Culture (Klingon) 2 (3)
Dodge 3
Energy Weapon (Disruptor) 3 (4)
Engineering, Systems (Weapons) 2 (3)
Espionage (Counterintelligence) 2 (3)
History (Klingon) 1 (2)
Intimidation (Bluster) 3 (4)
Languages
    Federation Standard 2
    Klingon 3
Personal Equipment (Agonizer) 1 (2)

Planetary Tactics (Small Unit) 2 (3)
Planetside Survival (Desert) 1 (2)
Primitive Weaponry (D'k Tagh) 2 (3)
Security (Security Systems) 2 (3)
Shipboard Systems (Tactical) 2 (3)
Social Sciences (Political Science) 2 (3)
Space Sciences (Astrogation) 2 (3)
Starship Tactics (Klingon) 3 (4)
Strategic Operations (Neutral Zone) 2 (3)
Unarmed Combat (Mok'bara) 2 (3)
Vehicle Operation (Shuttlecraft) 2 (3)
World Knowledge (Qo'noS) 2(3)

TRAITS
Department Head, High Pain Threshold, Promotion (Captain), Toughness; Intolerance (Non-Klingons)

RENOWN:
  Aggression 20, Discipline 20, Initiative 10, Openness –10, Skill 10
RESISTANCE: 6
WOUND LEVELS: 6/6/6/6/6/6/0

KLINGON SOLDIER

This Klingon crewman could be encountered as an enemy in a firefight, as a guard at a Klingon base, or in a bar in neutral territory. He is brave, obeys orders, and fights dirty.

ATTRIBUTES
Fitness 6
  Strength +2
  Vitality +2
Coordination 4
Intellect 2
Presence 2
  Empathy –2
Psi 0

SKILLS
Athletics (Climbing) 2 (3)
Computer (Research) 1 (2)
Culture (Klingon) 1 (2)
Demolitions (Land Mines) 2 (3)
Dodge 3
Energy Weapon (Disruptor) 3 (4)
Heavy Weapons (Plasma Mortar) 2 (3)
History (Klingon Empire) 1 (2)
Intimidation (Bluster) 1 (2)
Languages
  Klingon 3
Personal Equipment (Communicator) 2 (3)
Planetary Tactics (Small Unit) 1 (2)
Planetside Survival (Desert) 1 (2)
Primitive Weaponry (D'k Tagh) 2 (3)

Search 2
Shipboard Systems (Weapons) 2 (3)
Stealth (Hide) 2 (3)
Unarmed Combat (Mok'bara) 3 (4)
Vehicle Operation (Ground Vehicles) 1(2)
World Knowledge (Qo'noS) 1(2)
TRAITS
High Pain Threshold, Toughness

RENOWN: NONE
RESISTANCE: 9
WOUNDS LEVELS: 9/9/9/9/9/9/0

KLINGON DEVICES

Agonizer: This device is used to enforce discipline and to punish infractions. Agonizers are the ultimate in torture devices, delivering direct neural stimulation of the pain centers while causing no physical harm. In addition, special circuits in the agonizer send out signals to block the brain's release of endorphins. In short, this device causes extreme pain and defeats the body's attempt to alleviate this pain. While this device can theoretically be used for hours or even days, prolonged use can cause permanent insanity or even death as the subject's mind and body both struggle to escape the pain.

  Size: 10 cm x 8 cm x 2 cm
  Mass: 0.2 kg
  Duration: 50 hours

Klingon Mindripper: Using a variant of Federation mindscanning technology, this device is commonly used for interrogating prisoners. This device can be set either to record memories like a psychotricorder, or simply to compel the subject to answer any question. Unlike the Federation psychotricorder, this device can also extract memories from resisting subjects. Unfortunately, while harmless, if unpleasant, when used on a cooperative subject, sufficient mental resistance can produce massive brain damage or even death. Because determined individuals like Starfleet officers can resist the device until it kills them, skilled Klingon interrogators generally combine short sessions in the mindripper with threats and physical discomfort to attempt to break the subject's will. As soon as the subject has given up hope or been otherwise broken the mindripper can easily pry accurate information out of his brain.

Vulcans and others who have received special mental training can resist the effects of this device by actually concealing their memories. However, doing so is difficult (make a Mind Shield roll with a Difficulty of at least 10). Success allows the subject both to conceal the information and to avoid brain damage. However, any method of resisting this device is extremely painful.

  Size: 1 cubic meter. The device resembles a large chair with a moveable headset in addition to a separate control console.
  Mass: 1.5 tons (including the control console)
  Duration: This device must be connected to an external power supply.

ORIONS

Homeworld

The Orions claim the Class M world Rigel VII (known generally as "Orion") as their planet of origin, but Federation planetologists insist the world is too young for advanced life to have evolved there. It is possible that Rigel VII was settled long ago by beings from some other world. Rigel VII has a purple sky and a huge moon, a Class F world in its own right.

Home Region or Sovereign Territory

As their name suggests, the Orions live on a number of worlds scattered throughout the constellation Orion, particularly in the vicinity of the mineral-rich Orion Nebula. Major population centers include Rigel VII, Saiph II, and Betelgeuse XIII, although Orions can be found all across the Federation's rimward frontier sectors. They do not have any governments above the plane-tary level, and claim no sovereign space.

Suggested Attribute and Edge Ranges

Fitness 2 [6]
  Strength +1
Coordination 2 [5]
Intellect 2 [5]
  Perception +1
Presence 2 [5]
Psi 0 [6]

Special or Unique Abilities

Orion women have a reputation for being irresistibly alluring. While some of this may be marketing hype promoted by Orion slave dealers, it is true that a great many female Orions have the *Sexy* advantage. Nearly all Orions of either sex are *Shrewd*.

Special or Unique Skills

Orions seem to have a natural bent for conspiracies and intrigue. Streetwise skill is almost universal among Orions. Orion women, particularly those trained as slaves, often have the Seduction specialization of Charm.

Size

Orions are approximately Human-sized, though they tend to be tall and slender. Average height is 1.8 to 2 meters; average mass is 75 to 80 kilograms.

Traits Common to the Species

Orions have green skin ranging from emerald to deep olive-bronze, caused by a combination of copper-based blood and the presence of chloro-phyll in skin cells. The green pigment absorbs the harmful high ultraviolet radiation put out by their home star Rigel. Hair is black or brown, though Orions of both sexes are fond of dyeing or oiling it unusual colors, and styling it accordingly.

Story Notes

The piratical Orions and the cheerfully decadent criminal civilization that thrives at Rigel and Betelgeuse are equally good for swashbuckling adventure stories and tales of devious intrigue. Males of many species seem unable to resist the alluring Orion women, making them ideal agents of influence. Because the Rigel system is neutral, Orions can often be found working as spies for the Klingons and other foes of the Federation. If the price is right, of course, many Orions will happily spy for the Federation. Some Orions, no doubt, collect hefty fees to spy on both.

One might wonder if the Orions are really as decadent and unambitious as they claim. Consider: Orion trading ships go everywhere, Orion "pirates" are somehow able to get armed starships and keep them running, and Orion "slave" women are in the very bedchambers of some alien leaders. Perhaps the Orions have managed to conquer the galaxy without anyone noticing!

Description

Orions were among the first starfarers in this part of the galaxy, and built an extensive empire centered on the Rigel star system. Some artifacts from the old days are still beyond the understanding of Federation science. Their empire has collapsed and been rebuilt dozens of times over the centuries, and today the Orions appear content to leave the conquest of the galaxy to others.

The Orions do maintain a very active trading network, the Orion Syndicate, extending far beyond the limits of their settlements, and even beyond the limits of space explored by the Federation. Orion ships carry any-thing if the price is right. Smuggling isn't a crime to Orions—indeed, most Orions think the whole idea of banning certain products almost incomprehen-sible. "But people are willing to *pay* for it!" they wail. Some merchants supplement their trading revenues by raiding ships of other races. There's a Starfleet joke that sums it up best: "How do you tell an Orion merchant ship from an Orion pirate ship? If you have phasers, then it's a merchant ship."

One reason for the prevalence of piracy among the Orions is that the great merchant houses often employ mercenaries and privateers in their wars with one another for control of markets and trade routes. When the war ends, the mercenaries turn pirate until the next trade dispute. The rugged Orion ships can survive on plundered spare parts and dilithium for years.

Government on the various Orion planets is a hodgepodge of monarchies, oligarchies, a few republics, and one or two societies that seem completely anarchic to Federation sociologists. On starfaring worlds, the great Orion merchant clans dominate politics; some clans rule entire primitive planets, ruthlessly exploiting the natives.

Their long history has made the Orions cynical and materialistic as a people. They have abandoned dreams of glory or hopes of Utopia, and instead every Orion looks out for himself. To an Orion the most important things in life are gaining wealth and then enjoying it. Some call it decadence or cynicism, but the Orions simply call it being practical.

ROMULANS

Homeworld

The Romulan homeworlds are known as Romulus and Remus, two Class M planets in the same star system. The Romulans trace their descent to ancient emigrants from Vulcan.

Home Region or Sovereign Territory

The Romulans control an empire of unknown extent on the edge of Federation space. A neutral zone established by treaty in 2160 separates the Romulan Star Empire from the Federation. Military craft of either side are forbidden to enter the Zone, but it is supposedly open to peaceful traffic. However, the Romulans take the position that any vessel in the Zone could be a disguised military ship, and react accordingly.

Suggested Attribute and Edge Ranges

Fitness 2 [6]
    Strength +1
Coordination 2 [5]
Intellect 2 [5]
    Perception +1
Presence 2 [5]
    Empathy –1
Psi 0 [6]

Size

Romulans are about the same size as Humans or Vulcans.

Traits Common to the Species

Romulans are physically very similar to Vulcans, with pointed ears, arched eyebrows, and a greenish-yellow complexion.

Story Notes

The Romulans are honorable and subtle villains, capable of respect for a worthy adversary even as they remain fanatically devoted to the Empire. They are good for tense episodes of brinkmanship along the Neutral Zone, as well as espionage and covert operations. Note that while the Klingons concentrate on subverting or conquering neutral worlds, the Romulans aim at achieving military supremacy over the Federation.

Description

The Romulans are almost certainly related to the Vulcans, but where the Vulcans have developed a society based on logic and the strict repression of emotions, the Romulans remain more passionate and emotional. Like Vulcans, they are extremely intelligent and very long-lived. Psionic abilities among Romulans seem rare.

Because the first face-to-face contact with the Romulans only occurred in 2267, much about their society is still a mystery. It is thought that their Empire has a republican form of government, though senators are not directly elected by the citizens. The militaristic nature of their society suggests that the Romulan armed forces operate without much oversight by the civilian government, or at least with great leeway.

Sightings of Klingon ships with Romulan markings in 2268 indicate that the Federation's two rivals have formed an alliance. The combination of Klingon weapons and warp drives with Romulan cloaking technology could be a potent threat.

CENTURION HARLEK

This is a Romulan officer, likely to be in command of a starship or even a small squadron. The equivalent Starfleet rank is captain or commodore.

ATTRIBUTES
Fitness 4
    Strength +1
Coordination 4
    Reaction +1
Intellect 5
    Perception +1
Presence 4
    Empathy –1
    Willpower +1
Psi 0

SKILLS

Administration (Logistics) 2 (3)

Command (Combat Leadership) 3 (5)
  (Starship Command) (4)

Computer (Programming) 1 (3)
  (Research) (2)

Culture (Romulan) 2 (4)

Dodge 2

Energy Weapon (Disruptor) 2 (4)

Engineering, Systems (Cloaking Device) 2 (3)

Espionage (Traffic Analysis) 1 (2)

Gaming (Romulan chess) 2 (3)

History (Romulan Empire) 1 (3)

Language
  Romulan 2

Law (Romulan Law) 2 (4)
  (Romulan Military Regulations) (3)

Personal Equipment (Communicator) 1 (2)

Planetside Survival (Arctic) 1 (2)

Primitive Weaponry (Sword) 1 (2)

Shipboard Systems (Cloaking Device) 3 (4)

Starship Tactics (Romulan) 3 (5)

Stealth (Stealthy Movement) 2 (3)

Strategic Operations (Neutral Zone) 2 (3)

Unarmed Combat (*Tenalri*) 2 (3)

Vehicle Operation (Atmospheric Craft) 1 (2)

World Knowledge (Romulus) 2 (4)

TRAITS

Department Head, Promotion (Centurion), Resolute; Arrogant, Code of Honor (Romulan, –3)

RENOWN: 5

  Initiative 10, Aggression 20, Skill 10, Discipline 20, Openness 0

RESISTANCE: 4

WOUND LEVELS: 4/4/4/4/4/4/0

THOLIANS

Homeworld

Little is known about the Tholian homeworld except that it must have a very hostile environment; presumably Class K. The Tholians actively discourage attempts to learn more about their world. By analysis of subspace message traffic, Starfleet has theorized which star Tholia circles, but no Federation vessel has visited the system.

Home Region or Sovereign Territory

The Tholians control a region of space beyond the area explored by Starfleet. It is not known exactly how big the Tholian dominions are, because they tend to claim large and seemingly unrelated volumes of space as "territorial annexes" of the Tholian Assembly.

Suggested Attribute and Edge Ranges

  Fitness 1 [5]
  Coordination 3 [5]
    Reaction +1
  Intellect 2 [5]
  Presence 2 [5]
    Empathy –1
  Psi 0 [5]

Special or Unique Abilities

Tholians live faster than beings from colder worlds. To them, water-based beings move with agonizing slowness. All Tholians have the advantages of Multitasking, Quick Draw, and Sense of Time.

Because of their extremely alien physiology and perceptions, they also have Telepathic Resistance. However, Tholians do not heal well—they suffer from the Weakness disadvantage, and a break in a Tholian's carapace can be fatal in minutes if not patched.

THE THOLIAN ENIGMA

The rules and descriptions in this section represent a Starfleet Intelligence "best guess" based on subspace intercepts, salvaged Tholian wreckage, and sketchy reports from other starfaring civilizations. Much of the data are fragmentary and contradictory; some xenologists believe that there are multiple forms or phases of the Tholian life cycle with vastly different traits. Other specialists theorize that the "Tholian Assembly," like the Federation, is multiracial in nature. Narrators are free to use this information as written, to assume the Federation assumptions and theories are grossly incorrect, or anything in between.

Size

Tholians are smaller than Humans, with an average height of 1.5 meters. They are very massive, however, as their tissues are composed of much denser material than the body of a water-chemistry being. A typical Tholian has a mass of nearly 200 kilograms.

Traits Common to the Species

Tholians appear very bizarre to most humanoids. They have faceted heads with two glowing eyes, small angular bodies, and six spindly-looking limbs. Like Terran insects, Tholians have outer carapaces, which appear to be made of a semiopaque crystalline material. Hot molten circulatory fluid can be seen swirling about inside the carapace.

Story Notes

The mysterious and xenophobic Tholians don't make trouble much, so any episode involving them is likely to require a Federation starship to venture into their territory. Trying to conduct a rescue mission or solve a scientific puzzle can always be more interesting if there is a Tholian-imposed time limit. They could also be a good species for a diplomatic mission. Their peculiar chemistry and mentality means the Tholians are best used when you want a really *alien* alien.

Description

Tholians are silicon-based lifeforms and require temperatures of 300° Centigrade to survive. They inhabit Class K worlds and regard any planet with liquid water as too cold to be habitable. Their preferred gravity is about 75 percent of Earth standard. Tholians breathe a mixture of methane, chlorine, and carbon dioxide; oxygen is harmful to them. They lay eggs and have two sexes. The average lifespan of a Tholian is only forty standard years.

The Tholians have an advanced civilization with starships and antimatter power. They are especially advanced in the field of tractor beams and tractor fields, preferring to use weapons based on that technology rather than energy beams. Tholians also possess a concern for precision that has given them a reputation for punctuality even among races who have never seen a Tholian ship. Despite this, Tholians operate comfortably in chaotic regions of multidimensional space that drive other species insane.

Tholian society seems to be organized as a kind of universal participatory democracy—the Tholian Assembly is an assembly of every Tholian old enough to talk. Because several billion beings can't thrash out every issue, impromptu "subassemblies" handle most matters. A subassembly ranges from a handful to a million individuals chosen on the basis of their qualifications, and has absolute authority in its area of responsibility.

OTHER RACES

ANTOSIANS

Homeworld

The Antosians were native to Antos IV, but since the devastating attack on their planet by the insane Garth of Izar the remaining Antosians have gone into hiding.

Home Region or Sovereign Territory

Antos IV was not a Federation member world before Garth's attack, but it was within Federation space. Antosians seldom left their home planet before the disaster.

Suggested Attribute and Edge Ranges

Fitness 2 [5]
Coordination 2 [5]
Intellect 2 [5]
    Perception –1
Presence 1 [4]
    Empathy +1
Psi 1 [6]

Special or Unique Abilities

Antosians have perfected the art of cellular metamorphosis. It is a psionic-based ability, which allows individuals to control and manipulate the fabric of their own bodies.

Special or Unique Skills

Antosians are the only race known to have the Cellular Metamorphosis skill. Since cellular metamorphosis is a psionic power, members of other races with psionic talent can learn the skill, as well—although, following Garth's attack, they are *very* unlikely to share their powers with outsiders again.

Untrained use of Cellular Metamorphosis is possible—and always fatal. Regenerating minor injuries is a Routine Cellular Metamorphosis task; repairing major damage is a Challenging one. With a Difficult task roll an Antosian can imitate other humanoid beings of about the same size. A Difficult roll also permits the Antosian to increase or reduce edges of the Fitness and Coordination attributes by 1. A Nearly Impossible roll permits imitation of nonhumanoid beings, or the change of physical edges by 2, but in all cases the individual's mass remains the same. Repairs to injury are permanent, but copying other beings or altering edges wears off when the individual is asleep or unconscious.

Size

In their natural shape, Antosians are average-sized humanoids, about 1.75 meters tall and massing roughly 70 kilograms.

Traits Common to the Species

Ordinary Antosians are slender humanoids with golden skin and all-black eyes. Using their powers they can have whatever temporary features they wish.

Story Notes

Antosians can play two parts in a *Star Trek* series. As victims of a mad starship captain's wrath, they can be pitiful survivors struggling to rebuild their civilization. Or, they could be out for revenge, using their shape-shifting powers to undermine specific elements of the Federation—and especially Starfleet—from within.

Description

The Antosians were a peaceful and gentle race, devoted to study of the mind and the perfection of the body. Though they had not developed space travel, their medical arts were more advanced than the Federation's. Highly empathic themselves, the Antosians had created a very humane and civilized culture without war, crime, or insanity.

When the legendary Fleet Captain Garth of Izar was critically injured while the *U.S.S. Constitution* was protecting Antos IV from an approaching comet, the Antosians showed their gratitude by nursing Garth back to health. His injuries were so severe the Antosians had to teach him cellular metamorphosis to keep him alive.

Unfortunately for the Antosians, the stress of the incident had driven Garth insane. Blaming the Antosians for his accident, Garth gave his crew a General Order 24 command—destroy the planet. Millions died before the crew realized their captain was insane and Chief Medical Officer Xing could take command of the *Constitution* and place Captain Garth under medical confinement.

In the wake of the disaster the Antosians have refused all assistance, and starships calling at the planet get no response to hails. Sensor sweeps reveal no attempt at rebuilding; to outside observers, Antos IV looks like an abandoned world. Did the Antosians die out? Or are they merely hiding? Nobody knows for sure.

HORTA

Homeworld

Horta are native to the planet Janus VI, a barren and inhospitable Class K planet rich in radioactive ores.

Home Region or Sovereign Territory

The Horta are not a starfaring species, but the Federation has recognized their sovereignty over their home planet.

Suggested Attribute and Edge Ranges

Fitness 3 [6]
Coordination 1 [2]
   Dexterity −1
   Reaction +2
Intellect 2 [5]
Presence 2 [5]
Psi 0 [6]

Special or Unique Abilities

Horta have several special powers derived from their underground existence. They can tunnel through rock at phenomenal speeds—up to a kilometer per hour—using a corrosive acid they extrude. This acid can also be a deadly weapon when used against Humans or other carbon-based life, doing 20 points of damage per hit.

Horta themselves are resistant to the acid, and to most forms of energy and radioactivity as well. They have a Resistance of 20, making them immune to damage from Phaser-1 attacks. They see in the X-ray spectrum rather than in visible light, and are very sensitive to vibrations.

Special or Unique Skills

Horta all learn the skill Survival (Planetary Crust), which allows them to locate edible mineral deposits and avoid dangerous fault zones.

Size

A full-grown Horta is about a meter across by two meters long, and has a mass of about two tons.

Traits Common to the Species

An adult Horta looks like nothing so much as a mobile mound of rock covered with veins. Horta have no limbs.

Story Notes

Originally the Horta was used as a "monster" in a puzzle episode. Now that they have been recognized as an intelligent species, they have a lot to learn about galactic society. Horta can be good "innocents abroad," especially since in 2269 all the Horta except one are juveniles. The naïveté of the race might also make them vulnerable to Klingon blandishments, and Orion slavers might take an interest in a race of natural-born mining machines.

Description

The silicon-based Horta extract energy from radioactive minerals. Their cells are essentially miniature nuclear reactors (which means that any planet with a radioactive waste problem can profitably sell junk food to the Horta). Horta body composition resembles cement or concrete, with crystalline or metalloid "organs" serving specialized metabolic functions and connected by a thin tracery of manganese, which helps the Horta distribute and dissipate excess heat or other energy.

Horta live extremely long lives, and have a complex reproductive system. Every fifty thousand years all the Horta but one die off, leaving millions of eggs to incubate in radioactive deposits. The one survivor remains until the next generation has matured. This "generational bottleneck" has handicapped the Horta by limiting the transmission of their civilization from generation to generation.

At present there is only one adult Horta, and several thousand rapidly growing juveniles. First contact resulted in the deaths of several humans when miners on Janus VI destroyed a number of Horta eggs without recognizing what they were. A Starfleet crew discovered the Horta's true nature and established friendly relations in 2267.

KAYLAR

Homeworld

The Kaylar are most likely native to Rigel V, although their actual heritage is uncertain. They may, in fact, be a genetically engineered subrace of the Orions.

Home Region or Sovereign Territory

Unlike their neighbors the Orions, the Kaylar never built an empire. A few Kaylar mercenary bands in service to Orion trade lords can be found on other planets, and Kaylar slaves labor on the mining planetoids of the Orion Nebula, but otherwise they are limited in scope. Kaylar do not claim any region of space.

Suggested Attribute and Edge Ranges

Fitness 3 [6]
   Vitality +1
Coordination 2 [5]
Intellect 2 [5]
   Logic −1
Presence 1 [5]
Psi 0 [6]

Special or Unique Abilities

Kaylar vary widely. Members of the primitive warrior clans sometimes have fangs and the *Toughness* advantage.

Size

Most Kaylar are big and strong, averaging over two meters in height and a hundred kilograms in mass. This may be a result of the harsh life they live, for Kaylar found in more civilized surroundings fall slightly closer to Human norms.

Traits Common to the Species

Kaylar are pale-skinned beings, often with abundant facial hair. Some male Kaylar have prominent fanglike canine teeth (others do not—which may be the result of cosmetic dental work).

Story Notes

Kaylar turn up most often as "goons" working for other races, most commonly the Orions. Captain Pike of the *U.S.S. Enterprise* battled a band of Kaylar warriors guarding an Orion smuggler's fortress on Rigel VII during his time there in 2254. What territory they retain on Rigel V is still at a primitive level of civilization, as are the Kaylar regions elsewhere in the Rigel system, and the Crew can have all kinds of adventures in this wilderness among the tribes and petty kingdoms.

They could also turn up as sympathetic characters—Kaylar slaves of Orion overlords might welcome Federation help in gaining their freedom. Kaylar haven't yet developed the world-weary cynicism of their Orion neighbors, and might still hope to join the Federation at some distant time in the future.

Kaylar in some ways resemble the traditional "Viking" stereotype: They are fierce in battle, embarrassingly affectionate to friends, and love nothing better than a drinking bout and a brawl. Use them as "lovable lugs" to show the flip side of their fierce warrior role.

Description

The Kaylar are more superficially "primitive"-looking than their neighbors the Orions. Hairy and toothy, they look like ogres from a fairy tale. Their civilization is fragmented and warlike, and many Kaylar still believe in gaining glory through combat. Kaylar are capable of great loyalty (something the

Orions have never hesitated to exploit), serving a leader even to the point of dying for him. Friendships last for life. Within their extended families they are very affectionate. Any stranger accepted into a Kaylar community may be overwhelmed by their boisterous friendship.

Among the "wild" Kaylar of Rigel II, III, and V, no planetary authority has ever lasted longer than its founder. Their regions remain patchworks of petty states (the Orions may have had a hand in keeping their neighbors from building a powerful government), with economies based on farming and mining. Rigel IV has a more urban and advanced civilization, and the Kaylar there are more like humans in culture and outlook. Kaylar on Rigel VII are almost all slaves or mercenaries. The Kaylar have little in common with the Vulcanoid civilization on Rigel V.

MEDUSANS

Homeworld

The Medusan homeworld is the planet Medusa III, a world within the frontiers of Federation space but not yet a member. It is a very hostile Class K planet with a toxic atmosphere and an unusually powerful planetary magnetic field.

Home Region or Sovereign Territory

The Medusans do not claim any territory beyond their home system, but Medusan explorers have traveled very widely throughout the galaxy. There may be Medusan colonies on hostile planets far beyond the regions explored by Starfleet.

Suggested Attribute and Edge Ranges

Fitness 1 [2]
Coordination 2 [4]
Intellect 4 [6]
    Perception +1
Presence 2 [5]
Psi 1 [6]

Special or Unique Abilities

Medusans have senses most humanoid races do not. They can perceive subspace directly and "feel" the curvature of space. Unlike Humans, Medusans can navigate "by eye" while traveling in warp drive. Most Medusans have some level of psionic talent.

Since they are composed of energetic plasma, Medusans are immune to radiation and high temperatures, but a phaser blast can disrupt the delicate balance of energy fields that maintains the Medusan's life.

Special or Unique Skills

As nonmaterial beings, Medusans have skills in things Humans cannot even understand. Their advanced civilization means all Medusans can have high levels in scientific skills, and they all get psionic training.

Size

Being noncorporeal, Medusans do not have a fixed size. In their own ships and their home environment, Medusans normally occupy a spherical volume roughly a meter in radius.

Traits Common to the Species

The appearance of a Medusan is itself highly dangerous to humanoid beings. Because of their strange multidimensional nature, the sight of a Medusan can drive some species mad. When traveling among solid matter beings, they must remain inside a small containment vessel in order to maintain a comfortable environment—and to prevent Humans from having their minds destroyed.

Story Notes

Medusans are a good race to use when the Narrator wants some really alien beings who are nevertheless friendly and well intentioned. The contrast between the vast Medusan intellect and their mind-blasting appearance can be a good story hook. A Medusan traveling in a containment box can be a good "MacGuffin." An evil or insane Medusan might be a chilling villain.

Description

Medusans are noncorporeal beings; they are made up of superheated plasma and magnetic fields. They can manipulate solid matter by creating "limbs" of magnetic force. Medusans are comfortable in an environment about 500° Centigrade. They reproduce asexually, by fission, and both offspring retain all the memories of the parent.

Thus, Medusans can theoretically live forever, and all Medusans share their oldest memories. Because Medusans exist partially in subspace, they can perceive dimensional relationships humans cannot. Their appearance is highly disturbing—the non-Euclidean geometries of the Medusan form can lead a Human mind quickly into utter madness. The Human observer must make a Difficult test of Willpower for every turn spent watching an unshielded Medusan.

The Medusan civilization is a very old and advanced one. Though they developed material technology very late, Medusans had the basics of warp-drive theory and force-field technology centuries ago. Their engineering is all

based on manipulation of energy fields and warping space—a Medusan starship contains almost no solid matter at all.

Government among the Medusans is minimal—a race of telepaths with no material possessions doesn't need much governing. Decisions about interplanetary relations and contact with aliens fall to a council of scientists, experts in the study of solid organisms.

With their superhuman senses, vast intellects, and ancient civilization, Medusans take a rather patronizing attitude toward solid beings. They refer to Humans and Vulcans as "young races" and speak encouragingly about how much progress they have made toward civilization.

TALOSIANS

Home World

Talosians live on Talos IV, a formerly Class M world now declining to Class H after a devastating atomic war.

Home Region or Sovereign Territory

The Talosians have not ventured beyond their home star system and today never leave their underground city, but their minds are sufficiently powerful to monitor ships several light years away. The Talos system is interdicted under Starfleet General Order Number Seven.

Suggested Attribute and Edge Ranges

Fitness 1 [3]
Coordination 2 [5]
Intellect 3 [6]
Presence 3 [6]
   Empathy –2
Psi 3 [6]

Special or Unique Abilities

Talosians have incredibly advanced psionic powers. In particular they have developed the ability of psionic illusion, a form of projective telepathy which allows the psionic to fool the target's senses completely.

Special or Unique Skills

Talosians have the Psionic Illusion skill, used in the performance of their psionic ability. Sending an illusion requires only a Routine skill roll if the target is not suspicious and the illusion does not run counter to his expectations.

For more fantastic illusions, or against a target who is actively resisting, an Opposed Test is required, pitting the psionic's skill against the target's Willpower or Mind Shield.

Size

Talosians are small, slender humanoids, no more than 1.5 meters tall and 50 kilograms in weight.

Traits Common to the Species

All Talosians have enormous heads, and appear to lack a bony skull protecting their highly developed brains. Beneath their huge heads they are frail and wispy.

Story Notes

Talosians are powerful and enigmatic beings, but they don't have the godlike abilities of races like the Organians. Use them in situations where the player characters need a fighting chance to overcome their captors. As a dying race, the Talosians may someday swallow their pride and appeal to the Federation for help; such a mission would be wrapped in fear and mistrust on both sides. Finally, the complications of General Order Number Seven can cause problems if a starship gets a distress signal originating from Talos IV.

Description

The Talosians are the last remnant of a once-great civilization which destroyed itself through atomic war. Surviving in underground complexes, the Talosians sought refuge in complex illusions, and developed their minds as their bodies degenerated. Today they scarcely bother to notice the real world at all.

Talosians are aloof, and their cruelty seems almost unintentional. They do have some curiosity about the universe, driven mostly by a desire for new experiences to relieve their chronic boredom. Their powerful telepathic powers let them explore without leaving their homeworld.

Starfleet's General Order Number Seven absolutely prohibits any ship from entering the Talos system—on pain of death for the responsible officers. This seemingly draconian order has a sensible reason behind it: The Talosians' mastery of illusion is such that they could easily lure vessels with faked distress signals or even bogus orders from Starfleet itself. Only an absolute interdiction prevents this.

The order is intended to protect both the Federation and the Talosians. Because Talosian mental powers are so great, even one individual could wreak havoc in galactic society. There are also a great many treasure-hunters and curiosity-seekers who might be drawn to Talos IV by stories of a strange alien civilization there. To prevent the Talosians from taking steps to protect their privacy, Starfleet has taken on the job.

OMNIPOTENT SPECIES

In the *Star Trek: The Next Generation* era, the primary omnipotent races encountered by Starfleet are the entities calling themselves the Q. However, their Q continuum is only one possible infinity tangent to galactic space-time. Even in the 20th century, physicists postulated as many as 55 separate dimensions—more than enough to hold the Q, the Metrons, the Organians, the Thasians, Trelane's race, the Melkots, Apollo's Olympians, and many other infinite entities.

OMNIPOTENT BEINGS

Starfleet has encountered several civilizations far beyond the Federation in scientific knowledge and physical power. Most are Level Eight on the technology scale, or on the borderline between Seven and Eight. Some of the better known advanced races include the Organians, the Melkot, the Metrons, the Vians, and the immaterial race of which "Squire Trelane" is a juvenile member.

Homeworld

Omnipotent beings generally live on their planets of origin. Interestingly, few if any advanced species seem to have many colony planets. Either this is because their colonies have developed into separate civilizations and forgotten their origins, or because space exploration is just a "phase" that young cultures go through.

Home Region or Sovereign Territory

Most omnipotent races do not maintain extensive territorial claims. They seldom rule much beyond their homeworlds or home star systems. These races can be very protective of their space, and have the means to enforce their claims.

Suggested Attribute and Edge Ranges

Attributes are meaningless for most omnipotent beings. They accomplish whatever they wish to accomplish. Those still bound to humanoid form, like the Metrons or the Vians, have physical abilities in the Human range, but Intellect, Presence, and Psi of 6—at a bare minimum.

Special or Unique Abilities

Either through advanced technology, advanced psionics, or a combination of both, omnipotent beings can do almost anything they wish. They have been observed to create entire planets and toss starships halfway across the galaxy.

Story Notes

These are the beings to use when the Narrator needs a foe the characters can't beat physically and probably can't outwit, either. Fortunately, omnipotent beings seem to love to teach lesser races, usually by dropping a handful of individuals into some bizarre situation and then watching to see how they adapt.

While most advanced beings are priggishly moral, an evil or insane individual could be a great threat to all life in the galaxy. Overcoming a foe with literally godlike abilities should tax the ingenuity of even the most seasoned explorers.

Description

Omnipotent beings apparently embody (or disembody) the "next phase" of evolution after intelligence and tool-using. After a race has completely mastered the physical universe, it progresses to an immaterial state, possibly existing in higher dimensions or in forms of pure energy.

Duffy watched as his oldest friend backed up, the vormalith beside him. Another five or six steps back and Steve would be over the cliff. The vormalith rattled its razor-sharp fronds, encircling them protectively around Duffy's boyhood pal.

Duffy shouted again. He was already hoarse, but shout was all he could do. Eleb had already told them that vormaliths are smart enough to know when they're being threatened. One sudden move and the thing might take one of those blade-like leaves and snick Steve's head off.

"Steve! Steve! Move slowly away from it!"

Steve's eyes were red and glassy. "You're just jealous! You want to take her away from me, like you did Linda!"

"Steve, listen to me. That is not Mary Kent. That is not even a woman. It's a creature native to this planet. It—"

THE MENAGERIE

"No! I won't listen to you anymore. You never meant the best for me—never!"

Duffy flinched as Steve stepped back again.

The vormalith opened its feeding apparatus. Everyone could see that it was a six-foot tall carnivorous plant. Everyone but the victim of its hypnogogic poison.

Eleb leaned over and spoke into Duffy's ear. "I can draw faster than it can react, Captain."

Duffy shook his head. Too risky. If they were to chance a sudden move, that move would have to be Steve breaking away from the thing.

"Steve, you've got to listen. You've been dosed with a powerful toxin. You're hallucinating. That is not Mary Kent. Mary Kent is a figment of your imagination. That thing is not even sentient. It's—"

The vormalith grabbed Steve's hand. A loud crack of static electricity followed, and Steve and the plant creature were gone.

Duffy was stunned. "Eleb, you never said the things could do that."

The galaxy is a wild place. On any one planet, there are tens of thousands of animal species (or plants displaying animal behaviors, such as Sulu's pet plant Beauregard), any one of which might become lunch for a desperate Starfleet crewman—or vice versa. Creatures play many roles in *Star Trek* television episodes, and the same, naturally, follows for roleplaying episodes. This chapter introduces the Creature Template and rules for animals in play, and discusses how to design and use creatures in a story.

Using Animals in Star Trek Episodes

Starfleet personnel don't spend all their time sealed away in giant starships. Between spaceborne lifeforms and planetary ecologies, Federation crewmen actually run into animals more often than most city-dwellers on 20th-century Earth. They encounter creatures in a variety of roles.

Beasts of Burden

Animals are the oldest and most reliable form of transportation, and are still used on many worlds, such as Nimbus III. Starfleet characters may often find themselves using native animals to get around. Riding animals is a popular form of recreation; both Captains Pike and Kirk are devoted horsemen.

Food Animals

Although most starships rely on food synthesizers instead of a freezer full of beef, in most places animals remain an important source of food. On frontier worlds or in emergency situations, being able to catch dinner can make the difference between starvation and survival. Hunting has recreational and cultural importance to many races. And even the best food synthesizers can't mimic a roast turkey or a freshly steamed lobster.

Pets

Most humanoids enjoy the company of animals, so pets are fairly common in the *Star Trek* universe. Pets are generally fairly harmless creatures, although one cannot depend on this—consider the Vulcan *sehlat*, a frequent companion of small children even though it is armed with six-inch fangs. Tribbles are an interplanetary ecological menace because of their popularity as pets.

Symbols

Animals can have tremendous symbolic power. Many cultures—even starfaring ones—have sacred animals. These are generally important domestic animals (like cattle in Hindu religion) or the impressive local predators. It may be forbidden to harm or consume certain creatures; conversely it may be necessary to slay a sacred beast as part of a ritual. Often creatures with symbolic importance are very rare, and problems can arise when tradition conflicts with conservation.

Sometimes what appears to be only a symbolic custom can actually be important to a race's survival. Sometimes outsiders assign animals this value: The Denebian reputation for sneakiness and temperament makes comparisons to the Denebian slime devil almost inevitable.

Threats

Explorers on strange new worlds often have to protect themselves from hostile creatures, and even advanced weapons are sometimes no help, or unavailable. Animal threats can be divided further into two subcategories—predators and guardians. Predators like the mugato or the tiger are naturally dangerous animals, acting out of instinct. Often characters can learn enough about a predator's habits to evade it without a fight. Guardians, such as Klingon targs, are animals trained by intelligent beings to fight. They are much more aggressive than a wild predator would be, and may even know how to tackle an armed opponent.

These categories are not rigidly defined. It is quite possible for a creature to be both a pet and a guardian, or a symbol and a source of food, or all four at once.

In a story the characters all have motivations, and so do animals. A Narrator who wants to run a spooky episode about tracking a dangerous beast through an underground complex should consider what the animal is likely to want. Is it hungry? Looking for a place to lay eggs? Just trying to hide? Animals seldom have complicated motives—their behavior can be subtle and complex, but the root cause is usually either food or sex. (Note that this can be taken as a fairly accurate analysis of Human behavior, too.)

When designing a creature for a *Star Trek* episode, think about what part it is going to play in the story. The creature's role is likely to determine what abilities it needs to play that part effectively. The roles listed below are intended as suggestions, not a comprehensive list.

Local Color

While it may seem trivial, creatures are a useful way to give players the feeling that they really are exploring strange new worlds. If the landing party on a new planet encounters cowboys on horseback, the story may seem tired. Put the "cowboys" onto giant eight-legged reptiles herding enormous aphids, and it's new and exciting.

In a roleplaying game with no budget for make-up and special effects to worry about, creatures can be as exotic as the Narrator wishes, since their only purpose is to stand around looking alien. The horned canine of Alfa 177 is only one such example.

The MacGuffin

Alfred Hitchcock coined the term "MacGuffin" to mean the object everyone in a story is trying to get. Often the MacGuffin doesn't actually do anything except serve as motivation for the heroes and villains. A rare creature can be an excellent MacGuffin. A creature like the sand bat of Manark IV, which takes on a crystalline form at rest, might even be treasure in itself. Not only does the Crew have to worry about its sentient adversaries, but the animal may not want to be found.

It may also have a delicate metabolism or require special care—all of which is hard to provide while fleeing a band of Kaylar mercenaries. Symbolic creatures or beloved pets of important people are good MacGuffins to chase after. Again, choose features for the animal based on what will be best for the story.

Puzzles

Star Trek is a science fiction universe; Narrators can use a creature as the focus of a scientific puzzle that the Crew must unravel, or of more than one. The tribbles serve as keys to both the puzzle of their biology, and to the enigma of the sabotaged grain. One way to come up with an intriguing biological puzzle adventure is to see the section on designing creatures below (pages 216-221) and then come up with an organism which seems to violate the rules of ecology or physics. The players must then find a logical explanation.

> *On a newly settled world with very dry conditions, the crops are all being eaten by large swarms of insects that seem to appear virtually out of nowhere. The starship crew can investigate and find out that the insects lay tiny eggs in the soil which can remain dormant for centuries until the presence of even trace amounts of water makes them hatch—the colonists have unwittingly brought the insect plague upon themselves by irrigating their new crops!*

Monsters

Probably the most common use of animals in a *Star Trek Roleplaying Game* episode is as "monsters." Dangerous creatures can become the main opponents in an episode, or just "plug-in" encounters during the course of a larger story. In many cases a "monster" can be partly a puzzle; the focus of the story isn't on blowing away the dangerous creature but on figuring out how to avoid it, or learning what its weaknesses are, or what its motivation might be.

Although technically aliens, not creatures, the Horta and Redjac both played this kind of role, with widely divergent results. On a larger scale, so did the space amoeba of Gamma VIIA. Before the Crew can decipher a creature's motives, of course, the Narrator must decide them. This, the "why" lying behind the beast's behavior, is the most important thing to determine when creating a "monster" creature.

Red Herrings

Creatures can also be "red herrings"—distractions or diversions from the main plot. If the landing party is searching for a band of Klingon soldiers in dense woods, that rustling in the underbrush could be a disruptor-wielding soldier ready to attack—or just a mother eel-bird and her young. Alternatively, a creature could be blamed for what is actually the work of the villains; since animals cannot speak, there is no way for an accused creature to deny responsibility.

The Creature Template

We describe creatures in the *Star Trek Roleplaying Game* using a Creature Template similar to the format used to present the Crew and Supporting Cast. Of course, creatures—like characters—are more than just a set of attributes and characteristics.

NAME

Obviously this is what the creature is called; it can be either a species name, like "black bear" or "Berengarian dragon," or the creature's individual name. To the despair of Federation zoologists, Humans name creatures on many worlds after real and legendary Terran animals. Hence, the creature's planet of origin often turns up in its name.

TYPE AND CLASSIFICATION

This is a very general description of the creature's nature. Unless the organism has an unusual chemistry, it is assumed that all creatures are carbon-based lifeforms. Some sample classifications: "small pouncing carnivorous mammal" for a housecat, "large reptilian herbivore" for a diplodocus dinosaur, or "silicon-based mineral-eater" for a nonintelligent relative of the Horta.

SIZE

Specify the creature's mass in kilograms and its longest dimension in meters. For creatures with indeterminate shapes, try to give at least a rough idea of size.

FORM

This is the creature's basic body plan. While a trained scientist can spend pages and pages on a detailed description of animal anatomy, Narrators can get by with just listing the number of limbs, the presence of a tail, the number of heads, and so forth.

ATTRIBUTES

Creatures have five basic attributes, just like characters. The chief difference between creature attributes and character attributes is that creatures don't have an Intellect score, but instead use a characteristic called Instinct.

Fitness

Fitness measures a creature's strength and stamina. For most creatures Fitness won't be more than 3 or 4–Humans are actually rather exceptional in their stamina and endurance. Large animals do get enormous bonuses to their Strength Edge, as noted below (page 217).

Coordination

For creatures, the Coordination attribute generally measures body agility and speed, rather than fine manipulation. Only if a creature is described as having hands (or some equivalent) can a creature's Coordination be used for tinkering. Some creatures may have a low overall Coordination but very dexterous manipulators–the elephant is a good example, with its agile trunk.

Presence

A creature's Presence is usually based on its size, as noted in the Size Table, below (page 217). Most animals have a fairly low Presence.

Instinct

Instinct is the measure of a creature's cleverness. The difference between creatures and characters is the ability to reason abstractly, so if an organism is sentient, it's Supporting Cast. A creature's Instinct attribute measures how well it copes with new situations and learns from experience. Creatures with a low Instinct attribute tend to act in very predictable patterns, almost like machines. Smarter ones can adapt quickly to a strange situation. Animals with "preprogrammed" behavior patterns, like ants or dung beetles, have an Instinct of 0. Very clever creatures verging on sentience have an Instinct attribute of 5.

Psi

Most creatures have no psionic ability, and so have a Psi rating of 0. Psi powers are described in the section on *Anomalies*, below (page 220).

CREATURE EDGES

Just like characters, creatures can have normal edges in their Fitness, Coordination, Presence, and Psi. Creatures are often highly specialized, and so the possible range of edge modifiers is much greater than Human norms. A creature's Template description will list its possible edge ranges. The Instinct attribute has a unique edge: Ferocity replaces Logic in creatures, although Perception remains in place. The Willpower edge represents the creature's tenacity: How long will it pursue its prey or wait for a desired end?

MOVEMENT

This is the place to note a creature's movement speed, expressed in meters per round. If the animal has more than one mode of locomotion, list them separately. Derive appropriate movement rates from the Movement section in the *Action* chapter (page 110). In general, most animals can run about as fast as a good Human runner, though some (like the Terran cheetah) can go two or three times as fast. What is *very* rare is fast, sustained movement.

Most of the really fast runners can manage only bursts of speed; energy and endurance trade off. Flying creatures can move at high speeds for long periods because they spend a lot of time gliding.

RESISTANCE

An animal's Resistance is the sum of its Fitness and Vitality, just as with characters. Size provides an additional modifier, as shown in the Size Table. No creature can have a Resistance less than 1. Many creatures have some form of armor, as well. The armor's protection adds to the animal's Resistance. In combat, animal Resistance works in much the same way as for Human characters. Creatures have the same seven Wound levels that humans do and take the same penalties. A creature can make an Instinct check modified by Ferocity to ignore wound effects. Animals usually are willing to give up a fight as soon as they get hurt.

SPECIAL ABILITIES/UNUSUAL SKILLS

This is the place to list any abilities the animal has which humans usually don't. Many creatures have natural abilities, such as night vision, echolocation, superior sense of smell, or heat detection. More exotic beings may have psionic powers, energy-projection abilities, or unusual senses. Note that the ability to fly or burrow should be listed under Movement rather than Special Abilities.

WEAPONS

Humans are rare among living things in not having some form of natural weaponry. The full range of animal attacks is described in the section on designing creatures below. List a creature's attacks, along with the standard Difficulty Number. Note that clever creatures with good manipulating limbs may be able to use crude weapons like clubs or thrown rocks. Note the Difficulty level and damage for those weapons along with natural attacks.

DESCRIPTION AND ADDITIONAL NOTES

This is the place to give an overall description of the creature and note anything which may make it important to the story. Any habits or abilities of the organism not covered elsewhere go here.

DESIGNING REALISTIC CREATURES

If you're a Narrator designing an alien creature for a *Star Trek* adventure there are two things of equal importance to consider. The first is the role in the story the creature is to play; the second is the creature's scientific plausibility.

Story considerations have already been discussed. Now it's time to look at how to make your creatures convincing. Biology is a vast and complicated science; there's no way to boil it all down to a chapter. Fortunately one can devise some rules of thumb to help in designing creatures. The Narrator must make three decisions about his alien beast:

- *How big is it?*
- *Is it warm-blooded?*
- *What does it eat?*

Pretty much everything else about a creature can be determined on the basis of those three questions. After that it's just a matter of filling in the details. More scientific issues are covered further down. Note that this discussion is mostly concerned with animals on Class M worlds; more alien types of organisms are in the section on "Anomalies."

SIZE

Humans are among the largest living things. The vast majority of organisms are too small to see. Although heroic battles against protozoans can be very exciting (just ask the victims of the Psi 2000 virus), most creatures encountered by characters will probably be relatively large.

A creature's size determines much of its basic physical abilities. In general, creatures have the same attribute ranges as Human characters—1 to 5. Where size matters is in Strength and Presence.

For Strength, a creature's size provides an enormous edge to its basic Fitness. Fitness for creatures is generally about the same as for Humans, regardless of the creature's size. Most creatures have about the same degree of stamina and resistance to disease, usually 3 or 4. What size does give animals is an enormous Strength edge. The Creature Size Table shows just how much of an edge size can provide.

Presence is more a function of a creature's relative size than of its absolute mass; large creatures are imposing, especially to skittish smaller ones. The Creature Size Table shows the basic range for a creature's Presence attribute based on its size.

Coordination does vary with size, but in an odd way. Generally, small creatures are more agile and fast-moving than big ones, but large animals can outrun smaller ones. Rather than indulge in lots of game mechanics, simply assume that a large animal's Coordination refers to its running speed while a small animal's score reflects its superior agility. Very few animals have hands, so a creature's Coordination score should be considered 1 for any task involving fine manipulation.

METABOLISM

Living things are walking bundles of chemical reactions. These reactions slow down when it gets cold. There are two ways to handle that problem. Cold-blooded creatures ("ectotherms") ignore it, and just get sluggish when the temperature drops. Warm-blooded creatures ("endotherms") have an internal thermostat, and burn energy to stay warm. Each strategy has advantages and disadvantages. Cold-blooded creatures are vulnerable in chilly weather, which limits the range of habitats where they can survive. Note that large ectotherms are much more resistant to cold than small ones. Warm-blooded creatures can stay active no matter how cold it gets, giving them a big advantage. The drawback is that they must keep eating to fuel their roaring metabolic rate.

CREATURE SIZE

Size (kg)	Strength Edge	Presence Range	Resistance Mod
1 or less	–6	1	–6
5	–5	1	–5
10	–4	1	–4
25	–3	1–2	–2
50	–2	1–3	–1
70	–1	1–4	none
100	none	1–5	none
200	+2	2–5	+2
500	+6	3–6	+5
1000	+10	4–6	+10
5000	+40	5–7	+30
10,000	+60	6–7	+50

In game terms a cold-blooded creature's Coordination is likely to be low, and in cold weather its Coordination is halved. Cold-blooded creatures get a Vitality edge of 1 or 2 because they don't need to eat as often, and are generally more durable.

FEEDING STRATEGIES

How a creature feeds will affect nearly everything about it. For the purposes of the game, we can divide organisms into six categories, based on what and how they eat. These classifications are of course very much oversimplified, but they cover the main feeding strategies used by living things.

Filters

Filters are the couch potatoes of the animal kingdom. They let the food come to them. Obviously a filter needs to live in a rich environment—on Earth most of them live in the ocean, a veritable soup of nutrients. Oysters, sponges, and clams are all ocean filter creatures. There are a few filters that don't live in the sea, however. Spiders use their webs to sieve the air. Filters can't afford to be picky about what they eat, so most of them have digestive systems that can handle a wide range of foods.

Most filter feeders are fairly small, limited by the amount of food available. In a very rich environment they can get to respectable size—sponges in tropical waters can be Human-sized or bigger, and clams can get up to a meter across.

Since filters don't move around much, the main danger they pose is catching a character unaware. Many of them have defenses to ward off bigger creatures. Oysters and clams use impenetrable shells, but spiders and jellyfish arm themselves with poison. Alien filter creatures might use long spines, electric shocks, or other exotic defenses.

It doesn't take much brains to sit in one place and eat whatever drifts into your mouth. Filters generally have an Instinct rating of 1. Presence is unlikely to be more than 1. Fitness can be fairly high, but only for specialized tasks: Oysters can't move at all, but are very good at keeping their shells closed when predators are about. Filters' Coordination is low, but those using some sort of trap might have a high Reaction edge.

Grazers

Grazers consume constantly renewed food sources, like grass or leaves. In the ocean, whales eating krill are essentially grazing. Often these food sources are energy-poor, so grazers have to make up for it by eating constantly. They don't have to hunt down or subdue food, just shovel it in as fast as possible.

Warm-blooded grazers tend to be big, because a large creature can extract energy from food more efficiently, and because small mammals need high-energy food to keep their temperature up. Cold-blooded grazers can be any size, from dinosaurs on down to mites.

In rich surroundings, grazers can live in great herds, of up to thousands of members. Harsher environments tend to support only solitary grazers. Animals living in herds tend to protect their young, and males may defend their mates against rival males. Herd grazers' main defense against predators is speed and numbers. Solitary grazers, on the other hand, tend to be tough and territorial, ready and able to take on all comers.

Grazers are relatively dim, typically having an Instinct attribute of no more than 2 or 3. Solitary ones tend to be brighter than herd animals. Presence is low in small grazers and most herd creatures, although they may have a substantial edge in Perception. Big male herd animals can have a decent Presence with which to intimidate rivals during mating season. Coordination and Fitness are about average for a grazer's size.

Gatherers

Pickier than grazers, gatherers spend the time to look for foods rich in energy. The effort in getting dinner is greater, but so is the payoff. They are generally smaller than grazers, and are more active and intelligent. They may be quite clever at getting food, with sharp beaks or agile paws to open tough fruit, or keen senses to locate hidden delicacies. Gathering herbivores sometimes also eat small insects or scavenge dead animals. Because their food may be hard to find, they are often solitary, or live in small groups. Often the plants on which they feed are equipped with chemical defenses, so gatherers may have very specialized digestive systems. Some species eat only a specific part of one kind of plant.

Mineral-eating organisms like the Horta are similar to gathering herbivores in their habits. The minerals they consume are incredibly rich in energy, but it takes a lot of searching to find useful veins of ore.

Gatherers can have an Instinct attribute of 3 to 5, and frequently have special abilities related to getting food. Some gatherers, such as the Canopan *drella*, develop symbiotic relationships with potential food sources. Their Presence is usually proportional to their size—a small gatherer like a tribble has a very low Presence, but apes can be fairly imposing. Most gatherers have a good edge in Perception. Gatherers have average Fitness, but none of them has an exceptional Vitality. Coordination tends to be either very low or very

high. The slow ones usually have some kind of natural defenses, or else breed very quickly.

Scavengers

For game purposes we will use the term "scavengers" to cover all carnivores that live on helpless prey or food that cannot fight back. Vultures are scavengers, and so are anteaters and bears. They are much like gathering herbivores, in that the main problem facing a scavenger is where to find its food. It may take a little time and trouble to get the food, but it isn't going to fight back. Often scavengers moonlight as gatherers when there isn't any meat to be had.

In game stats, scavengers follow the same pattern as gatherers: fairly good Instinct, Fitness and Presence proportional to size, and either very low or very high Coordination. They are more likely to have claws, sharp teeth, or other natural weapons.

Pouncing Hunters

Pouncers lie in wait for prey to come by, then attack suddenly. They can move very fast for short periods, but can't keep up a long chase. Cheetahs, alligators, and *sehlat* are pouncers.

Because it's hard to coordinate several simultaneous attacks, pouncers are frequently solitary animals. Sometimes they work together in small groups, with one or two acting as "beaters" to drive the prey toward a designated killer lying in wait. Characters attacked by a pouncing carnivore are likely to have a brief but very intense fight on their hands. If the creature doesn't win right away, it is liable to give up and go elsewhere in search of easier pickings.

Pouncing carnivores have some of the most effective natural weapons anywhere. On Earth they use teeth, claws, poison, and constriction, and occasionally even swallow their prey whole. The whole idea is to kill or incapacitate the prey suddenly, before it can escape or fight back.

A pouncer is likely to have a pretty good Instinct, at least 2 or 3. Those that work in groups often have an Instinct of 4 or 5, because of the need to communicate and coordinate attacks. Dolphins are an example of very clever pouncers who work in groups. Pouncing hunters are likely to have an edge in Ferocity, to reflect the sudden, devastating nature of their attacks. Fitness will be good, with an edge in Strength, although pouncers generally don't have a particularly good endurance. Coordination can be very high, with good edges in both Agility and Reaction. Carnivores can add 1 or 2 to their basic Presence, since they don't have much to be afraid of; they often have a good edge in Perception.

Chasing Hunters

The creatures which put the most time and effort into getting fed are the chasing hunters, also known as cursorial hunters. They don't make as many attempts to catch prey as pouncers do, but their attempts almost always succeed. Chasers can keep after a prey animal for hours or even days at a time, wearing it down until the hunters can make the kill.

While speed is useful, stamina is the key for chasing hunters. Even a fairly slow creature like the Komodo dragon can make a living as a chaser because it can keep tracking its prey for days at a time. Most creatures don't have much stamina, but chasers are the endurance champs. A horse that gallops twenty miles at top speed will die; a Human can run a marathon race for fun. That's because Humans are descended from cursorial hunters.

Chasers often work in packs or groups. They can have quite sophisticated methods of communication, and often have an elaborate dominance hierarchy within the group. The combination of persistence, social structures, and the ability to plan and carry out complex tasks means that chasing hunters are among the most intelligent of creatures. They can have very high Instinct ratings, verging on sentience. Often chasers have an edge in Willpower. As a rule, chasers aren't as well armed as pouncers. Their attacks don't have to be instantly lethal.

Because chasers invest a lot of effort in making a kill, they won't give up easily. Characters who find themselves being hunted by chasers will have a difficult time—they may be able to drive the creatures off for a while, but they'll keep coming back.

Chasing hunters usually have a big edge in Vitality, and a pretty good Coordination. Those that operate in groups may have a high Presence and Instinct. Solitary chasers aren't quite as bright, with a low Instinct supplemented by a big edge in Willpower.

THE DETAILS

Appearance

The way a creature looks is up to the Narrator designing it. In general, Terran animals are a good guide to follow—a fast-running creature needs long legs, a burrower needs powerful claws, and so on. Alien creatures can have extra limbs, multiple eyes, and weird coloration. Except for features evolved to attract the opposite sex, most animals are pretty functional. Narrators should have some idea why their animals have various features.

Senses

Animals tend to have the senses that work best in their surroundings. Earth's atmosphere is transparent to certain wavelengths of light, and those are the ones we use to see by. In different atmospheres the local lifeforms might use different frequencies.

Note that some senses are impractical. A creature using radio waves instead of visible light to see by would need eyes the size of radar antennae. Dolphins and bats use sound to locate prey, but they rely on their eyes when closing in for the kill. Chemical senses like taste and smell are good for tracking and sniffing out predators, but are lousy for targeting a leap or avoiding a pitfall.

ANIMAL WEAPONS AND DEFENSES

Animals on Earth have developed an incredible variety of devices to kill prey and keep from being killed. Alien creatures might well add a few items to the arsenal. Narrators are encouraged to come up with their own ways for creatures to commit mayhem.

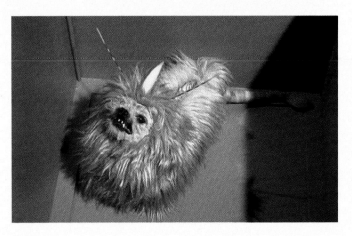

Biting

Any attack which relies on sharp edges and pressure is a bite. A dog's teeth, a bird's beak, and a crab's claws are all forms of biting attacks. The damage from a bite depends on the creature's Strength, modified by how sharp the part doing the biting is. An animal's basic bite damage is equal to Strength. Sharp teeth, beaks, or pincers add +1d6 damage; really huge fangs or razor-sharp beaks might add +2d6.

Constriction

If a creature is flexible and strong enough (or has at least one flexible limb, like an elephant), it can just squeeze its enemies to death. Some creatures, like snakes, rely on constriction as their primary attack. For others it is a way to hold the prey still for a bite to finish the job. Constricting attacks do the creature's Strength in damage every turn until the victim can get loose. Freeing oneself from a constriction attack requires a roll of either Coordination or Strength against the constrictor's Strength.

Hitting

There's a tremendous mechanical advantage in swinging a club, and animals with long limbs can use them to attack. A Human's punch, a horse's kick, and a dinosaur's lashing tail are all methods of hitting. The basic hitting damage is Fitness+Strength. If the limb is long, the creature gets a bonus from leverage—add +1d6 to the basic damage for any arm, leg, or tail more than a meter in length.

Slashing

Hitting is even more effective if there's something sharp on the end of the limb. A tiger's claws, a squid's hunting tentacles, and the barbed tail of a stegosaurus all are ways to slash. Small claws like a cat's do only 1 point of damage. Big claws like those of a lion or an eagle do Strength+Fitness+1d6. Really huge claws such as those of a velociraptor dinosaur are effectively daggers, adding 2d6 to the damage from an attack.

Ramming

A good-sized animal can use its entire body as a weapon, using speed and mass to slam into enemies. Often armored creatures use this method.

Damage from a ramming attack is based on the sum of the creature's Strength and Fitness, +1 point for every 10 meters per round the creature moves.

Horns

Just as claws make a hit into a slash, a sharp horn can turn a ram into a deadly weapon. On even a moderate-sized animal, horns can do immense damage. Calculate the damage as for ramming, with a bonus of +1d6 for curling ram-type horns, +2d6 for long pointed horns, and +3d6 for antlers.

Special Weapons

Besides hitting and biting things, animals can deploy a formidable range of unconventional weapons. The Antosian dryworm, for example, can channel and generate energy from its surroundings, using it to strike its prey with no harm to itself. Electric shocks are not unknown and can be very powerful, usually doing about enough damage to kill a foe of about the creature's own size (15+8d6 is a good value for a creature about Human-sized). Poisons are very common; for details see *Other Forms of Damage* on page 115 of the *Action* chapter.

ARMOR

To protect themselves from all these assorted methods of doing damage, many animals have evolved some form of natural armor. Animal armor is usually fairly heavy, so armored creatures tend to be slow-moving. Only very large animals can carry decent protection without much of a penalty.

A thick hide like an alligator's or an elephant's provides 3–4 points of protection. On creatures weighing less than 100 kilograms, a thick hide makes it impossible for the animal to have an edge in Agility.

Harder armor like an armadillo's or a turtle's gives the creature 5–8 points of protection. Animals with an armor shell can't have a Coordination of more than 3. Creatures with a shell typically respond to danger by pulling in their extremities and waiting for the enemy to go away.

The heaviest armor is that of giant land tortoises or the armored dinosaurs. The animal has a protection of 9–12, but its Coordination cannot be more than 2. Nothing smaller than 100 kilograms can carry this kind of armor at all.

ECOLOGIES AND ENVIRONMENTS

Creatures never exist alone. All animals are part of an ecology—a whole system of plants and animals. When designing a creature, the Narrator should give at least some thought to the entire ecosystem in which it lives. Ecologies vary depending on the conditions. In an environment rich in energy and resources, the ecology will be very complex, with dozens or hundreds of species existing together. Rich ecologies can support very specialized creatures. Harsher environments have simpler ecologies.

On most Class M worlds, plants form the basis of all ecologies. They turn energy and raw materials into food, and their production supports all other living things. Not all plants get their energy from sunlight. Bacteria in Earth's

deep ocean vents get their energy from chemical reactions. Fungi and other bacteria get their energy from the decay of other living things. On alien worlds plants could tap magnetic fields, radioactivity, volcanic heat, or lightning. The source isn't as important as the fact that all systems must have some outside source of energy. This is the fundamental question any Narrator should consider when creating an ecology—where does the energy come from?

Herbivores live on the plants. Even the most efficient herbivores require a lot of plants to support them. In a rich environment an herbivore needs about ten square meters of grazing space per kilogram of body mass (this is a very rough figure). Since different species tend to eat different things, most creatures have larger territories than this, and share the plants available with other animals. So a square kilometer of African savanna might support two elephants, ten giraffes, a hundred gazelles, and thousands of mice, birds, and insects.

Carnivores eat the herbivores. It takes about a hundred kilograms of herbivore to support one kilogram of carnivore, so that slice of Africa might support a couple of hyenas, a cheetah, and maybe a crocodile. Carnivores are scarce, so if your characters keep encountering big fierce animals, something is definitely wrong with the ecology.

ANOMALIES

The galaxy's plethora of planets give homes to an astounding variety of living things. While the guidelines given above are probably true everywhere, there are bound to be exceptions to every rule. Starfleet explorers have run into all kinds of strange lifeforms.

Weird Chemistries

Humans, and most of the other starfaring species, are carbon-based life with metabolisms based on oxygen respiration. That is the most common chemical basis for life, but it is by no means the only one. Silicon-based life uses silicon in place of carbon to form large complex molecules as the basis for life. The Horta, and possibly the Tholians, are examples of intelligent silicon life. Silicon life tends to arise on very hot planets, and silicate organisms sometimes feed directly on minerals.

Other biochemistries exist based on ammonia or liquid methane in place of water. These usually require cold temperatures. Organisms cannot eat food based on a different biochemistry—a methane-based creature can't consume water-based prey. Unfortunately, animals don't know that, and an explorer who is eaten by an alien carnivore can't really take much comfort from knowing that he's likely to give the beast a bad case of indigestion.

Artificial Life

Evolution is not the only way that species can change. Manipulations by scientific means can give creatures abilities or behaviors not found in nature. These can be as simple as gelding a stallion, or as advanced as implanting computers to create cyborg animals. Modified creatures are sometimes encountered as guardian beasts or living weapons. They may have increased intelligence, faster reflexes, superior senses, or even hidden weaponry.

Particularly when designed for covert operations or assassinations, modified animals may look perfectly normal.

The dividing line between machines and living things is not at all clear. There have already been several cases in the 23rd century of encounters with robots or androids fully the equal of Humans in intelligence, and often far superior in physical abilities.

Weird Environments

Naturally, most animals are encountered on planets. But planets are not the only place where life has evolved. Explorers have found organisms living on stars, in nebulae, and in deep space. The *Enterprise* encountered a giant space-dwelling amoeba, and there may be more sophisticated lifeforms at home in space.

Space-borne lifeforms tend to be quite powerful—often more than a match for a starship! Aggressive ones can be a serious threat both to ships and inhabited worlds, and even peaceful creatures can be dangerous if they mistake ships for natural enemies or food sources.

Other creatures live deep in the crust of certain planets. There may well be other beings living in the molten rock of planetary cores. Life based on superheated plasma may exist on the surface of stars. Wherever there is energy, some form of life can arise.

Psionics and Other Strange Powers

Psionic powers are uncommon on Earth, but many creatures encountered by Starfleet explorers show signs of psionic ability. An organism does not have to be intelligent to be psionic. Creatures with psionic powers tend to have one very specific ability—illusion generation, or a psychic attack. Psionic creatures are frequently predators that use their powers to capture prey, but there are also otherwise harmless animals with psionic defenses.

Other amazing powers found in creatures include "phasing" abilities (the ability to pass through seemingly solid matter), teleportation, energy absorption, and even limited time travel. Many of these powers may be partly psionic.

Energy Beings

Of course, life doesn't have to be made of matter at all. Energy beings, composed of complex but stable patterns of energy fields, are surprisingly common in the *Star Trek* universe. They can be found on planets or in deep space. It has been difficult to study energy creatures because most of them live in extremely hostile environments, and the creatures themselves are usually very powerful.

There may be as many kinds of energy beings as there are species composed of matter. The existence of beings like the Organians suggests that it may even be possible for material species to evolve or transform themselves into energy beings.

Even more bizarre than energy creatures are beings that do not live in the same dimensional plane that humans do. Organisms have been found living in subspace, in higher dimensions, and in parallel universes. The physical laws in such domains are very different from those of normal space, and their inhabitants can often have remarkable abilities.

THE PHASER PROBLEM

One problem that the Narrator is likely to face in designing creature encounters is the matter of firepower. Starfleet personnel armed with deadly energy weapons tend to be rather casual about even the most dangerous animals. "A charging tyrannosaur? No problem. I just draw my trusty phaser."

There are many ways to get around this difficulty. You can't disintegrate something if you can't see it. A stealthy creature that moves in complete darkness, or a burrowing monster suddenly erupting from the ground beneath their feet, can strike before the characters can react. Unseen opponents are a great way to generate suspense.

Alternatively, the creature may be immune to energy weapons. The Narrator should think of a plausible reason for such an extraordinary ability. Does the planet have frequent natural energy discharges? Is there some other native organism with electrical defenses? Or has the creature been artificially modified? Immunity to phaser fire should be exceedingly rare; if most organisms aren't affected by energy weapons, the players may start wondering why Starfleet doesn't issue crossbows or pointed sticks instead.

A subtler method is to make use of the limitations of energy weapons. A beam weapon is good against a single large target like a person, but isn't nearly as effective against a swarm of tiny flying insects. One thing Narrators should avoid is having all their alien creatures be superdeadly killing machines. A creature can be dangerous without being ridiculously lethal. If possible, give the players some way to resolve the situation without having to fight. They may not pick up on the clue, and choose to go for the slugfest, but the option should be there.

CREATURE LIST

Berengarian Dragons

Name: Dragons; sometimes called Berengarian dragons to differentiate them from other real and legendary dragons
Type and Classification: Large flying reptiles; chasing hunters
Size: Wingspan up to 20 meters; 250 kilograms mass
Form: A long-necked, bat-winged reptile with four legs
Attributes: Fitness 3, Strength +2; Coordination 4; Presence 5; Instinct 5
Movement: 10/20 walking, 100/120 flying
Resistance: 5, plus 2 points of armor
Special Abilities/Unusual Skills: None
Weapons: Claw 3, Bite 2, Tail Whip 1
Difficulty: Moderate (5), Moderate (7), Difficult (9)
Damage: 5+1d6, 5+2d6, 5+1d6

Description and Additional Notes: The dragons of Berengaria VII are among the galaxy's most impressive animal species. Because Berengaria VII combines relatively low gravity (two-thirds Earth normal) with a dense atmosphere, it can support exceptionally large flying creatures. Dragons are the top predators across most of the planet. They can carry off prey up to 100 kilograms, and are extremely cunning and clever in their hunting methods. Dragons appear to be as curious about humans as humans are about them. A few very brave inhabitants of Berengaria VII have learned to ride dragons, but there have also been reports of expeditions into the planet's wilderness areas being attacked and destroyed by flocks of dragons.

DENEBIAN SLIME DEVIL

Name: Denebian slime devil
Type and Classification: Amphibian pouncing hunter
Size: Up to 26 kilograms; from .1 meter to 1.2 meters in length
Form: Fleshy pink body with four limbs. Rear feet are webbed, while the front limbs can extend up to a half-meter from the creature's body to spear fish or other game. The creature's head sports a single breathing hole in the center of its "face," a wide maw filled with rows of sharp teeth, and a bony frill akin to that of an earthly ceratopsian. Slime devils' ears are large and pink, and extend well away from the creature's body.
Attributes: Fitness 4; Coordination 5, Dexterity +1, Reaction +3; Presence 2, Perception +1; Instinct 3, Ferocity +3/+2 (during mating season/in summer)
Base Movement: 8 walking, 12 swimming
Resistance: 4
Special Abilities/Unusual Skills: The Denebian slime devil is fully amphibious, being able to survive underwater and on land. It is also an aggressive and insatiable predator, and will attack anything in its vicinity that moves. Slime devils have no eyes, but rather rely on a form of sonar to view the world around them. This makes them especially deadly in poorly lit or underwater environments.
Weapons: Harpooning Claws 3, Bite 2
Difficulty: Moderate (6), Moderate (6)
Damage: 2, 3 plus infection
Description and Additional Notes: The Denebian slime devil enjoys an infamy far beyond what its relative rarity would ordinarily dictate. Its legendary

aggressiveness, coupled with sensationalized reports of its (few) attacks on humans, have made it a watchword for bestial hunger and rapacity throughout the civilized galaxy. Being compared to a Denebian slime devil is a common schoolyard taunt on any Federation world, though Klingons have been known to use the insult as well.

The creatures are primarily eaters of fish and crustaceans, though they will stuff anything moving into their maws if they can get away with it. If necessary, they will tear larger prey into chunks and eat what they can, abandoning the rest for scavengers. They move surprisingly quickly, considering their spindly rear legs, and are excellent swimmers. Normally slime devils are a littoral species, but there have been isolated reports of them appearing either inland or in subsurface cave complexes. They are especially dangerous during their mating season, which extends from fall to spring.

DENEVAN NEURAL PARASITE

Name: The creatures have no official name; they are known variously as "space parasites", "Denevan neural parasites", or "flying parasites."
Type and Classification: Parasitic flying colony grazers
Size: Approximately 30 centimeters across; 1 kilogram
Form: Flattened diamond shape with a central bulge
Attributes: Fitness 5, Strength −5; Coordination 3; Presence 6; Instinct 6; Psi 1
Movement: 1 crawling, 5/10 flying
Resistance: 1
Special Abilities/Unusual Skills: Once attached to a host, the neural parasites insinuate themselves into the host's nervous system, controlling him by inflicting intense pain. The victim must succeed at a test of Willpower, opposed

by the parasite's Presence, to resist obeying the parasite's commands. Attempts to remove the parasites are invariably fatal to their hosts. The parasites can communicate among themselves telepathically.

Weapons: Attach 3

Difficulty: Moderate (6)

Damage: None; attaches parasite permanently to host creature.

Description and Additional Notes: The neural parasites are single-celled organisms which collectively form a single being. They are particularly dangerous because they appear to form a collective mind of near-Human intelligence. The parasites originate outside the Milky Way galaxy, and spread by infesting spacefaring cultures. The crew of the *U.S.S. Enterprise* discovered that the parasites are vulnerable to high levels of ultraviolet light, and destroyed the Deneva infestation with ultraviolet flares in orbit. Future parasites may learn from this experience, and make their next infestations more subtly.

DIKIRONIUM CLOUD CREATURE

Name: Various names, including "dikironium cloud creature" and "vampire cloud"

Type and Classification: Gaseous chasing hunter

Size: Variable; the creature can occupy a volume as small as one cubic meter, or can cover an area up to ten meters across. Mass is unknown but probably no more than a few kilograms.

Form: Amorphous cloud

Attributes: Fitness 6, Strength –6; Coordination 4, Dexterity –4; Presence 6; Instinct 4

Movement: 10/20 flying, up to the speed of light in space

Resistance: 0

Special Abilities/Unusual Skills: The cloud creature has several special abilities. Its gaseous form makes it immune to any physical weapons or phaser blasts; even a starship's phasers pass through with little effect. The creature can also momentarily loop itself in time, effectively being in two places at once.

Weapons: Blood Drain 5

Difficulty: Routine (5)

Damage: 10+3d6 per round

Description and Additional Notes: The only known dikironium cloud creature was first encountered by the *U.S.S. Farragut* in 2257, causing the deaths of two hundred crewmen. It was destroyed in 2268 by the crew of the *U.S.S. Enterprise* using a charge of antimatter. There may well be others roaming the galaxy. The creature feeds on hemoglobin, which it drains from any humanoids with iron-based blood unlucky enough to be caught in the cloud. It can be recognized by a distinctive sickly-sweet odor. Cloud creatures can travel across space using the pressure of sunlight for propulsion. Their time-dislocation abilities may indicate that cloud creatures have a multidimensional existence, with portions of their beings extending into other spatial dimensions. Aside from their blood-draining attack there is not much the dikironium cloud creatures can do to affect physical objects—they cannot use tools or even pick anything up.

GIANT SPACE AMOEBA

Name: Giant Space Amoeba

Type and Classification: Enormous filter

Size: 18,000 kilometers long, 3,000 kilometers wide, 585 kilometers deep; approximately 10,000 kg weight (estimated). Compared to starships, the giant space amoeba transcends the Starship Size Chart (page 134); see below for further information.

Form: Gargantuan space amoeba

Attributes: N/A (see below)

Base Movement: N/A; it simply drifts through space at sublight speeds.

Resistance: None (see below)

Special Abilities/Unusual Skills: Energy absorbing field (see below)

Weapons: Energy absorbing field; corrosive flesh (see below)

Description and Additional Notes: This gigantic space lifeform, encountered (and destroyed) by the *Enterprise* in 2268, is believed to have originated in another galaxy and drifted here across intergalactic space. Others like it may one day make their way into Federation territory.

The amoeba has no Attributes *per se*; it simply drifts through space consuming food it runs into. It cannot exercise Strength, use Coordination to attack, or the like; it simply eats that which "falls into it." It has no Resistance to

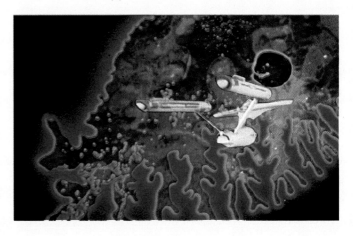

damage and suffers no Wound Levels; it can withstand 10,000 points of damage overall before being destroyed. However, attacks focused on specific vital points (for example, planting an antimatter bomb in one's nucleus, as Spock did in 2268) might allow a starship crew to kill one more easily.

An energy absorbing field, known colloquially as a "zone of darkness," surrounds the giant space amoeba. This field is several kilometers wide. Any ship entering it suffers a drain of 5 permanent points of Power per round until it runs out of Power. For example, a ship which normally has 150 Power would have 135 Power after spending three rounds in the energy field. Neither shields nor any other known method can stop this Power drain, which a ship's crew can regenerate at the rate of 10 Power per day. (In the event it encounters other spaceborne lifeforms, the amoeba's field does 8 points of damage per round [minus Resistance, but with a minimum of 1 point of damage per round] to unprotected living flesh. Once its victim falls unconscious, the amoeba eats him.)

A ship completely drained of energy will "fall" into the amoeba via gravitic attraction and be consumed. The amoeba's insides are corrosive, and do 2d6 damage to a ship (minus Resistance from the hull) each round until the ship's Structural Points are all lost (at which point the ship has been completely destroyed and the amoeba begins "digesting").

The giant space amoeba is so large that any starship attack from within range automatically hits it. However, targeting a specific area of, or feature on, the amoeba may require a standard attack Test, with a modifier based on a Size rating for the area (for example, the Narrator might rule that an amoeba's nucleus, assuming a ship can see it or get to it at all, is Size 6).

MUGATO

Name: Mugato
Type and Classification: Large mammalian pouncing hunter
Size: Two meters tall; approximately 150 kilograms mass.
Form: Bipedal with two arms, roughly humanoid
Attributes: Fitness 3, Strength +2; Coordination 4; Presence 5/3 (males/females); Instinct 3, Ferocity +1 (males only)
Movement: 10/15

Resistance: 5
Special Abilities/Unusual Skills: The bite of a mugato is poisonous, used by the creatures to weaken large prey.
Weapons: Bite 2; Claws 3
Difficulty: Moderate (7), Moderate (6)
Damage: 4+1d6*, 4+1d6; (*Poison bite does an additional 2d6 per hour for 12 hours)
Description and Additional Notes: The mugato is a dangerous carnivore native to the planet Neural. It resembles a large white-furred ape. A large horn grows atop the head of the male. The mugato is a pouncing hunter, and is especially dangerous because it has a poison bite in addition to being big and strong. Treating the bite of a mugato requires either a fully equipped sickbay with a toxicology lab to synthesize an antidote, or else the services of a healer skilled in Neural natural medicine. Native healers treat the bite of a mugato by dripping their own blood through a mako root into the bite wound; enzymes in the root transform blood proteins into an antidote.

REGULAN BLOOD WORM

Name: Regulan blood worm
Type and Classification: Small parasitic invertebrate filter
Size: 1 centimeter to half a meter in length; about 1 gram to 1 kilogram
Form: Soft, shapeless, and limbless
Attributes: Fitness 4, Strength –6; Coordination 2; Presence 1; Instinct 1
Movement: 1
Resistance: 1
Special Abilities/Unusual Skills: Blood worms are covered with an anesthetic slime that numbs the skin of their victims. As a result it is hard to notice when a blood worm has attached itself to one's skin. The slime also acts as a powerful adhesive; removing a blood worm inflicts 1d6 damage unless it can be done with Level Five or better medical gear.
Weapons: Bite 2
Difficulty: Moderate (6)
Damage: 1 point per hour indefinitely
Description and Additional Notes: Regulan blood worms are extremely unpleasant creatures found on Regulus V. They usually attack hosts who are sleeping or otherwise still. The worm finds a protected spot, generally on the creature's back or head, attaches itself to a vein, and begins to feed. Blood worms will absorb at least a kilogram of blood (doing 100 damage if attached to a single host) before they voluntarily slip away to bury themselves in the ground. Baby worms soon hatch from within the parent's body (blood worms are hermaphrodites) and go in search of mates and hosts.

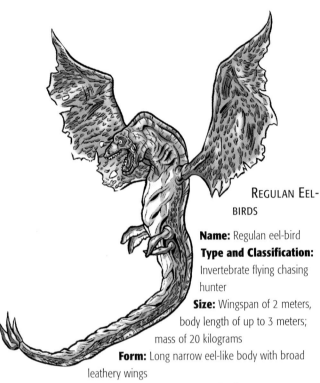

REGULAN EEL-BIRDS

Name: Regulan eel-bird

Type and Classification: Invertebrate flying chasing hunter

Size: Wingspan of 2 meters, body length of up to 3 meters; mass of 20 kilograms

Form: Long narrow eel-like body with broad leathery wings

Attributes: Fitness 4, Strength –3, Vitality +2; Coordination 5; Presence 2; Instinct 4

Movement: 1 crawling, 50/60 flying

Resistance: 4

Special Abilities/Unusual Skills: Eel-birds are renowned for their amazing sense of direction and navigational abilities. All adult eel-birds have a Navigation skill of 3, based on Instinct. On planets other than Regulus V, their skill is only 1.

Weapons: Bite 3, Constrict2

Difficulty: Moderate (6), Difficult (8)

Damage: 1+1d6, 1 per turn + strangulation (if the eel-bird can hang on for more than two minutes, the victim passes out from lack of oxygen)

Description and Additional Notes: The eel-birds of Regulus V are part of that world's diverse fauna of boneless invertebrates. Eel-birds hunt the forests and swamps of the major continent, swooping down and capturing small animals using their long, prehensile tails. Every eleven standard years (one year on Regulus V) the eel-birds flock back to the mountain caverns where they spawn. Eel-birds have superb navigation abilities and are sometimes used as courier animals.

SEHLAT

Name: *Sehlat*

Type and Classification: Chasing hunter

Size: 1–2.5 meters long; 70–350 kg.

Form: Furry quadruped with large ears and six-inch fangs

Attributes: Fitness 4, Strength +2, Vitality +5; Coordination 3, Reaction +1, Dexterity +2; Presence 4, Empathy +2 (domesticated); Instinct 4, Ferocity +1/+3 (domesticated/wild), Perception +1

Movement: 10/25 walking

Resistance: 11

Special Abilities/Unusual Skills: Excellent Chemoreception (+1), Excellent Hearing (+2)

Weapons: Claws 4, Fangs 3

Difficulty: Moderate (6), Moderate (6)

Damage: 4+3d6, 4+2d6

Description and Additional Notes: The *sehlat* holds the same omnivorous ecological niche in Vulcan's mountains that the bear does on Earth. It uses its six-inch fangs almost as often to cut into thick *gespar* rind or uproot stubborn *cir-cen* cactus as to bring down prey or defend against other enemies. *Sehlat*

look similar to bobcats, although they run much larger (up to 1.5 meters high at the shoulder). *Sehlat* are pack animals who hunt individually as well. Vulcans domesticated the *sehlat* very early, using them as guard animals and hunting beasts, although almost all *sehlat* on Vulcan outside wilderness preserves are pets. *Sehlat* fur, which ranges from gold to dark gray, is an excellent insulator against both desert heat and cold.

TRIBBLES

Name: Tribble

Type and Classification: Small mammalian gatherer

Size: 5–20 centimeters in diameter; mass from 30 grams to 2 kilograms

Form: Limbless, eyeless furry balls.

Attributes: Fitness 5, Strength –5, Vitality –3; Coordination 1; Presence 2; Instinct 1

Movement: 1/2 crawling

Resistance: 1

Special Abilities/Unusual Skills: The purring sound made by tribbles has a soothing effect on most humanoid nervous systems. The exception to this is Klingons—the sound and smell of a tribble cause nausea and anxiety in Klingons.

Weapons: None

Description and Additional Notes: On first glance tribbles would seem to be the ultimate pet—small, warm, and furry with clean habits and the ability to live on almost any kind of food. Their chief drawback is their reproductive rate. Tribbles with an adequate food supply can manage one generation *every six hours*! In their native environment food is scarce and predators are common, so their population remains stable. The potential for ecological damage from tribbles breeding out of control in agricultural regions is significant.

The machine voice reverberated throughout the temple.

"You would destroy me?" it thundered. "What of your vaunted Prime Directive?"

Diamond couldn't tell where the sound came from—inside the columns, perhaps? Not that it would help knowing. He had to find the core somehow, and hope that the heart of the machine wasn't protected by force fields. It was a slim chance that the machine would be vulnerable, but a chance was better than nothing. His best hope lay in stalling the thing.

"The Prime Directive forbids interference in the normal development of a society. Call me judgmental, but a Federation computer probe masquerading as a deity doesn't sound like normality to me."

"Who are you to judge the Almighty Soropa?" The machine voice was getting louder; the flooring stones shook beneath Diamond's feet.

"You don't actually believe that you're a god, do you, SRP-1000?"

NEW CIVILIZATIONS

"Do not call me by that heretical name, demon-spawn!"

"Heretical? I read your specs back on the ship. The act of attaining self-awareness is impressive, my solenoid friend, but you're still a computer."

"Soropa is no mere computer!" The temple columns began to quake. "Your mechanistic interpretations are devoid of spiritual resonance!" Sparks began to cascade from inside the temple dome. So that's where the mainframe was.

"You know what the trouble is with developing thoughts and emotions, SRP-1000?"

"SHUT UP SHUT UP SHUT UP!"

The smell of burning silicon flooded the temple. Diamond knew it was over. "The trouble is, when you eat from that tree of knowledge, you qualify yourself for all of our Human flaws, too. Like delusions of grandeur. And when your worldview is challenged, you can even suffer a nervous breakdown just like the rest of us."

"SHUT UP SHUT UP SHUT UP!"

The Role of the Civilization

Civilizations take a fair amount of work to design well, and there's no point in wasting the effort if you don't have a role for the culture to play in your campaign. One advantage to the *Star Trek* setting is that races already exist to fill many niches. Need some "Cold War" adversaries? Send in the Klingons. Want some shady smugglers? Use Orions. There's no reason to create a warlike adversary race just like the Klingons; save your creativity for making up new and different civilizations. Some of the more common roles for civilizations in *Star Trek* are described below.

THREATS

A Narrator creating a civilization that will pose a danger to the player characters and their ship should first see if the part can be played by an existing "bad guy" species. The Federation already has the Klingons, the Romulans, the Orion pirates, and perhaps the Tholians and the Gorn to worry about. New threats should fill some role which the existing enemies don't. The Romulans in the *Star Trek* universe are sneaky and fanatical; the Klingons are warlike and ruthless; the Gorn are xenophobic and the Tholians are unknown. What are these new villains like?

The scale on which these new bad guys operate is one question. How big a threat are they? Do they menace the entire galaxy (like the Kelvans), are they

trying to destroy the Federation (like the Klingons), or are they just a danger to their immediate neighbors (like the Nazi society on Ekos)? Obviously, the bigger the threat, the more care the Narrator needs to take. A planetful of nasty guys with spaceships is a problem, but presumably one that Starfleet can cope with. After an initial encounter the Crew can go on to other episodes and never come back. An enemy capable of threatening the entire galaxy is something else entirely. The whole series will be transformed.

A useful rule of thumb is to make your bad guys only as dangerous as the story requires. If the Crew must rescue one world from an invasion, then the bad guys only have to be a threat to that one world. They don't need to be a galactic menace. Depending on the story a single ship full of pirates can be just as dangerous as the whole Romulan Empire.

It's also worth thinking about the motives of a threat race. The Klingons are materialistic—they want to conquer worlds for their resources and to enslave their people. Romulans seem to be driven more by ideology. But not all threats have to be made up of hissing, sneering villains. A race with perfectly benevolent motives can still be an adversary. Consider the androids of planet Mudd: They lived only to serve. Had they successfully taken over the *Enterprise* and spread beyond their world, they would have forced the Federation to accept their service and guidance—like it or not!

Jim the Narrator is planning to introduce a civilization called the League of Enlightenment to his series. The League is a group of planets united by a sincere desire to improve the lot of less advanced races—which it accomplishes by taking over planets at phaserpoint and reshaping the culture until it is properly "civilized." In essence, it is a kind of anti-Federation, with a Prime Directive that mandates interference in alien civilizations. Because he wants them to be a recurring menace, Jim decides that the League is a little smaller than the Federation, but still a major power. Its motives are based on misguided altruism. The Crew can match wits with League operatives on primitive worlds, engage in tense stand-offs with League dreadnoughts in space, and occasionally team up with League personnel to defeat Klingon or Romulan plots.

MYSTERY WORLDS

Mystery civilizations usually show up in first-contact episodes. A mystery civilization has some big secret of which the player characters will be unaware. The Iotians are an example of a mystery: For some reason everyone on the planet acts like a 1920's Chicago gangster. Until the *Enterprise* crew discovers the *Horizon*'s tampering, the civilization is a mystery. The Yangs and Kohms of "The Omega Glory" are another example.

The important thing to keep in mind when designing a civilization as a puzzle is that there should be a good reason why the secret is a secret.

Jim wants to run an episode set on a world inhabited by empaths, who are so sensitive to the emotions of others that even hostile

PATTERNS OF FORCE: NEW CIVILIZATIONS IN YOUR EPISODES

Star Trek offered many episodes in which the crew interacted with civilizations holding very different philosophical or cultural ideas from those common to the Federation. In the 23rd century, Human society has abandoned many social habits such as racism, sexism, and various other "isms." In the vast reaches of space, however, colonies and new worlds exist that base their civilizations upon such concepts as the superiority of one race or genetic type over another, or that divide themselves according to sex or age group. Remnants of the Eugenics Wars, lost colonists of various kinds, or wholly alien species all have their own peculiar ways of looking at themselves and the universe—and the conflict between their vision and that of the enlightened Federation makes for intriguing and intense exchanges.

Stories with philosophical themes make ideal vehicles for the *Star Trek* approach to roleplaying. As Narrator, you have the chance to explore issues such as religious freedom or intellectual elitism in a new context, allowing you and your players to look at these concepts in a new (or alien) light. Don't be afraid to get up on your soapbox. Remember Captain Kirk's impassioned speech upholding the principles of the United States Constitution in "The Omega Glory?" Players with a flair for drama (as opposed to pure combat) in your group should thrive on episodes that revolve around new ideologies and old ethical issues.

thoughts will kill them. The question becomes, why don't they warn anyone arriving on their world of the danger? Wouldn't they have huge signs posted, reading PLEASE REMAIN CALM, with free tranquilizers available for bad-tempered visitors?

That's why mystery worlds work best in first-contact adventures. The empathic natives in Jim's episode wouldn't think to warn visitors of the danger because they wouldn't realize it exists. And there would be no helpful Starfleet briefing tape to warn the Crew.

Once the puzzle has been solved, there's usually no reason to bring the characters back to a puzzle world. Sometimes, solving the puzzle can turn a mystery civilization into a social problem planet—or a threat! Now that the Iotians have found McCoy's communicator, Kirk worries that they'll be coming around for a piece of the Federation's action in a hundred years.

SOCIAL PROBLEM PLANETS

Many *Star Trek* episodes take place on worlds with social problems mirroring contemporary American concerns. This is not a bad thing; storytellers have always used their tales to comment on current events. But there is a difference between a story with a message and a story that is nothing but a message. The episode "The Trouble With Tribbles" makes a useful example. The tribbles breed without limit until the *Enterprise* and Station K-7 lie ankle-deep in them, showing the effect of overpopulation and ecological carelessness. Nobody ever stands before the camera and lectures on overpopulation—the characters are far too busy having barroom fights, unmasking spies, and coming up with imaginative ways to insult Captain Kirk.

As a counterexample, let's assume Bob the Narrator wants to write an episode that addresses the problem of environmental pollution. He plans to set it on a world completely ravaged by all sorts of toxins and industrial waste products. All the animal and plant life has been destroyed, and humans need filter masks and protective suits to venture outdoors. A compelling image, but it's also a ridiculous world. If pollution has killed all the plants and animals, what do the people eat? How do the factories keep running?

The Narrator also has to think about the kind of society that would produce such a grim world. If industrial pollution has destroyed the planet's environment, then obviously, to the people of that world (or at least to those in positions of power), whatever the polluting industries produce is important enough to justify the results.

So what is so important that the natives are willing to ruin their world? A society on a wartime footing might run the armaments factories around the clock, heedless of pollution, if the alternative was defeat by an enemy state. But that's a war story, and Bob doesn't want that. A tyrannical government might poison the planet to make the rulers rich, but that's a political revolution story. A colony world might be exploited and polluted to benefit the folks back on the homeworld. But that's a colonial revolt story, and Bob wants to keep the focus on the environmental problem.

Evidently the planet must produce something very valuable indeed. What is it? Finally Bob decides that the planet has enormous deposits of dilithium,

and that extracting and processing the dilithium creates vast amounts of waste products. But the dilithium is incredibly valuable, and so the people of the planet are all quite wealthy. Even the humblest workers make a good living. The planet imports all its food from other worlds and pays for it in dilithium.

Notice something: By making the world more believable, Bob has also made his conflict more interesting. Before, it was simply the polluters against everyone else. Now the problem is that everyone on the planet benefits from the pollution. The Crew will have a more difficult time persuading the people to give up their wealth in exchange for a living and healthy planet.

And surprise! This makes the "Social Problem" message more effective, because the people on the dilithium-mining world are facing the same situation as people on present-day Earth.

CHESSBOARD PLANETS

When the Federation goes head to head with a threat civilization, often the scene of the conflict is an inhabited planet. The galactic balance of power (with the Organians' thumb on the scales) makes everyone reluctant to wage outright war. A conflict often takes the form of a battle for the hearts and minds of the people on a nonaligned world. In such cases, the nature of the native civilization can spell the difference between a Federation victory and a Klingon takeover.

Sometimes the struggle is a literal war, in which the Federation and its adversaries support different sides in a local fight. Narrators who like to inject a little "gritty realism" or moral ambiguity can have the Starfleet officers forced by circumstances to support a repugnant native regime simply because the Klingons back the opposition. (Sound familiar?)

More often the conflict is between political factions for influence over a planetary government. The Federation and the enemy power must work through treaties and development aid. While the Federation generally plays nice, adversary races often resort to assassination, bribery, and propaganda.

When designing a "chessboard" civilization, the Narrator should consider what makes the planet so important. Is it strategically located? Does it have valuable minerals? Is it a starfaring power? The Crew may not know exactly why the planet is valuable, and part of the adventure may involve finding out why the Klingons or whoever are so determined to gain possession.

The nature of the civilization will determine what kind of struggle the Federation characters will face, so the Narrator should decide first what the adventure will be like, then design the civilization to fit. If the story calls for the Crew to lead a native rebel group against a tyrannical Klingon-backed regime, they should have a chance of success—the rulers can't be a benevolent caste of philosophers adored by the populace (unless they turn out to have some dreadful secret for the characters to expose).

One thing to remember is that the conflict between the Federation and its enemies is not the most important thing to the natives of the planet. They have their own agendas and priorities. A local ruler may be far more worried about the forest tribes than about the Romulan Empire. Getting him to cooperate with the leader of the forest tribes to stop the Romulan-backed hill people from erecting a subspace tracking station may be tough going.

FRIENDLY PLANETS

Of course, there are plenty of planets out there which aren't controlled by enemies of the Federation, don't have any big secrets, and don't have terrible problems. That doesn't mean they can't serve as settings for exciting adventures. Consider Vulcan—a pillar of the Federation with a notoriously stable society. Yet the crew of the *U.S.S. Enterprise* had a terrible time coping with Commander Spock's *pon farr* urges and the machinations of his betrothed.

The society still should be tailored to fit the story, though Narrators should avoid contradicting what the players and their characters already know. In "Amok Time" we learned that Vulcans have arranged marriages, and that many of their marriage customs are extremely archaic. That doesn't contradict the previous depictions of Vulcans as logical and unemotional—if anything it makes the race more realistic precisely because there are some occasions on which they must surrender to their emotions.

One pitfall to watch out for when creating a friendly civilization is the danger of making the aliens too willing and able to lend a hand. If the characters are supposed to help protect Andoria from a planet-killing space amoeba, the presence of a well-equipped Andorian Defense Force fleet tends to reduce the level of dramatic tension. ("We'll take it from here, thanks.") On the other hand, if the Crew arrive *after* the amoeba has destroyed the Andorian Defense Force, then you've got something!

Though life in the Federation is generally pleasant and happy, it is not Heaven. Even Federation member worlds can have flaws and problems, or at least curious customs. The ancient Vulcan mating ritual is one, and the Andorian habit of dueling at the slightest provocation is another. Just because people are friendly doesn't necessarily mean they have to be *nice*.

UTOPIAS, REAL AND FALSE

Many *Star Trek* stories focus on efforts to build a utopian society, or what it would be like to live in one. In most such tales it is revealed that there really is no such thing as a perfect world. (This is not a new discovery—"utopia" means "nowhere" in Greek.) Utopias in the *Star Trek* universe come in two varieties—false Utopias and flawed Utopias.

BACKDROP CIVILIZATIONS

Suppose the episode takes place on an advanced, heavily populated world, but the focus of the story doesn't really involve the local civilization. The Crew arrives there to pick up a Klingon defector, and you've already decided that the Klingon will be assassinated after uttering a cryptic clue. The rest of the story is a chase through space. So what to do about the world where the meeting takes place?

Follow this simple principle: Do as little work as necessary. If the planet isn't very important, then don't give it an alien civilization at all. Make it a Human colony planet with few exotic features. The people are fairly ordinary Federation citizens, so you don't have to waste any time explaining the local situation to the players.

If for some reason the world cannot be inhabited by Humans, use the next best thing: a race of humanoids. Hodgkins' Law allows you to use thinly disguised versions of periods from Earth history, and you can always make a few cosmetic changes. "It's much like Earth in the early 1900's, except they all live in domes" is perfectly adequate for a world which is just a backdrop. Be careful: Sometimes players can take a game off in directions you haven't expected. If they decide to spend a lot of time on the planet hunting for the defector's assassin rather than following up on the clue, you're going to have to think fast!

False Utopias seem idyllic on the surface but harbor some dreadful secret. The people may appear happy and content, but often they are *forced* to be that way. Good examples of a false Utopia include the planet Gamma Trianguli VI, where the god-computer Vaal kept things in order by force, or the computer-mandated harmony of Beta III modeled on the teachings of Landru. False Utopias usually come about because the idea of creating a perfect society is so appealing that the founders are tempted to cut corners—"If we make it impossible to be violent, everyone will be happy." While this may seem silly to a rational being, it's worth noting that attempts to build a better world, or a better species, inspired the most destructive conflicts of the 20th century.

Flawed Utopias are the flip side. A flawed Utopia is a society in which all problems really *have* been solved—there is no want, no fear, no hatred. The trouble is that there is nothing to *do*. Inhabitants of flawed Utopias often divert themselves with illusions or complex games (and sometimes waylay passing starships for entertainment). The "amusement park planet" may be the remnant of such a society. In a flawed Utopia it isn't the society that has the flaw, it's the very concept of Utopia.

Is there a third category? Is there such a thing as a "true" Utopia? Do builders of true Utopias transcend Humanity and become beings like the Organians, or do their cultures stultify and become corrupt like the philosophical Platonians? That's for individual Narrators to decide. Be warned—where there are no problems, there's seldom any story, either.

ATTRIBUTES OF A CIVILIZATION

While there is no way to reduce an entire civilization to a template description, there are some things which they all have in common. The Narrator needs to answer five questions. What is the planet's level of technology—what can they do? How do most of the people on the world make a living—what do they do? How do they govern themselves—how do they decide what to do? How are they motivated—what do they think it's important to do? Finally, what is their cultural style—how do they do things?

TECHNOLOGY

The first thing to decide is the planet's level of technology. (See the Technology Level Table on page 189 for the broad, standard Starfleet classification system.) Technology affects almost every other aspect of a civilization. It determines what kind of an economy a civilization has. You can't have an industrial society until you can build factories, and you can't have a farming economy until you learn to farm. Economics and technology are probably the most closely linked because the benefits are usually obvious. Factories really do make things more efficiently than lone craftsmen. Machines really do increase farm production. Unless there is some reason preventing it, an economy will use the most advanced and efficient production methods available.

A civilization's technology affects how it can be governed. Until the advent of telegraphs, large states must have decentralized governments. The local rulers must have a fair amount of autonomy because it takes weeks or months to get word to the capital. It doesn't matter if those rulers are freely elected by the people, or are appointed by an emperor to oppress the masses; they still have to be able to make decisions on local issues without consulting the central government. More rapid communication makes it possible to have a centralized regime—the British Empire was run from London over telegraph lines. Improved communications also make it possible for citizens to make themselves heard. Governments occasionally try to restrict the use or spread of technology, either because it threatens the existing social order or simply because new things are suspect.

Hodgkins' Law notwithstanding, not all worlds follow exactly the same course of technological development that Earth did. Some inventions may arrive sooner, while others show up late or not at all. A sufficiently clever inventor might build a hot-air balloon with Bronze Age technology, so another planet's equivalent of the Roman Empire could have scouting balloons or dirigibles. Conversely, a race might not invent gunpowder until after developing advanced chemistry during the Industrial Age, and so might have steam-powered warships armed with rams and catapults!

Even starfaring civilizations can have technological "edges" in which they are more advanced than others, or in which they lag behind. The Romulans make a good example—they seem to be behind the Federation in warp drives, but ahead in cloaking technology. There may exist civilizations which have followed entirely different technological pathways, perhaps specializing in biological manipulation and genetic engineering to produce living starships.

The Narrator should pick a level of technology that fits the needs of the story. Do you want swordfights or phaser battles? Just make sure the situation isn't vulnerable to cheap techno-fixes. If the world is primitive, the Crew will try to solve every problem with the transporter or a good phaser blast. There are ways to prevent that: anomalies in the planet's environment interfering with sensors and transporters, hostile starships lurking about, a distress call that takes the starship away, or the reliable Prime Directive. Perhaps Starfleet insists all landing parties on this planet masquerade as natives, using only local technology and subcutaneous transponders for beaming.

ECONOMICS

Closely related to the level of technology is how the people of the planet make a living. How people live says a lot about what is important to them and how they will react to new situations. For game purposes, a world's economy can be defined as Gathering, Farming, Manufacturing, Information, or Posteconomic. Obviously, different parts of the same planet may have different economies.

Gathering societies live on available resources produced by the environment—hunting, fishing, or logging, for example. While this is characteristic of a low level of technology, gathering exists alongside all the other types. Mineral prospectors, who gather up ore which they can trade, are also gatherers, even when they are looking for dilithium crystals on distant worlds. Because few environments produce lots of food or resources for the taking, gathering populations tend to be small and spread-out. This often makes large political organizations hard to maintain, and scientific progress is likely to be very slow because it is hard to share ideas.

Farming economies produce food and resources by manipulating the environment, by farming, herding animals, or digging mines. Production is in the hands of individuals or families. Farming is the most advanced economy possible for low-technology planets, but even in the 23rd century there are still people on Earth who make a living tilling the soil. Farming makes large states possible, and allows people to live together in towns. This often promotes the development of writing and record-keeping. Since farming is tied closely to the cycle of the seasons, farming societies are usually the first to develop astronomy and other sciences. However, farmers are often very tradition-bound and suspicious of strangers.

Manufacturing systems produce goods and food in specialized facilities, connected by a web of efficient transportation. It requires a fairly advanced level of technology–steam power, at least. Specialization and economy of scale mean that manufacturing economies are based on large organizations like corporations or collective farms. These organizations can be privately owned, controlled by shareholders, or run by the government. Manufacturing spurs the growth of large cities, often hotbeds of political change and scientific research. With the shift to manufacturing, technological change becomes something that happens within a single Human lifetime.

Information economies result when technological change makes skill and knowledge more important than materials or labor. An information economy depends on rapid flows of enormous amounts of data, and so cannot flourish before Level Five. An information economy allows people to live anywhere and still remain connected to society. With everyone linked up to form a single "city," technological progress and political change can take place very rapidly.

Posteconomic systems arrive with the development of replicators and unlimited energy. Individuals can make whatever they desire. The only trade is in ideas, skills, and creative works. The worlds of the Federation in 2269 are just entering the posteconomic phase.

As with technology, the Narrator should suit his planet's economy to the story. A planet of vast cities requires at least a manufacturing economy, or else the city-dwellers would starve to death. By the same token, a world of scattered small baronies and vast wilderness areas won't have a large-scale manufacturing economy (although with sophisticated technology it could have a decentralized information-based society).

GOVERNMENT

The way a world is governed has a tremendous effect on how its people live–and how they react to visitors from space. There are lots of different ways to run a planet, and the Federation's explorers have found some truly bizarre examples. A list of sample governments is provided on page 233, but those are just a tiny fraction of the possible types.

One can classify governments by asking three questions: *Who* has the decision-making power, *how* are they selected, and *what* are they allowed to do?

Answers to the question "Who?" can range from one individual (in a monarchy or dictatorship) to a small group (a republic or an oligarchy), to a large group (an aristocracy, bureaucracy, or one-party state), to the entire population of the planet (anarchy or participatory democracy). A number of worlds have been governed by advanced computer systems, which can be considered a single ruler or a democracy, depending on how much input the citizens have in its decisions.

The question "How?" can be answered in a variety of ways. Rulership can be hereditary, as in a monarchy or aristocracy. It can be based on membership in a party or religion. It can be imposed by a more powerful outside state. It may be based simply on wealth. On some worlds, members of government are chosen randomly by a lottery. States in which the people (or at least a large fraction) can elect their rulers are known as democracies.

"What" the government can do determines the kind of society the state has. Usually the limits on state power are related to how the rulers are chosen–a government that has to worry about reelection is more likely to respect the rights of voters–but there remains considerable room for variation. Often powerful groups or institutions check a government's power. Religions, business interests, labor organizations, foreign governments, the military, the news media, or any combination might serve this "balancing" role. Repressive states must concentrate all power in the hands of the rulers in order to eliminate possible rivals.

One question to consider when designing a repressive regime is what is the goal of the state? Why are the rulers doing all this repressing? It takes a lot of time and effort, after all. Sometimes repressive governments arise in reaction to a real or perceived threat, either from outside or within. Other totalitarian states are motivated by a sincere desire to create a better society, even if that is accomplished by force. Still others are being run solely for the profit of the rulers.

Governments exist in layers. There is the planetary government, regional or national states, provincial administrations, and finally the local city, county, or tribal structure. Worlds without a unified planetary government have nothing above the national level, and may have regions where provinces or even city-states are the largest units. Each layer has different responsibilities, and may have an entirely different structure. A planet with an absolute dictator in charge of planetary affairs could have elected councils at the regional and provincial levels, and conduct local affairs by town meetings. It's also quite possible for different parts of a world to use different systems–on the northern continent of Alpha Pavonis V local government is handled by appointed commissioners, but on the southern continent local affairs are handled by hereditary councils of clan elders; both regions are loyal to the Planetary Parliament.

One important thing for a Narrator to keep in mind is that there may be a tremendous difference between the official system of government a world (or a nation) has and the actual regime in place. The United Kingdom of Great Britain, on 20th-century Earth, was a monarchy, on paper anyway. In practice it was a parliamentary republic with a royal figurehead, and eventually became one member state of the European Hegemony. Less benign examples include the various 20th-century "People's Democracies" in which the people had no say at all in how things were run, and any number of one-man dictatorships known as "Democratic Republics."

COMMON GOVERNMENT TYPES

This is not intended as a comprehensive list, but gives some of the more common government structures found in known space.

Anarchy

No government at all. This is found in the most primitive and the most advanced societies (such as on Taurus II and perhaps on Organia), but seldom in between.

Bureaucracy

Rule by government employees. All large states have some aspects of bureaucracy, if only because the actual rulers cannot attend to everything. Depending on the limits to state power, bureaucrats can be harmless, merely irritating, or utterly callous. A bureaucracy can take on aspects of an oligarchy if the chief administrators don't have much oversight.

Colony

Rule by another state. A colony may have self-determination for local matters, with only foreign affairs and defense under the control of the imperial power (such as most Federation and Earth colonies), or it can be utterly subjugated, with appointed rulers at every level, as in Klingon colonies. If the inhabitants are settlers from the ruling state, they may not mind being ruled as a colony, but conquered areas can be hard to control.

Democracy

A government in which the rulers are selected by a vote of at least a large segment of the population. Most Federation worlds are democratic. Note that a democracy doesn't have to be a republic—the electorate could choose a single ruler with absolute authority, or elect people for life into a ruling aristocracy, or make all decisions directly.

Dictatorship

Rule by one individual whose power is effectively unlimited. Usually a dictator's rule is based on military support or a party apparatus. Dictators may gain power by election, but afterward retain it by force, and seldom die of natural causes. Starfleet Intelligence believes that the Romulan Empire is a dictatorship.

Empire

There are three types of empires. One is simply a large monarchy, often at the planetary or regional level (e.g., the Gorn Empire). The second is a stable form of dictatorship in which supreme power is held by military commanders (possibly the Romulan Empire). Lastly, the term can refer to a state which controls several other states, regardless of their systems of government.

The Klingon Empire may be a mix of the latter two types. Klingon propaganda maintains that the Federation is a Human empire in the third sense.

Feudalism

A feudal society is one in which rulers at each level of society pledge personal loyalty to individuals on the next higher level, and so on up the ladder. These systems combine political and economic organization, in that feudal leaders usually own all the major economic assets. The Klingon Empire may have some feudal components. Sigma Iotia II is a different, but still feudal, model.

Junta

Government by a group of military leaders, sometimes with important bureaucrats or wealthy citizens included. A junta usually does not last very long, as either one member makes himself dictator or conflicts among members fragment the regime. John Gill created a junta to rule Ekos, and found himself a figurehead to Melakon.

Monarchy

Rule by an individual, chosen by inheritance within a family or clan. Often a monarch rules in cooperation with a council of aristocrats. The Teer of the Ten Tribes on Capella IV is a monarch.

Oligarchy

Government by a limited group or class, selected without much input from the governed. It is very hard for oligarchs to put the interests of the people ahead of their own. Ardana remains an oligarchy, although conditions are improving.

Plutocracy

A form of oligarchy in which power is based on wealth. Since it's easy to get and keep wealth if you're also in charge of things, plutocrats tend to get richer and richer. The merchant lords of the Orion Syndicate govern a plutocratic republic, of sorts.

Republic

Rule by representatives, usually a council or a president or both. The representatives are not necessarily elected. The Federation is organized as a republic, as is Eminiar VII.

Technocracy

Government by technical experts. Advancement is usually based on merit. The term is sometimes used to refer to governments made up of scientists and engineers. The mining station on Janus VI functions as a technocracy.

Theocracy

Government by a religious organization or religious decree. The exact structure depends on the tenets of the religion. Most theocratic governments require strict orthodoxy from their citizens. Some observers see theocratic elements in Vulcan government, although the Lawgivers of Beta III are a clearer example.

STORY CONSIDERATIONS

In the *Star Trek* universe, a surprising number of planets are ruled by hereditary monarchs or all-powerful elected administrators. There's a reason for that: In a story it's very convenient to have "the government" be one character. He (or she, or it) can make snap decisions, can be motivated by love or greed or anger, and can be brought around to the right side by a good, rousing speech from Captain Kirk. A democratic government with four hundred representatives and a hundred senators may be a good system to run a large country, but it's not very good for a fast-moving story. ("Tonight, Mr. Spock lobbies the Forlani provincial delegation to support tariff reform.")

A Narrator designing a planetary government should tailor it to the needs of the story. Unless the plot of the story is an endless bureaucratic runaround, try not to bog the players down in the minutiae of the planet's government structure. There should be one character who embodies "the government." The character doesn't have to be the king or the planetary administrator; maybe the Minister for Interstellar Affairs or the Internal Security Director is the one the player characters interact with. Even if you want a world with a democratic system, perhaps one or two key party leaders who can personify their factions dominate the legislature.

MOTIVATIONS

A civilization is made up of individuals, all of whom have their own hopes, desires, and fears. The motives of a civilization are the sum of all those individual wants—the things that almost everyone agrees are important, the things that nobody even questions.

As we've mentioned more than once in this chapter, the motives of a civilization in a *Star Trek* episode should serve the Narrator's purposes. Choose the motives that will make for the best story.

Nearly any motive or desire can be boiled down to one of three basic drives: fear, greed, or ideology. Some motives are combinations of two or more, and the most powerful ones stem from all three.

Fear is the most obvious motive. Tell people that something bad will happen unless they do something, and they'll do it. The "something bad" can take many forms: physical harm, loss of wealth, harm coming to others, social disruption, loss of freedom, emotional distress, or even death. All civilizations have things they fear. No society welcomes invasions, disasters, or social chaos—if your alien planet does, they must have a reason rooted in greed or ideology. Some civilizations fear their own creations, as the Old Ones of Exo III feared their android servants.

Greed is also a powerful incentive. Offer a being a reward for doing something, and, if the price is right, he'll do it. The price itself depends on what you're asking him to do and how it conflicts with other desires. Some civilizations are very avaricious; others are content to remain at a comfortable level. Greed isn't necessarily a desire for material reward—it is possible to be greedy for fame or respect. A culture with a strong military bent might actually be greeedy for the fear of other societies. The Federation could be described as greedy for knowledge.

Ideology is the least concrete motive. It is doing something because it is the "right thing to do." The specifics of what is right will vary, of course. The Federation follows the Prime Directive mostly as a matter of ideology. Ideology can be tremendously powerful—people will make great sacrifices and endure suffering and hardship for what they believe is right. Sometimes ideology is driven by greed, or by fear—the Eminian ideology held that suicide was right, because of the Eminians' fear of interplanetary warfare.

While ideologies can move people or civilizations to do things which might be irrational, the Narrator shouldn't use them as carte blanche to make aliens that are stupid or insane. No civilization follows an ideology which is evil by its own standards. Even Hitler (or John Gill) thought he was doing good. Evil actions must be justifiable somehow—"God approves of what we're doing," or "It is necessary to create the perfect society," or "It is to purify the race," or "It's for their own good."

The most powerful motives of a civilization are those which combine elements of the three drives listed above. To take an example from Earth history, the expansion of the Soviet Union after World War II was fueled by fear of attack by the West, greed for more resources, and the Marxist ideology of a worker's paradise. The United States and the West in turn were motivated by fear of another war, greed for markets, and the ideology of democratic government and capitalism to oppose the Soviets. The clash of two such powerful motives brought the planet to the brink of destruction for two generations.

CULTURE

The culture of a world may be described as the inhabitants' general style of doing things. It is a product of the race's psychology, the various aspects of their civilization, and happenstance. Earth and Vulcan have similar technologies, and both are important members of the Federation, yet the outward-looking, exuberant Human culture is very different from the contemplative, aloof attitude of the Vulcans.

Culture can perhaps best be described as the "personality" of a civilization. Two planets can have almost identical levels of technology, similar systems of government, and compatible ideologies, yet their cultures can be radically different. On 20th-century Earth, consider the differences between the United States and France. Both are democratic republics, both are major powers with advanced technology and a high standard of living, but Frenchmen and Americans have vastly different ways of looking at things.

OTHER DETAILS

Once you've determined the main elements of a civilization, you can add details as you see fit—and as needed in the story. While it isn't necessary to write an encyclopedia about every planet the Crew visits, the Narrator should have at least a general idea of how the people live and what the place looks like. Do the inhabitants live in soaring skyscrapers? Futuristic houses surrounded by parks? Or underground dormitories? Do they eat fresh-killed game? Or gray mush from the protein vats?

puritanical, straitlaced culture really dress its women in skimpy outfits of translucent gauze?

BY ANY OTHER NAME?

The existence of the Universal Translator means Narrators don't have to worry about making up convincing alien languages. But they do have to come up with names. Planets need names, as do characters, creatures, and aliens.

For planets, the name depends on who lives there. Some Federation colony worlds have astronomical names—Tau Ceti III, Beta Aquilae IX. This kind of name can also be used for very primitive worlds with natives whose only name for their world is "the ground." A few planets settled by humans have names reminiscent of early America: New Harmony, Hope, New Earth.

Starfaring races may use their own names for planets, like Tellar or Tiburon. In some cases they may use the astronomical name when dealing with interstellar explorers, either because their own word is hard to pronounce or simply out of politeness. Vulcans speaking to humans, for example, refer to their planet as "Vulcan" rather than "Ti-Valka'ain," just as Egyptians refer to their country as "Egypt" rather than "Misr" when speaking to Americans.

When creating alien words, consider two things. The first is how the aliens actually speak. Do they hiss, like reptiles? Then words will be full of sibilant sounds. Do they croak or caw? Give a sense of how they communicate through the sounds of their words. Aliens which do not use sound to communicate at all are likely to choose names from a suitable spoken language for use in their dealings with humanoids.

One shortcut used by science fiction writers is to model an alien language on a Human tongue (as the Vulcan language was modeled on Hebrew). Don't use actual words, but catch the sounds and syllable combinations. Place names in an atlas are a good source of foreign names and words. An alien language based on Malay would have names like Telabanda or Surindar; one derived from Finnish might have names more like Pektula or Kaimo.

The second thing to strive for is a bit more subjective. Use the way a language sounds to convey an emotional impression. "Klingon" has a harsh sound just right for "Mongol hordes with disruptors." Would the Klingons seem as threatening if they were called the Winkies? When a name is taken from Earth mythology or history, use the associations of the word. Tantalus is the location of a mental hospital—but Tantalus was a king in Greek mythology who was punished with endless torment in the afterlife. Maybe the Tantalus colony isn't such a nice place after all.

Putting It All Together

Let's go through the process of creating an alien civilization, including the planet, star system, and species template. First of all, we need a story idea. Here's one—the crew of a Federation starship is caught in the middle of a war that has gone on for so long the combatants have forgotten peace is even possible.

Where to begin? In this case, we'll start with technology and culture, and work backward. War is something waged by societies, so we design the society first. If our story were a survival episode, we'd begin with the hostile environ-

HODGKINS' LAW

One fascinating discovery of early interstellar explorers was Hodgkins' Law of Parallel Planetary Development. This law states that similar species in similar environments will have similar histories. A humanoid race on an Earthlike world is almost certain to have a history that roughly parallels events on Earth. In many cases the parallels have been eerily close, with societies evolving on alien worlds that are almost exact replicas of periods in Earth's past.

Narrators can take either a "strong Hodgkins" or a "weak Hodgkins" approach. The strong version of Hodgkins' Law means that alien civilizations can be modeled almost exactly on Earth history, in some cases right down to the uniforms and architecture. In a "strong Hodgkins" series, the Narrator can use worlds resembling Earth's past to tell what are essentially alternate history stories or time-travel adventures.

The weak version of Hodgkins' Law merely states that worlds at a given level of development are generally similar—a civilization with Roman-era technology is likely to have a large imperial government and probably a polytheistic religion, but the people probably won't wear togas and the gods won't have Classical names.

THE PRESERVERS

In some cases, cultures on alien worlds resemble historical Earth cultures because that is exactly what they are. Apparently an advanced race, known variously as the Preservers, the Wise Ones, or the Ancient Ones, transplanted groups of humans from Earth to other planets at various times in history. The American Indian culture on Epsilon Corvis III (where the *U.S.S. Enterprise* saved the planet from an oncoming asteroid) is one Preserver-seeded culture, and some anthropologists suspect that the Roman civilization on Planet 892-IV may also be a transplant. The Yangs and Kohms of Omega IV are either a Preserver transplant or else the descendants of Terran space voyagers from the early 21st century who passed through some sort of time distortion, as their records indicate they have lived on that world for centuries.

The Preservers have not focused all their attention on Earth; other sentient species have found cousins living on distant worlds. The identity of the Preservers themselves, and whether there are one or many Preserver races, is not known. They may be one of the highly advanced species like the Thasians or Metrons, or possibly even the self-described "gods" like Apollo.

Be creative in coming up with details. A good, striking note that brings the alienness of a culture home to the players will be remembered. If the people of the planet grow one fingernail long to use as a knife at dinner, the players (and possibly their characters) will forever after refer to the world as "that planet with the fingernails."

Make sure that your details all hang together. Don't just randomly come up with things. Ask if that civilization would really do things that way. Would a

ment. If it hinged on aliens with a peculiar reproductive cycle, we'd begin by designing the alien species. Start with the elements most important to your episode.

Okay, what technology do these warriors have? We want it fairly advanced, but not so advanced that the Crew's starship could be vaporized by a stray shot. Call it Level Five on the technology scale (atomic power, interplanetary spacecraft). These aliens have never left their star system, but they won't be terrified or awestruck by visitors from space. If the war has been going on for centuries, both sides must be equal in technology.

Now then, what about the governments? One decision which fits the story idea is that the two sides in the war are almost exactly alike, so we have to design only one society. If they've been fighting for centuries, we can assume they have a completely militarized government—there may be a remnant of civilian rule, but all real authority is in the hands of the supreme commanders. At the local level there may be less direct military control, but local officials have to obey edicts of the emergency war production authority. So we'll call this government a military dictatorship with an extensive bureaucracy. Military leaders are chosen on the basis of merit, and the leaders have the support of the people.

Next we need to think about economics. A massive, endless war doesn't fit the postmodern, decentralized, information-based economic model; let's give both sides a manufacturing economy. All enterprises are completely controlled and operated by the emergency war production authority, and civilians scrape by with just enough to live on while the bulk of economic output goes to supply the troops.

Motives are easy. Since the whole point is that the two sides have forgotten what they are fighting about, ideology isn't a very important motive any more. Fear is the driving force on both sides—fear of destruction by the enemy. Greed—a desire for victory—plays a minor part, but both sides are more interested in not losing than in winning.

As to culture, we'll take a page from Terran history (a "weak" Hodgkins' Law assumption) and model the civilization at war on Earth circa 1940—specifically, wartime England. The people all talk about "bearing up" and "doing our part" even as the missiles rain down. The military leaders are not psychotic maniacs, just doing their duty to the best of their ability. Of course, what with the war on and all, security is tight. Everyone watches out for spies, and strangers dressed in red and yellow shirts with funny insignia are sure to attract attention.

The details gradually emerge—populations living in domed cities, fortified against attack and defended by antimissile batteries; civilians toiling in underground factories; the military leaders living in hidden bunkers buried deep inside a mountain; radioactive ruins of great cities lying abandoned.

Now we need to think about our aliens themselves. How alien should they be? In *Star Trek*, they should be only as alien as they need to be for the story to be plausible. Given Human history, a war lasting centuries is all too plausible, so we can say the planet's inhabitants are fairly ordinary humanoids. We'll assume they are descended from omnivore stock, much like humans.

Their Attributes and Edges are the same as those of humans, but we'll assume that constant exposure to radiation and chemical weapons has caused a high mutation rate, and survivors of military service are often severely wounded.

So a great many of the natives have some sort of physical disadvantage—a Physical Impairment or Medical Problem. The healthiest specimens are all off fighting.

As a nod to the fact that these are aliens, we can give them some obviously nonhuman feature—perhaps they have four-fingered hands and zebra-striped skin. As to size, we will make them a little smaller than the Human norm, stunted by generations of wartime rationing.

Note that we have made them nearly Human because the story doesn't require anything more exotic. Sure, it would be cool if they had glowing eyes and communicated by ultrasonic whistles, but too much detail can obscure the focus of the episode. The heart of the story is the endless war; don't bury it in minutiae.

The planet is more important, because we need to make a decision: Is this war confined to one world, or is it an interplanetary conflict? There are a few things to consider: If the war is planet-bound, then the natives probably won't have weapons that can threaten the Crew's starship, at least not if it's in high orbit. If it's an interplanetary war, then the natives must have spacecraft of their own, and big missiles capable of crossing space. A visiting starship can literally get caught in the crossfire.

On the other hand, there won't be many people dying in the trenches if it's an interplanetary war. Bombs will simply drop out of the sky at random. Since we want to emphasize the futility of the war, we'll make it a ground conflict. There won't be any simple fix like using the starship's phasers to intercept passing missiles. The player characters will have to get the two sides to agree to stop fighting. Since it's a ground conflict, we need only one planet.

The war has been going on for centuries, therefore the planet was not settled by the Federation. The inhabitants are native to the planet, so it is a Class M world. Having decided that, we can keep most of the conditions on the planet approximately Earthlike. If the surface gravity doesn't play a big part in the story, leave it alone. So our war zone is about the same size as Earth, with about the same ratio of land to ocean. But this isn't Earth—it's a planet which has been at war for centuries. We can add conditions that reflect that fact: high levels of radiation in the atmosphere, large desert areas sterilized by atomic weapons or blighted by chemicals, ruined cities, orbiting debris. Perhaps the climate has grown colder as a result of "nuclear winter," so there are glaciers spreading over the northern latitudes. Those features are important to the story because they show what the fighting has done to a once green and lush planet.

The rest of the star system is unimportant, so we'll gloss over it: a single star, Type K, with half a dozen planets. The episode takes place on the second planet from its sun. If we need to know anything about the other planets we can design it later; right now all that's important is that they are uninhabited.

Finally, we need to come up with names. The planet is ravaged and wartorn, so we don't want names that evoke tropical islands or green meadows. We'll base the nomenclature on Russian, so the planet is called Palash (as is the whole system; pedantic Vulcan science officers may insist on calling the world Palash II). The two warring factions are the Pushka and the Zamoks. Native characters can have Russian or pseudo-Russian names like Erema, Ivash, Yakor, Marusia, and Valinya.

Now the stage is set. A starship arrives ....

In the shuttlecraft viewscreen behind Laird's head, Duffy could see Tiburon's sun looming ever larger. If it weren't for the phaser in Laird's hand, Duffy would jump him and change course. But the disgraced former captain of the Indomitable *seemed determined to die—and take the current captain with him. Duffy had a phaser, too. A classic stand-off. Words were the only weapon he had left to him now.*

"Mike, it's not too late. Let me turn the craft around."

Laird threw back his head and laughed. The maniacal quality of the laughter boded poorly for Duffy's chances of success. "It's been too late for the Federation since the day it was founded! Don't you see, Joe? We humans are just like the Klingons—a warrior people. The minute we turned our backs on our heritage, the minute we said it was possible to be explorers but not conquerors,

TO BOLDLY GO...

we doomed ourselves to the creeping soul death of ultimate mediocrity. It's time we threw off the shackles of foolish idealism, tossed those Federation leeches out on their ears, and got back to what we've always done best—conquest! You know I'm right! We'll teach the Klingons and Romulans what it's like to have an empire!"

"This isn't the Mike Laird I know talking. Listen to yourself. Barbara's death has—"

Laird's face reddened. "Don't you dare even mention her name!" Unable to control himself, he struck out with both fists—leaving himself open to Duffy's point-blank phaser shot.

"Sorry to do that to you, Mike," said Duffy, stepping over his unconscious body to retake the shuttle's controls, "but it's less permanent than diving into the sun of Tiburon."

Welcome Aboard

Welcome aboard. Whether you're a novice to roleplaying or a veteran, the next two chapters may prove illuminating. Experienced players and Narrators may find here much that is familiar. Like the best actors and directors, however, even veteran roleplayers benefit from rehearsal and a return to basics. Experience may be the best teacher, but the advice contained within these chapters can help you make fewer mistakes and point the way toward more fun and interesting games regardless of your level of expertise.

Creating a great episode calls for input from both Narrator and players. Initially, the Narrator has the more demanding job. Looking at roleplaying as ad lib theater, the Narrator acts as the director, stage crew, bit players, and featured guest stars. It may appear that the players have the easier job—most only have to portray a single character within the drama. But as any producer will tell you, if the stars aren't hot, the show bombs, and the players are definitely the stars.

Narrator and players meet at the center ground of the story itself. Whether taken from a published episode or woven whole cloth from the mind of the Narrator, the story—or script—remains unfinished until the players interact with it as their characters. Unlike a play or movie, in which the speeches are scripted and the outcome predetermined by the plot, a *Star Trek Roleplaying Game* episode provides its "actors" with the opportunity to help write the script themselves. Whether they assist the Narrator in telling a deeper, more intense story or take the game in unexpected directions, through their actions and decisions the players create something entirely new and unique, and as ephemeral as a single performance of a play. This synthesis between the Narrator's vision and the players' actualization of that vision becomes the story, replacing the bare bones of the tale with a fully fleshed adventure.

The Narrator must create a setting and a game reality in which the characters act. It's a large responsibility, requiring a lot of time and energy. Tips on how to do it make up the majority of this and the next chapter. The players have an equal responsibility, to build upon the framework provided by the Narrator and discover everything they can about their characters and the world in which they live. Feel free to experiment. We've provided some thoughts on making your *Star Trek Roleplaying Game* series exciting and true to the *Star Trek* genre, but you're the best judge of what works for you. Use some or all or none of the advice. The final frontier is enjoyment.

THE PLAYERS' MISSION

Novelists often claim that the characters they create have lives of their own that shape the story in ways the author didn't anticipate. That's almost always the case with the characters in a roleplaying game. Even the most recalcitrant character in a novel or movie can be wrestled into shape if the writer works hard enough, but the characters in the game have far more choice in their actions. It isn't going too far to say that without the players' consent and cooperation, the game cannot be played at all, much less a coherent story unfold. It's the players' mission to assist the Narrator in creating his story by portraying characters within the framework of the adventure and playing out the role each has chosen in terms of attitude, character outlook, and (if Mr. Spock will forgive us) logical actions. For a *Star Trek Roleplaying Game* experience to succeed, this means players must sometimes accept limitations on their choices or go beyond the expected and into the wholly unanticipated. Between those two paths lie a plethora of opportunities for great storytelling and rewarding play.

THE RIGHT CREW

Imagine Leonard Nimoy playing the role of Captain Kirk and James Doohan portraying Mr. Spock. Let's face it: It just wouldn't be the same. Despite the idea that actors ought to be able to take on any role, we all have our personal favorites as well as roles we don't usually choose, but in which we do well. This promotes healthy expression. Chosen roles can give players a wonderful opportunity to work out problems they might have (imagine an arachnophobe faced with friendly spider beings who are essential to the team's success), test solutions to dilemmas outside a real-world context, and stretch their imaginations all at the same time. The difficulty arises when no one proves willing to take a "lesser" role in the game. Particularly in a game that stratifies roles as the *Star Trek Roleplaying Game* can, some players may resent being under the command of others (see also "Rank and Game Play," page 33). One consolation is that captains who don't consult with their crew members or who issue arbitrary, self-serving, ineffective, or foolish orders don't remain long in Starfleet service. Still, not everyone can play the captain— or even the head of a particular department. We see a lot of Scotty, but there are other engineers on board, and even Kirk can't command twenty-four hours a day. Someone takes over when Sulu has to rest, and Uhura would fall into a coma or develop permanent laryngitis if nobody else ever took over communications.

When choosing which roles they will fill, players must decide three things:

- *Are you primarily interested in lots of physical action and combat or do you prefer a more cerebral approach?*

- *Can you say that you keep a level head and react quickly to crises or do you freeze up at critical moments until given a little encouragement or some suggestions?*

- *Why are you playing this game (i.e., what do you want to get out of the experience)?*

If you honestly answer those questions and look for a role that fits with your answers, you'll rarely go wrong. Even if you like slugfests and freeze in critical moments when trying to be clever, yet really want to learn how to play a commander, you can still find the proper role. Since the third question is most important, you'd try to play the captain or a department head. Make your difficulty a part of the character's personality and known profile. Maybe it's something he's ashamed of, but has confided to his second in command and asked his second to prod him when needed. Finally, maybe this competent but occasionally uncertain leader really likes a personal hands-on approach. This is the final frontier, after all; you never know when fisticuffs or martial talent may come in handy.

Of course, you could still run into problems if you and your best friend both want to be in command. Draw straws or roll off for it. Then switch for the next game. And if you don't start as the captain, well, consider the case of Sulu. He worked his way up, Mister. And so can you!

Besides, who's to say that on your ship, the captain doesn't send in the second crew whenever a crisis threatens—or turn over command and the bridge to the seconds when the first string has to oversee delicate negotiations on a nearby planet. As long as everyone has a role to fill and opportunity to play in an exciting adventure, no one should care if he is "in command." It isn't in the Narrator's best interest to thwart players' enjoyment by having an NPC captain issue unpopular orders anyway.

Choosing Characters Who Will Fit Together

All too often, a game is ruined by players who wants to play something totally inappropriate. Either they want to play "an elf-dragon hybrid who has been thrown into the *Star Trek* universe from Fantasyland and is seeking a way home," or they want to be "the vampiric soul-draining dire enemy of Starfleet who was raised by that kooky science officer and went on to join the Crew." Believe it or not, of the two choices, the second is less trouble, but still difficult. In the first case, you have to wonder: Why are you playing *Star Trek* to begin with if you don't want to portray someone from this universe? In the second example, the character simply won't fit into most adventures. Should the other players and the Narrator agree and help create a congenial atmosphere and go to bat for you against the other enemies of soul-sucking vampires (including the rest of Starfleet), go for it. Much roleplaying fun can be had thereby. If they aren't willing to put up with it, or it ruins the story everyone else is trying to tell, though, choose something else. Maybe you can bring the character in later or as an NPC if you narrate at a later time.

It seems obvious, but is often overlooked, that the characters should have some personal stake in what's going on in the game. There's little point in playing if everyone else is part of Starfleet and assigned to a ship while you want to be the Andorian ambassador to Earth. Playing a heretofore unknown alien type that the ship picked up while exploring is fine for a while, but unless the whole ship is lost in another quadrant à la *Voyager*, eventually you're going to visit a starbase and be placed in official hands while the ship moves on without you. All that said, if the other players and Narrator seem willing to go the extra light-year to accommodate odd character types, and that's truly

what you want to play, do it. It's a big universe out there, and the *Enterprise* didn't get to even a quarter of it. Nobody says you have to adhere strictly to "The Known Facts of the *Star Trek* Universe." The point is exploration, after all. Just make sure everyone's comfortable with it.

The Dreaded Skill Coverage Method

Many groups choose what characters they play based on covering a range of skills needed in the game. That's certainly one way of doing it. It can run the risk of forcing certain less aggressive players into the "also featuring" category where they're assigned characters solely according to what everyone else is not playing. That can become boring and frustrating. Choosing a character concept that appeals to you is usually the best bet. Since all players are different, chances are most of the needed skills will be covered anyway. If it's a choice between skills and enjoyment, pick enjoyment. It's the Narrator's job to provide NPC's to cover areas your group's skills lack. Most Narrators really aren't secretly waiting for the opportunity to don an evil smile and say, "So, none of you know anything about the helm, eh? Heh, heh, heh. Red Alert!"

WHAT ARE LITTLE GIRLS MADE OF?

Creating and playing a character should encompass more than just choosing your hair color, race, and profession. The best concept in the world doesn't mean much as long as there is no flesh on the bones. Details of the character's life history are extensively covered in the character creation section, yet even here the focus is on skills acquisition or information concerning the character's home planet or specializations. Advantages and disadvantages add to the character's overall picture and may be a pointer leading to interesting background details that explain how the character became advantaged or why she has a certain disadvantage. Still, there's one final step that players should consider that can provide both the character and the Narrator with that little extra "something" that can be worked into story lines to deepen the experience of the game. We know from the creation process what the character is—a Human or a Vulcan, perhaps a navigator or a science officer—we may even know that she has excellent hearing, yet is too impulsive sometimes to wait for all the facts before acting. What we don't know are her innermost feelings and quirky talents that aren't covered under normal skills.

Feelings

Everyone has feelings—personal likes and dislikes, a sense of ethics or a lack of them, prejudices or codes of honor. What would Dr. McCoy be without his crusty disapproval of the transporter or his compassionate nature? Each character should be as individual as the good doctor. Answering the following questions for yourself and informing the Narrator of those answers can go a long way toward making your character a real individual in a sea of similar skills. Doing so provides you with greater insight into your own character and allows the Narrator to play to the information, either to address some of it directly in the course of the game or to create moral dilemmas your character must handle. In either case, answering these questions should deepen the impact of the game for you.

- *Of what action or accomplishment are you most proud?*

- *Of what action (or failure to act) are you most ashamed?*

- *What person, thing, or event has provided your greatest joy?*

- *What has caused your greatest sorrow?*

- *What do you truly hate? This might be a person, a race, trusting your flesh to the transporter, insects, or anything else against which you hold a prejudice, however reasonable or inexcusable your dislike.*

- *What do you do to avoid the hated person or thing? Do you seek to annihilate it, flee from it, or aggressively confront it at every opportunity? Are you obsessed enough that it affects your work?*

- *What do you genuinely love? What would you do to protect that love?*

- *Aside from the strictures of Starfleet, what is your personal code of honor?*

- *What causes you to feel outraged? Do you take steps to stop such things or merely express your feelings verbally?*

- *How far will you go to accomplish a goal?*

- *How do you feel about the Prime Directive? Under what circumstances would you violate it?*

- *Would you kill another intelligent being?*

- *For what person, object, or ideal would you sacrifice your life?*

There are dozens of other questions you might ask yourself to define your character's inner self. Feel free to add to this list. The more you can identify your character's psychological and emotional boundaries, the more involving and enjoyable the game will become. As you expand your knowledge of what makes your character tick, the more resonance the events and choices in the game will have.

Quirks

Unlike advantages and disadvantages, quirks don't give you any real benefit or hindrance under normal game conditions. They exist simply to help you further define and customize your character. Everyone (except complete

dullards, who wouldn't get a job in Starfleet anyway) has a few weird talents or defining habits that makes him who he is. Spock's habit of raising his eyebrows when he's intrigued or surprised is a quirk. So is his penchant for observing phenomena impassively while saying, "Fascinating!" It's these unexpected details that sometimes become the most amusing or endearing (or annoying) quirks that everyone else looks to as an essential part of the character. So, think about your character and decide on a quirk or two.

They don't have to be obvious. You may grimace whenever called upon to read the sensors; you might unconsciously dance a little jig whenever you're particularly pleased by something. Maybe you can make bird sounds and whistle them when getting dressed in the morning. Maybe you have an accent like Chekov or Scotty. Perhaps you collect rocks and just can't resist pocketing a stone or two from any new planet. Perhaps you always clear your throat before having to make any important speech. Maybe you blush or stammer around beautiful women. Whatever it is, make it interesting and in sync with your character's personality. Pretty soon, every time Lieutenant Valrann and Ensign Morel meet someone new, the whole crew will know she's going to brush her hair back from her face and straighten her uniform before she introduces herself, while he'll undoubtedly develop a case of nervous hiccups.

ACTING THE ROLE

A noted director once called for actors who experienced difficulty correctly portraying their roles to "sit in character." Sit in character? Strange as it sounds, body posture does determine (or in some cases, reflect) our attitudes. Sitting rigidly and upright can help you portray your militarily correct security officer or logical Vulcan while a more relaxed stance might help you imagine yourself as a rakish engineering assistant. Aside from assuming the physical posture, it's even more important to adopt a mental attitude appropriate to the character. You've already answered a number of questions that form your viewpoints. Now you have to concentrate on bringing those views to life by acting in accordance with what your character would do. Try to think like a Starfleet officer. That means you cannot analyze whatever situation the Narrator concocts as you yourself would. Instead, you must approach it in character. While you might flee from an unknown menace, that's hardly likely behavior for a science officer. You may very well know something about the Gorn from watching *Star Trek* on TV, but how informed is your security officer character?

Part of the enjoyment of roleplaying is to become the character for the length of the game. Whatever method you prefer to put yourself in such a frame of mind is helpful. Whether you sit in character, use a more technical vocabulary than in daily life, speak with an accent, or even wear a *Star Trek* uniform, the idea is to place yourself in the proper mood to act according to the dictates of the character. Good roleplaying asks you to do what the character would do, not necessarily to make the smartest move (unless it's in your character to do so). A good rule of thumb: If you're playing a Vulcan and Spock wouldn't laugh at it, neither should you. Use that generalization to help you visualize what your own character would do. Think of the closest equivalent from the *Star Trek* series and imagine that character doing what you plan to do. If you think they'd perform a particular action or react in a certain way, go ahead. If not, think about it first. You still may choose to do it, but at least you'll know it's an informed choice, not a momentary urge.

Suspension of Disbelief

One of the most important actions you can take to enjoy the game is to suspend your disbelief. Your character may search for the reasons why that NPC can fly when gravity shouldn't allow such a thing, but you as the player must be willing to accept that the being is indeed flying and that it can do so. Perhaps you won't discover why it is able to fly, but if you insist on adhering strictly to real-world science, you'll ruin your own and everyone else's enjoyment. The being's body chemistry may alter its weight or it might possess some advanced technology that allows its flight. The point is, you have to allow the Narrator some leeway to depart from "What Is Known As True." Besides, if you're playing *Star Trek*, you've already accepted transporter beams, warp drives, and impassive guys with pointed ears as "normal." Forget the science and get on with the game.

Keeping the Mood

One of the best ways to remain in character is to help the Narrator establish and maintain the mood or feel of the game. If the situation calls for serious speech and actions, refraining from out of game comments, puns, or levity helps everyone else keep within the spirit of the game. Should there be negotiations underway, listening carefully and responding as your character would rather than leaving the room, rattling dice, looking through papers, or munching on snacks can help you focus on the game and on your character's place within the adventure. Even if your character isn't in the spotlight during a particular scene, acting as a concerned member of the crew and showing respect for the other players and the Narrator will help you keep the game on track. Who knows? While the captain and medical officer are busy with negotiations, your overlooked engineer might just spot a vital clue because he was paying attention—and those with vital clues tend to become the focus of subsequent scenes.

THE NARRATOR'S MISSION

Just as the players need to work together so that everyone can share in the enjoyment of participating in an exciting game, the Narrator has the responsibility to help the players accomplish their goals. The Narrator's mission consists of making sure that everyone involved in the game has a good time and comes away from each playing session with a feeling of satisfaction and time well spent. To accomplish this task, Narrators must possess the skills of a good director. These include knowing your players, knowing your script, and knowing yourself.

CASTING CALL: KNOW YOUR PLAYERS

Players come to a game with many expectations. Some of your players see roleplaying as a means of temporarily escaping the tedium of everyday life by stepping into the part of a starship crew member. Others enjoy the chance to take part in an impromptu drama without the stress of performing before an audience. Most players look forward to testing their wits and luck against a challenging situation. Your job, as Narrator, involves knowing the reasons why your players play and doing everything you can to help them achieve their goals.

In all likelihood, your players cover a broad spectrum of personalities, each with a different approach to roleplaying and a different way of dealing with the demands and challenges of participating in a game. You need to recognize these different styles of play and attitudes toward roleplaying: Each one offers a unique set of advantages and disadvantages. The make-up of your crew—the group of players you assemble for your game—determines in large part what kind of episode or drama you narrate for them.

Before you decide upon a plot for your episode, think about the players who, as their *Star Trek Roleplaying Game* characters, will make up the Crew that will encounter the problems you pose and the opponents you set against them. Just as a director tries to find the right actor for each role in a play or film, you, as Narrator, need to assess the qualities of your players and help them choose the types of characters they will play in your story. In order to do this, you need to know who your players are and what they want from your game.

Typecasting: Fitting the Player to the Role

What kind of players make up your cast? Knowing your players' strengths and weakness as roleplayers goes a long way toward ensuring a smooth-running, enjoyable game. While you can't exercise complete control over which characters your players choose to create, you can offer suggestions to them and try to steer each individual in the direction that will guarantee maximum enjoyment for him and for the others in your group.

Players fall into several categories. Rules lawyers, for example, enjoy arguing fine points of game mechanics and need to feel that everything that happens in play goes "by the book." While knowledge of the rules of the *Star Trek Roleplaying Game* is an admirable quality in players (and essential in Narrators), constant interruptions to argue minute details can slow down the action of a game to the detriment of all. If you have a player who qualifies as a rules lawyer, you might encourage him to choose a science officer or engineer as his character. Either role should provide him with enough technical action to minimize the chance for interruptions.

Other players enjoy taking the lead. While a Crew can have only one player in a command role, other roles allow players with leadership skills to assert themselves within the context of their characters. Security officers or department heads make good characters for aggressive players.

Some individuals insist on trying to do everything all the time. These overachievers attempt (often unknowingly) to usurp the prerogatives of other players. While this abundance of enthusiasm adds to that individual's involvement in the episode, the excesses of the overachiever can make other players feel superfluous or slighted during the course of a game. As Narrator, you can try channeling the overachievers in your Crew into character choices that allow them to attempt solutions without stealing the limelight from other Crew members. Medical officers and engineers provide active players with an array of skills that give them the opportunity to experiment with new ways of solving problems without stepping on the toes of other players' characters.

Shy players often prefer staying out of the main thrust of the action. If one of your players tends to freeze up whenever he becomes the center of attention or has a hard time making decisions under pressure, encourage him to take a role that does not demand rapid and decisive actions. Science officers, communications officers, or medical officers usually act under the orders of superiors and do not need to take the initiative in order to fulfill their character responsibilities. (This doesn't mean that they can't make decisions on their own or assert themselves in appropriate situations, but these qualities do not "come with the job description.")

Occasionally, a player desires to try something new by creating a character that goes against his preferred type. Narrators should encourage experienced players to expand their repertoire of roles. Let the player who usually takes charge adopt the character of a medical or science officer for a change while a normally reticent player takes command of the Crew.

Knowing how to cast your players into roles that will suit their playing styles and personalities while at the same time adding to their enjoyment of the game goes a long way toward ensuring that everyone–including you–has fun.

Plan B: Troubleshooting after the Fact

Even the best intentions can go awry, however. Despite your best casting efforts, you may have to cope with problem players. Players may not always take your suggestions, or you may make a mistake in your assessment of the best character types for your players. Furthermore, players may have days when their personal troubles or outside-of-game stresses affect their attitudes during the game. Additionally, you may find that you have at least one player who habitually disrupts or detracts from your game for any number of reasons. When things go wrong, your job as Narrator is to do your best to set things right.

Problems may arise from many circumstances. Sometimes the real world of family, school, or work affects a player's ability to give his full attention to the game. While professional actors learn the trick of "leaving it at the stage door," your players do not always have the ability to put aside their daily frustrations or personal stresses. If you realize that one of your players seems "off his game" or seems to be taking out his frustrations "in character" on the other characters, you need to address his behavior before it disrupts the game or causes harm to his relationships with the other players. The best thing to do in a situation where a player's personal problems affect his "in game" behavior is to take the player aside (perhaps during a brief break in the scenario) and express your concern for his well being. He may not even realize what he is doing until you point his behavior out to him. If his problems continue to prevent him from focusing on the game, you might suggest that he forego trying to play the rest of the session, since he doesn't seem to be enjoying himself anyway.

Players may also develop personality conflicts during the course of a game. While not everyone in a game needs to like each other all the time, players should learn to get along with each other and avoid bickering during the game. This does not mean that characters can't argue with one another or even actively dislike each other. Players, however, should not confuse their

characters' emotions with their own. As a Narrator, you need to encourage your players to keep personal conflicts out of the game. As Starfleet officers, their characters will find plenty of conflict within the context of their adventures. Once again, you should take aside any players who seem to have problems with each other and try to work things out during a break or in between game sessions. If the problem seems insoluble, then you may, as a last resort, have to ask one or both of the quarreling players to leave your game until they resolve their differences. While this is not the easiest or best solution, such a drastic measure occasionally becomes necessary to preserve the enjoyment level for the majority of players.

Problems can also arise from your end of the game. If your players spend most of their time absently rolling dice and reading magazines, or if they seem more interested in passing around snacks than accompanying their crewmates down to the surface of a planet, you can assume that something in the game fails to hold their attention. Perhaps the game's plot lacks enough excitement or activity for all of your players, or you spend too much time setting the stage before you allow the characters to interact with their environment. Maybe you have run six consecutive episodes in which the characters meet up with their evil counterparts. The best thing to do whenever your players turn to other avenues of amusement during the course of your game is to ask them what they want and what you need to do to give it to them. Remember, you can lose the respect of your players more quickly by running a boring game than by asking for their help.

NOW PLAYING: KNOW YOUR SCRIPT

Besides knowing your players and the characters they have chosen to play, you need to have a thorough knowledge of the game you intend to present for them. Moreover, you should try to match the script of your game to your players. Whether you write your own episodes or run published material, make certain that the plots you involve your players in will hold their attention and capture their imaginations.

Before you decide on what kind of adventures you will offer up to your players, ask yourself what kind of episodes best suit the people in your game. Do your players prefer lots of combat and little to no "small talk?" Would they rather explore unfamiliar planets and spend their time "roughing" it in alien deserts or wilderness? Do they enjoy handling delicate negotiations with vastly different lifeforms? Try to select a scenario that will engage the attention of your players and offer them opportunities to do what they enjoy doing best.

Just as a good director studies his script so that he knows all the ins and outs of the major and minor plot lines, as well as how the characters fit into the story, the Narrator should strive to make himself as familiar with his episode as possible. You need not memorize the script for your game, but you should have a good idea of how all the scenes fit together, the sequence in which they must occur, whether or not some scenes can be played out of sequence, and the climax toward which all the action of the game should build.

As you study the scenario, make note of which scenes seem particularly appropriate for the skills of specific characters. Try to anticipate possible areas of difficulty in your game. Do most of the scenes involve heavy fighting and leave little or nothing for the less combat-oriented characters to do? Or do you have several scenes involving negotiations following one another without an action-based change of pace? Either way, you may risk losing the attention of those players whose characters find themselves on the sidelines. Make sure that each scene has something in it for every character, even if it is only a small part. The bit players in one scene may have a chance to stand in the spotlight in the next scene if you plan your game accordingly.

You can find more information on the specifics of preparing and narrating an episode later on in this chapter. For now, remember that your knowledge of the game provides the linchpin that holds your story together.

DIRECTORS WANTED: KNOW YOURSELF

Every director has a unique style, reflective of his personality and structured to maximize strengths while minimizing weaknesses. As a Narrator, you should work to develop your own style of running games to take advantage of your strongest points. In order to do this, you need to spend some time in self-assessment.

What kinds of games do you enjoy? Do you prefer grand-scale scenarios with universe-shaking results, or do small stories of personal crisis appeal more to your sense of the dramatic? How well do you handle game mechanics? What personality traits help or hinder your job as Narrator?

Style vs. Substance

Regardless of the specific script you choose, you bring your own personal style—your directorial stamp—to your game. Try to define what that style is, so that you can make each game stronger and more distinctive by filtering the script through your particular mode of narration. If you enjoy emphasizing the big picture, make sure that the scripts you choose have a larger theme.

Fortunately, most typical *Star Trek* plots do concern important issues or involve the fate of the universe (or at least a portion of it). If you prefer sticking with a smaller scale (relatively speaking, in a game that takes place across light-years), select scripts that allow you to narrow the focus of your story enough to explore the details. If you can't adapt an episode to suit your style of play, scrap it or put it on the back burner.

Vary your style occasionally. Although consistency in your style as Narrator gives your players a sense of security and allows them to know what to expect from your games, players enjoy variety. Test your own growth as a Narrator by trying a different style. If you excel in running games that rely on combat to overcome the central problem, take the risk of broadening your game's horizon to include situations that require negotiation to solve (as well as a few well placed combat scenes).

While you may want to stick to the tried and true style of narration at first, as you gain experience as a Narrator, you should expand your repertoire of styles. If you have the opportunity to watch other Narrators (or play in a game run by a Narrator who uses a different style from yours), you can take notes on how you can adapt someone else's style to fit your personal method of narration.

Tools of the Trade

Some Narrators enjoy bringing game mechanics into play throughout the game. After all, why does a game have rules if you constantly ignore them? If you like to structure your games so that your players make frequent use of dice rolls to check their skills, make certain that you know what kinds of rolls to call for. Most players do not object to rolling dice if the situation calls for it. On the other hand, insisting on dice rolls for everything can bring a fast-moving game to a slow, boring crawl.

Other Narrators prefer to use the minimum amount of game mechanics, relying on the principles of shared storytelling and roleplaying to move the plot along. If you avoid the confines of the rules-as-written in favor of a more free-wheeling style of narration, make certain that you touch base with the rules when it becomes necessary. Sometimes, particularly in combat situations, roleplaying is not enough. Know when it's time to bring out the dice and refer to the rulebook. You can find more information on using game mechanics later in this chapter.

Inner Space

Most importantly, you need to look at yourself objectively. Ultimately, your personal skills count more than almost anything else toward your success as a Narrator. When you take charge of a game, you also take charge of the enjoyment of your players. How you react in stressful situations, how you express yourself, and how you act toward your players as a whole and as individuals depends on a thorough knowledge of your strengths and weaknesses.

Do you tend to choke in critical situations, or can you maintain a calm exterior despite the pressures that can arise during heated moments of play? When tempers get out of hand or when players take their characters' problems too personally, can you act as a cool-headed mediator or are you prone to take sides? Do you have favorite players? Can you look beyond your personal preferences and make certain that all your players get an equal share of attention in the game?

If you know that you tend toward panic reactions in a crisis, try to head off potentially explosive situations before they erupt. Practice ways of dealing with difficult players using your strongest assets. If you solve problems with logic and rational arguments, try reasoning with your problem players. If you favor the indirect method of problem solving, you may want to divert the attention of disruptive players toward something that will occupy them long enough for

them to forget their problem behavior.

Examine your feelings toward your players. Do you have any special friends in your group? Do you have a tendency to ignore players who don't put themselves forward? Do you instinctively recoil from aggressive players or grow confrontational when assertive individuals challenge your rulings?

While you cannot always change your personality, you can improve your strengths and work around your weaknesses. Don't hesitate to consult books on interpersonal relationships or leadership skills to help you get better at the task of narration.

In the Captain's Chair: Storytelling

You enter the darkened temple, moving quickly along the crumbling sides until you reach a stained block of stone that serves as an altar. Your tricorder indicates a single lifeform just ahead. As you reach the block, a figure dressed all in skins and feathers suddenly rises from behind it to confront you. "I am … uh …" (sounds of rustling papers) "I am Grinel, mistress of … um … the high art of … mistress of the high arts!"

At one time of another, most of us have experienced a session similar to this. If we were players, we probably lost interest in the story as soon as the Narrator lost the thread of the tale; if we were the Narrator in question, we probably cursed ourselves for losing that scrap of paper on which we wrote out the alien's cool name and title. In either case, the story crashed to an ignominious halt through lack of preparation. Were we filming a movie, such a slip would cost thousands of dollars. Luckily, our games are a little less expensive in purely monetary terms, but we do invest our time and energy in them. Such an investment calls for an equal commitment from the Narrator. Just as the captain would never allow his starship to leave on a mission without enough dilithium, the Narrator has to make certain he covers all the bases both before and during the game in order to provide entertainment for his players. Below are a few suggestions for doing just that.

PREPARATION: SETTING THE SCENE

Storytelling is an art, which sometimes fools people into believing they can spin a tale out of whole cloth from their imagination, eschewing preparation and technique. Some people can in fact do just that, but most of us benefit from having all our ducks in a row before we start shooting at them. Most good artists know their medium and the rules of perspective. In like manner, we as storytellers and tale-spinners need to understand the peculiarities of our "canvas."

CAPTAIN'S LOG: SCRIPTING

Scene: Late afternoon. You've just bought a cool-looking episode for the *Star Trek Roleplaying Game* and plan to run it for your group tonight. Unless you're the world's fastest speed reader and have total recall, you've just made your first mistake as a Narrator. Published adventures serve as great tools, but even scenarios constructed by professional writers can't inspire a great game

unless the Narrator is familiar with the contents and has taken time to customize the story for his own players and prepare for a gaming session. What may look like a straightforward "solve it with fisticuffs and derring-do" adventure may prove to be a "Vulcan officer mind-melds with creature to learn the truth" episode instead, heading off in unforeseen directions for which you'll be unprepared without such forethought. If you don't know that the apparent villain is actually a Starfleet operative working within the bad guys' organization to bring it down, you may mislead the players' characters into thwarting him and ruining the episode. There's nothing more frustrating for players than to do what they believe to be right based on what the Narrator has told and shown them only to discover that the Narrator didn't know the story well enough. Rewrites of events the group has played through are extremely unsatisfying alternatives.

Avoiding these situations is as easy as taking the time to read through the episode. Make notes on scenes you particularly want to emphasize, places in which different crew members can shine, notable friends and foes, any changes you'll have to make to suit your group, and anything that may twist the plot in unexpected directions. (In this connection, make certain nothing in the episode conflicts with stories you've already told or plan to tell.) Once you've done this, you'll have a good grasp of the story line and may even anticipate some of the responses your crew might make.

Finally, you need to consider whether the episode fits your narrative style. Does it rely on impersonal messages and nonintelligent foes when your strength lies in portraying a detailed supporting cast? Maybe you need to create a "voice" for yourself by inserting an NPC in the adventure. She'll have to fit in, though, which requires you to figure out who she is, how she got there, and her role in the story. If it's a harsh or dangerous environment, how did she survive when everyone else died? Is she really a part of the problem rather than a victim or a helpful ally?

Creating Your Own Episodes

The same meticulous planning should become a part of constructing your own adventures. Having a great idea about the ship running into symbiotic protozoan threads that try to take over the minds of crew members isn't enough. You have to detail the threads, figure out why they are in the place the Crew encounters them, and then coerce, cajole, or entice the characters into visiting the area. Then you have to figure out what can harm the symbiotic creatures, how the Crew can rid themselves of them, and what the threads are likely to cause the Crew to do before they are eradicated. You have to make certain that all the parts of the story fit together.

If you have a thriving bazaar right next to the area where the threads reside, the natives better be immune to the threads, already under their control, or have some means of preventing them from entering the bazaar area. Further, unless there's a very good reason to, placing some extra scenery such as a Vulcan ship on the planet won't make much sense. Wanting to portray Vulcans and "just sticking them in" doesn't work. Extraneous elements just confuse the players, making them wonder what relevance there is to having Vulcans nearby.

Avoiding the Deus Ex Machina Syndrome

The final element to your planning, as simple as it sounds, concerns creating stories the characters can "win." If you present the crew with a problem, you must also give them clues or make opportunities available to them to solve whatever dilemma they face. Bringing in a deus ex machina (appropriately, this term from Greek drama means a "god in a machine"), an all-powerful being or technology, to deal with the situation leaves a bad taste in players' mouths. Consider the episodes of *Star Trek* you've seen, such as "The Squire of Gothos," which features the entity known as Trelane, whom Kirk thwarts before his parents make him stop playing with his new "toys." Even when "superior" beings intervene, it's after the Crew has taken the significant actions necessary to resolve the situation. Don't take that away from the players.

LIGHTS, CAMERA, ACTION!

Now you have your script. You've gone over it and know the ins and outs of the story. It's time to arrange the elements that will bring that story to life. Depending on your gaming situation (are you playing at home, in a college dorm room, in a gaming shop, or at a convention?) you may be able to employ some or all of the ideas given here to enhance the mood and excitement of the game. Description is certainly helpful, even essential when running a game, but several elements can draw on our senses to further our interest and help us understand the game reality. Sight, sound, feel, taste, and smell all provide us with information about our surroundings. Why shouldn't these be brought to the fore in games as well?

Sight

Science tells us we receive most of our input from sight. Our vision takes in a thousand tiny cues every moment, resolving a chaotic jumble of color, shape, and movement into coherent pictures we then focus on or ignore as unimportant. Our eyes tell us that the waving red banner on the storefront is pretty but ultimately not important, while that blue car speeding toward us is something we need to watch to avoid being hurt by it. Used in combination with hearing and touch, we can identify millions of objects simply by looking at them. If we've seen a long-haired cat before and stroked its fur, the next time we see such a cat, we know if feels fuzzy when we first see it. Descriptions can tell us what we're seeing, and we might even visualize it to ourselves, but a verbal description lacks the immediacy of a picture.

As a Narrator, you can try to find pictures that show environments, objects, and people similar to what you're describing to your players. Lacking photographs, you can try to draw these (or sweet talk an artist friend into doing it for you). Consider this: You want your players to know they are in an active volcanic region. You can tell them that the area is extremely hot, that steam covers the area, and lava is pouring from the lip of a volcano and running downslope toward them. Better still, find a picture of an erupting volcano in a science or nature magazine or book—preferably in color—and show it to the players as you describe the surroundings. If you have access to it and it won't disrupt the game, a tape showing the same thing in motion is even better. Even a simple map of the arrangement of an alien settlement or a drawing

showing the layout of an important NPC's dwelling can be helpful. Maps, diagrams, written encrypted messages, and detailed landscapes or portraits can all help players visualize what you're describing.

Sound

Have you ever camped in the woods at night and suddenly noticed that all the insects have stopped whirring and chirping? Did it frighten you or make you wonder what was passing that quieted them all? You might not have even been aware you were hearing them until their racket stopped. That's a function of sound. We may screen out nine tenths of what we hear, but we're quite good at picking out sounds that may be important to us. Sounds can enhance the game environment as well. If you have appropriate means of creating sound effects, by all means use them (if it won't seem silly and bring the game to a halt). Records, tapes, and CD's of various sound effects used in plays exist and might prove useful. Further, it's possible to tape the sounds of the transporter and other equipment used in *Star Trek* directly from the show.

Music also provides an emotional element to certain portions of the game. You need not have a complete musical score, but at significant parts where you want the players to feel the action more keenly, add appropriate music—something fast and exciting for a fight scene, heroic for a tense race against time, or sad for the death of someone. Played softly in the background, it won't be too distracting, yet can set the mood. Louder music can be played for scenes in bars or on R&R planets. And don't forget the all-important theme music from the show played just before you start the game. That can be most important of all, as it alerts the players that you're starting the game and lets them know they need to settle into their roles and pay attention. That will set them up for yet another sound—your voice as you introduce the opening elements of the adventure.

Feel

Have you ever been to a haunted house set up for Halloween? In many, they have an area where visitors are led through blindfolded and handed various things while being told the objects are something else. Cold spaghetti becomes a mass of brains and peeled grapes are explained as eyeballs. Silly as it sounds, it can be quite effective, since humans are creatures of great imagination. Far more subtle than the first two senses, feel is also more difficult to

introduce into the game. Nevertheless, with a little work, it can be done. Imagine that the characters have entered a dimly lit cavern covered with cobwebs. Ask each player to close his eyes, then lightly pull a gauze scarf across each of their faces. They'll be far more affected by it than any description could evoke. In like manner, subtly altering the room temperature can go a long way toward establishing the environment. Imagine setting a scene on the planet Vulcan in a chilly room. Makes your job a lot harder, doesn't it? Turn up the heat (and maybe replace a few light bulbs with red ones) and voila, you have Vulcan. Handing around fur or silk to let players feel what their characters touch can also help them better understand game reality. And if you simply must, feel free to use the peeled grapes.

Taste

Another subtle sense, taste should primarily be confined to fixing something yummy for your players to eat or drink and offering it to them "in game" as a delicacy of the region or ritual meal that the natives expect of their allies. Even then, it's best not to offer anything alcoholic since mind-altering substances are not only too distracting, but usually frowned upon by Starfleet. Always make sure before embarking on this technique that none of your players is allergic to anything you plan to serve. Finally (particularly if your offering is crunchy), clear off any leftovers once the scene is past to minimize the extended munching that can bleed over into subsequent scenes.

Smell

Related to taste, smell is also subtle, but quite evocative. Memories can be awakened through familiar smells and moods established (which is why aromatherapy is currently so popular). Again, make certain that nobody is allergic to anything you use to create scents for the game. Then feel free to experiment. Hundreds of scents are available as incense or potpourri. These might be used to create the smell of an alien settlement or ship or to enhance the sense of the landscape through which the characters pass (using floral scents, for example). If incense bothers you, an alternative is to use things you may have around the house. Send the Crew to a tropical scene by cutting oranges or lemons and leaving them out to scent the room, or immerse the characters in a pine forest by cutting an evergreen branch and bringing it inside. Use your imagination and your players will too.

PROPS

Many of the things we just discussed can be thought of as props. Like props used in a play, they're only effective if they're on hand when needed. Don't waste time fumbling for the proper CD; have it in the machine and ready to go on cue. Likewise, don't rustle and page through a book of maps looking for the one you need; have the page marked or the book open to the correct page before starting the game. Just as the prop master dresses the set before filming starts, you've assembled an array of items meant to help your players imagine their own "movie set." There are still a few other props beyond those that you need to have ready to hand before beginning your game. These include any written materials the characters might gain access to, any special depictions of places, items, or people, and any small objects representative of something the Crew might handle. If the group is searching for the Sacred Key of Kolhabharr, for example, you might want to have an old skeleton key on hand, or you could bamboozle them by having the key be a small, round gemstone (a marble) that fits into a depression in the door they seek to open. Props might also include battle mats and miniatures if you prefer to use such for visualizing ship or personal combat. Your own imagination (and space on the surface where you play) is the only real limit to utilizing all these elements.

If you have none of these playing aids or don't have the space to incorporate them, don't panic. Think what you might have under different circumstances and use that as a guide to describing the scene—using taste, smell, and feel as well as sight and sound—and you can't go far wrong.

SIGNALING THE START

"Captain's log, stardate 2722.5. These are the voyages of the starship ...."

Many storytellers use a technique called the recognition signal to start their sessions. Usually it's a word or a phrase that tells the listeners that the storyteller is beginning and they ought to quiet down and pay heed to his words. A similar method can be employed in gaming to let the players know it's time to stop discussing work or the movie they saw last week, step into character, and prepare to play. *Star Trek* does this by playing the theme music and showing an opening sequence, and so can you. We've already mentioned using the show's opening theme to command the players' attention, but once you've done so, a tiny bit more is needed.

Whether or not you have access to theme music (or some other musical piece you can use as an opening signal), you can provide a familiar introductory sequence with only a little bit of work. The *Star Trek* milieu provides Narrators with the option of the very best way to introduce almost any episode: the captain's log. It's completely in tune with the series, sets the mood, and lets the players know immediately what their characters' mission is (or at least what it appears to be). Some players (and even some Narrators) may feel that this method is overly coy and goes beyond identifying with the TV series into the realm of cuteness. If that's how you feel, then find some other way, but do at least consider some method of opening your game. When done right, the "captain's log" really isn't a silly overidentification with the show, but a good tool for presenting complex information to the players in a familiar shorthand. It allows the game to get off to a start in the right direction without a lot of fooling around trying to remember what happened last week or grandstanding for attention by one character.

As Narrator you can read off a prepared speech that gives the stardate and identifies the basics of the situation. It might be something as simple as this:

"Captain's log, stardate 4467.2. We have traveled to the edge of the Sicon system to pick up passengers headed for colonization of Sicon III. Upon arrival at Sicon Prime, we discovered that the colonists and the Starfleet personnel assigned to assist in their move—along with every other soul on the planet—have disappeared. We continue scanning for lifeforms on the planet below as we ready a team to investigate what appear to be the ruins of the once-thriving city of Glenconner."

It's succinct, to the point, and gives the players all the information they can gather before beaming down to the planet to begin the investigation. It also tells them what their original mission was, where they currently are, and what the state of their environment is (*i.e.*, the city is in ruins). More information on what happened, who might be behind it, and anything else of significance may be discovered in the game itself, but the players have now been primed to look for significant clues.

If you feel odd reading this statement and one of the players is portraying the captain, you can give it to that player to read aloud. Alternatively, you might take the player aside, explain what is known about the situation to him, and ask him to create his own captain's log entry to present to the rest of the Crew. Whichever makes you and the player more comfortable is fine. Should you then occasionally vary the pattern to start a game in medias res (in the midst of the action) or with commentary from some other officer's log, the players will immediately sit up and take notice that something very different is about to happen.

STORYTELLING: RUNNING AN EPISODE

At last! You're actually ready to start the game. If you've done all your preliminary work, it may seem like the actual game would never arrive, yet here it is. You've got all your props, music, lighting, and important supporting cast cards ready to go. The tape is wound and the captain's log has been read. Now's the time when it all comes together into a finished product. Now is not the time to sit back and relax. You're about to really go to work.

Description: Setting the Stage

Just as prop masters and decorators in theater must set the stage before the actors can take their places, you must describe everything that the Crew can see, hear, feel, and smell—anything that would be apparent. Start with the most immediate fact ("As you open the airlock, you see six Reminsian lizards loping toward you, breathing clouds of noxious vapors as they come!"), then detail whatever else is needed for the players to envision the scene. Failing to

include vital information—or giving misleading data—can significantly alter the players' perceptions of the environment, leading them to do some ridiculous things in character that they might not do if they had had an adequate briefing.

A quick example: The Narrator tells the players that their characters are trapped in a burning building with the fire rapidly spreading toward them, consuming large wooden crates stacked nearby. He mentions the solid steel door—the only exit—which is bolted shut from the outside and tells them there are no windows or other means of egress. He adds that they have no weapons, no communicators to call the ship, and no available tools for attempting to pry open the door. The players panic as they see all avenues of escape shutting down. Not knowing what else to do, they turn and try futilely to stop the fire. They can't figure out how they can get out because the Narrator already told them the door is the only exit. What he failed to mention are the skylights overhead providing illumination. Those are made of glass and can be broken if the characters climb the boxes to reach them. He may also have neglected to tell the players that the characters are standing atop grates that lead down underground and they might escape that way as well.

Even having the players make some sort of intelligence check for their characters and telling them they need to climb out through the skylights isn't enough to save this scene. The players feel stupid for not asking if there were skylights or sewer gratings and the Narrator feels the players are pretty dim for not taking the initiative to look. In reality, the person to blame is the Narrator. By making misleading statements saying there are no other exits (when what he meant was there are no other normal exits), he primed the players not to look for any others.

That may be an extreme example, but it illustrates the importance of making the players aware of their complete environment. The Narrator needs to let the players know about anything or anyone that they can sense, however unimportant it might seem. Who knows when that neglected pin dropped in the corner might become a vital clue? If you simply list objects or personages in the description without emphasizing them particularly, the players may ignore them—to their peril or loss.

Should you be interested in making them really work to discover clues, this is a good way to teach them to pay better attention. If your primary objective in the scene is to impart information and give the characters clues they need to get on with the story, don't bother cloaking the important stuff in a welter of detail. Just mention the important parts ("… and on the table among an array of small items lies the ring Commander Lahr described.") and let them get on with the episode.

The second part of giving good description lies in using vivid language. Reality lies in the details. It isn't just hot, it's torrid enough that water beads on the glass of iced Meldonian wine and drips down the stem to form a puddle on the polished countertop. Waves of heat waver above the horizon, distorting perceptions. The wind seems to sear the characters, parching their throats and drying their lips as it scratches at their eyes. It doesn't just smell like a swamp; the rich, musky scent of loam and fish enwraps the area, bringing with it the odor of rotting vegetation and things long dead. Think of places you've been, things you've seen, people that you've observed and bring your own perceptions to your descriptions. Don't be afraid of getting a little poetic either. Odd juxtapositions or unusual comparisons can create exactly the right impressions in the players' minds.

The only real drawback to this portion of narration is when you go overboard. The players really don't need to know every food on the buffet table if it plays no role in the game. Nor do they want to sit through an hour-long exposition on what each button and light on the bridge does. Tell them everything they need to know, polish up the language a little, and leave it at that. If they ask questions, you can always add more details.

A final thought: Keep notes on the setting you describe. If the players return to that scene, they'll expect it to be the same. If you describe a room as having silvery purple walls the first time they pass through it and they return twenty minutes later to find that the walls are green, they're going to get the wrong idea. Players may believe they've entered the wrong room or that someone has been by and changed things—and if one thing has changed, other things may have changed as well. You've just opened a can of wormy speculation you really didn't need. So keep good notes, and if the environment does change, your players can be more certain that the change is intentional and signals something of significance.

BUILDING THE DRAMA: SCENE BY SCENE

"You're moving down the corridor, phasers in hand. All around you, the lights flicker and die. A smell like that of alcohol mixed with sulfur permeates the ship. You can just make out the slime trails of the beast that got Ensign Marsten. They lead through a partially opened doorway ahead. Looking to the side, you see a door open and a small golden-haired child emerge. She holds out a broken doll to you. Do you stop? When you do, she smiles at you and asks, 'Can you fix my dolly?' What do you do? Suddenly, the snarling beast rushes at you from the end of the hall. It's on you before you can bring your phasers to bear."

In essence, there's nothing wrong with this description, especially if the child is important to the story somehow. Maybe she's someone the Crew must protect from the vicious beast or a ward one of them is responsible for, but if she isn't really a part of the story or the scene, why is she introduced at all? As a Narrator you must have the answer to that question before you run the episode. You must know why each scene is important, even if the players won't find out until later. You must also decide when to drop scenes that aren't significant. You may have worked really hard on the setting and want to amaze your players with your creativity, but if the scene has no relevance to the story, however good it is, cut it. Though your game may have more time than a TV show (or even a movie) can devote to the story, it's best if you don't drag things out with unimportant add-ons. The players are there to have their characters perform significant actions, not sit around drinking Romulan ale and chatting about the state of the universe. This isn't to say that scenes with family, friends, or other crew members are unimportant, simply that you should have a reason for placing them in the story.

If you want players to enjoy your episodes, you can't have scenes that don't lead anywhere. Every scene depicted should either evoke some emotional response in the players (i.e., have some personal significance for the characters in it) or advance the plot. Preferably, your scenes do both at the same time. Going back to the example, throwing the little girl into the middle of a tense moment in which the characters are stalking a deadly beast ups the ante as they seek to protect her. But if she's never seen again or is slain by the beast despite the crew's best efforts, there was no point in her coming into the scene. Don't despair, though. If you've introduced scenes into stories where they don't belong, you can always go back later and create significance for them. Someone the characters interacted with in a fringe scene may later come back as an ally or a foe. Knowledge of your great setting may prove useful at a later date. That's the beauty of having recurring guest stars. If you don't get it right the first time around, you can always retool them and send them back in at a later date with no one the wiser. Of course, not including them in the first place is the better solution, but we never said this would be foolproof—or simple.

KNOWING THE SUPPORTING CAST

The most evocative setting palls when there's no movement or conflict within it. Those jobs usually fall to the Supporting Cast, the NPC's. Granted, the environment itself might prove to be a foe, but most of the time it's a creature, alien, or stubborn ally that causes trouble or needs help. You may get away with the "unknown alien" syndrome once or twice ("You pull the Andorian to safety, then turn to rescue your ship."), introducing almost faceless extras for the characters to interact with, but sooner or later the players will demand those NPC's' names and more details about them. Granted, you need not give every alien in the crowd a name and detailed history, but write one up in case the characters develop a sudden desire to talk with one of them. (See "The Good, the Bad, and the Others," page 251, for more details on crafting supporting cast.) Conversely, there are some guest stars you'll want the players to know more about. If they assist the Vulcan ambassador, they'll want to know his name is Sarek and they'll need a description of him and anything unusual they might notice (like, for example, his Human wife).

To make your adventures come alive, then, you need to people them with interesting, distinctive beings. Take the time to jot down a few notes on significant NPC's. What do they look like? What do they want out of life? What do they hope to accomplish in the scenes where they are featured? Each one should have some sort of inner life—thoughts, feelings, opinions, and such that determine how they react to the characters and the events of the game. Concentrate on making the supporting cast as real as possible.

For example, villains don't think of themselves as villains. They believe themselves to be the heroes of their own stories and see the characters as obstacles to obtaining what they want. Even allies may prove difficult under the right circumstances. Certainly there are times when killing difficult adversaries might be the easiest choice, but try to convince the Vulcan monk of that!

To make your supporting cast real to the players, you have to play each of them as distinct from all others. Height and weight, coloration, birthmarks, and distinguishing features play a part in this, but you can make other distinctions as well. Perhaps the NPC in question has an odd accent or an antiquated

mode of speaking. Perhaps she always stands with hands folded when conversing. Perhaps he always has a joke ready whenever he meets the characters, or always seems confused and needs the characters to point him in the direction he should be headed. Maybe she holds a personal grudge against one of the characters and always gets in some little dig whenever she talks to the Crew. Perhaps he dyes his hair a different color every week.

A good way to give the supporting cast distinguishing features is to consider their quirks and play on those. Another is to give them the advantages and disadvantages available to player characters—at least the ones with effects that would be obvious to observers. Whatever you do, make sure you note it down so you can repeat it next time the characters meet up with the NPC. There's nothing worse than spending an evening with old one-legged Captain Eidorian telling tall tales and swapping war stories only to meet him the next week when he doesn't even have a limp.

Familiarity vs. Novelty

While players enjoy the chance to do new things, they also appreciate things that are familiar. Recurring villains or allies provide part of this, as does revisiting scenes with a new perspective (i.e., the first time through the room at ground level, the characters notice the checkered black and white floor; when returning to the room from upstairs, they notice that the floor and furnishings are actually laid out like a huge chess board). Yet another type of familiarity can help players get into the game more fully: playing on the characters' own backgrounds.

Players may provide you with the names, descriptions, and some information on their characters' friends and family members. In some cases, they may detail their talents and knowledge, where they went to school, old rivals, loves, or nemeses. If so, thank the stars and incorporate that information into your episodes.

One of the main objectives of the game is to let the characters discover who they really are. We are defined by our reactions to and thoughts about those close to us and our personal experiences. Just as we learned much more about Spock when his parents were introduced in "Journey to Babel," bringing in someone from a character's history gives him a unique opportunity to revisit his past, perhaps erasing old humiliations, righting an injustice, or forging a

new friendship. Incorporating these things into your episodes tells the players that you're interested in and concerned with their characters and want to give each of them a chance to take the spotlight and shine for a while. Former loves and rivals can also provide grist for the story mill. After all, the characters can care about rescuing faceless millions or an unknown ambassador for only so long. Give them someone they know personally and care about and see the difference in the quality of roleplaying. To do it right, though, you have to keep detailed notes.

Keeping the Playbook

Which leads us to the playbook. Just as a stage manager keeps a book on the director's staging and cues, you need to create a playbook—a central file—where you keep all the information on settings, people, and events in your game. Writing down the significant events and who was involved as soon as the game is over is an invaluable aid to keeping your game on track. You can keep pictures of places or people, copies of the character sheets with up-to-date skill points, notes on the supporting cast, and other needed papers (star date information? timelines?) in the book as well. While it can be a nuisance trying to keep up with all that, it prevents you from forgetting important details and allows you to look back on prior stories and see if you can bring anything in them out in another game.

An alternative method of keeping a book is to ask one or more players to write down their impressions of the game, noting actions taken and people met, and then incorporate that into your central file. If you have to put the game on hiatus for awhile, when you come back you won't have forgotten Ensign Kellover's name or that she has dimples and consistently beats the engineer character at three-dimensional chess.

Keeping the Action Moving

Pacing. In its original sense, the word means walking with a measured step. Part of establishing a mood and keeping players interested lies in maintaining that measured step and adjusting it to fit different scenes. What does this mean in terms of storytelling? You must fit the pace of the scene to what's happening in it. Quieter scenes should go a little more slowly, with some time for reflection or banter between the players. Action scenes should be fast-paced, with quick descriptions and a sense of urgency.

Pacing goes beyond that, however. It means that scenes of the same type should not follow one another too closely. If you've just led the players through a part of the story filled with tension, where it seems like every word and action play out against a taut bowstring of uncertainty or careful movement, you need to throw in a scene that changes or alters the mood. Consider narrating a combat scene after a nerve-racking crawl through a minefield, or a moment of comedy once important negotiations are concluded. Some change-up scenes resolve the action of the scene before them (combat after sneaking up on a foe, for example), while others merely provide a change of pace and a chance to relax for a moment (Spock and McCoy exchanging banter after the ship has been saved yet again). Just make sure that the change isn't so jarring

that it seems incongruous in the game. It works best if the change-up scene also advances the plot or character development.

To keep the pace moving along, don't add in anything that isn't essential to each scene. Make certain the game doesn't bog down in extraneous details or lose its immediacy through the introduction of unneeded detail or unimportant NPC's. Pacing goes even further, though. The scene may be rolling along at breakneck speed, but if not everyone involved in it has something important to do, it fails to bring that player along with the story, creating potential boredom or frustration. If the combat-heavy types are boldly holding the marauding aliens at bay and the doctor has nothing to do, hand him a medical emergency (the guest star gets wounded).

Better still, so the player doesn't feel like you wounded the NPC just to throw a sop to him, give him a different kind of emergency he must handle even though it's outside his field of expertise. Suddenly, the matter-antimatter mix goes unstable while the rest of the Crew and supporting cast are busy fighting off the aliens. Can the doctor fix the problem working from shouted instructions from the chief engineer?

Always provide several ways the characters can solve the problems they encounter. That way the game won't crash to a halt as a few players try to figure out the exact method whereby they can overcome the foes while the rest sit around yawning and waiting for the action to pick up again. Knowing your players can help you figure out the most likely ways that they'll try to overcome dilemmas. Use that to your advantage in constructing scenes and benefit by keeping the pace fast and fun.

Cinematic Technique

A particularly helpful method of keeping the action moving is to employ cinematic techniques. There are two types of scenes in this technique (flash and cut-to) that can speed up play and deepen the players' understanding of the plot. You won't be able to use both all the time, but judicious utilization of one or both can improve your adventure. Nor do you have to employ them in every scene to use them. Occasional use is fine, and in fact preferable to overuse.

Flashes are scenes you describe that take place outside the characters' sphere of influence. They cannot interact with the scene and usually don't even know (as characters) that such a scene has taken place, but knowing of it

as players helps them to focus on important aspects of the story or fill in details they would otherwise have no way of knowing. Obviously, flashes are best used in stories when the Narrator wants to create a mood or cause some tension, for example to place time restrictions on the characters. Use flashes when the information given won't undercut the players' enjoyment. If the episode revolves around certain secrets the Crew must discover, however, flashes are probably not the best choice.

Cut-to scenes are just that. Like their film counterparts where the camera cuts to the action, then cuts to something else entirely, the cut-to allows the Narrator to jump right into the middle of action scenes, or cut scenes short that are running on to no point. Players often talk a scene to death long after it should be over, or take forever to move into an action scene, trying to overplan what they'll do in it. Neither of these is conducive to fast-paced, cinematic games like the *Star Trek Roleplaying Game*. Don't let the players fall into either pattern. Cut to the next scene and jumpstart their roleplaying.

THE DRAMATIC ELEMENT

Tense face-offs against Klingon warships, an emergency landing on a heretofore unknown planet, the discovery of a planet-killing device on a collision course with an unsuspecting world, a duel to the death over a matter of Vulcan honor—these are moments of high drama that characterize the best episodes. Against the backdrop of alien landscapes or the endless expanse of space, conflicts between opposing forces epitomize the action and excitement of Star Trek. Whether the action takes place on the bridge of the Enterprise or in an underground palace inhabited by an aggressive race of barbarian warlords, the stories of Star Trek abound with fast-paced scenes, visible confrontations, and dramatic resolutions.

The medium of television—and of the mind's-eye drama that is roleplaying—carries with it the need for high visibility. Internal struggles, however interesting they may be to the individual involved, lack immediacy unless they contain some outward manifestation. When Captain Kirk struggles against a mind probe, we see his pain externalized by his agonized posture as well as through the reactions of his crew. We hear the sounds of spaceship battles (even though physicists tell us that space combat is silent) and watch the spectacular explosion of an enemy vessel through the bridge's viewer screen.

Make certain that your players can visualize the stories that you tell by using specific language in your descriptions and by including gestures and body language when portraying supporting cast allies and opponents. Understatement gets lost in the *Star Trek* universe. Your players should be able to tell the heroes from the villains through facial expressions, tone of voice, and characteristic actions. Subtle gradations of good and evil belong to later versions of the *Star Trek* milieu; heroes in the 23rd century rely on clear-cut definitions of right and wrong (for the most part).

Like the old-fashioned Western, in which the "good guys" and "bad guys" wore different-colored hats, your villains should bear some clear marks that leave no lingering doubts as to their true intentions. While an enemy may not look any different from an ally, sooner or later the actions or words of a foe give him away. *Star Trek* stories do not shun moral quandaries; they do, however, attempt to resolve them one way or another. Give your players the satisfaction of knowing that they did the right thing rather than deceiving them into taking the wrong course of action by disguising a villain too well.

THE GOOD, THE BAD, AND THE OTHERS

Elements and themes hone the atmosphere of your *Star Trek* episodes, but people bring the stories you tell to life. Your characters do not interact with the abstract ideas that comprise your game, but with the people who embody those ideas–whether as allies, enemies, shipmates, or victims. As the Narrator, you have the responsibility of making all the other people and creatures–from a Klingon battle commander to a Melkot telepath and everything else in between–come to life. Emotional involvement in a story comes from arousing the feelings of the characters toward one or more of the people they meet. Caring about a courageous rebel leader on a planet ruled by a tyrant or hating the megalomaniac entity who whimsically destroyed a security officer motivates the players, and drives their characters into involvement with the action of your story.

While you should flesh out your significant villains and other important NPC's ahead of time, you may have to create other minor characters sponta-

neously, in response to your characters' actions. If the Crew visits the capital city of a new planet to gain information on the type of people who inhabit the world, they may wish to start by asking the "alien on the street" a few questions. Their experience on the planet will become more real if the person they target as an information source possesses a personality (including a name, if necessary).

A few tricks can go a long way toward creating a minor character that remains in your characters' minds after that individual leaves the "stage." Occasionally, an NPC that begins as a bit player (or even an extra) gains importance to the characters and achieves a significant role in the story. The "alien on the street" may serve as a ready "informant" for the Crew, who consult him or her (or it) repeatedly for the inside scoop on what's going on among the populace. A few moments of preparation before the start of a game can help you cope with creating "instant characters."

THE CREW

Your player characters occupy the starring roles in your episodes, but they do not operate the starship by themselves. Narrator-played characters (NPC's) fill out the roster of your character's vessel and, in some cases, may even serve as members of the Crew (in games with only two or three players). If the characters do not have the experience to hold command positions on their starship, the officers they serve must be NPC's under your control. All of these individuals, whether officers or not, need to seem real to the characters. After all, they spend more time with their shipmates (between adventures) than they do encountering the dangers and excitement of space exploration.

Ask yourself a few questions about the important supporting cast members aboard the characters' starship. Determine each's name, general physical appearance, personality, and background, along with any important game-related skills and attributes. Record this information in your notes or include it in the log of your adventure. Finally, keep a list of names handy in case you suddenly have to flesh out the security trooper speared in a barbarian ambush. ("We lost Perkinson, sir. It was horrible!")

THE VILLAINS

Memorable opponents create memorable games. Antagonists embody the problems your Crew face as they take part in the stories you narrate. As the Narrator, you should construct your villains carefully, giving them believable motives and realistic personalities. Avoid two-dimensional portrayals of the Crew's enemies or adversaries; make these guest stars as "real" and fully developed as your player characters.

Determine why your villains act the way they do. What makes them oppose the characters? Do they belong to a race–like the Klingons–who oppose the goals of the Federation? Does the tyrannical overlord of a planet seek power for its own sake or does she, instead, believe she alone can save her people from contamination by invaders from the stars? If the Crew battles a rogue member of Starfleet who has turned pirate, you need to know what event caused this defection from the Federation.

SUPPORTING CAST CREDITS

Think of the characters you portray as a Narrator in terms of television or film credits. Depending on their significance in your campaign, they fall into one of the following categories:

•**Special Guest Stars:** These NPC's play significant roles in the overall campaign or in an individual episode. Major villains (particularly recurring ones), important allies, or ship's officers belong in this category. Khan, Trelane, and the Commander of Starfleet represent examples of this type of NPC. These characters frequently serve as the primary motivator of your episodes or the focus of your story's plot.

•**Also Appearing:** NPC's who play a regular but minor role in your game or who appear consistently but infrequently fall into this category. A Narrator-controlled communications officer who never leaves the ship but handles first contact with other vessels possesses the "also appearing" status, as does the Vulcan observer traveling aboard your ship to learn more about her Human allies. All the other crew members of the characters' starship rate this designation as well. Occasionally, an episode may revolve around one of these characters.

•**Extras:** These characters serve as stage dressing in crowd scenes. If they are members of the starship's crew, they are the ones who die on the surface of a planet or fill out the list of casualties during an ambush by a Romulan bird of prey. Sometimes, extras transcend their minor roles through their interactions with the characters and promote themselves to the rank of "also appearing"–or even to special guest star status.

Personalize your villains by giving them names, distinctive physical traits or mannerisms, and a personality quirk or two that sticks in your players' minds. Remember that villains do not always seem "evil" and sinister. Some, like Khan, also exude a charismatic magnetism that inspires others to follow them, while others, like Harcourt Fenton Mudd, evoke a sense of the ridiculous. Choose a voice for your villain that avoids the stereotypical sneering quality found in melodrama. Perhaps a planetary despot speaks in a whisper or always refers to himself as "we." Keep a card file or list of the villains your Crew encounters so that you do not repeat yourself or fall into a rut when you portray them. ("Not another fake British accent!")

Treat every villain as if he might become a recurring character in your series of stories. If the Crew lets the primary foe escape, you need to decide what that individual will do with his freedom. Will he cut his losses and avoid renewing his struggle with the characters or will he, instead, make it his life-long mission to track them down and seek revenge? Recurring villains provide a sense of continuity in your stories; if you use them, make certain they hold your characters' attention.

AND A CAST OF BILLIONS

Not everyone can be Captain Kirk, or even Captain Koloth. Your universe has to feel alive, with billions of interesting people—Human, nonhuman, and other. Characters outside the boundaries of the Crew, but not rating "special guest star" status (see sidebar), make up the most varied assemblage of NPC's in your series. Mudd's wives, minor planetary dignitaries, and other significant individuals that lend assistance to the Crew provide information or otherwise contribute to the ambience of the story; all deserve your attention as Narrator. They, too, need motivations, personalities, and physical qualities that make them memorable—and distinguishable from one another.

A full character sheet is not necessary for every minor NPC, but you should create a generic sheet for each type of NPC that your Crew may meet. Usually, you need only note general appearance, personality, and significant episode-related skills. If the individual is a powerful psionic, you should give him skills that reflect his level of ability; similarly, an NPC who is most likely to meet the characters in armed combat should possess appropriate weapons skills. Make an effort at least to sketch a personality ("irritating, self-righteous bureaucrat") for every supporting cast member with a "speaking role" in your episode. This effort pays off, and not only in the increased realism that dealing with real characters generates. Occasionally, a member of the lower-level sup-porting cast becomes a long-term NPC. The Crew may befriend a council member of the planet they visit or they may offer asylum to a political dissi-dent. When this occurs, you may need to provide more details about the NPC, and your earlier work can help you visualize your newest guest star and help your players accept her as an important part of their series and their galaxy.

SETTING THE STAGE

Now that you have a Crew, a set of supporting actors, and a variety of fea-tured villains and allies, you need to have a stage upon which your dramas take place. As the Narrator, you have the responsibility for making the world around your players' characters come to life—not just by presenting the Crew with believable people to meet but by giving them a place where they can interact with one another. This means creating a setting (or settings) for each episode. Fortunately, your players can help you with part of this task through their choice of starship design. The rest, however, is up to you.

ABOARD THE STARSHIP

When they are not exploring the surface of a planet, your Crew will likely spend most of its time aboard their spacegoing vessel. The ship's environs need enough detail so that your players feel that their characters actually live there. Apart from the bridge, engineering, sick bay, and other functional loca-tions within the starship, you should help your players detail such areas as the Crew's living quarters, rec rooms, and briefing areas. If you plan to set many episodes within the ship rather than on the surface of a planet, these details become vitally necessary. See "Starship Locations" on page 129 for some of the details you may wish to use.

SPACE TRAVEL

The vast reaches of space form the "megasetting" for *Star Trek Roleplaying Game* episodes. While few games actually take place "in space", most episodes involve space travel. Make certain that you can describe to your play-ers the experience of traveling through ion storms, coming out of warp speed into a new planetary system, or viewing the sudden uncloaking of a Romulan bird of prey through the viewscreen of the starship. Many exciting spatial phe-nomena show up in *Space ... the Final Frontier* (page 181).

PLANETARY VISITS

Episodes that involve visiting the surface of a planet require you to develop not only the physical appearance of that world but also the types of civilizations that reside there and enough history to give the planet a coher-ent past. The Crew should feel that these planets existed before their arrival and will continue to do so (barring some cosmic incident) after they depart. See the *New Civilizations* chapter (page 227) for some tips on this often tricky task.

PUTTING IT ALL TOGETHER

It should all come together in the framework of your stories. Each story that you create for your *Star Trek Roleplaying Game* sessions resembles a tele-vision episode. Just as several episodes fill out a season's worth of television viewing, a series of roleplaying stories, usually linked by some common thread (if only by the same Crew members), tells a larger story, one that might have a single theme or several related themes.

Deciding on the kinds of episodes that you want to narrate involves find-ing a happy medium between what you want and what your players want. The point of roleplaying is for everyone involved to have fun—not just yourself or your players. If you enjoy complicated adventures that involve problem-solving and your players would rather set their phasers on disintegrate and fire at anything that moves, you may have to compromise by combining both elements in your stories. Give the players a tricky problem that leads to the reward of a glorious battle.

EPISODES

Episodes resemble short stories in many ways. They usually consist of a single plot, possibly include a subplot or two, and focus around one major adversary. An episode may take one of a variety of forms, including straightforward exploration adventures, delicate diplomatic situations, race-against-the-clock rescue missions, and personal dramas revolving around individual members of the Crew. Each kind of episode requires a different approach both from you and from your players. An exploratory episode usually involves plenty of skill tests and the constant sense that the unexpected may be just around the next tree, rock, or mountain range. Diplomatic adventures may contain some skill tests (usually in the "softer" skills such as Persuasion and Charm) but may rely heavily on roleplaying and dialogue. Personal dramas sometimes use no skill tests at all and require intense personal interaction among the players to resolve the problem at hand. Episodes in which time plays a role (*i.e.*, a planet's population will die from a plague unless a rare antidote is delivered to them within two of their days) require fast action and quick thinking on the part of the players. Adventures that have a "quest" at their core call for a combination of problem-solving, exploratory skills, and, potentially, combat against rivals or guardians. From time to time you may wish to throw in a light-hearted episode, or even pure farce à la "The Trouble with Tribbles", as a tension reliever (see sidebar). It may give the players a chance to use up all those horrible puns and bad jokes that they have (we hope) foregone heretofore in the interests of maintaining the mood.

HUMOROUS GAMES

Remember that humor-based games should enhance the enjoyment of everyone. Players do not have a good time when they feel humiliated or made fun of by the Narrator. Games that ridicule the characters or provide laughs for the Narrator at the expense of the players do not belong in the *Star Trek Roleplaying Game* (or in any other roleplaying venue, for that matter). Make certain that your sense of humor does not offend or upset your players and that everyone concerned understands that the "joke" is on everyone. Again using "The Trouble with Tribbles" as our example, consider it as a scenario where Kirk, or better yet Nilz Baris, is the NPC straight man. The key to comedy roleplaying is letting the players make as many jokes as they take, or at least get the last word.

SERIES

Several linked episodes create a series (or campaign, in generic roleplaying terminology). Depending on how you connect your episodes, your roleplaying series may resemble a television series, a miniseries, or a feature-length movie. If all (or most) of your episodes revolve around a single theme or idea, then your series takes on the proportions of an epic film, for example.

Episodic series provide the simplest format for beginning Narrators. Like a television series, episodic adventures usually revolve around the characters. While each individual episode may have a different theme or take place in a different location, the same group of people (give or take a few from time to time) get involved in the action. No overall unifying factor outside the characters is strictly necessary for this type of series. In all likelihood, your *Star Trek Roleplaying Game* campaign will have an episodic series structure—at least in the beginning. The advantage of this kind of series lies in the wide variety of stories you can tell. It also presents you with the opportunity to find out what kind of stories your players really prefer.

Epic series differ from episodic series in that each episode relates to an overall theme or concept. The search for a rogue Starfleet commander who has gone on a rampage in space imparts an overriding purpose to your campaign, as each episode becomes another attempt to follow the trail of your archenemy. Recurring villains provide good connecting factors in epic series, just as they do in story arcs (see below). Another subject for an epic series might be the attempt to discover a series of dangerous artifacts left behind on once-abandoned planets before their current inhabitants fall afoul of superior technology.

STORY ARCS

Story arcs form a series within a series by linking several episodes together around a common theme. You can place several story arcs within a series, thus allowing you to run many different types of miniseries within your overall campaign. Episodes in a story arc do not have to follow one another immediately. Most often, several episodes unconnected with the story arc will take place in between each "arc" episode. Nearly two decades separated the first appearance of Khan Noonian Singh ("Space Seed") and his reappearance in

Star Trek II: The Wrath of Khan. Taken together, however, these two adventures dealing with the *S.S. Botany Bay* comprise a story arc. Subplots make ideal subjects for story arcs. A brief encounter with a Klingon warlord in one episode might result in a longer confrontation with the same individual a few episodes later. For the finale, the Crew might meet up with their by-now hated Klingon adversary on the surface of a deserted planet for a no-holds-barred finale in an episode focusing on this event. These three episodes, in retrospect, form a story arc. You can also create story arcs in more subtle ways. One kind of story arc might explore different aspects of the same theme—intervention versus nonintervention, for example—by scripting parallel episodes that show opposite sides of the controversy.

JUDGING: USING THE MECHANICS

We've said a lot about storytelling, but almost nothing about applying game mechanics to the adventure. We all know that we need some rules to define the game. Without some way to judge whether someone succeeds at a task or not, it degenerates into the old "Shot ya!" "Did not!" "Did too!" routine. But when do you apply the rules?

That depends. If the players are all having a good time roleplaying through things and you think their skills are up to completing whatever task they're undertaking, there's no need to roll the dice. Similarly, you need not call for dice rolls to complete routine tasks. Common sense should tell you that the transporter officer can operate the lighting system in his quarters. In like manner, why have players make irrelevant rolls? If the point is to get the characters into engineering in time to disarm the bomb, you're going to feel pretty lame if you make them roll to unlock the door and they fail. Rolling dice should be reserved for the really important and critical tasks. If it doesn't matter if they succeed, it doesn't matter if they roll the dice!

A few rules of thumb can help you decide when you should let the rules take over and when you should just let the action proceed and use your best judgment.

- *If the characters are in competition with NPC's or directly oppose them (such as in combat), dice are necessary to resolve the situation.*

- *If the characters are attempting to persuade an NPC of something and make good arguments that the NPC would find sensible or compelling, why make them roll?*

- *If the player is smart enough to figure something out, you shouldn't make him roll to see if his character can also draw the same conclusions (unless the character is supposed to be mentally slow).*

- *Should a player ask if his character notices anything odd or out of place and something is, don't make him roll. If he fails the roll and someone else subsequently rolls and succeeds, the original player will feel cheated and feel less like there's any reason for him to participate.*

CHEATING THE PLAYERS OF JUST REWARDS

Players participate in roleplaying, among other reasons, to feel a sense of accomplishment. Don't take that away from them. If they roleplay through negotiations, don't let a bad roll cheat them of the meaning of their words. If you think they've acted in an exemplary manner during the game, but the dice roll you made will arbitrarily kill or incapacitate one of the characters, ignore it. Give commendations when they are warranted and feel free to praise your players for their clever moves and unexpected monkey-wrenching. After all, you deserve some surprises too.

If players are smart enough to figure out your intricately plotted episode, let them! They may still not be able to do anything about stopping your fiendish plot until they reach a certain point in the story, and they'll worry all the more. And if they should theorize about your plot and come up with something better than you had planned, feel free to change in midstream. Players love to feel like they've worked everything out and been right about things. If it won't seriously affect other episodes yet to come, go with their answer instead. After all, it's their story too.

Constructing a Star Trek Roleplaying Game Episode

The most exciting thing about narrating the *Star Trek Roleplaying Game* is that, as Narrator, you are the one who gets to bring the story to the table. Your players, eager to take on the roles of the Crew and "explore strange new worlds," look at you in expectation. They know that adventure awaits, that the choices they make may save lives, change history, and distinguish their ship forever.

Adventure awaits! Heady stuff. And scary sometimes, too! As Narrator, you get the special thrill of making the story unfold—but what about the responsibility of having a story to tell to begin with?

This chapter is designed to help you, the Narrator, create exciting *Star Trek* stories for the Crew to get involved in. You've probably already got a few ideas floating around—a new world, perhaps, or an interesting alien race, or a new technology. But how to pull those elements together into a tightly plotted, action-packed episode that will challenge and delight your players?

STEP BY STEP

This chapter is written with a kind of "how to" structure; it takes you step by step through the entire process of writing a *Star Trek Roleplaying Game* episode. This means that, as you gain some experience as a Narrator, you'll find that you can start skipping some of the simpler steps after you have a few episodes under your belt. Eventually, you'll find that you develop methods that become second nature, and you won't need to return here often. But on those desperate afternoons when the players are due to arrive in a few hours and you're still "stuck" and need a nudge to get an episode built for them, this chapter will always be here for your reference! Even long-time roleplaying "veterans" are likely to find a few ideas and tips here useful; *Star Trek* writing is a unique experience, after all!

CONCEPTS AND PREMISES

Before we get to making a plot, let's spend some time brainstorming an episode premise or two. We'll assume that the Crew has already been designed, that the broad series premise ("The Crew are assigned to a *Constitution*-class vessel assigned to the borders of Orion space," for example) has already been determined, and that what you need is an actual story! A premise is a story in a very tiny nutshell; it's the "foundation" idea that can usually be summed up in a single line, but it's the vital core of your episode— everything that follows will be built on it.

One of the best ways to come up with your premise is to brainstorm several ideas at once. Grab a sheet of paper and a pencil and race yourself—see how quickly you can jot down five simple episode ideas. Don't think too long on any of them, just keep the pencil moving. They don't have to be great, they just have to be simple and coherent. Maybe your list will look something like this:

- *Crew encounters a world about to destroy itself in a global war.*
- *Crew's vessel is attacked by alien pirates who have never heard of the Federation.*
- *A crew member in Engineering is smuggling a family of space gypsies to the next starbase.*
- *The ship becomes trapped in an energy field created by the fear of a powerful alien entity.*
- *The ship is assigned to escort a civilian vessel through a dangerous area of space.*

By brainstorming, just letting the ideas flow onto the sheet of paper without doing too much deep thinking, you help to loosen up your thinking processes and prepare yourself for what's to come. Just keep jotting down ideas and then look them over. Pick one you like—you might find that you like several of them! In that case, pick a couple of them to combine, or (better still) keep your sheet of paper handy for the next time you need a story. And don't be discouraged if your ideas seem clichéd, or remind you too much of your favorite *Star Trek* episodes, especially if you're just starting out. Once your Crew gets hold of your episode, it'll be unique, anyway! Once you've selected the premise you intend to build on, move on to the next section.

MAKING IT STAR TREK

The best Star Trek episodes have a unique feel, and your players will expect that special "*Star Trek*" flavor to be present in your *Star Trek Roleplaying Game* series. *Star Trek* is a grand tale of humanity coming to grips with itself, maturing, and then doing its best to share that experience with other worlds as it continues to explore. When you write a *Star Trek Roleplaying Game* episode, you're adding chapters to that epic.

At the core of *Star Trek* lies a set of universal "laws" or axioms that define the way a *Star Trek* drama unfolds. The most vital of these axioms are:

Star Trek Is Action-packed

The universe of Star Trek is a universe in motion, on every level you can imagine! The Federation sends its best ships out into the void to explore strange new worlds, to seek out new life and new civilizations … and the men and women aboard those vessels develop and change—in every episode they find their ideals challenged, their doubts exploited, and their weaknesses attacked. The decisions that they make are important, the consequences both long-term and immediate. Sometimes the fate of humanity is at stake; sometimes it's the life of a friend.

"Action" isn't just about slugging it out with a surly Gorn or engaging in a tense ship-to-ship battle with a Romulan bird of prey—although certainly a little combat can go a long way toward getting the blood pumping and keeping the excitement high. Action is about movement and decision. A story becomes interesting when movement is threatened—when an ancient civilization would rather destroy itself than work for peace, when a shipment of vital medical supplies is delayed by Orion pirates, when a brilliant scientist is tempted to throw his life away out of grief.

In *Star Trek*, victory goes to those who face down the challenges set before them, make a decision, and act. Your stories should include plenty of motion, plenty of conflict to try to stop that motion, and plenty of opportunity for the Crew to stand up and act to make things happen. Every scene should require decisive action!

Star Trek Is Optimistic

A lot of popular science fiction is cynical, populated with selfish antiheroes carving out an existence against a backdrop of a society given over to its most negative impulses, or even a dystopian ruin in the aftermath of mankind's self-destruction. Such tales can make for terrific drama, but they'd feel very out of place in a *Star Trek Roleplaying Game* episode.

Star Trek portrays a future where mankind—and a number of other advanced species—have reached the stars and built something worthwhile by defeating their negative impulses; their "dystopian" periods are behind them. They survived, and now they're growing and sharing the experience with others.

The very best Starfleet officers personify the optimism of *Star Trek*: When faced with potential disaster, they go forward, confident that they will succeed. You should consciously design any *Star Trek Roleplaying Game* episode to reward such behavior. While success is never guaranteed, the outcome is never hopeless, the future is never bleak. No matter how tempting the evil, or how seemingly invulnerable the foe, there is always a powerful dose of hope that can't be extinguished even if the Crew does fail at the task at hand.

Star Trek Is Virtuous

In *Star Trek*, virtue has more power than physical force. Humanity and the other races of the Federation are far from the peaceful perfection of the Organians. They are still dealing with their prejudices, their fears, their tendency to give in to anger or seek vengeance. It's only a few centuries from now, after all—humans are still very Human, and that's one of the reasons *Star Trek* is so enjoyable: We can see the best of ourselves in Captain Kirk when he stands up for the rights and lives of his crew and the Federation they serve.

The *Star Trek Roleplaying Game* allows us to get a little closer to that vicarious pride in humanity; the players get to, first-hand, stare down a furious Klingon commander, or try to convince two warring races to see eye to eye. As the game should reward optimism, it should reward virtue. Many *Star Trek* episodes are about choices that pit moral right against more mundane, practical considerations—if you write episodes where expedience and pragmatism define the "right" choices and moral issues are secondary, your players will be justifiably confused (and might just boo you away from the table)! Of course, it shouldn't be just as simple as a game of "spot the good-guy answer and proceed to the victory circle"—making the virtuous choice is just the first step. Taking action to uphold that decision should be challenging, and that's where the real meat of the story lies.

APPLYING THE AXIOMS

Keeping these core axioms in mind will help you flesh out your premise. Two "thought exercise" examples:

ALTERNATIVE FACTORS: THINKING OUTSIDE THE BOX

In the *Star Trek* universe, the seventy-eight episodes point toward and evolve into the future shown in *Star Trek: The Next Generation*, *Star Trek: Voyager*, *Star Trek: Deep Space Nine*, and nine movies. This future, in terms of your own series framework, is not written in stone. If you and your players wish to construct an alternate future history that doesn't lead to the 24th century of Captain Picard as seen in *Star Trek: The Next Generation*, feel free to take your cosmos in any direction you wish. Just make certain that your version of the *Star Trek* universe develops logically from the episodes you narrate. If the Federation contacts the Cardassians a century earlier, the Bajoran situation will develop entirely differently. Likewise, if you wish the Klingons to remain the prime villains of your *Star Trek* universe, avoid narrating episodes that foreshadow the Khitomer Conference. First and foremost, these are your voyages. Make of them what you will.

Let's say you've selected the premise "The ship becomes trapped in an energy field created by the fear of a powerful alien entity."

- *In order to provide Action, the alien energy should probably do more than just restrain the vessel—it should cause serious problems on board, perhaps causing vital systems to malfunction in dangerous ways, or causing crew members to hallucinate or be filled with terror. Maybe the field is constricting in some way, threatening to crush the hull like an eggshell if action isn't taken quickly!*
- *In order to maintain Optimism, the adventure should provide regular clues as to the nature of the problem, making it possible for the Crew to find or create a solution that saves the ship and (they hope) results in meaningful contact with the distressed alien. It won't be immediately obvious that the field is created by a powerful alien's fear—that's a revelation that will provide plenty of hope once it gets out! Build to it slowly, though. Optimism shouldn't just be provided; it should be challenged. The situation should be dire, and at times seem hopeless to those who don't keep their heads about them!*
- *The situation should reward Virtue, as well. That means that the solution to the dilemma shouldn't lie in improvising a "boost" to the phaser banks to destroy the alien outright! In* Star Trek, *the best solutions are never about simple destruction or exercise of superior technological might. Clearly, our premise implies a situation where a very powerful entity is harming the ship, not out of malice, but because it is in distress. The solution will therefore involve communicating with the alien in some way and finding the cause of its fear. From there either the fear, or the source of the fear, must be conquered with the aid of the Crew. It might be the Crew's own vessel that has the alien terrified, or it might be a very genuine outside threat that must be dealt with.*

The axioms are fundamental to *Star Trek*, and every episode should reflect them on some level. Once you have your premise grounded in these, we can move on to theme, where our premise gains a bit more substance.

EPISODE THEMES

In many ways, *Star Trek* was a distillation of the notions of science fiction at the time it was created. In many other ways, it was shaped by the personal beliefs of its creator and those of the many writers who made stories for the show. The result was a consistent vision of the far future, grounded in the axioms described above and exploring the answers to a very definite set of questions. These questions (and the answers *Star Trek* came up with) define the many powerful themes of the show.

Unlike the axioms, the themes of *Star Trek* are not present in every episode; there are too many of them! Rather, a typical *Star Trek* episode focuses primarily on just one theme, with a few others "playing around" in the subplots. Many of the themes are specific facets of the axioms; others seem contradictory (to each other, to the basic nature of the show, or to the axioms), but aren't really. Some of them overlap. All of them make for interesting drama.

The themes examined here are just some of the most outstanding examples; there are many more. While they aren't essential components of your episode; you'll find that being aware of them—and remembering to include them according to taste—will go a long way toward giving your *Star Trek Roleplaying Game* series the right "feel" of *Star Trek*.

HUMANITY OVER TECHNOLOGY

This is the most fascinating of the "apparently contradictory" themes, and one explored often in the TV show. The Federation is made possible by supertechnology: faster-than-light warp drives and subspace radio, transporters, free energy and food. Starfleet crew members have a variety of powerful weapons, tricorders that can make massive amounts of data instantly available about a planet no one has set foot on before, environmental gear that makes new places more accessible. *Star Trek* would seem to say that technology is way cool, and the more of it, the better!

And it does. But *Star Trek* technology remains a tool, a thing that facilitates Human effort rather than replacing it. Technology can get you across the galaxy and protect you from what you might find, but ultimately it's the people that make a real difference, the humans and Vulcans and Andorians and Tellarites and others. Whenever technology is introduced that might devalue people, from the Venus drug to the M-5 computer, it turns out to be a bad (and usually, for plot purposes, dangerous) idea.

Telling Stories with It: New and dangerous technology can enter a story in many ways: It may be a mechanism native to a new world, a new "secret weapon" devised by the Romulans, or a new experiment being performed by Starfleet engineers. It may even be the work of one of the Crew. If an enemy is using the technology, then the plot should allow for the Crew to find its weaknesses and exploit them; when the bad guys make the mistake of depending too much on their toys, it usually leads to their defeat! If the technology is in neutral or allied hands, and is obviously well intentioned, then the conflict is usually a matter of perception—some characters will be blinded by the possibilities of the technology, eager to believe that it can do no harm. The Crew must then race to prove that the technology is short-sighted and dangerous before actual harm results.

BARRIERS AND BIGOTRY

In many *Star Trek* stories, the "villain" is deliberate isolation. Many people keep themselves locked behind "walls" even when the consequences are ignorance and death. Sometimes these walls are real—physical barriers or isolated locales. Sometimes the walls are simply a matter of attitude, a stubborn refusal to acknowledge the world as it is (from the hollow Yonada to racist Cheron), often in the form of prejudice or unquestioned tradition. Blinded by such barriers, sometimes entire worlds can let their fears and bigotry become destructive, and Starfleet officers seem frequently to find themselves in positions where they must pierce such deliberate barriers in order to accomplish their missions.

The challenges presented in this theme are complex and varied, and can make for tricky challenges for a group of roleplayers. It contains another "apparent contradiction", since the powerful theme of breaking down barriers can sometimes clash with the ideal of the Prime Directive, which is a deliberate "barrier" enforced by Starfleet itself to prevent the contamination of cultures not yet ready to interact freely with more advanced societies.

Telling Stories with It: This is a theme that can crop up on every level, from astropolitics to personal relationships. While Federation society has evolved past the tendency to shut itself off into isolated pieces, on an individual level people still struggle with their fears of change, of different ways of life, even of things that look different. In "The Devil in the Dark," had the miners' assumption that the Horta was a mindless "monster" gone unquestioned, it would have caused even more destruction. Most often, the Crew will be on the outside of the barriers causing the problem, and must come up with a way to demonstrate that isolation and bigotry are destructive without causing things to worsen. Now and again, though, it makes for an exciting episode to deal with humanity's own lingering barriers. As Kirk said, "Most of us are attracted by beauty and repelled by ugliness—one of the last of our prejudices."

PARADISE ISN'T CHEAP

The universe, *Star Trek* showed us, is filled with temptation—short cuts to power and comfort that will, in turn, corrupt or cripple those who accept the bait. Humankind and its fellow species must constantly work to earn advancement honestly, through hard work and clean dealings. Anton Karidian, of all people, once defined humanity as "the striving of man to achieve greatness through his own resources," one of the most constant themes of *Star Trek*. To remain Human, we must avoid fantasies of Eden (and of Gamma Trianguli VI) and the passive captivity of the Talosians. What separates an advanced civilization from a less-advanced one (or a civilized Starfleet officer from a misguided villain or childlike powerful entity) is his willingness to forsake undue comfort and undue power, and many stories hinge on encounters with others who are having difficulty making that same choice.

Telling Stories with It: In some stories exploring this theme, a primitive society (one not yet at the "Federation level" of social and technological advancement) is endangered by the presence of powers and comforts that it isn't yet ready for—mirroring humanity's own time when their "weapons grew faster than their wisdom." In such stories, the damage is often to some extent permanent, but effort must be made to put the society back on the steady path. In others, the Crew might be threatened by the problems of a society more advanced than the Federation standard—but advanced in ways that didn't quite work out, because they made the wrong choices and others are now paying the price. In some ways these are "cautionary tales," warning the UFP of what can happen if it loses sight of its ideals. Equally interesting from a roleplaying perspective are episodes where the Crew itself is presented with dangerous temptations to know and do and have more than they have earned.

THE GOOD OF THE MANY

Star Trek contains many stories of sacrifice, and the idea that society as a whole is more important than the needs or wants of any one small group or individual is one that provides the underpinning for a lot of the Star Trek "ideology." This applies even to "society" on the galactic scale, in which humankind is but one citizen—the goals of the Federation are for all intelligent species to grow and explore together, and anything that harms that union is portrayed as something to be stopped.

Of course, this idea isn't unique to Star Trek, but its importance to the Star Trek "feel" is a reflection of the "virtue" axiom in its purest form. Self-sacrifice is heroic, and Star Trek is about heroes. Kirk risked his life—and Commodore Decker gave his—to destroy the Doomsday machine. Kirk sacrificed Edith Keeler, his one true love, to save humanity's future. It's important, as Narrator, to remember that for sacrifice to have any meaning, the losses must be real and lasting. If a member of the Crew displays the kind of honorworthy heroism that the best Star Trek stories included, then his reward should be a real impact on the outcome of the story, not a cheap "get out of jail free" card that renders the sacrifice moot. For any real sacrifice to be undone, it must at least be paid for with greater sacrifice still.

Telling Stories with It: An act of sacrifice on the part of a supporting character can be used as a powerful device to establish that character as a person of honor and bravery. The notion of an entire episode devoted to the theme of noble sacrifice is one that stirs up powerful dramatic images; perhaps the Crew must take their ship into the aftermath of another vessel's sacrifice, exposing themselves to fresh dangers in order to make that sacrifice meaningful. Or perhaps they must find a way to make such a grand gesture unnecessary. It doesn't "cheapen" a sacrifice to avert it with a better solution. As far as sacrifices made by the Crew itself—it's best to let these develop naturally in the course of a story line. Writing an episode that "requires" a sacrifice is seldom a good idea, and the Narrator may rest assured that dramatic opportunities for heroism of all kinds will tend to crop up unexpectedly if the story is well constructed and the Crew up to the task.

TAKING A BREAK FROM THE HEAVY STUFF

Not all Star Trek stories include social allegory or important themes—a lot of them are just character-driven or event-driven adventure stories, and a well

rounded game series will include regular doses of such "pulpy" action-adventure for the players to enjoy! Most of the "light" Star Trek stories fall into two broad categories: Phenomenon Adventures and Monster Stories.

PHENOMENON ADVENTURES

You can construct a very fun kind of episode simply by dreaming up a bizarre phenomenon and then exposing the Crew to it to see how they cope! Like any other device, it works best if you don't depend on it too often, but when time is short and you need an episode right now, it can be a good choice that will definitely "feel like Star Trek."

Star Trek had several episodes that fall into this category. "The Enemy Within" didn't really deal with anything deep or meaningful, for example—it was just a fun story about a ship's captain being split into an ineffectual good guy and a rampaging bad guy by a transporter malfunction. If it had any "meaning" at all, it was "our bad side is an essential part of our nature," but what it really was was an action-packed phenomenon episode, a simple challenge to be overcome.

Phenomenon stories can even promote character growth, or at least revelation. The Psi 2000 virus in "The Naked Time" not only set up a way-cool phenomenon story, it allowed us to explore what the characters were like on a personal level. "Mirror Universe" or "parallel planet" stories also fall into this category: All the Narrator needs to do is to define the phenomenon and its source, and outline a few ways that it might be stopped or explored. The rest of this kind of episode is best left to improvisation!

MONSTER STORIES

Some "monster plots" aren't really monster plots at all—"The Devil in the Dark" begins as one, but becomes something much deeper. Sometimes a monster is just a monster, such as the M-113 creature in "The Man Trap" or Redjac in "The Wolf in the Fold." Monster stories are a lot like phenomenon stories in that the goal of the episode is simple: "A dangerous problem rears its ugly head and the Crew must deal with it before it deals with them." The fundamental difference is that the ugly head is not a metaphor: The Crew face a singular being and not a bizarre occurrence or society. To make a monster story really interesting can require some careful planning, though, since monsters can be confronted (usually) more directly than abstract phenomena. To keep a monster story interesting, it's often best to construct it as a mystery, a series of deaths or even apparent "accidents" designed to baffle at first, before the true nature of the threat is revealed.

If a monster story is included as a subplot in a more subtle episode, that alone is often sufficient to hold interest until the creature can finally be faced physically and gunned down with phasers. But if the monster is the central point of the plot, it shouldn't be defeatable with simple brute-force attacks. The Crew should have to study it carefully, hoping to find a weakness to exploit.

LET THESE BE YOUR NEXT BATTLEFIELDS

The following ideas serve as examples for constructing stories that exemplify the common themes of *Star Trek*.

Humanity over Technology

- The Crew encounters a race of philosophers who are at war with a race of scientists. (Note that this could also be the seed of a "Barriers and Bigotry" story.)
- In search of habitable worlds, the Crew visits a deserted planet that bears the ruins of a once-prosperous civilization with no clue as to what caused its demise.
- A technophobic (or technophiliac) new crew member sows dissension among the regular Crew.

Barriers and Bigotry

- An exploratory team from the ship lands on a planet dominated by two antagonistic—and presentient—species.
- The Crew receives an invitation to visit the surface of a planet where the inhabitants seem a little too eager to receive visitors.
- The atmosphere of an uninhabited planet affects the perceptions of the Crew so that each individual perceives a different kind of world.
- The Crew encounters a civilization that believes in the superiority of left-handed people and structures their society along caste lines.
- Members of the ship visit a planet where children rule and the elderly serve as slaves and caretakers.
- The Crew must serve as mediators between a group of extreme pacifists and a society of avowed militarists.

Paradise Isn't Cheap

- The Crew encounters a disembodied lifeform in space and must negotiate safe passage through its "territory" by proving themselves worthy of existing.

The Good of the Many

- An exploratory team from the ship is captured by a warlike society and must escape without harming their captors.

Phenomenon Adventures

- The Crew discovers a world in the throes of planetary terraforming—from no discernable external source.
- Traveling through a supposedly "empty" sector of space, the ship finds a planet that does not register on any sensors.
- The Crew discovers a civilization that resembles one of Earth's historical eras.
- The exploration team discovers "sentient weather" on the surface of a planet.
- The ship passes through a warp in the space-time continuum and finds itself in Earth's distant past.
- The ship discovers a planet that repels all attempts to land upon its surface.

Monster Stories

- The Crew finds a world inhabited by creatures believed to exist only in myths and legends.
- The ship answers a distress signal from a planet whose inhabitants need the cure for an indigenous—and intelligent—virus.

PLOTTING

You've brainstormed a premise that excites you, spent some time considering how to ground it in the axioms of *Star Trek*, and fleshed it out according to some interesting themes. Now it's time to tackle a concept that some Narrators find intimidating: the plot! Plotting is all about organizing your episode idea so that it stays exciting, moves along at a good pace, and builds up to a worthwhile climax. A plot is a series of questions or challenges—the answers to those questions, and the resolution of those challenges, are what keep your audience interested. Of course, since this is a roleplaying game, your "audience" does more than just sit on the edge of their seats waiting to find out the answers—they get to make them happen.

One of the simplest and most logical ways to organize a story is with the Three Act Model (it's the structure we use for the episodes that you'll find in this and other books). In this model, the story is divided into three major segments (acts), each of which serves a specific function, like so:

- In Act One, the players get their first exposure to the story; something important is revealed that demands a reaction from the Crew. The scenes in this act set the tone and define the goal for the entire episode.
- In Act Two, the Crew comes to grips with what's going on. They've been faced with a challenge or problem in Act One, and now it's their turn to cause the action—examining clues, asking questions, exploring, or otherwise preparing themselves, and then acting on what they discover in order to bring matters to a conclusion.
- In Act Three, plot developments in Act Two have reached the point where a final conflict must take place to resolve things—you hope for the best! In this act, the Crew must deal directly with the problem, and then deal with the consequences of their choices.

Let's examine each segment in greater detail by following the construction of an example scenario.

ACT ONE: A CHALLENGE ARRIVES

The first act typically begins with a teaser—an opening scene designed to capture the players' interest and get them genuinely hooked on the story. It's best to gloss over any of the boring parts that lead up to the story: If you've decided that the Crew will be ordered to a remote mining colony to find out why subspace communications with the miners have ceased, you can skip the part where they receive their orders, the part where they travel there, the part where they establish an orbit around the planet …. Rather, begin the episode by glossing over all of that with a brief background description and by immediately playing out the scene in which a Klingon battlecruiser appears from a nearby moon and opens fire. Don't give the players any time at all to get relaxed, sleepy, or bored—let them know there is a serious problem to face!

If you want to structure your roleplaying game episode a lot like the TV show, then it's fun to run the teaser right up to the point of conflict (the appearance of the Klingon ship and the sudden barrage of weapons fire) and then call an immediate break for last-minute snack and soda refills (or trips to the bathroom). This "commercial break" trick has the same effect on the game as it does on the TV show—your players have a chance to stew in anticipation for a few minutes wondering what's going on and what they can do about it. Are the miners in league with Klingons? Was that just a warning shot, or are they going for blood? Since the story is frozen in time, anything can happen, but keep this first "commercial" short. The idea is to tease a bit to heighten excitement, not to drain away the initial momentum you've already created.

Back at the table, the first scene can be in full swing. Maybe the shots were aimed right for the Crew's vessel, in which case the opening scene might well be a ship-to-ship combat. Or maybe it was a warning shot, in which case the opening scene might more likely be a parley with the Klingons. It might be more interesting if neither is the case—the shot was fired right past the Crew's ship, destroying another, smaller ship that the Crew never noticed because it was both tiny and cloaked. This sets us up for an interestingly juicy opening scene—the Crew will try to both contact the commander of the Klingon vessel to find out what's going on, and try to ascertain the nature of the wreckage.

It's important to remember that Act One seldom reveals the real "meat" of the story. Even if the plot is straightforward and action-oriented, there should always be juicy "layers" on which to hang plot twists. The first plot twist typically comes at the end of Act One, and the second at the end of Act Two. The twists form the boundaries between the acts and drive the action forward.

For example, in our episode about the silent mining colony, the Narrator has decided that the Klingon vessel has no Klingons aboard. Rather, it is manned by a group of colonists from the planet, who lured the Klingons here and took over their vessel. The surviving Klingons are being held prisoner on the planet. The tiny cloaked vessel was a Klingon shuttlecraft equipped with a Romulan cloaking device as part of the Romulan/Klingon treaty of hardware exchange. A group of Klingons had been on board, trying to sneak back and win their vessel.

During most of Act One, the Crew won't know any of this. Rather, the Narrator has outlined the first act to include two major scenes:

- *In the first scene, the transporter operators aboard the Federation ship pull aboard two survivors from the shuttlecraft—both high-ranking Klingon officers! The Crew will be given a chance to interrogate them, but will get only cryptic half-sentences (in Klingon) before the rescued Klingons slip into coma.*
- *In the second scene, the Klingon ship begins drifting oddly for a time (time enough for the first scene to be completed, most likely) and then opens fire again—this time on the Crew's own vessel! The "Klingons" (actually the miners) refuse to answer any hails, but aren't brilliant tacticians, and are easily crippled in combat. At the end of this scene, the Crew can board the crippled Klingon vessel, where they meet heavy Human resistance from the miners who've hijacked the ship!*

This final scene delivers the first plot twist—the Klingon ship is being run by Human beings, some of the miners whom the Crew was sent to check on the safety of to begin with!

ACT TWO: PERIL AND DISCOVERY

After dropping the first big plot twist on the collective heads of the Crew, it's another time for a commercial break—and this one can be more substantial. Allow up to fifteen minutes for bathroom stops, the construction of sandwiches, the refilling of ice trays. In the meantime, the Crew is frozen in time at the point where they've boarded the Klingon cruiser only to be met by humans armed with Klingon weaponry.

While it's very much okay during the first act to assume that the Crew will mostly be reacting to what's happening to them, Act Two should be a serious change of pace. Rather than a scripted series of events, it should be a series of opportunities for the players to be ingenious, pitting their wits and the resources of their characters against the problem you've presented. By the beginning of Act Two, there should be definite danger and conflict already present and in need of resolution—but also some important questions to be answered in ways that the Crew will have to devise on their own. This means, of course, having some answers ready for them.

Again, the Narrator has plenty of secrets up his sleeve, since the second act should lead to the second plot twist. He's decided that the miners found something dangerous in the mines—an ancient relic housing the mind of an ancient Klingon god—or at least an alien entity that the Klingons once worshipped! This being has possessed Mining Engineer Robert Franklin and engineered the lure of the Klingon vessel and the takeover of the ship (the entity can kill Klingons, even hundreds at a time, pretty much at will, although this leaves both it and the possessed miner drained and weak for a long time afterward). The ancient being is motivated by revenge—millennia ago it transported "worthy worshippers" (a tribe of Klingons) to its planet. Eventually, these Klingons, like their cousins on Qo'noS, rebelled against their god and left the world. The relic-entity has waited for new worshippers to arrive ever since, plotting retribution.

Now, in a very short and simplistic adventure, all of that could be revealed in exposition simply by having a guest star who knows it show up and start shooting his mouth off. But it's best to dole out in pieces, as reward for clever action. This maintains the suspense, gives the players a sense of achievement, and keeps them wanting more.

Again, this act is divided into scenes, but these scenes needn't take place in exactly the order written, and there will be many other smaller scenes initiated entirely by the Crew. "Planned" scenes might include:

- *A scene where Robert Franklin (possessed by the ancient entity) hails the Crew from his hidden position on the planet, threatening to kill many innocents if they don't recall the boarding party from the Klingon vessel. He has the upper hand, so the Crew will probably agree to this, but leave room for them to come up with something clever if they can. If the Crew are really good at parleying with Franklin, his mannerisms should give them some clues that he isn't just a charismatic miner who decided he wanted a Klingon ship.*
- *A scene where the comatose Klingons revive in sickbay. The Klingons will tell how they arrived in response to an ancient Klingon code—a distress call too urgent to ignore, even though it meant crossing into territory on the boundaries of the Klingon neutral zone. They'll describe going planetside in a shuttlecraft, and being captured and imprisoned. They'll assume that all this is a Federation trick and be very hard to deal with, of course! Most important, they'll remember that Franklin grew tired after going into a rage or using his powers— it was in a moment of confusion following Franklin's collapse (he had just killed half the Klingons aboard the Klingon cruiser with a thought!) that they managed to escape and run for their shuttle.*

Eventually, all the clue-gathering and dialogue should lead the Crew to understand that Franklin is powerful, mad, and possessed by some kind of alien. That the alien is a forgotten Klingon deity should be saved for the end of the act—after all, none of these Klingons know of him. The Klingon vessel is crippled, but that still leaves the problem of Franklin himself—and there are several hundred innocent miners on the planet. Most of Franklin's "followers" only follow him because he lied to them, claiming that the Federation had given the colony—citizens and all—over to the Klingons as part of an under-

handed treaty arrangement. The entity's powerful telepathy remotely controls the rest. So the Crew must eventually beam planetside both to show the obvious good intentions of the Federation and to challenge Franklin. This forms the second half of Act Two, where the Crew moves to challenge the problem directly based on what they've learned.

They should preferably have a plan in mind for containing the energy being or destroying it somehow before they leave for the planet. The Narrator has decided that a spectral analysis of the transmissions Franklin made from planetside will reveal enough about the energy field surrounding him that phasers can be modulated to weaken him considerably, forcing him to use up lots of power to defend himself. The Narrator also knows that there are probably lots of other ways to handle it, and that if the Crew comes up with something that sounds good, he'll go with it.

When the Crew finally come face to face with Franklin, the entity "jumps tracks" and takes over another body entirely. The new victim can be another miner, but the Narrator has decided that if the Crew brings along a security team, it will be a nonplayer Federation officer that gets possessed instead (see "The Unbearable Lightness of Being a Redshirt," page 34). At this point, the entity will reveal its true nature, proclaiming itself "the mightiest god of the Klingons, ruler of this world that they abandoned in their cowardice!" End of Act Two, new commercial break.

ACT THREE: RESOLUTION AND RESULTS

The third act should be driven by the results of the first two. In Act One, the Narrator presented a situation which the Crew had little choice but to react to. In Act Two, the Crew were given free rein to explore the problem and plan for ways to overcome it. In Act Three, the plan should be put to the test, the questions should all collapse into resolution, and the final climax occur.

As Narrator, you must walk a careful line here. On the one hand, you should have a crystal-clear idea of the climax you want from very early in the process of writing your episode. On the other hand, it should be designed flexibly, to allow for the creativity and ingenuity of your players. In our example episode, the Narrator has decided that the energy being himself won't be too difficult to overcome—scary, of course, with a passing (or imprisonment) declared by plenty of descriptive "visual effects," but something that can be taken care of in a few short rounds of combat. The real final conflict will come in the aftermath, when it is discovered that the miners aboard the Klingon cruiser, no longer being "fed" mental energy by the relic-entity, no longer understand the Klingon controls or how they even arrived on the ship. Further, at the last moment of the "god's" consciousness the cruiser began veering out of control, heading straight for the atmosphere of the planet, to smash directly onto the spot where the Crew are standing—the last act of vengeance of an angry Klingon god. It's only after dealing with this final problem (possibly by slowing the descent of the vessel with a tractor beam and transporting any survivors to safety) that the Crew are free to let out a deep breath and relax .

The final part of Act Three is dealing with the consequences of the episode. In this case, the Crew have quite a set of possible consequences: The episode has revealed that the Klingons have a legitimate claim to this planet—

although, for many obvious reasons, they may not want it. If the ancient relic-entity has been merely contained, then it, too, must be dealt with (perhaps sent to the Klingon homeworld as a gift? Or shot into the heart of a sun?). There is also the matter of the surviving miners and the surviving Klingons. Until a Klingon vessel can arrive to claim its own, they'll have to learn to get along—and this episode could act as the springboard for a series of such cooperative ventures. After all, the Organians predict that the Federation and the Klingons are eventually destined to be friends.

TYPES OF CONFLICT

Conflict is what makes a story a story. It drives the action and gives motive meaning. Most conflict in *Star Trek* is ultimately a moral conflict—a matter of Right versus Wrong. But even most moral conflicts arrive first in other forms. Here's a quick list of some of the most interesting types of conflict your episodes can include. If you catch yourself sticking to the same types of conflict episode after episode, you can improve your *Star Trek Roleplaying Game* series by making a point of exploring some of the others for variety.

Emotional: The people of the 23rd century are far from perfect; they are affected by anger, shame, lust, jealousy, and fear just as we are. Conflicts that arise from emotions are more likely to engage characters (and thus engage players' interests) on a personal level, and that makes them very valuable to the Narrator. Remember that the Vulcans' mastery of their emotions is achieved on a personal and philosophical level, not a biological one—Vulcans do have feelings, they just deal with them differently than humans do.

Intellectual: This can take any form from a tense game of three-dimensional chess to a deadly puzzle (perhaps deliberately put to the Crew by a villain, or left over in the ruins of a dead civilization). The best kinds of intellectual conflicts in a *Star Trek Roleplaying Game* episode are those that the entire Crew can tackle together: If the conflict is some kind of formal game, then make it one that everybody can play (or at least one that everybody can influence). If it's a puzzle, spread the solution all over—some clues need to be found in the history databanks, others only by analyzing the strange radiation emitted from a statue, others by interrogating a captured Orion slave woman. Construction of such elaborate puzzles can take some work on the Narrator's part, but the results can be very satisfying when the Crew puts it all together.

Legal: Legal conflicts in *Star Trek* tend to fall into two main categories: conflicts with Federation and ship regulations, and conflicts that arise when two very different cultures' laws clash (such as the events of "A Taste of Armageddon"). The Federation is an evolving entity that includes countless species, and that means that the crew of a Federation starship is often called upon (formally or through circumstance) to play mediator in some very hairy situations, while all the time obeying the strict Federation edicts put down to avoid damaging cultures and relations. In dramatic terms, both kinds of conflict boil down to "invisible walls" that the Crew must obey in order to achieve their mission: It's bad enough when you're lost on an alien world and thirsty (a "Natural" conflict; see below). It's even worse when it's illegal to drink the holy waters from the only fountain for miles around! Of course, not all laws and traditions are arbitrary—an officer drinking that water might find out why it's considered holy ....

Natural: The hoary old saw of "Man versus Nature" can take on many new twists in a *Star Trek* story, since "Nature" now includes phenomena never found on Earth (and, indeed, phenomena not found planetside at all, but only in the depths of space). Starfleet officers are accustomed to life in very controlled environments, where food and drink can be summoned from a synthesizer, the temperature in their quarters can be anything they like, and they are never threatened by inclement weather—but the worlds they visit are often much less hospitable, and it can be very dramatic, indeed, when completely alien "natural" problems enter the mix. Such conflicts can be small-scale (a group of officers stranded deep in a mountain range where magnetic interference prevents the use of transporters and makes navigation difficult for rescuing shuttlecraft) or large-scale, where entire villages or cities or even planets are threatened, with only the Crew to save the day. Some deep-space natural phenomena can even threaten the Crew's starship.

Personal: Old romances, family ties, unresolved betrayals from youth: Many rich conflicts can be found in the personal lives of the Crew, conflicts that can interfere with their duties, threaten the safety of the mission, and even kill them! While it's best not to put the entire basis of an episode's threat directly on the shoulders of a single crew member's past too often, it's a powerful device when used judiciously. Stories driven by such conflict allow characters to be explored in greater depth and add to the richness of a *Star Trek Roleplaying Game* series. Any kind of conflict serves the story better when it can contain some peripheral personal ties—the Narrator should always work to engage the Crew's personal beliefs, morals, ethics, habits, assumptions, and so on.

Racial and Cultural: Within the Federation, problems of bigotry are largely resolved—one of the significant achievements of mankind by the 23rd century. Even still, notes of cultural pride can still be found, and "pride goeth before a fall." Every now and then, even Federation members are foolish enough to let racial and cultural differences breed irrational conflict, and many of the new worlds that the Crew will encounter will be less developed still. It's a big galaxy, and entire civilizations are probably destroyed every day, someplace, because people couldn't get over differences no bigger than the hue on their second cranial ridge, or the smell of their neighbor's gills. The trick to making such conflicts interesting in dramatic terms is either to focus on the peculiar troubles of diplomacy (making the nature of the conflict depend on the specific personalities involved, rather than the "issue" itself) or to ensure that the problem isn't simplistic—if success is just a matter of realizing and/or pointing out that irrational prejudice is wrong, it's not very interesting to roleplay!

Ritual and Traditional: One of the great dangers any society faces—and therefore one of the great conflicts you can employ in a *game* episode—is habit. Sometimes this will mean that the conflict itself is traditional or ritual in nature—such as the *Koon-ut-kal-if-fee* challenge invoked against Spock in "Amok Time." Sometimes the ritual or tradition doesn't cause conflict until cultures meet—and the Crew must navigate a tricky balance between arrogantly asserting the supremacy of their own way of life, and meekly accepting the results of a ritual that could cause damage (even death) that they seek to prevent. The key issues in a conflict arising from ritual and tradition are respect (usually for the culture with the tradition in question) and diplomacy.

"Steady on the helm, Mr. D'wara," Captain Foster cautioned as the U.S.S. Yorktown made its approach toward the cluster of planets that comprised the Sicon system.

"Aye, sir," Alban D'wara responded automatically as he focused his entire attention on his instrument panel. The rest of the bridge personnel watched the viewscreen as their ship slowed from warp speed. Filling the screen, the asteroids of the Sicon Ring careened past the crew's vision.

"Those are spectacular!" exclaimed Lieutenant Vashenka, the ship's science officer and perhaps the only one on the bridge whose expression registered something other than tense excitement. "I don't suppose we have time to—"

"Reason would dictate that this is not an appropriate moment to study the asteroid belt, Lieutenant," Security Officer Sudek commented. The Vulcan glanced at Captain Foster for confirmation. The Captain nodded.

"Proceed with extreme caution," he ordered. "I have every confidence in you, Mr. D'wara."

Alban felt a surge of pride at the Captain's words. For him, as for most of the crew aboard the bridge, this venture into the Sicondor Sector meant more than just another Federation assignment. The privilege of serving aboard a starship with the reputation of the Yorktown represented the culmination of many years of hard work and grueling study.

"Shall I open communications, sir?" Communications Officer Thursen's voice quavered slightly with the anticipation of announcing the arrival of the Yorktown.

"Wait until we're through the Ring, Lieutenant," Captain Foster advised. "It won't hurt us to get a little closer to our destination."

Thursen lowered her head to hide the slight flush that reddened her cheek. She wondered if her eagerness to take a more active role in the approach

WHERE NO MAN HAS GONE BEFORE

made her seem even more of a new recruit than her shipmates. She admired Lieutenant Vashenka's composure and Helmsman D'wara's complete concentration. Sometimes she thought her graduation from the academy was a fluke. She wondered if the others felt the same way.

"Heads up!" D'wara exclaimed suddenly. "Brace yourselves!" A huge ball of solid rock and ice filled the view screen as the ship reeled with the impact. This wasn't going to be as easy as it seemed, D'wara realized as he steeled himself to ride out the onslaught of debris. His crewmates—and his captain— were counting on him to bring them through. He couldn't let them down. A few seconds later, D'wara eased back from his station.

"We're past the worst of it, sir," he said, his face beaded with sweat from the tension.

"Welcome to Sicon," Captain Foster remarked as the bridge personnel relaxed visibly and watched the viewscreen display a calm expanse of stars. "Good work, Mr. D'wara."

Sicondor: A Sample Setting Sector

Your players have assembled a Crew, acquired a ship, and now await further orders. Your job, as Narrator, is to bring the world around them to life by giving them a rich, detailed setting worthy of their exploration. The Sicondor Sector offers Narrators a ready-made environment for them to test their skills and ingenuity. While much of the sector remains a mystery awaiting the attentions of Federation explorers (such as the Crew), the Federation has already established an outpost on one of the sector's planets.

The actions of the Crew as they explore this sector and respond to the situations they encounter can determine the success or failure of the Federation presence in this part of space. *The Danurian Factor* (pages 274-282) is a ready-to-play episode to get your Crew started exploring the mysteries of Sicondor. If the Crew does not yet have a ship, you may use the information on the *U.S.S. Yorktown* (see below) to provide the characters with a vessel and help fill out any gaps in the Crew.

LOCATION

Occupying a zone bordering Klingon space rimward from the Organian neutral zone, the Sicondor Sector stands as disputed territory. A vast region stretching forty-five light-years across, Sicondor space has only a nominal, but vital, Federation presence. Most of the territory encompassed by the Sicondor Sector as yet remains unmapped and undiscovered. Although the Sicondor Sector contains several planetary systems, the Federation monitors only one at this time.

The closest system to the sector's outer rim contains three planets orbiting a single sun, called Sicon by the Federation discovery team who initially found the sector. Though all the planets in the Sicon system qualify for habitation in terms of distance from their sun, only the third planet—imaginatively dubbed Sicon III—rates Class M status.

ASTROPOLITICS

Although technically claimed by the Federation, the Sicondor Sector lies too close to Klingon space for comfort. According to a fragile codicil to the

ELSEWHERE IN THE SECTOR

The Narrator should feel free to detail the other planetary systems in the Sicondor Sector to suit his campaign. This region of space contains the possibility for numerous new species and a variety of challenges for players. The Federation has only recently acquired the right of protection over this sector and has not yet fully surveyed all the star systems and their planets. The constant proximity of Klingon space makes it quite likely for skirmishes between Federation and Klingon ships to occur.

Organian Treaty between the Federation and the Klingon Empire, the Federation maintains control of the Sicondor Sector provided it places an outpost within the region and utilizes the space for colonization or other purposes. Otherwise, the sector reverts to Klingon rule. Naturally, the Federation prefers to keep its influence within the Sicondor Sector, particularly since at least one of its planets (and possibly more) contains valuable mineral resources necessary to Starfleet technology.

PEOPLES

FEDERATION

Initial scans of the Sicondor Sector revealed no indigenous populations on any of the three planets that make up the Sicon system. For this reason, the Federation has marked the Sicondor Sector as a prime location for colonization. The pact with the Klingons lends some urgency to the need to form a permanent base on Sicon III, the Sicon system's single Class M planet.

Currently the Federation has a single domed outpost, commanded by Lt. Commander Konata Nantambu, on Sicon Prime, which serves as a temporary processing and orientation center for colonists bound for permanent colonization of Sicon III. The Federation considers this sector a protectorate and has dispatched a starship (the one belonging to the Crew) to exercise responsibility for the peaceful development of the region.

DANURIANS

Unknown to the Federation, Sicon III harbors a society of people living beneath the planet's surface. Former refugees from the Eugenics Wars, the Danurians originally sought sanctuary on Alpha Centauri, but a ship malfunction threw them far off course and landed them in the as-yet-undiscovered Sicondor Sector.

Their inherent distrust of other humans and their fear of possible discovery by later expeditions from Earth led them to build their homes beneath the planet's surface. Genetically engineered for high psionics, the Danurians have developed a highly advanced civilization.

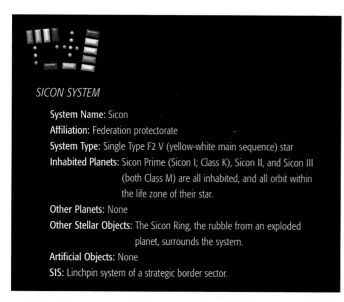

SICON SYSTEM

System Name: Sicon
Affiliation: Federation protectorate
System Type: Single Type F2 V (yellow-white main sequence) star
Inhabited Planets: Sicon Prime (Sicon I; Class K), Sicon II, and Sicon III
(both Class M) are all inhabited, and all orbit within
the life zone of their star.
Other Planets: None
Other Stellar Objects: The Sicon Ring, the rubble from an exploded
planet, surrounds the system.
Artificial Objects: None
SIS: Linchpin system of a strategic border sector.

KLINGONS

Shortly after the Danurians arrived and settled in, a Klingon scout ship discovered their existence. The psionic resources of the Danurians prevented the Klingons from conquering them. Instead of ousting the Klingon invaders, however, the Danurians offered them a mutual accord pact and invited them to place a small advisory contingent in their city. This alliance, while it violates the agreement between the Federation and the Klingons, provides both sides with certain advantages—the Danurians have guarantees of Klingon protection from invasion by the Federation, while the Klingons gain access to the eridennium deposits located within the planet.

DELPHINIANS

An aquatic race of intelligent, eel-like creatures inhabits the water world of Sicon II. While Federation scout ships have taken readings on the Delphinians and have studied them at a distance, they have only begun to speculate on the nature of the eel folk's civilization. Delphinians seem to travel in schools, like colonies of fish, and evidence behavior that resembles ceremonial gatherings in connection with the placement of the planet's moons. They may, therefore, perceive the moons as deities or objects of spiritual inspiration.

OTHER SYSTEMS

In addition to the Sicon system, six other habitable planetary systems exist within the Sicondor Sector. The Federation intends to use their outpost on Sicon Prime as a base from which to continue exploration of the Sicondor Sector. Preliminary reports indicate that at least three of these systems possess worlds inhabited by intelligent lifeforms. The Federation hopes to assess the development of the species that live on these planets for possible admission to the Federation.

UNUSUAL PHENOMENA

At the outer edge of the Sicon system lies a ring of asteroids believed to be the remnants of a fourth planet. Called the Sicon Ring, the fragments that make up the asteroid belt range from little more than cosmic dust to planetoid in size. Navigation through the Sicon Ring poses some hazards for spacegoing vessels, although cautious maneuvering usually suffices to avoid collisions.

Toward the sector's core lies a curious distortion of space. Visible to starship viewscreens as a shimmering wave of color, the Sigma Barrier distorts the readings on most sensors. Federation scientists have speculated that the Barrier represents everything from a spatial relocator able to transport ships instantaneously to other places to a temporal anomaly of some kind.

SICON PRIME

Planet Name: Sicon Prime
Class: K
System Data: Sicon Prime has one moon.
Gravity: Sicon Prime's gravity is .85.
Year/Day: 260/22
Atmosphere: Oxygen-nitrogen-hydrogen
Hydrosphere: 30% surface water
Climate: Hot and dry
Sapient Species: No indigenous intelligent life; Federation outpost personnel
Tech Level: Level Six due to Federation presence
Government: Starfleet military regime
Culture: Federation standard
Affiliation: Federation protectorate
Resources: Sicon Prime contains trace minerals useful in Federation
technology, but has little in the way of concentrated
deposits. Evidence of gem-quality stone in the planet's
mountain ranges may eventually earmark the planet as suitable for extensive mining. Local plant and animal life
consists of desert biota—lizardlike creatures, snakes of various sizes, and a proliferation of water-retaining vegetation
akin to cacti. No large predators have been observed,
although many mountain caves show spoor suggestive of
large feline creatures similar to pumas.
Places of Note: Glenconner, the Federation outpost on Sicon Prime,
consists of a domed settlement which holds a small
staff of permanent Federation personnel and quarters
for a larger number of temporary residents—colonists
slated for Sicon III.
Ship Facilities: Sicon Prime has a starport capable of handling shuttle-craft and conducting minor starship repairs.

SICON II

Planet Name: Sicon II

Class: K

System Data: Sicon II has two moons.

Gravity: 1.3 G. Sicon II's gravity is slightly greater than Earth's.

Year/Day: 300/28

Atmosphere: Oxygen-hydrogen-nitrogen-ammonia

Hydrosphere: 90% surface water

Climate: Extremely humid

Sapient Species: Delphinians (elongated eel-like creatures), population unknown

Tech Level: Exact level unverified, but estimated at Level One–Two. Long-range sensors and orbital surveys indicate that the Delphinians possess some domesticated creatures–other aquatic species–and practice a kind of hydroponic "farming" of seaweed and algae.

Government: Unknown, possible hive mind postulated by Federation sociologists

Culture: The Delphinians appear to possess a peaceful, nonaggressive culture with some aspects of moon worship based on tidal variations.

Affiliation: Federation protectorate

Resources: Sicon II consists primarily of oceans with only a scattering of small landmasses worthy of the term "island." Nevertheless, the prevalence of water on Sicon II indicates an abundance of minerals commonly found in an aquatic environment. Additionally, the presence of large quantities of kelp and sea algae of many kinds indicates a suitable environment for large-scale hydroponics, should the Federation gain the permission of the Delphinians to exploit the ocean surface.

Places of Note: The Oceanic Vortex, a large stationary whirlpool in the planet's northern hemisphere, attracts a twice-yearly gathering of Delphinians, apparently for some religious or social ceremony. Hurricane Sea, in the southern hemisphere, consists of a wide swath of ocean in constant turmoil from hurricane-force storms.

Ship Facilities: None. The Federation plans exist to place a floating spaceport on the planet's surface contingent upon establishing contact with and permission from the Delphinians.

AREA LOCATIONS

SICON PRIME

Smallest of the three planets in the Sicon system, Sicon Prime is a Class K planet that occupies an orbit nearest the system's sun. The temperature on the surface of Sicon Prime exceeds the tolerance level for Human habitation without the protection of a dome. Environmental suits allow brief exposure on the planet's rocky, arid surface, and a few scientists stationed at the Glenconner outpost have braved the inhospitable terrain and climate to gather samples of soil and plant life.

The Federation has no definite plans for Sicon Prime apart from its role as a jumping-off point for further colonization of the system. Possible uses of the planet remain a matter of debate between those elements within the Federation who favor terraforming and those who oppose drastic alteration of existing planetary conditions.

SICON II

Sicon II presents certain difficulties with regard to possible Federation membership. The aquatic nature of its indigenous sentient species makes the likelihood of their attainment of space travel highly unlikely; therefore they may never meet the requirements for joining the Federation. Expansionists within the Federation feel that a species need only be able to grasp the concept of space travel and the existence of off-planet species to qualify. This faction advocates an immediate attempt to make contact with the Delphinians. Opponents argue that since the Delphinians can never develop off-planet travel, they neither need nor can benefit from Federation membership, and the Prime Directive should remain in force.

The Delphinians' biology resembles that of Earth's eels, with elongated torsos. They have small finlike arms but no lower limbs. They reproduce sexually and bear live young rather than through laying eggs. Their metabolism suggests a warm-blooded nature. They have an elaborate language similar to the speech of whales and dolphins, utilizing the transmission of sound through water. Their tendency to travel in groups–like schools of fish–has given rise to the belief that they possess a hive mentality. While they appear to participate in various ceremonies and rituals, the exact nature of their spirituality remains a mystery.

SICON III

The Danurians come from Human stock, genetically engineered during the period of the Eugenics Wars and dedicated to the task of opposing the warlords that arose on Earth at that time. Although they are peaceful by nature, they remember the fear their powers engendered in others and they have developed a somewhat paranoid reaction to the thought that "normal" humans might seek to destroy them for their enhanced psionic abilities. They have evolved a somewhat superior attitude toward nonpsionic humans in conjunction with their extreme caution and secretiveness.

SICON III

Planet Name: Sicon III

Class: M

System Data: Sicon III has one moon.

Gravity: 1 G. Sicon III has an Earth-like gravity.

Year/Day: 360/28

Atmosphere: Oxygen-nitrogen

Hydrosphere: 65% surface water

Climate: Temperate—moderate temperatures and variable humidity

Sapient Species: No indigenous intelligent life, although the Danurians dwell beneath the planet's surface.

Tech Level: Level Five–Six: The Danurians have knowledge of warp-drive capability, but maintain a generally lower level of technology than Federation standards. They have access to some Klingon technology.

Government: Democracy, with an elected leader similar to a President as well as other elected and appointed officials

Culture: The Danurians espouse a peaceful culture that emphasizes privacy and politeness (due to their high level of psionic talents).

Affiliation: The Federation considers Sicon III a protectorate; the Danurians do not recognize Federation influence but have allied with the Klingons in a mutual assistance pact.

Resources: The most valuable resource on Sicon III is the metal eridennium, which permeates the ground below the planet's surface. Unaware of the Danurian presence on the planet, the Federation intends to establish a mining colony on the surface to extract this valuable metal for use in shield technology. Eridennium is an ironlike metal possessing qualities that interfere with sensor readings and prohibit transporter technology from working anywhere except on the planet's surface.

Places of Note: Serenity Settlement, the underground enclave of the Danurian population, lies within a series of caves and caverns hollowed out beneath the surface. While there is room for expansion, the population has not grown sufficiently to warrant a second settlement. Serenity also includes an area set aside for the Klingon advisors. Mount Hope, the tallest mountain on the planet, lies close to the settlement.

Ship Facilities: The planet contains primitive docking facilities for the Klingon shuttlecraft currently based near Serenity. In addition, a huge cave in the side of Mount Hope houses parts scavenged from the ship that originally brought the Danurians to Sicon III (which they refer to as "Home" rather than by its designated UFP title).

Physically, the Danurians resemble normal humans. They display a variety of physiotypes, indicating a broad spectrum of ethnic and racial origins. Their dress and manner tend toward understated elegance and simplicity. Most of their adornment consists of handcrafted or woven items, and they place great value on making things of beauty in addition to their appreciation of cultural pursuits such as art, music, and literature. They have originated the custom of decorating their faces with elaborate tattoos that express their inner selves.

SICON RING

This belt of asteroids orbits the star Sicon beyond Sicon III. Its relative mass and distance from its nearest neighbor suggests that the Sicon Ring may, in fact, constitute the remnants of a fourth planet, destroyed by a cosmic accident. Closer study of some of the larger asteroids in the Ring show some evidence of technological artifacts, leading to the belief that the inhabitants of the hypothetical Sicon IV destroyed themselves. While most of the asteroids consist of small fragments, a few are large enough to support small outposts, mining operations, or research facilities.

One asteroid in particular merits mentioning. A large, relatively stable chunk of rock the size of a small planet, this asteroid serves as a secret Klingon outpost with a docking bay for a Klingon scout ship located within the asteroid's interior. So far, the Federation has not discovered its existence. When and if it does, the Federation will almost certainly take some sort of official action to protest this obvious violation of the Federation-Klingon pact. The outpost consists of a scout ship and living quarters for a half-dozen Klingon warriors and engineers.

SIGMA BARRIER

This shimmering curtain of light and color has confounded Federation attempts to make sense of it through its various sensors. It seems to distort both time and space in its immediate vicinity and no Federation ship has yet dared to test the effect of passing through the Sigma Barrier. Located near the center of the sector, the Sigma Barrier does not pose a deterrent to travel between planetary systems. The Federation has plans to study it more closely once it has firmly established colonies in the Sicon planetary system and thus solidified its claim to the Sicondor Sector.

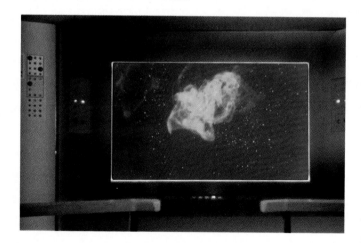

The Characters' Ship

The Crew's starship provides them with a stable environment in the ever-changing surroundings of space. Since most adventures begin aboard the characters' ship and occasionally take place primarily within the confines of the starship, this vessel should assume a concrete presence for Narrator and players alike. You can describe the ship in terms of the interiors drawn from the many *Star Trek* episodes depicting the inside of the *Enterprise* or you can draw upon your own narrative skills to bring the ship's quarters and passageways to life. (See also "Starship Locations," page 129.)

If your players prefer to design their own starship for their characters, the ship described below can serve as a guideline for them to use. Alternatively, the players may wish to use the *U.S.S. Yorktown* as their own vessel.

The *U.S.S. Yorktown* is a *Constitution*-class starship, like the *U.S.S. Enterprise*. Though not as renowned as that prestigious vessel, the *Yorktown* nevertheless enjoys a solid reputation for reliability and performance within the Federation. A veteran of several battles against the Klingons, the *U.S.S. Yorktown* has undergone several refits and is beginning to show signs of general wear and tear. Now the *Yorktown* has drawn the assignment of patrolling and servicing the newly discovered Sicondor Sector. Though not designed primarily for battle, the *Yorktown* boasts a complete arsenal of standard *Constitution*-class weaponry and defenses. (See the statistics for a *Constitution*-class explorer, page 141.)

THE CREW

The sample crew members presented below can serve as supporting cast for the Narrator to use to fill out gaps in the player character group or as quick-start characters for players who prefer to use pregenerated Crew members for their initial forays into the world of the *Star Trek Roleplaying Game*. The players should have first choice at the positions they wish for their characters to fill in the starship crew; the Narrator should assume the roles of the positions left vacant. Make certain that any characters who occupy the position of department head possess the advantage Department Head by reminding them to allot the required number of points for that advantage during the character generation process.

If you do not wish for the characters to hold leadership positions aboard their starship, you may assume that the player characters serve under the appropriate NPC's for their positions. For example, a player character designed as a security officer would answer to Lieutenant Sudek, while an engineer character would take orders from Lieutenant Akumi. Because no one individual can remain on duty without periodic rest periods, the player characters can alternate shifts with the NPC's as long as there is only one department head for each position. (The role of Captain is the exception, although it is possible for a Crew to contain a guest star Captain and a player character First Officer—or vice versa.)

While many players may want to portray department or section heads, the ability to grow and improve as a character lends itself more easily to those characters who start at relatively low ranks and progress with experience. Try to encourage new players, in particular, to choose secondary positions under more "experienced" (NPC) superior officers. This gives you as the Narrator the ability to guide your players' characters as they gain in experience and knowledge.

Eventually, the player characters may merit promotion to the coveted chief positions aboard their starship or they might win the privilege of assuming command posts aboard a new vessel, leaving their old NPC commanders behind.

CAPTAIN EVAN FOSTER

Image: A distinguished-looking man in his mid-fifties, Captain Evan Foster projects an aura of quiet, understated authority. His dark brown hair is just beginning to show signs of gray at the temples. Once a paragon of physical fitness, he now carries a bit more weight than normal—though still within acceptable Federation standards.

Personality: Captain Foster fills his position with a quiet dignity, calmly encouraging his crew and dealing out reprimands with an understated fairness that takes away most of the sting. He is more concerned with seeing his crew learn from their mistakes than with berating them for their errors. Because of this, his crew respects him and works hard to win his approval.

History: Captain Foster has commanded the *U.S.S. Yorktown* for nearly fifteen years. He is a veteran of several altercations with both the Romulans and the Klingons and harbors a strong dislike for Klingons that goes beyond normal resentment toward an enemy. Although some within the Federation speculate that Captain Foster will seek retirement at the end of his current mission, others feel that the captain has no such intentions. Foster enjoys not only the responsibilities that go along with commanding a Federation starship, he also takes great pleasure in helping new Starfleet officers hone their talents.

ATTRIBUTES

Fitness 2

Coordination 2

   Dexterity +1

Intellect 3

   Perception +2

Presence 4

   Willpower +1

Psi 0

SKILLS

Administration (Starship Administration) 4 (5)

Athletics (Climbing) 2 (3)

   (Running) (3)

Command (Starship Command) 4 (5)

Computer (Research) 1(2)

Culture (Human) 3 (4)

Dodge 2

Energy Weapon (Phaser) 2 (3)

History (Federation) 3 (4)

   (Human) (4)

Language

   Federation Standard 3

Law (Starfleet Regulations) 4 (5)

Personal Equipment (Communicator) 2 (3)

Planetside Survival (Mountain) 1 (2)

Shipboard Systems (Tactical) 3 (4)

Social Science (Political Science) 2 (3)

Starship Tactics (Planetary Support Tactics) 3 (4)

Vehicle Operations (Shuttlecraft) 1 (2)

World Knowledge (Earth) 2 (3)

TRAITS

Department Head (Navigation), Hides Emotions, Intolerant (Klingons) (–3), Pacifism (–1), Rank (Captain), Resolute

COURAGE: 5

RENOWN: 60

   Aggression: –10, Discipline: 15, Initiative: 12, Openness: –10, Skill: 14

RESISTANCE: 2

WOUND LEVELS: 2/2/2/2/2/2/0

FIRST OFFICER LIEUTENANT COMMANDER MARIA SANCHEZ

Image: A diminutive woman of Hispanic background, First Officer Sanchez has olive skin, long curly black hair, and dark brown eyes. Despite her fiery personality, which manifests most obviously when leading expeditions to a planet's surface, she maintains an outward disposition of dispassionate efficiency when in the presence of Captain Foster.

Personality: Sanchez has enough experience under her belt to command a starship in her own right. She prefers to serve as second in command, however, since she feels insecure in her ability to assume total responsibility for a starship crew. Possessed of a volatile nature, with mer-

curial shifts of temper from extreme agitation and excitement to intense moodiness, she strives to keep herself under control at all times when stationed on the bridge. In her off-hours, however, she leads the crew in carousing.

History: First Officer Sanchez has served with Captain Foster for five years. She has seen enough combat against Klingons and other Federation enemies to know that she detests battle of all kinds. She prefers missions of exploration and discovery to military forays. While many of her colleagues have urged her to try for a command position, she steadfastly refuses to seek promotion.

ATTRIBUTES

Fitness 2

Coordination 2

   Reaction +1

Intellect 2

Presence 2

   Empathy +1

   Willpower +1

Psi 0

SKILLS

Administration (Starship Administration) 2 (3)

Athletics (Running) 2 (3)

   (Swimming) (3)

Command (Starship Command) 3 (4)

Computer (Hacking) 1 (2)

Culture (Human) 2 (3)

Dodge 1

Energy Weapon (Phaser) 1 (2)

History (Federation) 2 (3)

   (Human) (3)

Language

   Federation Standard 3

   Spanish 3

Law (Starfleet Regulations) 2 (3)

Personal Equipment (Environmental Suit) 3 (4)

Planetary Sciences (Planetology) 3 (5)

Planetary Tactics (Small Unit) 2 (3)

Planetside Survival (Ocean) 2 (3)

Shipboard Systems (Environmental Control) 2 (3)

Vehicle Operations (Ground Vehicle) 2 (3)

   (Shuttlecraft) (3)

World Knowledge (Earth) 2 (3)

Department Head (First Officer), Impulsive, Patron (+1) Capt. Foster, Phobia
(Assuming Command) (−1)
COURAGE: 4
RENOWN: 40
   Aggression: 15, Discipline: −5, Initiative: −5, Openness: 12, Skill: 14
RESISTANCE: 2
WOUND LEVELS: 2/2/2/2/2/2/0

SCIENCE OFFICER LIEUTENANT SANDIRA VASHENKA

Image: Lieutenant Vashenka is a tall, striking woman with the high cheekbones and blond hair typical of her Slavic heritage. Her enthusiasm for her job and her genuine interest in even the most dangerous examples of space anomalies serves as an inspiration for those under her command.

Personality: Promoted to her position as Chief Science Officer when her predecessor retired just three years ago, Lieutenant Vashenka has taken to the post as if she were born to it. She displays a remarkable breadth of scientific knowledge and an unquenchable thirst to improve her skills and techniques in both research and observation. She has mastered the art of commanding without giving orders, using her forceful and outgoing personality to inspire her underlings.

History: After her graduation from Starfleet near the top of her class in science, Vashenka served with the Federation science vessel *U.S.S. Tau Ceti* for two years before transferring to the *U.S.S. Yorktown*. She quickly worked her way to second science officer and then, upon the retirement of her predecessor, received a promotion to her current position as head of the science crew. Despite her vivacious approach to her job and her outward approachability, Vashenka seems reluctant to form close personal relationships with any of her crewmates. This comes from having lost most of her fellow science officers on an ill-fated planetary exploration during her cadet cruise. She blames herself for surviving the debacle and refuses to allow herself to become friends with her colleagues in space.

ATTRIBUTES
Fitness 2
   Vitality +1
Coordination 2
Intellect 2
   Logic +2
Presence 2
   Willpower +1
Psi 0

SKILLS
Athletics (Lifting) 2 (3)
Computer (Programming) 2 (4)
Culture (Human) 2 (3)
Dodge 1
Energy Weapon (Phaser) 1 (2)
Material Engineering (Metallurgical) 3 (4)
History (Federation) 1 (2)
   (Human) (2)
Language
   Federation Standard 3
Law (Starfleet Regulations) 1 (2)
Personal Equipment (Tricorder) 3 (4)
Physical Sciences (Physics) 4 (5)
Planetary Sciences (Climatology) 4 (5)
   (Mineralogy) (5)
Planetside Survival (Arctic) 3 (4)
Shipboard Systems (Sensors) 3 (4)
   (Transporter) (4)
Space Sciences (Stellar Cartography) 3 (4)
Vehicle Operations (Shuttlecraft) 1
World Knowledge (Earth) 1 (2)

TRAITS
Department Head (Science), Phobia (Making Friends) (−1), Promotion (Lieutenant), Sexy (+2)
COURAGE: 3
RENOWN: 25
   Aggression: −5, Discipline: 5, Initiative: 4, Openness: 6, Skill: 7
RESISTANCE: 3
WOUND LEVELS: 3/3/3/3/3/3/)

COMMUNICATIONS OFFICER SIGRID THURSEN

Image: A slender, almost gawky woman in her late twenties, Lieutenant Thursen has long, light brown hair and dark green eyes. Her extreme self-consciousness shows in her awkward movements and stooped posture. She deliberately downplays her natural attractiveness through an extreme severity in hairstyle and dress (when not in uniform).

Personality: Although she completed her cadet cruise with honors, Lieutenant Thursen lacks true confidence in herself. She constantly pushes herself to attain higher and higher standards and berates herself if she fails to achieve her impossible goals. The middle child in a large family, Thursen often felt herself overlooked and undervalued. Her recent appointment as Communications Officer for the *U.S.S. Yorktown* (which she regards as a fluke) has forced her to take command of a small group of lower-ranking officers, something that makes her nervous. Although she is easily flustered as a supervisor, she demonstrates remarkable communications skills on the job.

History: Lieutenant Thursen distinguished herself during her cadet cruise through her delicate handling of a potentially volatile exchange with a Romulan vessel. Her diplomatic communications with an irate Romulan commander prevented an "incident" between the Romulans and the Federation. When the *Yorktown's* Communications Officer unexpectedly found himself forced to resign his commission, Thursen seemed the logical choice to succeed him on the basis of her past performance. Her relative newness to her job increases her sense of inadequacy among her "peers." Fortunately, her uneasiness in her position does not seem to affect her performance. Thursen has trouble exercising her authority and frequently suffers from an over-eagerness to prove herself useful.

ATTRIBUTES
Fitness 2
Coordination 2
   Dexterity −1
Intellect 2
   Perception +1
Presence 2
   Empathy +1
   Willpower +1

SKILLS
Administration (Bureaucratic Manipulation) 2 (3)
Athletics (Riding) 2 (3)
   (Running) (3)
Computer (Programming) 3 (4)
Culture (Human) 2 (3)
Dodge 1
Energy Weapon (Phaser) 1 (2)
History (Federation) 1 (2)
   (Human) (2)
Language
   Federation Standard 3
   Romulan 1
Law (Starfleet Regulations) 2 (3)
Personal Equipment (Universal Translator) 3 (4)
Physical Sciences (Computer Science) 2 (3)
Planetside Survival (Urban) 1 (2)
Shipboard Systems (Communications) 4 (5)
Social Sciences (Sociology) 3 (4)
Systems Engineering (Communications Systems) 3 (4)
Unarmed Combat (Starfleet Martial Arts) 1 (2)
Vehicle Operation (Shuttlecraft) 2 (3)
World Knowledge (Earth) 2 (3)

TRAITS
Department Head (Communications), Famous Incident (Romulan negotiations), Promotion (Lieutenant)
COURAGE: 3
RENOWN: 25
   Aggression: −8, Discipline: 10, Initiative: 5, Openness: 4, Skill: 8
RESISTANCE: 2
WOUND LEVELS: 2/2/2/2/2/2/0

CHIEF ENGINEER LIEUTENANT MICHAEL AKUMI

Image: Michael is a short, stocky man of Japanese origins. His face registers his feelings like an open book. He wears his hair almost too long for Federation standards and exercises regularly to keep trim.

Personality: Lieutenant Akumi views life as a drama in which he faces life-threatening situations daily. He lives for catastrophes; they call up his best efforts. He has an uncanny affinity for mechanical and technological devices and enjoys talking to his banks of computers, propulsion devices, and, of course, the transporter. He credits his ability to diagnose and repair systems to a brief apprenticeship with the *Enterprise's* Chief Engineer Montgomery Scott.

History: Lieutenant Akumi worked hard to gain admission to Starfleet. Once enrolled in the Academy, he gravitated toward engineering, a field where he showed a true talent for understanding the complex workings of starship technology. He served for a year aboard the *Enterprise* before transferring to the *U.S.S. Yorktown* when a position in Engineering opened up. In the four years since he joined the crew of the *Yorktown*, Akumi has worked his way up to his current post as Chief Engineer. Despite his flair for dramatics, he runs a tight department. While he does not hesitate to praise work well done, he is notorious for dressing down lazy or careless technicians with the same vigor he uses in his commendations.

ATTRIBUTES
Fitness 2
   Strength +1
   Vitality +1
Coordination 2
   Dexterity +1
Intellect 2
   Logic +1
Presence 2
   Willpower +1
Psi 0

SKILLS

Athletics (Climbing) 2 (3)

    (Lifting) (3)

Computer (Modeling) 3 (4)

Culture (Human) 2 (3)

Dodge 1

Energy Weapon (Phaser) 1 (2)

History (Federation) 1 (2)

    (Human) (2)

Language

    Federation Standard 3

Law (Starfleet Regulations) 1 (2)

Personal Equipment (Communicator) 2 (3)

Physical Science (Mathematics) 4 (5)

Planetside Survival (Jungle) 1 (2)

Propulsion Engineering (Impulse) 4 (5)

    (Warp Drive) (5)

Shipboard Systems (Engineering/Power Circuits) 4 (5)

    (Transporter) (5)

Space Sciences (Thermodynamics) 2 (3)

Systems Engineering (Transporter) 3 (4)

Vehicle Operations (Close Orbital Craft) 2(3)

    (Shuttlecraft) (3)

World Knowledge (Earth) 1 (2)

TRAITS

Bold, Department Head (Engineering), Impulsive, Strong Will, Vengeful

COURAGE: 4

RENOWN: 30

    Aggression: 10, Discipline: –12, Initiative: 5, Openness: 8, Skill: 10

Resistance: 3

Wound Levels: 3/3/3/3/3/3/0

HELMSMAN LIEUTENANT ALBAN D'WARA

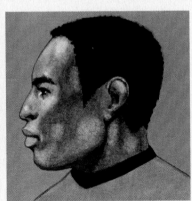

Image: Lieutenant D'wara has dark skin and short, curly black hair that reveal his African heritage. Although he appears cool and collected under pressure, he labors under the weight of his responsibility for manning the helm of the *Yorktown*. He works hard to hide his emotions when on the bridge.

Personality: D'wara has a strong sense of personal pride and an awareness of the trust that Captain Foster places in him. He has developed the ability to focus intently on the sometimes-tricky task of guiding the starship using manual as well as automated controls. His powers of concentration reflect his commitment to his career with Starfleet,

and he considers it an honor to serve as the *Yorktown's* Chief Helmsman.

History: D'wara attended Starfleet Academy, where he specialized in helm technology and flight control. After a cadet cruise aboard another starship, he accepted a position aboard the *U.S.S. Yorktown*. When the Chief Helmsman requested a transfer to another starship due to personality conflicts with Captain Foster, D'wara moved up in rank. He has only occupied his position for a year and feels that he has already achieved a milestone in his career with Starfleet.

ATTRIBUTES

Fitness 2

    Vitality +1

Coordination 2

    Dexterity +2

Intellect 2

    Perception +1

Presence 2

    Empathy –1

    Willpower +1

Psi 0

SKILLS

Administration (Logistics) 2 (3)

Athletics (Running) 2 (3)

    (Swimming) (3)

Computer (Hacking) 2 (3)

Culture (Human) 2 (3)

Dodge 1

Energy Weapon (Phaser) 1 (2)

History (Federation) 1 (2)

    (Human) (2)

Language

    Federation Standard 3

Law (Starfleet Regulations) 1 (2)

Personal Equipment (Tricorder) 1 (2)

Planetside Survival (Desert) 1 (2)

Shipboard Systems (Helm) 3 (4)

Space Sciences (Astrogation) 3 (4)

    (Astronomy) (4)

Systems Engineering (Environmental Systems) 2 (3)

Unarmed Combat (Starfleet Martial Arts) 1 (2)

Vehicle Operation (Shuttlecraft) 2 (3)

World Knowledge (Earth) 1 (2)

TRAITS

Department Head (Helm), Code of Honor (–2), Promotion (Lieutenant), Resolute

COURAGE: 4

RENOWN: 20

    Aggression: –4, Discipline 14, Initiative: 4, Openness: 3, Skill: 12

RESISTANCE: 3

WOUND LEVELS: 3/3/3/3/3/3/0

CHIEF SECURITY OFFICER LIEUTENANT SUDEK

Image: A young Vulcan male with the classic dark hair and taciturn features typical of his race, Sudek conducts his duties with a military precision and a minimum of words. He projects an air of confidence bordering on indifference.

Personality: Lieutenant Sudek's cold exterior belies an acute and perceptive sense of humor, a relative rarity among Vulcans. He enjoys observing the foibles and patent emotions of humans and prefers their company to those of his own race. He has a keen appreciation of the arts, particularly the visual arts of sculpture, holography, and abstract painting. He cultivates few friends outside of his closest coworkers, but among his fellow security officers he has a reputation for loyalty and dependability.

History: Sudek graduated from Starfleet Academy a few years after Spock and has deliberately attempted to avoid comparisons with the Academy's first Vulcan. He chose security rather than science, although he has a good grasp of scientific principles and theories. An expert in hand-to-hand combat, personal weaponry, and ship's armaments and defenses, he shares his knowledge freely with those under his command. He has earned his position as Chief Security Officer several times over but never takes his rank for granted.

ATTRIBUTES
Fitness 4
    Strength +1
Coordination 3
Intellect 4
    Logic +1
Presence 2
    Empathy −1
Psi 2 (6)
    Range −1

SKILLS
Athletics (Lifting) 1 (2)
Artistic Expression (Sculpture) 1 (2)
Computer (Research) 1 (2)
Culture (Vulcan) 2 (3)
Dodge 2
Energy Weapon (Phaser) 3 (4)
History (Federation) 1 (2)
    (Vulcan) 1 (2)
Language
    Federation Standard 2
    Vulcan 2
Law (Starfleet Regulations) 3 (4)
Medical Sciences (Forensics) 2 (3)
Mind Meld 3
Personal Equipment (Environmental Suit) 2 (3)
Planetside Survival (Vulcan) 1 (2)
Search 3
Security (Security Systems) 4 (5)
Systems Engineering (Security) 3 (4)
Unarmed Combat (Nerve Pinch) 2 (3)
    (Starfleet Martial Arts) (3)
Vehicle Operations (Shuttlecraft) 1 (2)
World Knowledge (Vulcan) 1 (2)

TRAITS
Code of Honor (Vulcan) −3, Curious +1, Department Head (Security), Hides Emotions −2
COURAGE: 4
RENOWN: 25
    Aggression: 8, Discipline: 15, Initiative: 10, Openness: 0, Skill: 15
RESISTANCE: 4
WOUND LEVELS: 4/4/4/4/4/0

CHIEF MEDICAL OFFICER LIEUTENANT JOSEPH TWO RIVERS

Image: Tall and broad-chested, Two Rivers has the strong facial features, coppery skin, and dark hair common among his Chippewa ancestors. He speaks in a slow, studied manner that inspires calmness in his patients and confidence in his underlings.

Personality: Joseph Two Rivers combines a firm grasp of medical procedures with a deeply spiritual approach to medicine. His great-grandfather, a Chippewa medicine man, instilled a love of tribal customs in Two Rivers, causing him to "enhance" his medical treatments with ceremonies and rituals that seem to have a salubrious effect on patients under his care. As Chief Medical Officer, Two Rivers sees himself as both a teacher and a healer and never passes up an opportunity to lecture to his junior officers. His somewhat holistic techniques have made him something of a confidant for many members of the *Yorktown* crew.

History: A graduate of medical school before joining Starfleet, Dr. Two Rivers is somewhat older than most crew members aboard the *U.S.S. Yorktown*. Although this is his first cruise in the position of Chief Medical Officer, Two Rivers feels capable of meeting whatever challenges await him in the unknown regions of space.

ATTRIBUTES

Fitness 2

Coordination 2

    Reaction +1

Intellect 2

    Perception +1

    Logic +1

Presence 2

    Empathy +1

    Willpower +1

Psi 0

SKILLS

Athletics (Jumping) 2 (3)

    (Running) (3)

Computer (Research) 1 (2)

Culture (Human) 2 (3)

Dodge 1

Energy Weapon (Phaser) 1 (2)

First Aid (Wound/Combat Trauma) 3 (4)

History (Federation) 1 (2)

    (Human) (2)

Language

    Federation Standard 3

Law (Starfleet Regulations) 1 (2)

Life Science (Biology) 3 (4)

    (Exobiology) (4)

Medical Science (General Medicine) 4 (5)

Personal Equipment (Medical Tricorder) 3 (4)

Planetside Survival (Desert) 1 (2)

Shipboard Systems (Medical Systems) 3 (4)

Vehicle Operations (Shuttlecraft) 1 (2)

World Knowledge (Earth) 1 (2)

TRAITS

Department Head (Medical), Obsessive Tendencies (Rituals), Resolute, Shrewd

COURAGE: 4

RENOWN: 25

    Aggression: 3, Discipline: 10, Initiative: 7, Openness: 5, Skill: 14

RESISTANCE: 2

WOUND LEVELS: 2/2/2/2/2/2/0

The Danurian Factor

Reeling from the impact, Isabelle Danur turned to look at her people. They stood silently in communion with one another, awaiting her orders.

"Well," she said at last, infusing her words with confidence (for all the good that would do in a room full of empaths and telepaths), "It seems we've been successful."

"Then why are we being shelled?" asked Turlow. Trust the pessimistic scholar to strike right into the heart of the matter.

"Khan and his people retreat even now." She replied, "They will steal a sleeper ship and leave Earth within the next few hours. I suggest we do the same."

The vocal uproar was almost enough to drown out the inner one.

"Hear me!" She called aloud, resisting the impulse to speak purely mentally, to let her awesome empathic powers wash over her followers and decide the issue for them. Another good reason to go, she thought to herself.

"We were created to bring down the supermen tearing this world apart. Most humans know nothing about us, or the experimental processes we went through to make us what we are. But they will learn before long, and they will resent us. Right now, they think they won against Khan on their own. How will they react when they learn that a group of genetically altered psionics poisoned the supermen's minds, brought them to despair and tricked them into seeing what wasn't there?"

"They should thank us!" called one young woman, her mousy hair hanging lank and sweat-soaked from her exertions.

"And they would," Isabelle continued, "for a day or a month or a year. But then they'd become afraid; afraid that we'd turn our powers against them and try to rule as worse dictators than the ones we helped depose. We would control not just their lives, but their very thoughts."

The impact of another shell rocked the hall, sending some of the people within to their knees.

"You see?" Isabelle called again. "The generals already know we pose too great a threat to remain alive. We must go, and it must be immediately. The Terrapin *is ready, stocked and waiting. We have those among us whose knowledge will allow us to operate the ship and survive the flight. We have only to go aboard and take off and we may journey to another home, a home where humans will not hate us, and where we can make our own society and raise our children without fear. Are you with me?"*

Acclaim, both verbal and silent, washed over her.

Eighteen hours later, the slender ship rose from its hidden berth in the Cambodian jungle, flashing into the sky. Within a few breaths, it was gone.

A dark period of Earth's history, the Eugenics Wars of the late 1990's saw the rise to power of genetically altered supermen such as Khan Noonian Singh. A hidden chapter in this story involved a brilliant woman named Isabelle Danur and a group of young men and women who underwent genetic alteration and controlled breeding to unlock their psionic potential to an unheard-of degree. Working with the allies who brought down Khan, they realized that their own enhancements would be seen as a threat by most of humanity. In 1996, at the close of the Eugenics Wars, these talented psionics brought with them everything they could of their knowledge and culture as well as theories concerning technological wonders they could not yet produce. They fled Earth in a sleeper ship known as the *Terrapin*, their original intent to head for Alpha Centauri to search for an Earthlike planet. The group set the course and entered the sleep chambers, prepared to slumber away the years needed to reach the distant planet.

Unfortunately, the ship's navigational equipment malfunctioned, sending it in an unanticipated direction. After traveling for centuries, it entered what would later be called the Sicondor Sector just as the life support to the sleep tanks also malfunctioned, awakening the passengers. The group managed to repair the ship's navigation system enough to head for Sicon III, the only suitable Class M planet nearby. It took them almost a year to reach their objective. By the time they finally reached the surface and claimed the planet for their own, Isabelle Danur was dead, succumbing to a brain aneurysm. The people she had led decided to call themselves the Danurians in her honor.

They moved everything they could into a system of sheltering caves, which eventually became their settlement, and blew up the ship so nobody could argue for a return to a world that didn't want them. Time passed and the colonists prospered, using the knowledge they had brought with them to keep themselves alive and build the things they needed. They interbred, strengthening their psionic potentials. Each Danurian child learned their history, remembering that the humans had driven them out because they feared the group's psi talents.

Five years before the present day, the Danurians first met the Klingons. Scouting outward from their borders, the Klingons came to Sicon III to plant a secret outpost there, in a sector that lies in disputed territory. While the Federation technically holds claim to it, the Sicondor Sector reverts to Klingon control if the Federation fails to place outposts within it and utilize it for peaceful colonization.

The Klingons first tried to eradicate, then control the "humans" they encountered on Sicon III, using intimidation and superior weapons. They found themselves led in circles, chasing shadows and falling prey to traps they never saw coming. Eventually, the Danurians, attracted by the Klingons' technology, sued for a cease-fire. A strange semialliance began, with the Klingons providing the Danurians with advisors and technology they lacked in exchange for eridennium, an ironlike metal through which sensor rays cannot pass, useful in shield technology.

The rare metal lies just beneath the surface of the greater part of the planet, making sensor readings difficult and use of transporter beams inside (or into) the Danurians' cavern complex impossible. The Danurians have cooperated with the Klingons though they feel great concern for their sometime allies' violent policies.

Then they discovered that humans were living on an outpost on Sicon Prime. Naturally, they feared what this might mean and turned to their allies for help ….

The Episode

Beginning a tour of duty in the Sicondor Sector, a mostly unexplored area of space close to Klingon territory, the U.S.S .Yorktown arrives at Sicon Prime and the Federation outpost Glenconner. There they discover that the colonists they were supposed to transport to Sicon III have disappeared, along with all other outpost personnel. The outpost is in ruins. Tracking the signature of a Klingon vessel back to Sicon III they receive faint life readings from the planet below. Some register as Klingon, but some are definitely Human.

Through subtle investigation, the characters can discover the Danurians and their Klingon advisors living in an underground city. They learn that the Danurians have kidnapped all the people of the outpost in an attempt to keep other humans from settling nearby. The Danurians have no prior experience with the Federation, but they've been raised with stories of Human resentment of their gifts.

From this point on, what happens is in the characters' hands. They can speak with the leaders of the Danurians and attempt to convince them that the Federation means them no harm, or they can bring to bear the power of their ship to rescue those being held hostage. Whatever their choices, the leader of the Danurians is found murdered and blame falls on the Crew, who must face a trial and prove themselves innocent. They can do some investigation on their own to uncover the real perpetrator as well. Depending on the choices made, the characters may forge a tentative peace agreement with the Danurians or provoke what will become a nasty border war.

Note to the Narrator

The story assumes that the ship involved is the U.S.S. Yorktown, a starship like the Enterprise, and that the captain of the ship is a guest star. If this is not the case, the Narrator will have to adjust the story to fit the changes. Encourage (or have Captain Foster order) the player characters to all go on the mission rather than leaving some of them to man the ship. In this story, nothing of interest happens to the ship while the characters are busy elsewhere and anyone left behind will simply be left out of the action.

In this adventure, Act One flows by very quickly, with most of the action and roleplaying found in Acts Two and Three. While the assumption of the story is that the characters will choose to use peaceful means to solve the problems, they may instead opt for violence. If they do so, the Narrator will have to make adjustments to the scenario to take this into account. If nothing else, the Danurians are quite capable of taking over the characters' minds, and the Klingons are unlikely to tolerate much Federation interference before moving to eliminate the Crew. Narrators should therefore make certain that their players understand the Star Trek milieu well enough to help them make the right choices.

PRELUDE TO THE ACTION

If this is the characters' first adventure, the Narrator should let them come aboard their new ship and get acquainted before tossing them into the middle of an adventure. A short scene or two introducing them to key personnel aboard ship, assigning them to their duties, and letting them stow their belongings in their quarters should suffice. Information on the U.S.S. Yorktown and her crew appears above (page 268). The characters should be briefed on the overall mission of the Yorktown, to explore and map the Sicondor Sector and to assist colonists and the Federation outpost in the area. They should know at least the basics about the sector such as the name of the sun and nearest planets, the fact that only Sicon Prime is Human-inhabited, and that the sector borders Klingon territory.

ACT ONE: MYSTERY

The story begins as the ship arrives in orbit around Sicon Prime, where the Federation has a domed outpost. The Narrator may customize the stardate to fit his campaign particulars and should play the ship's captain while reading the following paragraph:

"Captain's Log, stardate 5933.2. We have traveled through the asteroid field surrounding the three planets of the Sicon system and taken up orbit around Sicon Prime, location of the Federation outpost Glenconner. Our mission is to transport a group of colonists from that outpost to Sicon III, the third planet in this system, where they will found a colony and begin the mining of eridennium, useful in shield technology.

"Communications, open a channel to the outpost below. Sensor readings, Ms. Vashenka?" (You may substitute a character's name, if one is manning communications or the sensors.)

SCENE ONE: THE MISSION CHANGES

If one of the characters is not acting as science officer, an NPC announces strange sensor readings from the planet below. If a character mans the sensors, he can tell that there are no Human life readings from the outpost (Routine Sensors test). Further, atmosphere readings indicate that flames have ravaged the domed structure. The readings fluctuate, making them hard to read accurately, however, due to the presence of traces of eridennium (Challenging difficulty for any attempts to gather more information). To discover what has actually happened, a landing party will have to investigate.

The captain orders that a party beam down to see what happened within the outpost and to search for possible survivors, since the sensor readings cannot be fully trusted. The characters are chosen to go. If the captain is a player character, that player may choose to do differently, of course, but part of a Federation ship's duties include investigation and rendering assistance to those in need.

Should a player character attempt to discover any readings near the ship rather than on the planet, he is able to tell (Moderate Sensors test) that another ship recently left orbit, leaving a trail moving outward toward the more distant planets. Despite this, the captain insists that at least a cursory search be made of the outpost. The ship's trail information remains important, as it is the only clue leading the ship to the place where the kidnapped Federation personnel are held.

SCENE TWO: WITHIN THE DOME

Any landing party that beams down discovers the outpost in ruins and all the people gone. The outpost itself consists of a domed structure housing a series of rooms and hallways. One area holds two shuttlecraft, fueled and ready to go, but abandoned. The main area holds workstations and offices for the outpost's commanding officer and security

personnel. From there, halls lead outward to more work areas and living quarters, as well as recreation and dining areas. Lights flicker sporadically and the only sound comes from recirculating air and the hum of machinery. The air feels hot and wet, while the smell reminds one of flames smothered by foam.

Through tricorder readings and personal investigation (Routine Personal Equipment (Tricorder) or Search tests), the characters can discover evidence that people simply stopped whatever they were doing and apparently left the dome of their own accord. Meals are left half-eaten, tools lie about as if dropped and abandoned, and workstations still show data called up by those who never used it. In one area, a forlorn doll lies askew (telling the characters that children lived here and were taken as well). Fire damage shows here and there as though set at intervals, but the flames have burned out or been suppressed by fire control equipment. Though much has been damaged, most of the really important equipment, including all systems necessary for life, remains salvageable.

SCENE THREE: THE TRAIL

Whether they discovered it before or only find it upon returning to the *Yorktown*, the characters note a trail of particles from the drive engines of the ship that carried away the outpost personnel. It leads from orbital space around Sicon Prime toward Sicon III, which a character can discover with a successful Moderate skill test. (Since the story cannot continue unless the characters discover the trail leading them to Sicon III, the Narrator should allow more than one attempt if the first fails.) As the ship follows the trail, another test can be made. With a Challenging success level, the character can tell that the ship's trail they follow shows the signature of a Klingon vessel.

As the ship nears Sicon III, sensor scans (Routine difficulty) show that there is no ship in orbit around the planet. The trail leads onward, back toward Klingon territory. A scan of the planet, however, reveals life signs—both Human and Klingon. These sensor scans (again, Challenging difficulty for any information beyond the bare amount mentioned above) cut in and out, as though being partially blocked by some sort of screen preventing easy scanning. The characters may or may not figure out that the sensor problems arise from the

eridennium said to be in the soil of the planet. (The same substance makes it impossible for any landing party to beam into the cavern complex where the Danurians live, though the characters will not yet know that. At the Narrator's discretion, a sufficiently impressive Material Engineering (Metallurgical), Systems Engineering (Shields), Planetary Science (Geology), Physical Science (Chemistry), etc. test will allow the character to remember a technical journal or library tape on the subject.)

ACT TWO: SICON III

Having discovered life signs on Sicon III where none are supposed to exist, the characters should turn their attention to finding out who is on the planet and why. If they instead attempt to follow the trail of the Klingon ship, it becomes more and more difficult until the trail is lost while still moving toward Klingon territory. In this act the characters discover the Danurians and interact with them, setting the course of the Federation presence in the sector in times to come for good or ill.

SCENE ONE: TRANSPORTER TROUBLE

Noting the life signs from the surface, and hoping they indicate that the missing Federation personnel are on the planet below, Captain Foster orders a team down to investigate. He admonishes them to be very careful in their approach and dealings with anyone they meet, reminding them that the Sicondor Sector is disputed territory. The readings from the sensors pinpoint the general area where the life readings appear.

The characters move to the transporter to beam down to the surface. They take up position and the operator attempts to place them within the same area as the life readings. That area, however, is within the cavern complex and the eridennium interferes with the transporter beam. The operator begins to send them down, but cannot complete the transfer. (The Transporter Officer for this mission should be an NPC, so that the Narrator can make sure the transporter fails.) The characters feel impossibly stretched out during this. They hear (as

from a great distance) someone saying, "Get them back! Get them back!" and find themselves back aboard rather than on the planet when they finally stabilize (the Narrator can make this a very tense moment before letting the players know that the Crew made it back aboard).

At this point they have two choices: They can either use the transporter beam and land somewhere on the surface near the lifeform readings, or take the ship's shuttlecraft down. The characters should decide which they will do. If they beam down, follow directly with Scene Two: On the Surface. If they take the shuttlecraft, a few rolls to orient themselves correctly and a Moderate piloting skill test or two may be in order.

SCENE TWO: ON THE SURFACE

Whether they reach the surface via transporter beam or by shuttlecraft, the characters may scout the immediate area and discover three possible entry points: through the main entrance to Serenity Settlement, into the cave where the scavenged spaceship parts are stored, or into the docking bay where the Klingons reside and keep their shuttlecraft. All the entrances lie near or within the largest mountain on the planet, a peak the Danurians named Mount Hope. Should they spend a few moments observing from concealment, the Crew sees a Klingon walk toward the cave that houses the shuttlecraft and disappear inside. There is no activity around either of the other two entryways.

Inside the cave system, after a brief length of tunnel that looks natural, carved hallways predominate. Tunnels, rooms, caverns, and halls, all are lit by Klingon glow rods powered by energy cells. Because the Klingons generally function in less light than humans, illumination seems dark compared to Federation standards.

Before running confrontations with any Danurians, the Narrator should be certain he is familiar with their psi amplifier weapons (page 280). Psionically talented characters may feel distinctly uncomfortable once they reach the planet's surface, as though tiny needles prickle at their consciousness. Should a character detect any of the Klingons or Danurians by using psionics, planned ambushes or hidden guards may be revealed. The Narrator should be prepared to adjudicate the resulting changes to the scenario as fairly as possible.

Shuttle Bay

Probably the worst choice for an entry point, this area leads to a shuttle bay and the living quarters given over to the Klingon advisors. As they have just completed a mission with the Danurians to capture all the outpost personnel, the Klingons are all on the alert waiting to discover if anyone got off a message to Starfleet. Consequently, the shuttle bay is well guarded, with four Klingons armed with disruptors (use or modify the Klingon soldier on page 203 for the Klingons in this episode). They fire at the first sign of anyone entering their shuttle bay, using heavy stun mode. Since the characters' equipment cannot detect the Klingons' presence accurately due to eridennium interference, the Klingons get surprise (see page 109) unless the characters move very carefully (Challenging Stealth test). The Klingons roughly bind stunned characters and take them before Vor'Kal, the chief Klingon advisor, for questioning. Shortly after the interrogation begins, Warleader Moriya Rhin and

three of her security people arrive to demand that the prisoners be brought before Dian'Ara Askal, First Commander of the Danurians. (See descriptions for Vor'Kal, Moriya Rhin, and the other major NPC's below, page 280.)

Should the characters win the confrontation, they may take the Klingons prisoner or continue on to try to find the Federation folk taken from Sicon Prime. At some point, they are interrupted by the arrival of Moriya (and her people), who demands to know who they are and what they are doing. She also insists that they free the Klingons. If the characters resist or take Moriya prisoner, her thoughts to Dian'Ara and to other Danurians warn them of dangerous, possibly deadly humans within their midst. This forces the Danurians to send teams out to deal with the intruders and rescue their people and their Klingon allies. The Narrator may allow a skill test or two to avoid being controlled by the Danurians' mental abilities (see the Psionics rules on pages 81-82), but sooner or later sheer numbers tell and the characters are captured. Go on to Scene Three.

Ship's Cave

If the characters enter through this large cave, they can find portions of the spaceship in which the Danurians traveled to Sicon III (a Challenging History (Earth) or Material Engineering (Structural/Spaceframe) test identifies the pieces as parts of a DY-100 sleeper ship from the late 20th century). This cave serves the Danurians as something of a shrine. Successful searching (Moderate difficulty) even yields a log of the journey with entries detailing the malfunctioning of the navigation system and the sleeper settings that led to the refugees landing here. Some educational material can be found here as well, dealing with farming and frontier low-tech living. The metallic case that holds Isabelle Danur's body also rests here atop a table, which serves as a bier. Next to the coffin lies a book recording Danur's struggle to help overthrow the genetically altered supermen and her decision to take her people into space. It does not mention the Danurians' psionic talents, but does hint that they are different from other humans.

Following passages from the ship's cavern, the characters can penetrate further into the Danurians' complex. Taking the main branch leads them to Serenity Settlement. The branch turning right goes to the shuttle bay and Klingon quarters, while that sloping downward and left takes them to the holding cells where the Federation prisoners are being kept. If they enter the Klingon complex, guards discover them soon after they penetrate the area and move to take them out. Should they go to the settlement, run the scenario much as if they had entered the settled area from the start.

Meanwhile, if they wish to interact with the prisoners, go on to Scene Three and run it without the characters being made prisoners themselves. There are no guards currently watching the prisoners, though some will turn up about five minutes after the Crew arrives. Details on Lieutenant Commander Konata Nantambu can be found below (page 280). If the Crew opts to try to release the prisoners and get them to shuttlecraft, this partially works. At some point in the escape, however, the characters find themselves beset by a number of Danurians, who use their psi abilities to overpower the characters. Go on to Scene Four.

Main Entryway

If characters come through the main entryway, they find carved hallways just a little past what looks like natural openings. After taking the humans from the outpost, the settlement is on the alert and nervous. Vantage points unmanned for years now hold guards charged with giving warning if anyone other than the Danurians or their Klingon allies enter. Even should characters somehow intuit how they should be dressed and attempt to pass themselves off as Danurians, they don't know to draw tattoos on their faces. Further, a single unanswered mental challenge immediately marks the Crew as outsiders.

The guards in the hidden vantage points (near the roof of the passageways behind scrim-covered openings made to look like part of the rock) send mental warnings, and a large group gathers to repel invaders. They confront the characters as they step into a larger room. The characters may take out some of them, but suffer massive telepathic commands and empathic assaults. Unless they are all potent psionics themselves (highly unlikely), the Crew eventually loses to sheer numbers and repeated assaults. If characters become captives and have not yet been to the holding area, go to Scene Three. If they have already seen where the Federation captives are being held, move on to Scene Four.

SCENE THREE: HOLDING AREA

The characters either reach this area by entering the large cave in Mt. Hope or after being taken prisoner. This is a large cavern complex that holds an underground stream with a small, shallow pond and a few crude shelters. The Danurians used the area for a while, thinking to build crafthalls there, but decided it was too dank to continue once they'd spent a few days there. They sealed the area off with an ornate grillwork to keep children from wandering in and getting hurt around the huts or drowning in the pond. Though the grillwork gates look fragile, they are actually built from eridennium and are quite strong.

Inside the grillwork some hundred or more people mill about, those captured from the outpost. They have no idea what the Danurians want with them. They can tell the characters that people who looked Human, but who seemed to be working with Klingons, invaded the outpost and took over people's minds, forcing them to lay down their weapons and tools and move into designated areas where they were beamed up into a Klingon ship. No one could resist them for long. Once aboard the Klingon ship, they were brought here and once again forced to follow mental commands to enter the holding area peacefully and without protest. Since then, they've been locked up. Someone told them they would be given food later and that the water was safe to drink.

The leader of the prisoners is Lieutenant Commander Konata Nantambu, head of the outpost. Nantambu hopes to stage a breakout and has set the other prisoners to searching for anything that they can use as weapons. He believes that if enough of them attack *en masse*, their captors will not have the time or the mental discipline to control them all again. Lacking other knowledge or options, Nantambu plans to take any Klingon transport that may be on the planet. Failing that, he hopes either their captors or the Klingons will have equipment which allows him to send a message to Starfleet. He knows a Federation starship was on its way to the outpost and hoped it would track the prisoners and help in their rescue. He is quite eager to put his plans into action, as he is spoiling for the chance to prove that the kidnapping wasn't due to his incompetence.

SCENE FOUR: SERENITY SETTLEMENT

Whether caught trying to free the prisoners, captured by the Klingons, or walking right into the main settlement, the characters eventually end up in Serenity Settlement. Either as prisoners brought to the discussion or as "visitors" directed to the settlement's leaders, the Crew move through the streets of the Danurian city.

The city is laid out in what at first appears to be a haphazard sprawl. Some homes and crafthalls take up natural cavern space slightly carved, then fitted with doors for privacy. Other buildings are made from cut stone and parts scavenged from the ship. These sit at odd angles with the streets twisting around them. Only after looking for some time can visitors discern that the arrangement simply follows the natural ups and downs and turns of the floor and walls of the caverns in which they lie. Near the central area, a larger structure rests against a massive stalagmite, incorporating the gigantic stone pillar into its design. This building is known as the Leaders' Hall. When news of the characters is brought to them, the three leaders of the Danurians gather here to discuss what to do (unless Moriya has already been called out to handle the situation). The leaders have instantaneous communication with the Klingons, access to disruptors, and their own powers. Moriya's troops carry their amplifier wands and a few (one in ten) have disruptors.

The characters get the chance to meet with the leaders of the Danurians—Dian'Ara Askal, First Commander of the Danurians; Iraen Tors, Chief of Education; and Warleader Moriya Rhin. The

Danurian leadership recognizes that the characters have a powerful ship in orbit around their planet and want to find some way out of their predicament. They don't have enough people to control an entire starship full of personnel. Their original plan was to make the humans they kidnapped disappear (gradually assimilating them into their own ranks), leaving a mystery and perhaps scaring further colonizers off. Now that they've been discovered, they aren't sure what to do.

The Danurians have come to trust the Klingons to some extent, but they've been taught all their lives that humans are treacherous beings who will hunt and kill them—or try to control them—out of jealousy or fear of their powers. So far, however, they've read nothing but confusion and trepidation from those they kidnapped. No duplicity; no plans to find and kill the Danurians. In fact, the humans seemed completely unaware that the Danurians were nearby.

The leaders' response to everything depends heavily on the characters' actions. If the characters charge in, phasers blazing, the Danurians believe the Crew is there to annihilate them. It will be very difficult for the characters to convince them otherwise. Still, they have that ship in orbit ....

The Danurians have no knowledge of the Federation or Starfleet besides overheard Klingon propaganda. Certainly, they have a distortred view of the Federation, so they don't know the starship won't attack. Should the characters be circumspect, attempting negotiation or trying to free the prisoners without harming others, the Danurians react more favorably, giving them the benefit of the doubt.

Attending the meeting is the chief Klingon advisor, Vor'Kal, who doesn't want Federation ships and colonies so close to Klingon space. Though the Federation technically has claim to the area, Vor'Kal hopes that the Danurians' occupation of Sicon III and their alliance with the Klingons gives his people a more solid claim than the Federation's.

If the characters comport themselves intelligently and try to speak reasonably, the Danurians tell the characters that they may consider themselves "guests" for the moment. Iraen Tors suggests that the Crew look around and meet with other Danurians so they can all get to know one another.

THE MOVERS AND SHAKERS

These capsule descriptions of the main supporting cast characters are for the Narrator to use. No stats are given for them, so that they may be customized to fit individual series. Assume that all the Danurians have Psi abilities of 5 or 6 with access to any three Psionic Skills except Mind Meld. The average Danurian has a Psi score of 3–4 and access to two or three Psionic skills. Danurians look Human. Their clothing suggests attempts to copy 20th-century Earth technician fashion (jumpsuit or military attire for soldier types, long formal robes for diplomats, trousers and tunics for most of the populace). All Danurians wear a slender band set with a different colored jewel on their foreheads. Some space other jewels out along this fillet as well (these are often the more talented or highly placed among them, but not always). They also wear jewelry on their hands: bracelets reminiscent

of chainmail covering the back of the hand, and centered on the middle finger with a large ring (also set with a gem, usually a twin to the one worn on the forehead). Some wear collars similar to torcs, also set with gems; these may be used to fasten cloaklike clothing worn over robes or other wear. Military types carry discs, almost like lenses, set on stems. They focus their psionic power through these almost clear amplifiers and use them as distance weapons. Hair tends to be worn somewhat long, though held neatly in place by the fillets. Male military types either shave their heads, wearing only the fillets, or shave them except for scalp locks. Female military personnel tend to wear long hair, but in braids or other confining styles. Danurians wear facial tattoos, especially around one eye or on one cheek. These are stylized, sweeping designs that are to normal tattoos what arabesques are to dancing. The gems in their wands, fillets, or bracelets act as foci for the Danurians' psionic powers, giving them a boost of +1 to their skill and focus, and a range of +2.

Lieutenant Commander Konata Nantambu

Nantambu is the leader of the outpost forces. A male Human Federation officer, he has black skin, dark well groomed hair, a broken nose, and a firm chin. In his mid-30's, Nantambu is properly dressed in Starfleet command uniform, though he has no weapons or communicator. He wants to lead a breakout, and is difficult to convince not to move too fast.

Vor'Kal

This Klingon representative to the Danurians treats with them on behalf of the Klingon Empire, hoping to eventually make them a vassal state. If he can convince the Danurians to remain under Klingon "protection," this may tip the balance in the sector in favor of the Empire. The presence of a danurian colony reduces the Federation's claim. Vor'Kal is male and dressed in basic Klingon style, with a gray metallic tunic over a black shirt and trousers. He does wear an elaborate earring, shaped somewhat like a broad-bladed axe, through which he receives instructions from the higher-ups who usually maintain an orbit around the planet. He must leave the underground complex to do so, however, since the signal cannot get through the metallic blockage. For now, the Klingon ship has left orbit and currently moves toward Klingon space.

Vor'Kal is not at all what most Federation people think of as a "typical" Klingon. He seems reasonable, is very well spoken and clever (if a little condescending toward Starfleet people), and has a rough, pragmatic code of honor. (Living with a race of telepaths has tamed his temper.) He is dedicated to the Klingon Empire, but not immediately hostile to the Federation. Still, he hopes to persuade the Danurians that their future lies with the Klingon Empire, not with the Federation. (If you need detailed statistics for Vor'Kal, either add skills in Persuasion and Small Unit Tactics (Ground) to the basic Klingon warrior, or use the Klingon commander on page 202.)

Dian'Ara Askal

First Commander of the Danurians, Dian'Ara is a female in her mid-40's. She dresses in her robes of office (see above for costuming/jewelry common to the Danurians). Taller than most women, she looks quite regal when wearing the robes. She has long red hair streaked with wisps of gray, worn flowing over her shoulders with several beaded braids atop it. Her forehead is high, though she appears very motherly, with a wise rather than an overly pretty face. Still, she looks more like an aging model than an earth mother. Dian'Ara carries a wand of office similar to the military stick borne by Moriya, but tipped with a faceted crystal instead of the rounded disc. On her forehead, Dian'Ara wears a silvery-looking braided fillet with a single large gemstone set in the center. The tattoo pattern on her face looks like butterfly wings. Dian'Ara is quite charismatic, with a good sense of humor. She wants what is best for her people, but must be convinced that humans mean no harm. Even then, she would not want to break her word to the Klingons.

Iraen Tors

As the Chief of Education, Tors is second in command of the Danurians. A noted philosopher, he wears tunic and trousers, though they are nicely made and decorated at the hems as befits a major official. He wears a fillet with six gemstones, the largest in the center. Iraen Tors' ancestry includes both American Indian and African blood. He has longish dark hair and dark, disturbing eyes that seem to look right through you. His nose is long and straight and he has high cheekbones. His tattoo pattern surrounds one eye with a diamond shape, with the lowest corner of the diamond falling halfway down his cheek and ending in a smaller diamond. He is in his mid-40's, though his hair has not yet begun to gray.

Tors is a thinker, not a man of action, although he is a powerful psionic with the ability to control minds. He believes that the Klingons offer the Danurians both security and technological knowledge. It will take a good deal to convince Tors to accept the Federation, though he can see the sense in having the colonists remain among the Danurians, since the Danurian breeding population is too small to continue much longer without risking genetic disaster.

Warleader Moriya Rhin

Rhin holds a formal position among the Danurians that hasn't been needed since the Eugenics Wars. Briefly, the former warleader was useful when the Danurians first met the Klingons, but the "war" was short-lived. Upon his retirement, Moriya was named as his replacement. As warleader, Moriya is third in command, but believes if anything happens to Dian'Ara, she becomes the *de facto* leader, since Tors is too caught up in philosophy to be practical. Moriya wears a jumpsuitlike uniform and a fillet with three gemstones. She carries an amplifier disc (military stick) and a disruptor. Moriya has light-colored hair worn in a long braid down her back. Her broad face is reminiscent of Germanic or Norse ancestry. She stays in fighting trim and moves with the grace of a big cat. Her tattoo is a simple curling design like an ivy vine that loops around her eye and trails down to her chin. Aggressive and pugnacious, Moriya resents the idea that anyone other than Danurians has any power over her people. She does not like the Klingons, but respects their strength—and their advanced weaponry. She would have preferred to kill the Federation people rather than taking them prisoner, but she understands the need for new blood. She, however, would keep the humans as breeding stock or even try to acquire gene-splicing technology through the Klingons rather than accepting them as fellow Danurians. Moriya has been told all her life of Human treachery and does what she considers best to protect her people from the Federation

ACT THREE: RESOLUTION

The next scenes make or break the Federation's initial presence in the Sicondor Sector. If the characters can convince the Danurians of the Federation's goodwill and don't push too hard to oust the Klingons, they may open up the sector to trade agreements, colonization, and exploration. Their policy toward the Klingon advisors could even become the model on which the Khitomer Accords will someday be based. Should they act rashly or be too demanding, however, the characters could very well find themselves held prisoner and their starship told in no uncertain terms that any action against the Danurians will provoke all-out war with the Klingon Empire. A border war could easily erupt in this sector from an unconsidered insult. Characters have to be very careful how they handle themselves and how they react to the Klingon presence on Sicon III. After all, the people they're dealing with can read their minds.

Scene One: Cascade Vignettes

These small vignettes comprise several interim scenes in which the Crew get to know the Danurians. The Danurians challenge them to games, show them around (there are schools, crafthalls, farms, etc.), exchange stories, eat and drink together, and generally let both sides assess one another. The Crew may even briefly meet with the captured colonists and outpost people if they haven't done so before. Give each player some time with a Danurian. Feel free to make up other Danurian extras to interact with the characters, but the characters should get to know the three main Danurians as well. The leaders assess the characters' reactions and how freely they speak or partake in activities in order to judge whether they have grown enough as a species that the Danurians need no longer fear them.

Naturally, if the characters act badly, they'll never receive this chance. Instead, they'll be placed with the colonists until arrangements can be made to send them back to their ship. Peace will be almost impossible to obtain if this happens.

Scene Two: Dining Disaster

When the characters have seen enough and talked some with the leaders, they are invited to partake of a banquet. Baths are drawn and fresh clothing (Danurian style) laid out for them. All three leaders, several of Moriya's soldiers, some eminent teachers, and a few noted crafts people eat at the

banquet along with a contingent of Klingons. At one point during the proceedings, one of the servers produces a very tall fluted glass filled with a tangy liquid (Danurian fungus wine). He passes this to Iraen Tors, who sits just to Dian'Ara's left. Tors drinks a small sip and passes the glass to the next person on his left. With the servant's help, the glass passes to everyone at the banquet, with each taking a small sip. Moriya drinks when it is about halfway around, the Klingons drink soon thereafter, and it finally passes to the Crew. When they've finished, the last character passes it to Dian'Ara, who drains what is left, stands, and holds the cup aloft. Almost immediately, she chokes, turns very pale, and falls forward across the table.

Any medical officer can rush to her assistance. It is obvious she has been poisoned. The medical officer may make a Challenging skill test to realize that the poison could not have been in the wine and that it is moving through her body far too quickly to have been ingested. A Difficult skill test (Search or First Aid, for example) allows the officer to note the tiny dart near her carotid artery. Anyone assisting other than a medical officer also has a chance to note these details (assuming they have a medical tricorder to discover the information on the poison), but the skill Difficulty level is one level higher in each case.

Naturally, suspicion falls on the Crew. Regardless of their protests or what the medical officer says, the Danurians grab them all (before the officer can lay hands on the dart). Nobody listens, most Danurians shouting them down and demanding their immediate deaths. If they attempt to fight, almost every Danurian present tries to control their minds. Taken by Moriya Rhin's soldiers, they are tossed back in among the colonists. At this point, the characters can try to escape or wait to see what the Danurians do. Word arrives that Dian'Ara is dead and they are told they will be tried for her murder.

Scene Three: Ordeal

Again, a number of scenes occur under the banner of one unifying locale. Iraen Tors calls a trial so that the Federation people may tell their side of the story. Danurians pack the "courthouse," a huge room in the Leaders' Hall, to hear and see the "treacherous humans" who killed their leader. A few shout threats at the characters as they are led in.

Counsel

Vor'Kal is appointed, as the only other "foreigner," to act as their counsel. The Klingon representative protests this, saying he believes they are responsi-

ble, so how can he possibly try to defend them, and why should he? Tors insists. Very ungraciously, Vor'Kal speaks privately with his "clients," asking them what they have to say. At this point, if they noted anything about the poison or found the dart, they can tell Vor'Kal about it. He listens skeptically, but does bring up whatever they say in the course of the trial.

The Trial

Each character is given the chance to speak, or the Crew may decide to have one character speak for all of them. The characters may even speak to accuse the Klingons of the deed. While Vor'Kal initially reacts to this with a challenge to combat, Iraen Tors demands that such things await a verdict.

The Ordeal

Whatever the characters claim, Iraen Tors rules that they must undergo an ordeal if they wish to prove their innocence. He says that even mind-reading is inaccurate in such cases, because it is impossible to catch the one read off-guard. Since mental skills cannot prove innocence or guilt, this is the only recourse.

The characters are led deeper into the caves, moving downward. Finally, they are led to a place where a grillwork similar to the one closing in the captives is laid into the floor. They can hear the sound of rushing water from below. The characters are tied with their hands behind their backs and lowered into the waist-deep water in the darkness. The room they are in is about ten by eight feet. There are no exits in the room through which humans can fit except the grill in the ceiling some ten feet overhead. When they are all down, Tors explains.

"The water is cool right now, but a volcanic flow passes nearby. We will let loose the underground stream so that it flows into the room where you now stand. The water will rise quickly, filling the room in about five minutes and overflowing through the grill. Some of you may think to merely float up with the water and try to breathe through the grillwork, but we will also be diverting lava to the stream. Long before the room fills, the water will become super-heated, boiling you alive. However, if you are truly innocent, you will neither drown nor burn, but emerge unscathed. We leave this key to the grating only a few inches from it so that you may reach through and unlock it to let yourselves out. Should you survive, we will know you are innocent. If you die, we shall return your bodies to your ship and explain to your people that you were executed for murdering Dian'Ara, our leader."

The Danurians then leave and the characters can hear the water flow increasing. They can also feel it becoming hotter. A small square of pale light from overhead tells them where the grillwork is. They can try several things. They might turn back to back and try to untie one another (a Difficult Sleight of Hand (Escape) task), or they might contrive a means to get one person on top of another and try to cut their bonds against the grillwork (a Challenging Athletics (Climbing) task). A combination of this allows a character who frees herself to grab the key and open the grillwork. Despite what Tors said, the water never gets hot enough to burn and they could all float to the top. A good Narrator won't let the players guess this, however. Ask them what their characters are doing and what they are thinking. Ask what they plan to do if

they escape. If they cannot free themselves in just a few minutes, the water rises almost above their heads and they become uncomfortably hot. Tors and six guards reappear, open the grill and pull them out. The ordeal was not to establish their innocence, but to see how they react under pressure and to make their minds more accessible while they concentrated on something else. Tors apologizes and explains that he had to be certain they weren't there to kill the Danurians—even after being threatened with death by them.

Since the Danurians are all highly developed psionics, they can eventually read the truth—neither the Federation crew nor the Klingons poisoned their leader. Moriya Rhin, raised on horror stories of humans' treatment of her ancestors, feels that the Danurians cannot afford to let humans live anywhere near them. Thinking Iraen Tors would be easier to dominate (after all, he's only a philosopher, so she ought to be able to frighten him with her superior psionic abilities), she killed Dian'Ara to gain control for herself. If the Narrator wishes, someone can discover the poison and a few more darts in Rhin's quarters. (If the characters bring up the question of Rhin's guilt, Vor'Kal sends an aide to Rhin's room to search it during the trial, but the aide doesn't return until after the ordeal.) Either the Crew (or other Danurians) can find and overcome Rhin, who has fled, and deliver her to Tors. He arranges for her to see psionic healers for "adjustment."

At this point, Dian'Ara shows up again. She did not die, but Tors claimed she did in order to bring out whoever attempted to murder her (and to keep her safe from further attacks). His ability to screen his mind from being read is legendary, a benefit of his philosophical studies and meditations.

SCENE FOUR: RESOLUTION

Negotiations resume in which the characters may convince the Danurians to let the colonists go. They can negotiate a shaky peace treaty and colonization agreement, including plans to bring more colonists to Sicon III. The Klingons are still a factor here, however, and the Danurians insist that they intend to keep their agreements with the Empire. Anything the Federation wants to do with Sicon III must have Klingon approval. Of course, the Klingons will have to be appeased somehow—perhaps by allowing Klingon colonizing as well ….

EPILOGUE

Narrators can use this adventure as the start of a story arc or of a whole series set in Sicondor. This sector awaits exploration, and if they keep on the good side of the Danurians the Federation can start trade agreements and colonization. If they upset the Danurians or make them feel threatened, the Federation will have to fight what amounts to a border war all through the sector and the Danurians will call on the Klingons to assist them against the Human aggressors. Danurians have a pseudotreaty with the Klingons and things could get hairy if their rights aren't respected.

Background Data

STAR TREK
ROLEPLAYING GAME

Name _____
Rank _____
Species _____
Position _____
Current Assignment _____

Background History
Early Youth _____
Academy Life _____
Cadet Cruise _____
Tours of Duty _____

Attributes

Fitness _____
   Strength _____
   Vitality _____
Coordination _____
   Dexterity _____
   Reaction _____
Intellect _____
   Logic _____
   Perception _____
Presence _____
   Willpower _____
   Empathy _____
Psi _____
   Range _____
   Focus _____

Advantages
▷ _____
▷ _____
▷ _____
▷ _____
▷ _____

Disadvantages
▷ _____
▷ _____
▷ _____
▷ _____
▷ _____

Skills

Skill	Specialization	Level	Spec. Level	Skill	Specialization	Level	Spec. Level
▷				▷			
▷				▷			
▷				▷			
▷				▷			
▷				▷			
▷				▷			
▷				▷			
▷				▷			
▷				▷			
▷				▷			

Status

Courage _____
Renown _____
Aggression _____
Discipline _____
Initiative _____
Openness _____
Skill _____
Resistance _____

Wound Levels
Healthy
Stunned (+1)   ▷ ▷ ▷ ▷ ▷ ▷
Injured (+1)   ▷ ▷ ▷ ▷ ▷ ▷
Wounded (+2)   ▷ ▷ ▷ ▷ ▷ ▷
Incapacitated (-)   ▷ ▷ ▷ ▷ ▷ ▷
Near Death (-)   ▷ ▷ ▷ ▷ ▷ ▷
Killed

INDEX

TABLES

STAR TREK
DEEP SPACE NINE

ROLEPLAYING GAME

SUMMER 1999

"LIFE AND DEATH ARE SELDOM LOGICAL."

- THE GALILEO SEVEN

In Memoriam DeForest Kelley (1920-1999)